P9-ARN-476

MODERN PLANE TRIGONOMETRY

WILLIAM L. HART

Professor of Mathematics, University of Minnesota

MODERN PLANE TRIGONOMETRY

D. C. HEATH AND COMPANY BOSTON

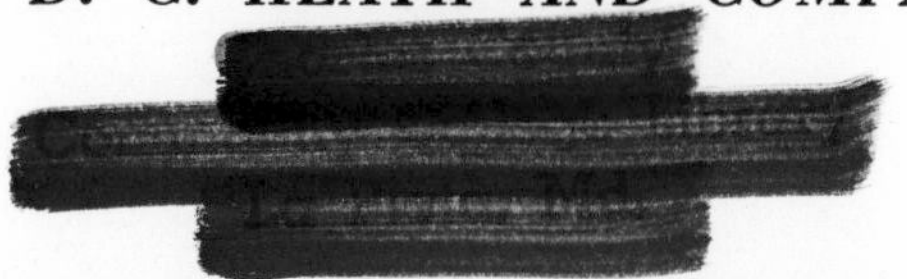

Printed in the United States of America
Printed March 1965

Library of Congress Catalog Card Number: 61-6092

PREFACE

This text is designed for college freshmen, or for college-capable students in a high school, who may desire to study calculus later. It has long been an accepted fact that the trigonometry course for such students should devote major attention to analytic trigonometry, because of its importance in the study of calculus. Hence, no text on trigonometry for these students deserves to be labeled as a particularly modern book if its sole claim to this distinction consists of emphasis on analytic features. Naturally, the present text exhibits this emphasis. However, in addition, the analytic content is designed to be distinctly in tune with the best modern curricular trends in both secondary and collegiate mathematics. While attaining this objective, the text also presents logarithmic computation and the numerical applications of trigonometry in a substantial fashion, arranged to facilitate various degrees of emphasis by the teacher. If desired, the book can be easily adjusted to a relatively brief course centered on analytic material with a minimum of numerical work, for students who need only increased sophistication in their acquaintance with the basic content. Or, when the text is taught with no major omissions, it provides for a course giving generous attention to both analytic and numerical aspects, with ample provision for supplementary work by the superior students. All of the discussion is couched at a mature level. It is clear that, with the indicated objectives for the book, a strong foundation in algebra is a prerequisite for appreciation of the content. Attention is called particularly to the following characteristics of the text.

SPECIAL FEATURES

Topics for orientation, in the substantial first chapter:

The concept of **a set** * of objects.

Notion of a **variable** and its **domain.**

Review and rephrasing of terminology about **solutions of equations** and about **identities.**

* Presented simply *without introducing set algebra,* which is discussed in Note 6 of the Appendix.

Fundamentals of analytic geometry through the stage of the **distance formula** and the **graph of an equation.**

General concept of a **function,** with modern terminology.

Graph of a function when its domain and its range both consist of single numbers.

Emphasis on the distinction between **a function** and **its values.**

Extensive study of the geometric trigonometric functions, classically defined with their domain as all angles,* *before* the student's attention is distracted from this trigonometry for the *general angle* by numerical applications of *right triangles.*

Use of the distance formula of analytic geometry:

To obtain simple **general proofs of the addition formulas,** and thus to eliminate their unsatisfactory classical geometric proofs.

To prove the law of cosines for a triangle.

Emphasis on the standard analytic trigonometric functions of numbers as a natural and essential development:

Their introduction on the basis of knowledge of the geometric trigonometric functions of angles,† considered as *measured in radians,* with *a change in the interpretation of the domain.*

Their use in graphing, conditional equations, identities, and definitions of the inverse trigonometric functions.

The treatment of inverse functions:

Early discussion of the **general notion of an inverse function** (single-valued), at the beginning of the chapter on logarithms.

Substantial study of **the logarithm function as the inverse of the exponential function,** before logarithmic computation is discussed.

Introduction of the **standard inverse trigonometric functions** (single-valued) in the simple fashion desired for calculus, as inverses of the trigonometric functions of numbers *on restricted domains.*

Supplementary work provided for superior students:

Various topics and problems earmarked with a black star in the routine chapters of the text.

A complete optional chapter on **complex numbers.**

* With exceptions for the tangent, cotangent, secant and cosecant functions.

† Note 3 in the Appendix introduces the standard analytic trigonometric functions of numbers without any original contacts with angles, by use of the "*winding*" device. The author decided that this approach, although interesting, deserves only minor emphasis, to avoid removing the student too far from useful intuitional reactions involving the geometric trigonometric functions with domains consisting of angles.

An extensive note in the Appendix introducing the **algebra of sets,** with appropriate exercises for the student.

Several other notes in the Appendix with interesting content.

Reordering of analytic topics:

Early introduction of the addition formulas, proved by use of analytic geometry.

Proof of the reduction formulas by use of the addition formulas, to eliminate cumbersome geometric proofs.

Heavy emphasis on use of radian measure for angles because of its utility in calculus, and in the development of the standard trigonometric functions of numbers.

Proper attention to use of degree measure, because of its importance in applied mathematics and in numerical applications of trigonometry:

Use of a symbol such as $x°$ (read *x degrees*) to represent an *angle*, with the *number* x carefully distinguished from the *angle* $x°$.

Recognition of the *so-called graphs* for the trigonometric functions of angles in degree measure as *true graphs*, in the sense of Chapter 1, of related functions whose domains consist of *numbers* (a first variety of trigonometric functions of numbers).

Moderate use of degree measure in applications of trigonometric identities, and solution of conditional equations.

Treatment of computation and numerical applications:

Special attention to questions about **the accuracy of computation.**

Inclusion of the author's extensive *Logarithmic and Trigonometric Tables*, to offer the teacher freedom of choice in providing experience with **three-, four-,** or **five-place computation** in various exercises.

Listing of **answers for both four-place and five-place logarithmic computation** in appropriate exercises.

Reasonably complete, but not overemphasized, treatment of applications of right triangles.

Arrangement of the chapter on oblique triangles *to permit restriction to use of just the* **laws of sines and cosines,** before the remaining classical content is met.

PEDAGOGICAL AIDS

The book employs devices common to all of the author's texts to assist both the teacher and the student.

Illustrative examples are used profusely.

The problem material for the student is extensive.

Review or miscellaneous exercises occur frequently, with a long summarizing review exercise coming near the end of the text.

The problems in exercises are arranged roughly in order of difficulty, where feasible.

Answers are given in the text for almost all of the odd-numbered problems; answers for even-numbered problems are furnished free to the student in a separate pamphlet when requested by the instructor.

William L. Hart

CONTENTS

MODERN PLANE TRIGONOMETRY

1

BACKGROUND TOPICS

1. Introduction

In the history of mathematics, we find that the subject called *trigonometry* was first developed because of its usefulness in the indirect measurement of angles and distances, particularly in surveying, astronomy, and navigation. The corresponding numerical aspects of trigonometry remain indispensable in the directions just mentioned, and also in modern engineering, the physical sciences, and various other fields where mathematics is applied. However, with the discovery of calculus, a large new field of usefulness arose for trigonometry, with *analytic aspects*, as contrasted to *numerical applications*, of the subject being involved. Trigonometry gives rise to certain numerical features associated with *angles*, and leads to introduction of the so-called *trigonometric functions* of angles.* It is found that these functions and their analytic properties are an essential basis for a large part of calculus. The present text will give a rounded presentation of the trigonometric functions, with attention paid to both their numerical applications and the analytic properties of the functions. However, the major share of the emphasis will be given to so-called *analytic trigonometry*, because of its importance later in calculus. Thus, the treatment is oriented largely with respect to the needs of the student who will study mathematics at least through the stage of calculus. Simultaneously, ample acquaintance will be given with numerical trigonometry, both for motivation at elementary stages and for use in applied mathematics.

2. Certain terminology concerning real numbers

When we mention a *number*, we shall mean a *real number* unless otherwise specified, because *imaginary* † *numbers* will seldom occur. Real numbers are classed as positive, negative, or zero, which is not said to be either positive or negative. A symbol such as 5, V, $\sqrt{25}$, $(3 + 2)$, etc., for a particular number (in the preceding cases for *five*) sometimes is referred to as a **numeral.**

* Eventually, even the idea of an *angle* will drop out in our development.

† See page 208.

Any single letter introduced hereafter without a previous description will be a symbol for a number. A letter, such as x, representing a single number, or perhaps any one of a certain set of numbers, may be called a **literal number symbol** (or **literal numeral**); we then speak of *the number* x. A *value* of a number expression is one of the numbers which can be represented by the expression.

A real number is called a **rational number** if it can be represented as a fraction p/q where p and q are integers and $q \neq 0$. Thus, any integer p is a rational number because $p = p/1$. Any real number which is not a rational number is called an **irrational number.**

ILLUSTRATION 1. In elementary algebra, it is proved that no integers p and q exist such that $\sqrt{2} = p/q$. Hence, $\sqrt{2}$ is an irrational number. At an advanced stage in mathematics, it is proved that the familiar number π is irrational.

The **absolute value** of a real number b is defined as b *itself if* b *is nonnegative,** and as $-b$ if b is *negative.* The absolute value of b is represented by the symbol $|b|$.† We say that two numbers b and c are *numerically equal* if $|b| = |c|$; then, b and c differ at most in sign. We observe the following properties of absolute values.

$$|b|^2 = b^2; \qquad |bc| = |b| \cdot |c|;$$

$$\left|\frac{b}{c}\right| = \frac{|b|}{|c|}, \quad \textit{if} \quad c \neq 0.$$

ILLUSTRATION 2. $|5| = |-5| = 5$; 5 and -5 are numerically equal.

ILLUSTRATION 3. If b and c represent numbers, the fraction $\frac{b}{c}$, sometimes written b/c, is read "*b over c*," or "*b divided by c*." Also, b/c sometimes is referred to as the "**ratio** *of b to c*," which may be written "$b : c$."

3. Directed line segments

In an efficient development of trigonometry, it proves essential to employ a moderate amount of analytic geometry. In our discussion of content from this field, we shall deal with situations on a given line,‡ or in a given plane. Let us assume that a unit of length has been specified. Then, in this book, the word *length* or the unqualified word *distance* will refer to a *nonnegative number* which is the measure of some distance in terms of the given unit of length. By the *distance* between any two points in a plane, we shall mean the length of the line segment joining the points.

A line l is said to be a *directed line* if it is agreed that one direction on l is

* *Nonnegative* means *zero or positive.*
† The *absolute value* of a number sometimes is called its *numerical value.*
‡ The word *line* will mean *straight line.*

called *positive*, with the opposite direction *negative*, as in Figure 1. Also, *directed distances* on l in the corresponding directions will be positive and negative, respectively, and a direction is assigned to each line segment on l. To indicate that a segment is directed or traced *from a point A to B* on l, the segment is named AB. Then, we define the *value* of AB as the *directed distance from A to B*. Thus, if A and B coincide, $AB = 0$. If AB has *positive direction*, the value of AB is *positive* and is equal to the *length* of the segment. If AB has *negative direction*, the value of AB is the *negative of the length* of AB. In any case, the absolute value of AB is equal to the length of AB:

Fig. 1

$$|AB| = (\text{length of segment } AB). \tag{1}$$

If a segment is directed *from B to A*, we refer to the segment, and also to its value, as BA. Since AB and BA have opposite directions,

$$AB = -BA \quad or \quad AB + BA = 0. \tag{2}$$

Sometimes, we shall use $\overline{AB}$ instead of $|AB|$ for the *length* of AB.

ILLUSTRATION 1. In Figure 1, the positive direction is indicated on the line by an arrowhead (common usage); then

$$AB = -2; \qquad BA = 2; \qquad |AB| = |BA| = 2.$$

The student already has met directed line segments in the familiar representation of real numbers on a linear scale, as in Figure 2. If x is any real number, we associate it with that point P on the scale for which $x = OP$, with OP taken as positive or negative according as P is to the right or the left, respectively, from O. On the real number scale in Figure 2, we call O the **origin** and x the **coordinate** of P. We shall use "$P{:}(x)$" to abbreviate "*point P with coordinate x.*"

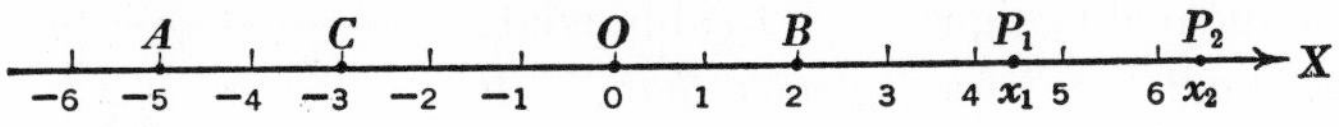

Fig. 2

For any three points A, B, and C on a directed line, as in Figures 3 and 4, it can be seen that

$$AB + BC = AC. \tag{3}$$

In (3), if we think of the *value* of each segment as *the measure of travel in a specified direction*, then (3) simply states the fact that travel *from A to B*, followed by travel *from B to C*, is equivalent to travel *from A to C*.

Fig. 3

Fig. 4

ILLUSTRATION 2. In Figure 2 on page 5, $AB = 7$, $BC = -5$, and $AC = 2$. We verify that $7 + (-5) = 2$, as stated in (3).

THEOREM I. *If** $P_1:(x_1)$ *and* $P_2:(x_2)$ *are on a number scale, then*

$$P_1P_2 = x_2 - x_1; \tag{4}$$

$$(\text{length of } P_1P_2) = |P_1P_2| = |x_2 - x_1|. \tag{5}$$

Proof of (4). In Figure 2 on page 5, $OP_1 = x_1$, $OP_2 = x_2$, $P_1O = -OP_1$. On applying (3) to (P_1, O, P_2) in that order, we obtain

$$P_1P_2 = P_1O + OP_2 = OP_2 - OP_1 = x_2 - x_1.$$

ILLUSTRATION 3. In Figure 2 on page 5, the coordinates of B and C are 2 and -3, respectively. From (4), $BC = -3 - 2 = -5$; the distance between 2 and -3 is $|BC| = |-3 - 2| = 5$.

We use the number scale as a background for geometrical language where each *number* may be talked of as a *point*. Thus, to remark that b *is close to* c will mean that *the distance* $|b - c|$ *is small.*

If no agreement is made as to positive and negative directions on a line l, it is said to be *undirected.* Then, all distances measured on l are positive, and it is immaterial whether we use AB or BA for a segment of l with A and B as end points. In this case, the value of either AB or BA is the length of AB.

Note 1. To avoid ambiguity, if a line segment or distance is *directed* (and thus possibly is *negative*), this will be definitely stated. If we refer to a directed segment AB on a line where, previously, no positive direction has been assigned, we agree that AB has positive direction.

If b and c are real numbers, we say that b *is less than* c, or c *is greater than* b, if b is to the *left* of c on the number scale. We use the inequality signs "$<$" to abbreviate "*less than*" and "$>$" for "*greater than.*" If $b < c$, as in Figure 5, the directed segment from b to c on the number scale has the value $(c - b)$, which is *positive* because b is to the left of c. Hence,

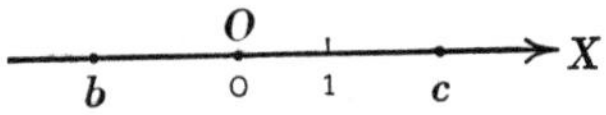

Fig. 5

$$\textbf{"}b < c\textbf{" means that } (c - b) \textbf{ is positive.} \tag{6}$$

ILLUSTRATION 4. $-5 < 2$ because -5 is to the left of 2 on the number scale, and also because $2 - (-5) = 7$, which is *positive.*

ILLUSTRATION 5. To indicate that x is positive, we write $x > 0$. To state that x lies between b and c, where $b < c$, we write $b < x < c$, which may be read "*b is less than x and x is less than c.*"

* We read "$P_1:(x_1)$" as "P,1 *with coordinate* x,1," or simply "P,1,x,1."

EXERCISE 1

Read the symbol in words and find its value.

1. $|3|$. **2.** $|-4|$. **3.** $|-2|$. **4.** $|-6|^2$. **5.** $|-2|^3$.

6. Mark A:(2), B:(− 3), C:(− 6), and D:(− 8) on a number scale and compute AB, CD, $|BC|$, and DA.

Plot the points on a scale. Find AB, BC, and AC by use of Section 3, and check $AB + BC = AC$. Also, compute $|AB| + |BC|$ and $|AC|$.

7. A:(− 7); B:(− 3); C:(− 1). **8.** A:(9); B:(− 1); C:(− 5).

9. A:(− 2); B:(− 6); C:(0). **10.** A:(8); B:(− 6); C:(− 3).

11. A:(− 5); B:(7); C:(2). **12.** A:(9); B:(− 8); C:(0).

Insert the proper sign, $<$ or $>$, between the numbers.

13. 2 and 5. **14.** − 12 and 3. **15.** − 3 and 0. **16.** − 4 and − 7.

Consider a number scale and state the facts by use of inequality signs.

17. x is negative. **18.** x is to the left of − 4.

19. x is to the right of 6. **20.** x is between − 3 and 6.

21. x is between − 7 and − 3. **22.** x is between 0 and − 6.

23. With the understanding that each literal number symbol represents a real number, state the proper answer to each of the following questions. Is b positive? Is $-x$ negative? State the value, in terms of b, for * $\sqrt{b^2}$ if b is positive; negative; zero.

4. The concept of a set of objects

In referring to a **set** of things, we shall take the word *set* as an *undefined term*. Each object in a set will be called an **element** or a **member** of it. In mentioning any set T, we imply that T is *well defined;* that is, we have the means to recognize whether or not any specified object belongs to T. A **subset** S of a set T is a set consisting of some (possibly all) members of T.

ILLUSTRATION 1. We may refer to the set T of members of the United States Senate. The two senators from Illinois form a subset of T.

If a set T has just *n members*, where n is a positive integer, we call T a *finite set*. If a set T is not a finite set, then T is said to be an *infinite set*. In such a case, corresponding to any positive integer n, there exist more than n members in T.

ILLUSTRATION 2. The set, T, of all integers, and the set, R, of all real numbers are infinite sets. The set, P, of all positive integers is a subset of T, and also of R. The set, A, of all rational numbers and the set, L, of all irrational numbers are infinite sets.

* Recall that, if P is any positive number, $\sqrt{P}$ represents just the *positive* square root of P. See page 208 in the Appendix.

If S is a subset of the set T, we say that S is *included* in T, and write "$S \subset T$," read "*S is included in T.*" We have $T \subset T$. If all members of S are members of T, and if all members of T also are members of S, then S and T consist of the *same members* and we write $S = T$. It proves convenient to introduce the so-called **empty set,** or **null set,** consisting of *no* members, and represented by $\emptyset$. We agree to say that $\emptyset$ is included in every set. That is, for any set S, we have $\emptyset \subset S$. If $S \subset T$ and $S \neq T$, we say that S is a **proper subset** of T. In such a case, there is *at least one element* of T which is *not* in S.

ILLUSTRATION 3. In Illustration 2, $P \subset T$ and P is a proper subset of T. If H is the set $\{1, 2, 3, 4, 5, 6, 7, 8, 9, 10, 11, 12\}$, then the set $\{1, 2, 3\}$ is a proper subset of H.

In this text we shall mention sets frequently. The objective of the present section is to alert the student to the fact that the notion of a *set of objects* is fundamental in mathematics, and that various important concepts essentially demand use of the word *set* in definitions, and in their applications.

Note 1. In Note 6 of the Appendix, certain operations on sets are described and an introduction to so-called *set algebra* is presented, with an appropriate set of problems, for students desiring to learn such content. It will not be used in this text.

5. Variables and constants

A **variable** is a symbol, such as x, which may represent any particular thing of a specified set, S, of things (not necessarily numbers). We call S the **domain** * of the variable x. Each element of S may be called a *value* of x.

ILLUSTRATION 1. We may use y to represent any person in the United States. Then, the entire population is the domain of the variable y.

In this text, unless otherwise specified, the domain of any variable will be a set of numbers. If x is a variable with the domain S, then x may represent any particular number of S; each number in S is a *value* of x.

ILLUSTRATION 2. Let S be the set of all numbers $x < 2$. We could also define S as the set of all numbers $u < 2$. Thus, the letter, x or u, used as the symbol for an arbitrary number in S is of no importance.

In a given discussion, a **constant** is a number symbol representing a fixed number. A constant may be a numeral such as 3, $-\frac{5}{2}$, etc. Or, a constant may be a literal number symbol, such as b, c, etc., which is known to represent a single number. A literal constant, such as b, also may be called a *variable,* whose domain consists of *just one number.*

* Sometimes called the **universal set** for the variable.

ILLUSTRATION 3. In the formula $A = \pi r^2$ for the area,* A, of a circle of radius r, if we think of all circles, then A and r are variables and π is a constant.

In any mathematical expression in this text, except where otherwise specified, any literal number symbol, such as x, is understood to be a variable whose domain is the set of *all real numbers* x for which the expression has meaning as a real number.

6. Equations and inequalities

Consider an equation or an inequality in a single variable, x. Then, the following terminology applies.

DEFINITION I. *A* **solution** *of an equation* † *(or inequality* †*) in a single variable, x, is a value of x for which the equation (or inequality) becomes a true statement.*

A value of a variable x which is a solution of an equation (or inequality) in x is said to **satisfy** it. A *solution* of an equation in x sometimes is called a **root** of the equation.

ILLUSTRATION 1. The equation $2x^2 - x - 1 = 0$, or $(2x + 1)(x - 1) = 0$, has just two solutions, or roots, $x = -\frac{1}{2}$ and $x = 1$. The inequality $x < 3$ has infinitely many solutions, consisting of all numbers represented by the points on the real number scale of Figure 2 on page 5 to the left of the point representing 3.

Similarly, as in Definition I, a solution of an equation (or inequality) in *two or more variables* is defined as a set of values of the variables which *satisfy* the equation (or inequality), that is, *which make it a true statement.*

ILLUSTRATION 2. A solution of an equation in two variables, x and y, is a *pair of values of x and y* which satisfy the equation. The equation $x + 2y = 4$ has the solutions $(x = 2, y = 1)$, $(x = 4, y = 0)$, $(x = 0, y = 2)$, etc. In algebra, the student has probably learned that, as a rule, an equation in two variables can be expected to have infinitely many solutions.

An equation (or inequality) in certain variables is said to be **inconsistent** if it has no solution. If an equation or an inequality is satisfied by *all* sets of values of the variables involved, in the case of an equation it is called an **identity**; in the case of an inequality it is called an **absolute inequality.** If an equation is *not* an identity, sometimes we refer to the equation as a **conditional equation.** Two equations (or inequalities) are said to be

* Whenever we use a symbol for a concrete quantity, in agreement with common practice the symbol may represent a *number* which is the *measure* of the quantity in terms of an appropriate unit.

† The student should read Definition I, first, with *equation* used throughout and, second, with *inequality* used in place of *equation.*

equivalent * if they have the same solutions. Usually, when we refer simply to an *equation* we shall mean a *conditional equation.*

Suppose that A and B represent number expressions involving certain variables. Let h be any constant, *not zero,* and let K be a number expression which may involve the variables. Then, in algebra, the student has had experience with the fact that the equation $A = B$ is equivalent to each of the equations $hA = hB$ and $A + K = B + K$. Also, if h involves the variables, it was observed in algebra that the equations $A = B$ and $hA = hB$ are *not* necessarily equivalent.

ILLUSTRATION 3. The equation $x^2 - 4 = (x + 2)(x - 2)$ is an identity in x. The equation $(x + y)^2 = x^2 + 2xy + y^2$ is an identity in x and y.

ILLUSTRATION 4. The equation $x = x^2 + 5$ is equivalent to $x^2 - x + 5 = 0$. The equation $x + 3 = 2$ is *not* equivalent to $x(x + 3) = 2x$, because this equation has the root $x = 0$, which does not satisfy $x + 3 = 2$.

ILLUSTRATION 5. If x is a variable whose domain consists of just *real numbers,* then the equation $x^2 = -4$ is *inconsistent,* because the square of a real number is never negative. However, if the domain of x consists of all *complex* † *numbers,* then $x^2 = -4$ if $x = \pm 2i$, and thus the equation $x^2 = -4$ is *not* inconsistent.

To solve an equation means to find all of its solutions, if there are only a finite number of solutions, or to describe the solutions clearly if they are infinite in number.

Note 1. The *set of all solutions* of an equation (or inequality) sometimes is referred to briefly as its **solution set.**

7. Polynomials and polynomial equations

A **monomial** ‡ in certain variables is defined as a *constant,* not zero, called the **numerical coefficient,** multiplied by *powers of the variables where the exponents are nonnegative integers.* If each of these exponents § is *zero,* the monomial is merely a *constant.* A sum of monomials is called a **polynomial** ‖ in the variables. A polynomial is called a **binomial** if the polynomial is the sum of two monomials, and a **trinomial** if the polynomial is the sum of three monomials. The **degree** of a monomial in certain variables is the *sum of the exponents* of their powers which are factors of the monomial. The degree of a polynomial in the variables is defined as *the degree of the monomial of highest degree* in the polynomial.

* We shall meet only simple applications of inequalities, and hence shall not mention operations on an inequality leading to equivalent inequalities.
† A complex number is of the form $(a + bi)$ where a and b are real numbers and $i^2 = -1$, or $i = \sqrt{-1}$. See page 193.
‡ Sometimes called an *integral rational term* in the variables.
§ A brief review of exponents is found in Note 1 of the Appendix.
‖ Sometimes called an *integral rational polynomial.*

ILLUSTRATION 1. If a, b, and c are constants, not zero, while x, y, and z are variables, then $7ax^3y^2$ is a monomial, with the numerical coefficient $7a$, of degree 5 in x and y, and of degree 3 in x alone. The polynomial $(5a + 3bxy^2 + 2cy^3z^2)$ is of degree 3 in y alone, and of degree 5 in x, y, and z. Since $x^0 = 1$, any nonzero constant b can be thought of as being of degree zero in any variable x because $b = bx^0$.

If A and B represent polynomials in certain variables, the equation $A = B$ is referred to as a **polynomial** * **equation** *of degree n* or, sometimes, simply an *equation of degree n*, if the polynomial $(A - B)$ is of degree n in the variables. Polynomials (or polynomial equations) of degrees 1, 2, 3, and 4 in the variables are called, respectively, *linear*, *quadratic*, *cubic*, and *quartic* polynomials (or polynomial equations). With the degree $n > 4$, usually we do not use a special name.

ILLUSTRATION 2. We call $2x^2 - x - 1 = 0$ a quadratic equation in a single variable, x. We refer to $3x + 5y = 7$ as a linear equation in the variables x and y.

If a, b, and c are constants, where $a \neq 0$, the student has met the fact that the quadratic equation

$$ax^2 + bx + c = 0, \tag{1}$$

where the variable x may have imaginary values, has just two solutions (possibly identical) given by the quadratic formula

$$x = \frac{-b \pm \sqrt{b^2 - 4ac}}{2a}. \tag{2}$$

The roots in (2) are found to be real and equal, real and unequal, or imaginary † and unequal, when and only when the discriminant $b^2 - 4ac = 0$, $b^2 - 4ac > 0$, or $b^2 - 4ac < 0$, respectively.

ILLUSTRATION 3. The quadratic equation $2x^2 - 4x + 5 = 0$ has the two solutions

$$x = \frac{4 \pm \sqrt{16 - 40}}{4}, \quad or \quad x = \tfrac{1}{2}(2 \pm i\sqrt{6}).$$

EXERCISE 2

1. If T represents the set of all nonnegative integers $x \leqq 5$, write out all subsets of T consisting of three integers.
2. With T as in Problem 1, let S be the subset of T consisting of all integral powers of 2 contained in T. Write the members of S.

* Also called an *integral rational equation*.
† In case a brief review of imaginary numbers is advisable, see page 208.

3. If x is a variable whose domain is T of Problem 1, find the sum of all values of x; of the squares of all values of x.

4. If x is a variable whose domain consists of the set $\{1, 2, 3, 4, 5, 6\}$, and if $y = 2x + 3$, find the sum of all values of the variable y; write out the set of numbers which form the domain of y.

5. If the domain of x is $\{2, 4, 6, 9\}$ and $y = x^2$, write out the set of numbers forming the domain of the variable y.

Solve each of the equations; use the quadratic formula where desirable.

6. $3x - 7 = 0$. **7.** $15 - x = 4x$. **8.** $x^2 - 36 = 0$.

9. $x^2 + 9 = 0$. **10.** $2x^2 - 5x = 3$. **11.** $6 + 2x^2 = 7x$.

12. $x^2 - 2x = 2$. **13.** $4x^2 + 4x = 1$. **14.** $2x^2 + 9 = 8x$.

15. $8x^2 + 11 = 8x$. **16.** $4x^2 = 7x$. **17.** $3x = 5x^2$.

Prove that the equation is an identity.

18. $(y - 3)(y + 3) = y^2 - 9$. **19.** $(x + y)^3 = x^3 + 3x^2y + 3xy^2 + y^3$.

Prove that the equation is **NOT** *an identity, without solving the equation.*

20. $3x^2 - x = 5$. **21.** $2x - 5x^2 = 7$. **22.** $x + y = x^2 + y^2$.

Obtain three solutions of each equation.

23. $2x - y = 5$. **24.** $3x + 2y = 6$. **25.** $2x + 4y = 7$.

On a real number scale, the **graph of an equation** *(or inequality relationship) in a variable x is defined as the set of all points of the scale representing real solutions * of the equation (or inequality relationship). Graph each equation or statement involving inequality relations.†*

26. $2x - 5 = 0$. **27.** $x^2 - 3x + 2 = 0$. **28.** $x < 2$. **29.** $3 < x$.

30. $2 < x < 5$. **31.** $-1 \leqq x \leqq 3$. **32.** $-3 \leqq x < 0$.

33. $-2 \leqq x \leqq 4$. **34.** $-4 < x < 0$. **35.** $3 < x \leqq 6$.

8. Ordered pairs of objects and coordinates in a plane

A pair of symbols ‡ x and y is said to be an **ordered pair** in case each symbol is assigned to a specific place in two available locations. If the symbols are written in a line with a comma between them, we shall refer to the places from left to right as the 1st and 2d places, and shall call the corresponding symbols the *first* and *second components* of the pair. Two ordered

* If T is the set of *all real solutions*, the graph could be described as *the graph of* T on the number scale.

† Each problem presents a *mathematical statement*, which sometimes is called an *open statement* because a variable is involved. We meet simple mathematical statements in Problems 26–29, and compound mathematical statements in Problems 30–35. Thus, Problem 31 is read: "-1 *is less than or equal to x* **and** *x is less than or equal to* 3"; a solution of this statement is a value of x satisfying *both* of the coordinate statements joined by the conjunction "*and.*" The graph in each of Problems 30–35 is an *interval of numbers*, where one or both end points may have to be excluded.

‡ The symbols are not necessarily numbers.

pairs of symbols are considered identical if and only if the symbols in each place are the same for the two pairs. Thus, the ordered pairs of numbers (a, b) and (c, d) are identical if and only if $a = c$ and $b = d$.

To initiate analytic geometry in a plane, in some manner we associate an ordered pair of numbers, called *coordinates*, with each point in the plane. We proceed to introduce *rectangular coordinates*.

Consider a given plane subject to the postulates involved in elementary Euclidean geometry, as met by the student at the high school level. In this Euclidean plane, we draw two perpendicular lines, each called a *coordinate axis*, with one axis, OX, horizontal and the other, OY, vertical in the typical Figure 6. We agree that the axes and lines parallel to them will be *directed lines*, with the positive direction to the *right* on lines parallel to OX and *upward* on lines parallel to OY. On each axis, we establish a number scale with O as the origin. In doing this, we choose arbitrarily a first unit for scale distance on OX, and a second unit for scale distance on OY, where these units are not necessarily equal. We agree that, for coordinate purposes, distances in the plane along lines parallel to OX will be measured in terms of the scale unit on OX, and along lines parallel to OY in terms of the scale unit on OY. Let P be any point in the plane. Then, we present the following terminology.

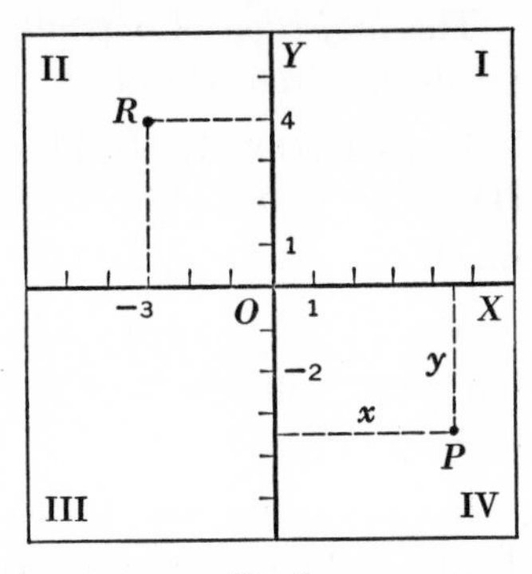

Fig. 6

I. *The horizontal coordinate, or* **abscissa,** *of P is the directed distance x, measured parallel to OX, from the vertical axis OY to P.*

II. *The vertical coordinate, or* **ordinate,** *of P is the directed distance y, measured parallel to OY, from the horizontal axis OX to P.*

The abscissa and ordinate of P together are called its *rectangular coordinates*. The intersection, O, of the axes is called the **origin** *of coordinates*. In (I) and (II) we have established a *one-to-one correspondence* between all ordered pairs of real numbers and the points in the plane. We shall use "$P{:}(x, y)$" to mean "*P with coordinates* (x, y)." We read "$P{:}(x, y)$" as "P, x, y." The axes divide the plane into four **quadrants,** numbered I, II, III, and IV, counterclockwise from OX.

Illustration 1. To plot $R{:}(-3, 4)$, erect a perpendicular to OX at $x = -3$ and go 4 units upward to reach R, in Figure 6.

Illustration 2. Recall that a geometric *locus* is a set of all points satisfying a specified condition. The locus of a point $P{:}(x, y)$ with $x = 5$ is the line perpendicular to OX and 5 units to the right of OY.

Note 1. Hereafter in our coordinate plane, unless otherwise specified, we shall assume that a unit has been chosen for distance measured in *any* direction, and that *this unit is taken as the scale unit on each coordinate axis.*

Note 2. "*To find a point*" usually will mean "*to find its coordinates.*"

★*Note 3. Oblique* coordinates can be introduced in a fashion similar to (I) and (II) by using intersecting axes OX and OY which are *not* perpendicular. In honor of the French mathematician RENÉ DESCARTES (1596–1650), who introduced the study of analytic geometry, any system of rectangular or oblique coordinates in a plane is called a **Cartesian system.**

9. Distance formula

The *projection* of a point P on a line l is defined as the foot of the perpendicular from P to l.

ILLUSTRATION 1. In Figure 6 on page 13, the projection of $R:(-3, 4)$ on OX is $(-3, 0)$ and on OY is $(0, 4)$. The projection of any point $P:(x, y)$ on OX is $(x, 0)$ and on OY is $(0, y)$.

Note 1. If A and B are any two points, at present "AB" will refer to the *segment* AB of the line through A and B.

Let $P_1:(x_1, y_1)$ and $P_2:(x_2, y_2)$ be given points. Figure 7 shows the projections M_1 and N_1 of P_1, and M_2 and N_2 of P_2 on the coordinate axes, with the associated values of one coordinate of each projection.

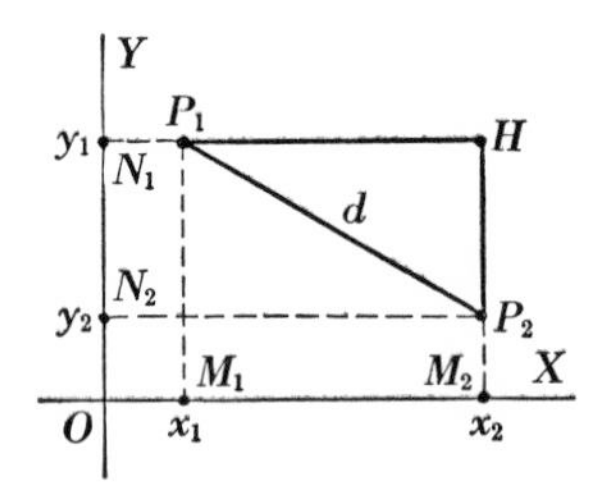

Fig. 7

THEOREM II. *In an xy-plane, the distance, d, between the points $P_1:(x_1, y_1)$ and $P_2:(x_2, y_2)$, or the length of P_1P_2, is given by the formula*

$$d = |P_1P_2| = \sqrt{(x_2 - x_1)^2 + (y_2 - y_1)^2}. \quad (1)$$

Proof. 1. In Figure 7, let H be the intersection of perpendiculars to OY through P_1, and to OX through P_2. Then, in the right triangle P_1HP_2, by the Pythagorean theorem,

$$(P_1P_2)^2 = (P_1H)^2 + (HP_2)^2. \quad (2)$$

2. From (4) on page 6,

$$P_1H = M_1M_2 = x_2 - x_1; \qquad HP_2 = N_1N_2 = y_2 - y_1.$$

Hence, we obtain

$$d^2 = (P_1P_2)^2 = (x_2 - x_1)^2 + (y_2 - y_1)^2. \quad (3)$$

On extracting square roots we are led to (1).

Note 2. Since $|P_1P_2| = |P_2P_1|$, and also because (1) involves *squares* of differences, the *order* of P_1, P_2 in (1) is immaterial. In (1), $|P_1P_2|$ can be rewritten merely P_1P_2 if P_1P_2 is undirected.

ILLUSTRATION 2. From (1) with $x_1 = 2$, $x_2 = -3$, etc., the distance between $A:(2, -8)$ and $B:(-3, 4)$ is

$$AB = \sqrt{(-3-2)^2 + [4-(-8)]^2} = \sqrt{25+144} = 13.$$

The distance d of $P:(x, y)$ from the origin $O:(0, 0)$ is called the **radius vector** of P and is found from (1):

$$\mathbf{d = \sqrt{x^2 + y^2}.} \qquad (4)$$

EXAMPLE 1. Find the point on OX equidistant from $A:(5, 4)$ and $B:(-2, 3)$.

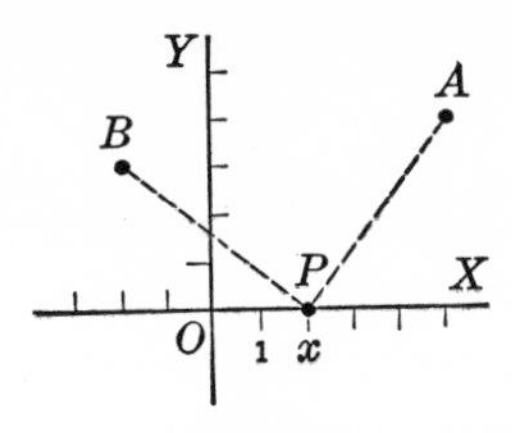

Fig. 8

SOLUTION. 1. Let the unknown point be $P:(x, 0)$, in Figure 8. Then $PA = PB$. This occurs if and only if $(PA)^2 = (PB)^2$. From (1),

$$(PA)^2 = (5-x)^2 + 4^2; \qquad (5)$$

$$(PB)^2 = (x+2)^2 + 3^2. \qquad (6)$$

2. From (5) and (6),

$$25 - 10x + x^2 + 16 = x^2 + 4x + 4 + 9.$$

Therefore, $14x = 28$ or $x = 2$. The point is $P:(2, 0)$.

EXERCISE 3

Find the other vertex of a rectangle with the given vertices.

1. (3, 4); (– 5, 4); (3, – 1). **2.** (– 2, – 1); (3, – 1); (3, 2).

3. A line l through (2, – 3) is perpendicular to OY. What is true about the ordinates of all points on l?

Describe and construct the locus of a point $P:(x, y)$ satisfying the condition.

4. The abscissa is – 3. **5.** The ordinate is – 4.

Plot the point and its projections M and N on OX and OY, respectively. Find the coordinates of M and N.

6. (3, 7). **7.** (2, 4). **8.** (– 2, – 5). **9.** (8, – 7).

If A represents the first point and B the second, find AB and $|AB|$.

10. (0, 8); (0, 5). **11.** (8, 4); (2, 4). **12.** (– 1, 3); (– 1, 5).
13. (2, 2); (9, 2). **14.** (3, 4); (3, – 12). **15.** (x_1, y_1); (x_1, y_2).

Find the distance between the points, or an expression for it.

16. (1, 2); (4, 6). **17.** (5, 0); (0, 12). **18.** (3, 7); (– 6, 7).
19. (7, 2); (2, 14). **20.** (– 1, – 3); (2, 1). **21.** (0, 0); (4, 7).
22. (0, 3); (4, 0). **23.** (– 2, 5); (– 2, – 1). **24.** (x, y); (3, – 4).

Prove that the triangle with the given vertices is isosceles.

25. $(-2, 8)$; $(-1, 1)$; $(3, 3)$. **26.** $(3, -1)$; $(3, -3)$; $(7, -2)$.

Prove that the triangle with the given vertices is equilateral.

27. $(-2, 0)$; $(8, 0)$; $(3, 5\sqrt{3})$. **28.** $(0, 2)$; $(0, -6)$; $(4\sqrt{3}, -2)$.

Prove that the points are the vertices of a right triangle.

29. $(-1, -1)$; $(1, 0)$; $(-2, 6)$. **30.** $(3, 2)$; $(5, 3)$; $(0, 8)$.

31. Prove that $(-2, 4)$, $(-4, 1)$, $(6, 2)$, and $(4, -1)$ are the vertices of a parallelogram.

32. Find x if the distance between $(x, 2)$ and $(6, 6)$ is 5.

33. Find y if $(-3, y)$ is equidistant from $(-3, 2)$ and $(5, 6)$.

34. Find a point on OX equidistant from $(-1, -1)$ and $(3, 5)$.

10. Graph of an equation in two variables

Consider an equation in two variables x and y, whose domains possibly do not consist entirely of real numbers. On page 9, we defined a *solution* of the equation to be a *pair of corresponding values of x and y* which satisfy the equation, or which make it a true statement. Hence, a solution is an ordered pair of numbers (b, c), where the first component, b, is a value of x and the second component, c, is a value of y.

Illustration 1. In $3x - 5y = 15$, if $x = 0$ then $y = 5$ in order to satisfy the equation; thus, $(0, 5)$ is a solution of it. Another solution is $(8\frac{1}{3}, 2)$, obtained by placing $y = 2$ and solving for x in the equation. The given equation has infinitely many solutions because, if any value is assigned to x, a corresponding value can be computed for y from the equation so that (x, y) is a solution.

Hereafter in this chapter, let us assume that the domain of any variable consists of real numbers. Then, the *solution set* for an equation in two variables, x and y, is a set of ordered pairs of real numbers, (x, y). Suppose, now, that each solution (x, y) is taken as the coordinates of a point in a plane provided with an xy-system of coordinates. Then, the resulting points usually will make up one or more curves. This leads to the following terminology.

Definition II. *The* **graph,** *or* **locus,** *of an equation in two variables x and y is the set of points whose coordinates (x, y) satisfy the equation.**

Suppose that T is *any* set of ordered pairs of real numbers (x, y), and let us define *the graph of T* as the set of points in an xy-plane whose coordinates are number pairs in T. Then, in place of Definition II, we may say that *the graph of an equation is the graph of its solution set.*

* In graphing an equation in the variables x and y in an xy-plane, as a rule there is no necessity for using equal scale units on the coordinate axes.

To graph an equation will mean *to draw its graph.* To obtain it, we may substitute values for either variable in the equation and compute the corresponding values of the other variable, to form a table of representative solutions (x, y). The graph then is drawn through the points having the coordinates in the table.

ILLUSTRATION 2. To graph $3x - 5y = 15$, we form the following table of solutions by substituting $x = 0$, then $y = 0$, and other values of x or of y. We plot the solutions $(-5, -6)$, etc., in Figure 9, and join the points by a smooth curve, which is seen to be a line, l.

$x =$	-5	-2	0	5	6
$y =$	-6	$-4\frac{1}{5}$	-3	0	$\frac{3}{5}$

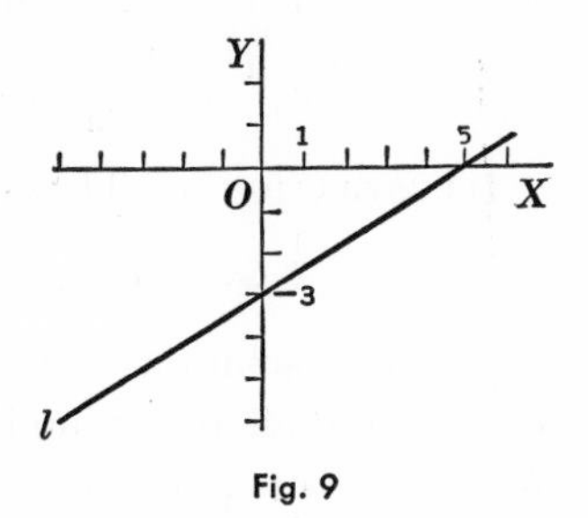

Fig. 9

From page 11, a *linear* equation, or an equation of the *first degree*, in variables x and y, is equivalent to an equation of the form $Ax + By + C = 0$, where A, B, and C are constants and A and B are not both zero. In Figure 9, we illustrated the fact * that, in an xy-plane where the units on the axes need *not* be equal, *the graph of a linear equation in x and y is a line.* To obtain it for a given equation, it is advisable to compute *three solutions* of the equation, although just two points determine a line.

The **x-intercepts** of a graph in an xy-plane are the values of x at the points where the graph meets the x-axis; the **y-intercepts** are the values of y where the graph meets the y-axis. Intercepts are useful in graphing, and are obtained conveniently as follows.

SUMMARY. *To obtain the intercepts of the graph of an equation in x and y.*

1. *To find the x-intercepts, place $y = 0$ and solve for x.*
2. *To find the y-intercepts, place $x = 0$ and solve for y.*

ILLUSTRATION 3. To graph $3x - 5y = 15$, we place $x = 0$ and find $y = -3$, the y-intercept. The x-intercept is $x = 5$. The graph, in Figure 9, passes through $(0, -3)$ and $(5, 0)$.

ILLUSTRATION 4. We may look upon $x - 8 = 0$ as a linear equation in x and y where y has the coefficient zero. Then, the graph of $x - 8 = 0$ in an xy-plane has an x-intercept, $x = 8$, but no y-intercept because we cannot have $x = 0$ in a solution. Hence, the graph is the line perpendicular to the x-axis where $x = 8$. Also, we could look upon $x - 8 = 0$ as an equation in a *single* variable, x; then, the graph of $x - 8 = 0$ on simply an x-axis would be the *single point* where $x = 8$, the only solution of the equation. The *context* should always show what viewpoint is involved.

* Proved in analytic geometry.

ILLUSTRATION 5. To graph the equation $y - x^2 + 2x + 1 = 0$, we first solve for y to obtain $y = x^2 - 2x - 1$; then we assign values to x and compute y to form the following table of solutions (x, y). The graph is a curve called a **parabola,** in Figure 10.

$x =$	-2	0	1	2	4
$y =$	7	-1	-2	-1	7

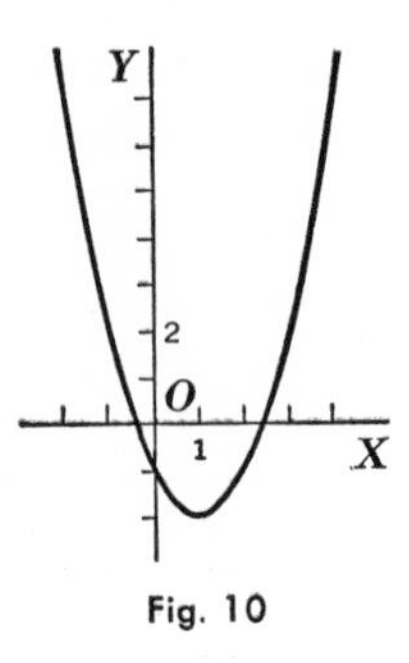

Fig. 10

ILLUSTRATION 6. The equation

$$x^2 + 5y^2 + 6 = 0, \quad or \quad x^2 + 5y^2 = -6,$$

has no real solution (x, y) because x^2 and y^2 are positive or zero for all real x and y, and hence $x^2 + 5y^2 \neq -6$ for any real point (x, y). Therefore, the equation $x^2 + 5y^2 + 6 = 0$ has no graph.

11. The equation of a locus

An equation of a locus in an xy-plane is an equation in x and y whose graph is the given locus.

ILLUSTRATION 1. An equation of the locus of a point $P{:}(x, y)$ which is two units to the right of the y-axis is $x = 2$.

In terminology from page 10, two equations in variables x and y are called *equivalent* if they have the same solutions, and hence the *same graph.* For instance, if one equation can be obtained by multiplying both sides of another by a constant, not zero, the equations are equivalent. If we can find one equation for a locus, then we can write infinitely many equivalent equations for it. As a rule, we refer to the particular one of these equations with which we deal as **THE** equation of the locus.

ILLUSTRATION 2. The locus of $3x - 5y = 15$ is the line l in Figure 9, page 17. This line also is the locus of $6x - 10y = 30$.

We may refer to an equation by giving it *the name of its graph.*

ILLUSTRATION 3. In Figure 10, we observe the *parabola* $y = x^2 - 2x - 1$.

EXERCISE 4

Graph each equation in an xy-plane.

1. $3x + 2y = 6$. **2.** $3y - 4x - 12 = 0$. **3.** $3x + 7y = 0$.

4. $x - 5 = 0$. **5.** $y = -7$. **6.** $x + y = 0$. **7.** $3x - 4 = 0$.

Graph the equation with $x = 2$, and other values of x near 2, used in the table of values.

8. $y = x^2 - 4x - 5$. **9.** $y = 3 + 4x - x^2$. **10.** $y - x^2 = 7 - 4x$.

Graph the equation with $y = -2$, and other values of y near -2, used in the table of values.

11. $x = y^2 + 4y - 5$. **12.** $x = 7 - 8y - 2y^2$. **13.** $2x + 8y = 2y^2 + 5$.

14. Make verbal statements to prove that $3x^2 + y^2 = -5$ has no graph.

15. Prove that the graph of $x^2 + (y - 2)^2 = 0$ consists of just one point.

★**16.** Let $[x]$ be used to represent *the greatest integer which is less than or equal to x*, where the domain of x consists of all real numbers. Graph the equation $y = [x]$.

★*Graph the equation.*

17. $y = |x|$. **18.** $y = |x + 1|$. **19.** $x = |y| - 1$.

12. Concept of a function

If x and y are variables, and it is said that "*y is a function of x*," we infer that there is some rule designating a value of y corresponding to each value of x. We shall make this terminology precise.

DEFINITION III. *Let D be a given set of numbers. Suppose that, for each number x in D, some rule specifies just one corresponding number y, and let R be the set of all of these values of y. Then,*

$$\left\{\begin{array}{l}\textit{this } \textbf{correspondence} \textit{ between the numbers of } D \textit{ and} \\ \textit{those of } R \textit{ is called a } \textbf{function,} \ F, \textit{ from } D \textit{ to } R,\end{array}\right\} \quad \textit{or} \qquad (1)$$

$$\left\{\begin{array}{l}\textit{the } \textbf{whole set of ordered pairs} \\ (x, y) \textit{ is called a } \textbf{function,} \ F.\end{array}\right\} \qquad (2)$$

Two current forms of terminology for describing a function are given in (1) and (2); other equivalent forms are met in mathematical texts. The correspondence in (1) determines the ordered pairs in (2); conversely, these pairs create the correspondence. Hence, merely personal preference is involved in deciding which of (1) and (2) is to be emphasized at any time.

In Definition III, each value of y is called a *value of the function*. The set D of values of x is referred to as the **domain** of definition of F, and R is called the **range** of values of F. From (2), we may refer to F as *a set of ordered pairs* (x, y). In view of (1), we may speak of F as *a correspondence between the domain D and the range R*, or as *a mapping of D on R*. We call x the **independent variable** and y the **dependent variable.** Frequently, the dependent variable is referred to as if it were the function, and we say

$$\textbf{y is a function of x,} \qquad (3)$$

which abbreviates "*y is the value of a function F corresponding to the number x in the domain of F.*" Thus, (3) means that to each value of x there corresponds *just one* value of y. In Definition III we refer to F as a function of a *single variable* because the domain D consists of *single numbers.*

ILLUSTRATION 1. Let D be the set of all x such that $1 \leqq x \leqq 3$, and let $y = 2x + 3$. If $x = 1$, then $y = 5$; if $x = 2$, then $y = 7$; etc. Thus, with x in D, the values of y make up the interval R, $5 \leqq y \leqq 9$, on OY in Figure 11, where the correspondence between x and y is indicated by representative arrows. This correspondence is a function mapping D on R. The formula $(2x + 3)$ gives the value of the function for any value of x.

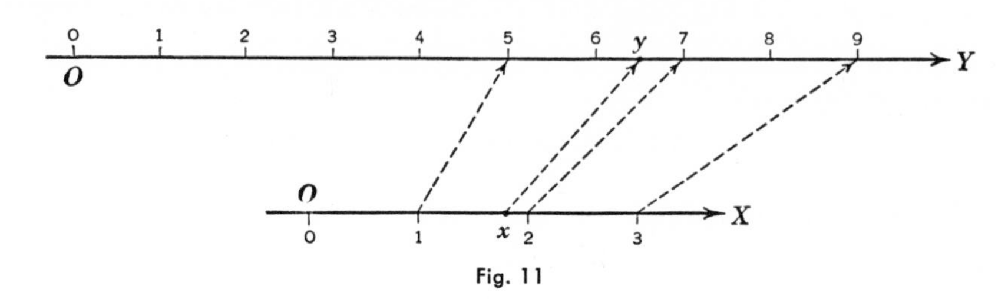

Fig. 11

Any formula in a variable x, specifying a single value for each value of x, defines a function whose values are given by substitution in the formula. However, a function may be defined merely by its tabulated values, or other means, without use of a formula. If a function is defined by a formula, the function frequently is named on the basis of the nature of its formula. Thus, in previous mathematics, we have met *algebraic functions*. Later in this text we shall emphasize the *trigonometric functions*.

ILLUSTRATION 2. In Definition III, if $y = k$, a constant, for all values of x, we say that F is a *constant function*.

ILLUSTRATION 3. Let F be the function whose value is $(\frac{3}{5}x - 3)$ at any real value of x. Let $y = \frac{3}{5}x - 3$. Then F consists of infinitely many ordered pairs (x, y), a few of which are in the following table. The pairs (x, y) forming F are the *solutions of the equation* $y = \frac{3}{5}x - 3$. Hence, in an xy-plane, the set of points whose coordinates (x, y) are pairs in F is the graph of the equation $y = \frac{3}{5}x - 3$ because F is its *solution set*. The graph is line AB in Figure 12, drawn through the points in the table. We also call AB the *graph of F*. We formalize the concept of the graph of a function as below.

$x =$	-5	0	3	5	6
$y =$	-6	-3	$-1\frac{1}{5}$	0	$\frac{3}{5}$

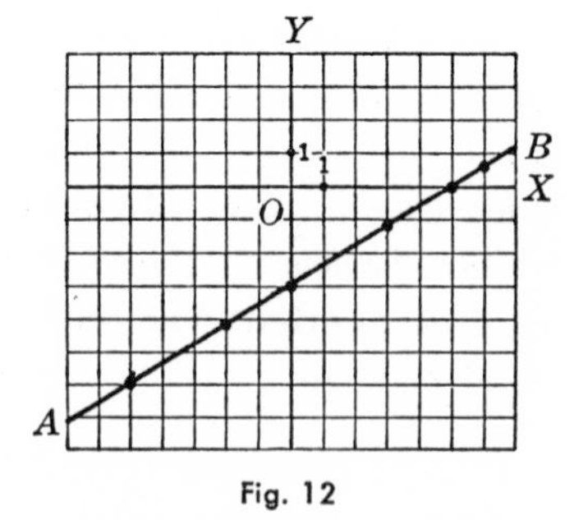

Fig. 12

DEFINITION IV. *In an xy-plane, the* **graph of a function,** *F, of a single variable, x, is the set of all points whose coordinates (x, y) form pairs of corresponding values of x and the function.*

The discussion in Illustration 3, and Definition IV, lead to the following working method: *to graph a function defined by a formula in a variable x, place y equal to the formula and graph the resulting equation.*

ILLUSTRATION 4. To graph the function whose value is $(x^2 - 2x - 1)$ at any value of the variable x, we let $y = x^2 - 2x - 1$ and graph this equation. The graph is the parabola in Figure 10 on page 18.

ILLUSTRATION 5. Let D be the set $\{0, 1, 2, 3, 4, 5, 6, 7, 8, 9, 10, 11, 12, 13\}$. Let F be the function such that, for any x in D, the value, y, of F is the *largest integral multiple of* 2 *which is at most equal to* x. Thus, if $x = 0$, then $y = 0$; if $x = 5$, then $y = 4$; etc. The range, R, of F is the set $\{0, 2, 4, 6, 8, 10, 12\}$. In Figure 13, the correspondence between D and R is shown by arrows. F consists of fourteen pairs (0, 0), (1, 0), (2, 2), (3, 2), · · ·, (11, 10), (12, 12), (13, 12). A graph of F would consist of fourteen points.

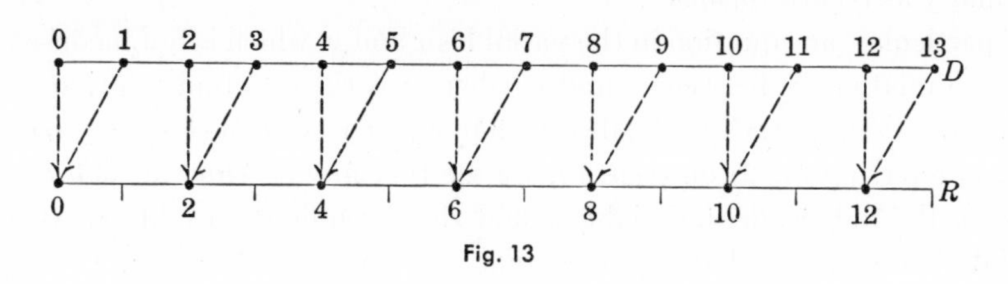

Fig. 13

Note 1. Usually, in graphing a function in a coordinate plane, we use the horizontal axis for plotting values of the independent variable.

In the description of a function, F, the letters used for the independent and dependent variables are of no importance. Thus, suppose that F is defined by stating that, for every number x in the domain, the value, y, of F is $y = 3x - 5$. The same function is defined by saying that, for every number u in the domain, the value, r, of F is $r = 3u - 5$.

ILLUSTRATION 6. When the values of a function are defined by a formula, we sometimes refer to it as if it were the function. Thus, we may refer to "*the function* $(x^2 + 7x)$," or to "*the function* $y = x^2 + 7x$," as an abbreviation for the following statement: * "*the function whose value at any value of x is* $(x^2 + 7x)$."

Note 2. In Definition III on page 19, if we change the word *number* to *object*, the definition describes a function F whose domain D is *a set of objects* of any variety, and whose range R is *a second set of objects*. Thus, D might consist of a set of people and y, with domain R, might be the color of the eyes of the person x of D. Functions of this nature are important. For instance,

* Let the *inverted* Greek letter epsilon, ∍, be used to abbreviate "*such that.*" Then, above, with F as the function, we may write $F = \{(x, y) \ni y = x^2 + 7x\}$, which is read "*$F$ is the set of all numbers* (x, y) *such that* $y = x^2 + 7x$." The preceding symbolism is a form of so-called *set-builder* notation for abbreviated description of sets.

in the next chapter, the trigonometric functions will be defined initially as functions whose domain consists of *angles*, not numbers.

★*Note 3.* In Definition III on page 19, since just one value of y corresponds to each value of x, sometimes it is said that a function, as thus defined, is *single valued.* If n is a positive integer greater than 1, and if Definition III were altered to read that n values of y correspond to each value of x, a function as thus defined would be called *n-valued.* We shall not use the concept of an n-valued function.

13. Functions defined by equations

Suppose that x and y are variables, and that T is any nonempty set of ordered pairs of numbers (b, c), where b is a value of x and c is a value of y. Then, we shall refer to T as a **relation** *between* (or *in*) *x and y*, and may speak of x and y as *related variables.*

In particular, an equation in the variables x and y, which is not inconsistent, defines a relation, S, between x and y, where S is the set of all solutions (x, y) of the equation. Hence we shall say that x and y are *related by the equation.* Also, in referring to (2) on page 19, we see that *any function, F, is a relation* between the independent variable x and the dependent variable y, with the special characteristic that *just one value of y corresponds to each value of x.* In contrast, a *relation T* between x and y is a *function* with x as the independent variable *when and only when the special characteristic just mentioned is true.* Thus, some relations are not functions.

Illustration 1. Sometimes a relation may be described merely by tabulation of its pairs of values of the variables. Thus, the following table of values of x and y describes a relation, T, in x and y:

$x =$	1	1	2	3	2
$y =$	2	-4	1	2	3

We see that T is *not* a function with x as the independent variable because there are *two pairs* $(1, 2)$ and $(1, -4)$ with $x = 1$. Also, T is *not* a function with y as the independent variable because there are *two pairs* $(1, 2)$ and $(3, 2)$ with $y = 2$.

Suppose that two variables x and y are related by an equation which, for each value of x, determines *just one value of* y such that (x, y) is a solution of the equation. Then, *its solution set, F, is a function* with x as the independent variable, or we may say that *the equation defines y as a function of x.* With an equation of this variety, sometimes we may obtain a formula for the values of F by solving the equation for y in terms of x. Similarly, an equation defines x as a function of y provided that, *for each value of y, the* *equation has just one solution* (x, y).) In either of the preceding cases, the graph of the equation is identical with the graph of the function F defined by the equation, because F is its solution set.

ILLUSTRATION 2. From $3x - 5y = 15$, we obtain

$$y = \tfrac{3}{5}x - 3, \quad \textit{and similarly}, \quad x = \tfrac{5}{3}y + 5. \tag{1}$$

Thus, for each value of x, there is just one solution (x, y); for each value of y, there is just one solution (x, y). Hence, the equation $3x - 5y = 15$ defines y as a function of x, and also defines x as a function of y. The graph of either of these functions in an xy-plane is identical with the graph of $3x - 5y = 15$, as seen in Figure 9 on page 17.

ILLUSTRATION 3. The equation $y - x^2 + 2x = 1$ defines a relation between x and y where y is a function of x because, with $y = x^2 - 2x + 1$, *just one value of* y *corresponds to each value of* x. This may be checked with the graph of the equation in Figure 14; a perpendicular to the x-axis at any point $x = a$ meets the parabola in just one point, (a, b), or there is *just one* value $y = b$ corresponding to $x = a$. On the other hand, if $c > 0$, a perpendicular to the y-axis at $y = c$ would meet the parabola in *two points*. Hence, the equation $y = x^2 - 2x + 1$ does *not* define x as a function of y, because *two values of* x *correspond to each admissible value of* y (except $y = 0$).

Fig. 14

In graphing a function in an xy-plane, as a rule there is no necessity for using equal scale units on the coordinate axes.

EXERCISE 5

In each of Problems 1 and 2, state the range R of the function F and write the complete set of pairs of numbers which form F. Construct a graph of F in an xy-plane. Also, prepare a diagram like Figure 13 on page 21 to show how F maps its domain on the range. The units need not be equal on the scales for x and y.

1. F has the domain $\{-4, -3, -2, -1, 0, 1, 2, 3, 4\}$ and the value of F for any number x in the domain is x^2.
2. The domain, D, of F consists of the integers $(1, 2, 3, \cdots, 15)$. The value of F corresponding to any number x in D is the largest integral multiple of 3 which is less than or equal to x.

Graph the function whose values, for any real number x, are given by the formula.

3. $3x - 2$.
4. $-2x + 5$.
5. $x - 7$.
6. 12.
7. $x^2 + 6x - 5$; use $x = -3$ in the table of representative values.
8. $4x - x^2 + 3$; use $x = 2$ in the table of representative values.

By solving for y, and then for x, obtain a formula for the values of the function of x, and also of the function of y defined by the equation.

9. $4x + 3y = 12$. **10.** $2x + y = 7$. **11.** $3x - 6y = 7$.

In Problems 12–16, after graphing the equation, state whether or not the equation defines y as a function of x, or x as a function of y. Then, obtain a formula for the values of any function which is met.

12. Graph $2y + 2x^2 - 4x = 5$, with $x = 1$ used in the table of solutions.

13. Graph $3x - 6y^2 + 24y = 5$, with $y = 2$ used in the table of solutions.

14. Graph $y = x^3$.

★15. With x on the interval $-3 \leqq x \leqq 5$, graph the equation $y = [x]$, where $[x]$ represents the greatest integer at most equal to x.

★16. With y on the interval $-2 \leqq y \leqq 4$, graph $x = [y]$.

14. Functional notation

Let F be a function with the domain D. Then, it frequently is convenient to represent the value of F corresponding to the number x in D by the symbol "$\boldsymbol{F(x)}$," read "*F of x*" or "*F at x*." Thus,

$$\left\{\begin{matrix} \boldsymbol{F(x)} \textit{ represents the } \textbf{value of } \boldsymbol{F} \\ \textit{corresponding to any number } x \textit{ in } D. \end{matrix}\right\} \tag{1}$$

We then say that $F(x)$ is a symbol in *functional notation.*

Illustration 1. If we write $F(x) = 3x^2 + x - 5$, this simultaneously assigns F as a symbol for the function, and gives a formula, $3x^2 + x - 5$, for the values of F. Thus, the values of F at $x = c$, $x = -1$, and $x = 2 + h$ are found to be

$$F(c) = 3c^2 + c - 5; \qquad F(-1) = 3 - 1 - 5 = -3;$$
$$F(2 + h) = 3(2 + h)^2 + (2 + h) - 5.$$

Sometimes it is convenient to refer to * "**a function $\boldsymbol{F(x)}$**," or to say that "*F is a function of x*," as an abbreviation for the statement that "*F is a symbol for a function where the letter x is to be used for the independent variable.*"

We use single letters such as G, F, H, g, f, k, etc., to represent functions. Occasionally we shall use a phrase such as

$$\text{"}\textbf{a function } \boldsymbol{y = g(x)}\text{"} \tag{2}$$

to abbreviate "*a function g where the value g(x) also will be represented by y.*" If we write $y = g(x)$, then x is a variable; y and $g(x)$ are variables having the same value corresponding to any value of x; the letter g alone is *not* a variable, and has no values, but is a symbol for *a set of number pairs* (x, y).

* The symbol $F(x)$ also gives the added information that F is a function of a *single* variable, which is useful knowledge after functions of *two or more* variables enter the field.

ILLUSTRATION 2. If $f(x) = 5x^2 + 2$ and $g(y) = 4/y$, then

$$[f(3)]^2 = [5(9) + 2]^2 = 47^2 = 2209, \quad f(x)g(x) = (5x^2 + 2)\left(\frac{4}{x}\right) = 20x + \frac{8}{x};$$

$$f(g(y)) = 5(g(y))^2 + 2 = 5\left(\frac{4}{y}\right)^2 + 2 = \frac{80}{y^2} + 2.$$

ILLUSTRATION 3. If $f(x) = \dfrac{\sqrt{4 - x}}{x + 2}$, then $f(x)$ is not defined if $x + 2 = 0$, or $x = -2$, because *division by zero is not an operation of algebra.* Also, if only real values of f are to be considered, $f(x)$ is not defined when $4 - x < 0$, or $4 < x$, because then $\sqrt{4 - x}$ is imaginary. Thus, $f(x)$ is defined just when $x \leqq 4$, excluding $x = -2$.

In terms of functional notation, the graph in an xy-plane of a function F of a variable x is defined as follows.

$$\left\{\begin{array}{l}\textit{The } \textbf{graph of a function } F\textit{, with the independent}\\ \textit{variable } x\textit{, is the graph of the equation } y = F(x).\end{array}\right\} \tag{3}$$

15. Functions of two or more variables

Let x and y be variables which are free to assume any ordered pair of values (x, y) in a certain set, D, of pairs of numbers. We may represent D as a corresponding set of points (x, y) in an xy-plane. Suppose that, to each point (x, y) in D, there corresponds just one number z, and let R be the set of all values thus obtained for z. Then,

$$\left\{\begin{array}{l}\textit{this } \textbf{correspondence} \textit{ between pairs in } D \textit{ and num-}\\ \textit{bers in } R \textit{ is called a } \textbf{function,} \ F\textit{, from } D \textit{ to } R\textit{,}\end{array}\right\} \quad \textit{or} \tag{1}$$

$$\left\{\begin{array}{c}\textit{the } \textbf{whole set of ordered triples of num-}\\ \textbf{bers } (x, y, z) \textit{ is called a } \textbf{function,} \ F.\end{array}\right\} \tag{2}$$

In (1) and (2), F is said to be a function of *two* independent variables, x and y, because D consists of *pairs* of numbers, (x, y). We refer to D as the **domain** of F, and to R as the **range** of F. We extend the functional notation to this situation and write $z = F(x, y)$, meaning that $F(x, y)$, as well as z, represents the value of F at the point (x, y) in the domain of F. Similarly, we may have a function of three or more variables. Thus, $F(x, y, w)$ would represent the value of a function F of three independent variables at the point (x, y, w) in the domain of F.

ILLUSTRATION 1. If $F(x, y) = 3x^2y + 8x + 5y^2$, then

$$F(2, -3) = -36 + 16 + 45 = 25.$$

Note 1. Hereafter, unless otherwise stated, in any reference to a *function* we shall mean a *function of a single variable.*

16. Polynomial functions

A function F is called a **polynomial function** *of degree n* in certain variables, say x and y, if $F(x, y)$ is given by a polynomial of degree n in the variables, as defined on page 10. With functional notation, we may now state that a *polynomial equation of degree n in x and y* is of the form $f(x, y) = g(x, y)$, where $f(x, y)$ and $g(x, y)$ are polynomials and $[f(x, y) - g(x, y)]$ is of degree n in the variables. The values of any polynomial function P of degree n in a single variable x are given by a polynomial,

$$P(x) = a_0 + a_1x + a_2x^2 + \cdots + a_nx^n, \tag{1}$$

where $a_0, a_1, \cdots, a_n$ are constants and $a_n \neq 0$. If $n = 0$, then $P(x) = a_0$ where $a_0 \neq 0$.*

Sometimes, in preceding terminology, the word *polynomial* is omitted, and we then refer, for instance, simply to *a function of degree n in x*, instead of to *a polynomial function of degree n*.

ILLUSTRATION 1. If f is a linear function of x, then $f(x) = mx + b$ where m and b are constants and $m \neq 0$. The graph of f in an xy-plane is the graph of the equation $y = mx + b$, and hence is a *line*.

ILLUSTRATION 2. If f is a linear function of x and y, then we have $f(x, y) = Ax + By + C$, where A, B, and C are constants and A and B are not both zero.

If F is a quadratic function of x, then

$$\boldsymbol{F(x) = ax^2 + bx + c,}$$

where a, b, and c are constants and $a \neq 0$. In analytic geometry, it is proved that the graph of a quadratic function is a **parabola.**

EXAMPLE 1. Graph the quadratic function $(x^2 - 2x - 3)$.

SOLUTION. 1. Let $y = x^2 - 2x - 3$. We assign values to x and compute y, as in the following table.

x	-3	-2	0	1	2	4	5
y	12	5	-3	-4	-3	5	12

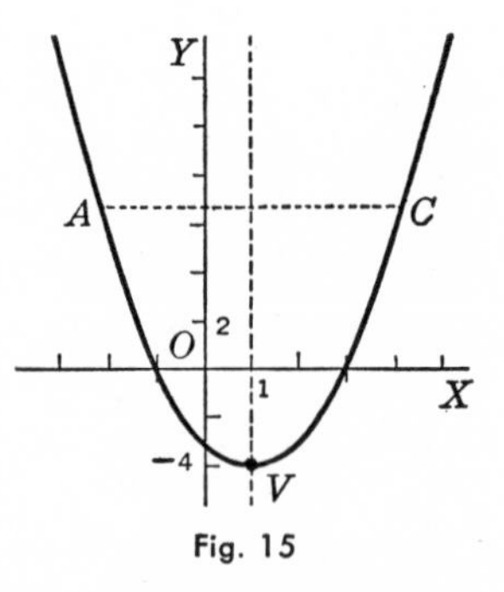

Fig. 15

2. The parabola through these points (Figure 15) is the graph of the function. The lowest point, V, of the parabola is called its *vertex*. At V, $y = -4$. This ordinate is the *smallest* or **minimum value**

* The constant function P, where $P(x) = 0$ for all values of x, is *not* referred to as a polynomial function of degree *zero;* in this case, $P(x)$ sometimes is called the *zero polynomial.* This notational matter will not concern us.

of f, and hence V is called the **minimum point** of the graph. The vertical line through V is called the *axis* of the parabola. It is *symmetric* to its axis, because *any chord* (such as AC) *of the parabola perpendicular to the axis is bisected by it.* The *equation of the axis*, through V, in Figure 15 is $x = 1$. This parabola is said to be **concave** *upward* (open upward), because the curve bends *counterclockwise* if we travel on it from left to right.

ILLUSTRATION 3. The graph of $y = -x^2 + 2x + 3$ would be a parabola concave *downward*, and its vertex V would be called the **maximum point** of the curve. The value of y at V would be called the **maximum value** of the function $(-x^2 + 2x + 3)$.

In analytic geometry, it is proved that the x-coordinate of the vertex of the graph of a quadratic function $y = ax^2 + bx + c$ is $x = -b/2a$. This value of x should be used in the table of values which is the basis for the graph in any particular case.

ILLUSTRATION 4. The graph of the cubic function $y = x^3 - 12x + 3$ in Figure 16 was based on the following table of values.

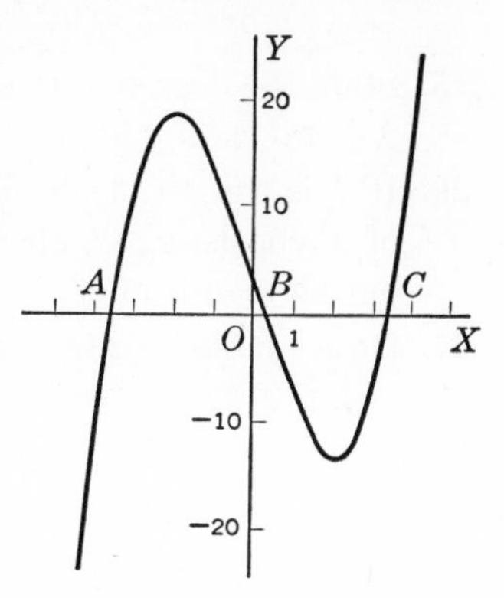

Fig. 16

When $x =$	-4	-3	-2	-1	0	1	2	3	4
Then $y =$	-13	$+12$	$+19$	$+14$	$+3$	-8	-13	-6	$+19$

EXERCISE 6

Graph the function whose values are defined by the given formula for all real values of x.

1. $2x + 3$. **2.** $-3x + 5$. **3.** -7. **4.** 5.

5. x^2. **6.** $x^2 - 4x + 7$. **7.** $-3x^2 - 6x + 5$. **8.** $4x^2 + 5$.

9. $-x^2$. **10.** $x^2 + 6x + 5$. **11.** $-2x^2 + 8x + 3$. **12.** $8x - 2x^2$.

In an xy-plane where the x-axis is horizontal, graph the given equation, which defines x as a quadratic function of y, or y as a quadratic function of x.

13. $x = 4y^2 + 2$. **14.** $x = 2y^2 + 8y - 6$. **15.** $x = -y^2 + 6y - 8$.

16. $y = 3 - 2x^2$. **17.** $y = 2x^2 - 4x$. **18.** $y = 6 - 4x - x^2$.

Graph the polynomial function f for which $f(x)$ is given.

19. $f(x) = x^3 - 3x^2 - 24x - 7$; use $f(-4)$, $f(-3)$, $f(-2)$, $f(-1)$, $f(0)$, $f(3)$, $f(4)$, and $f(5)$.

20. $f(x) = x^3$; use $f(-2)$, $f(-1)$, $f(-\frac{1}{2})$, $f(0)$, $f(\frac{1}{2})$, $f(1)$, and $f(2)$.

21. $f(x) = x^2(x - 2)^2$; use $f(-2)$, $f(-\frac{1}{2})$, $f(0)$, $f(\frac{1}{2})$, $f(1)$, $f(\frac{3}{2})$, $f(2)$, $f(\frac{5}{2})$, $f(3)$, and $f(4)$.

REVIEW PROBLEMS for Chapter 1

22. Mark A:(-3), B:(4), C:(-5), and D:(6) on a number scale and compute AB, DC, $|AD|$, and $|CB|$. Also, check the equality $AC + CD = AD$.

23. By use of inequality signs, state that the number x lies between -3 and 7 on the real number scale.

24. If the domain of the variable x consists of all real numbers, which of the following equations is (a) inconsistent; (b) an identity; (c) a conditional equation having solutions?

$$3x^2 + 5 = 0; \quad x^2 - x = 2; \quad (x - a)^2 = x^2 - 2ax + a^2.$$

25. State the degree of the polynomial $(5xy^3 + 3yz^4)$ in the variables x, y, and z, jointly; in y alone; in z alone.

26. If T is the set of all positive integral powers of -2, and S is the subset of T consisting of all members x of T such that $-15 < x < 30$, write out all members of S.

27. On a number scale, graph the solutions of the mathematical statement $-2 \leqq x < 5$, where x is a variable.

28. In an xy-plane, find the radius vector of P:$(-7, 24)$.

29. In an xy-plane, find the distance between P:$(-3, 5)$ and Q:$(2, 4)$. Use Table I.

30. In an xy-plane, find the point $(0, y)$ which is equidistant from A:$(4, 5)$ and B:$(3, -2)$.

31. In an xy-plane, prove that the triangle with the vertices $(0, -4)$, $(0, 16)$, and $(10\sqrt{3}, 6)$ is equilateral.

Graph the equation in the variables x and y.

32. $3x - y = 5$. **33.** $2x - 7 = 0$. **34.** $4x + 5y = 0$.

35. $y = x^2 - 6x + 5$. **36.** $x = y^2 + 4y - 7$.

37. $x = |y|$. **38.** $y = |x - 2|$. **39.** $x = [y] - 2$.

HINT for Problem 39. $[y]$ is the greatest integer in y.

40. The domain, D, of a function, F, consists of all integers x such that $|x| \leqq 9$. For each x in D, the value of F is that integral multiple of 3 which is nearest to x on the real number scale. (a) Find the range, R, of F. (b) List the set of ordered pairs of numbers which form F. (c) Construct a diagram like Figure 13 on page 21 showing how F maps D on R. (d) Construct a graph of F in an xy-plane.

41. If $f(x) = 3x + 2$ and $g(x) = x^2 + 3x$, find $f(-2)$; $g(3)$; $2f(3)g(-1)$; $f(g(2))$; $f(g(x))$.

2

TRIGONOMETRIC FUNCTIONS OF ANGLES

17. Directed angles

In elementary geometry, an *angle* was thought of as a ready-made figure, and the measure of an angle always was a positive number or zero. It is convenient now to add a dynamic concept to the figure for an angle.

Suppose that a ray, issuing from a point O in a plane, rotates in the plane about O in either a *clockwise* or a *counterclockwise sense* (or *direction*) from an *initial* position OA to a *terminal* position OB, as illustrated for various cases in Figure 17. Then, this rotation is said *to form, or generate, an angle AOB*, where we read the letters starting with the initial side (read in reverse) AO, followed by the letter locating the terminal side, OB.

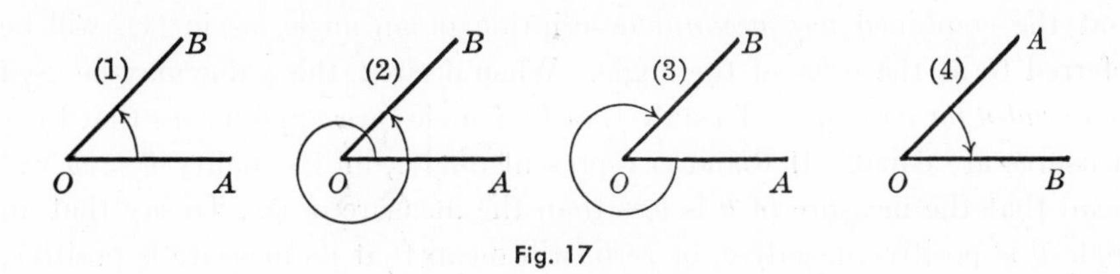

Fig. 17

SUMMARY. **An angle is an amount of rotation,** *which may be identified geometrically as the rotation of any ray in a plane about its end point, O, from an initial position, called the* **initial side** *of the angle, to a terminal position, called the* **terminal side** *of the angle. The end point O of the rotating ray is called the* **vertex** *of the angle.*

Various units will be introduced for measuring angles. *Regardless of the unit employed*, an angle generated by *counterclockwise rotation* will be assigned *positive measure*, and an angle generated by *clockwise rotation* will be assigned *negative measure.* We introduce the angle with *zero measure*, for the case where the initial and terminal sides of the angle coincide and no rotation is involved. In a figure, the sense of rotation for an angle can be shown by a curved arrow.

To introduce so-called *degree measure* for an angle AOB, as in Figure 18, suppose that the vertex O is placed at the center of a circle of radius r. Let s be the directed distance measured along the arc AB which is traced on the circumference of the circle as OA revolves into the position OB, where s is taken *positive* or *negative* according as the rotation is *counterclockwise* or *clockwise*, respectively. The circumference of the circle has the length $2\pi r$. If $s > 0$ and $s/2\pi r = 1/360$, we define the *measure* of $\angle AOB$ to be **one degree,** written $1°$. That is, as a measure of the *amount of rotation*, $1°$ is $\frac{1}{360}$ *of a complete revolution of OA counterclockwise.* In degrees, the measure, θ,* of any $\angle AOB$ is defined by

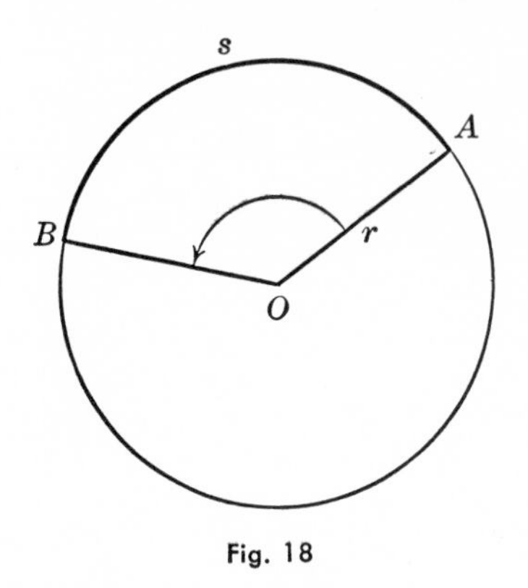

Fig. 18

$$\theta = \frac{s}{2\pi r}(360) \text{ degrees.} \qquad (1)$$

Thus, the measure given by (1) is a *positive* or a *negative number of degrees* according as $s > 0$ or $s < 0$, respectively, which agrees with our previous decision about the *sign* for measuring rotation. If $\angle AOB$ is generated by a complete revolution counterclockwise, so that $s = 2\pi r$ in (1), then $\theta = 360°$. The angular unit $1°$ is subdivided as in elementary geometry. Thus, we define *one minute*, $1'$, as $\frac{1}{60}$ of $1°$, and *one second*, $1''$, as $\frac{1}{60}$ of $1'$.

In any system of measurement (at present, in degree measure), we agree that the combined *measure-unit* description of an angle, as in (1), will be referred to as the *value* of the angle. When desired, this value may be used as a *symbol for the angle.* To state that two angles are equal means that their measures are equal. If θ and ϕ represent angles, an inequality $\theta < \phi$ will mean that the measure of θ is less than the measure of ϕ. To say that an angle θ is positive, negative, or zero, will mean that its measure is positive, negative, or zero, respectively.

ILLUSTRATION 1. In Figure 17 on page 29, the configuration AOB is the same in each diagram. In (1), $\angle AOB = 45°$. In (2), a complete revolution is indicated besides $45°$; $\angle AOB = 360° + 45° = 405°$. In (3), the rotation is $45°$ less than $360°$, clockwise; $\angle AOB = -315°$. In (4), $\angle AOB = -45°$.

Any positive angle between $0°$ and $90°$ is called an **acute angle.** Any positive angle between $90°$ and $180°$ is called an **obtuse angle.** An angle of $90°$ is called a **right angle,** and an angle of $180°$ is called a **straight angle.**

The description of an angle is incomplete until we are told its *sense* (*clockwise* or *counterclockwise*) and the amount of rotation used in forming the

* Frequently we shall employ Greek letters to represent angles and their measures. The letters α, β, γ, θ, and ϕ are called *alpha, beta, gamma, theta,* and *phi,* respectively.

angle. Any number of complete revolutions, clockwise or counterclockwise, may be added to any of the rotations in Figure 17 on page 29 without altering the initial and terminal sides of the angles. Thus, we see that infinitely many positive and negative angles of unlimited absolute values correspond to any given pair of sides for the angles.

If at any time an angle is shown by merely *drawing two rays* radiating from the vertex, without indicating the amount of rotation and sense, it will be assumed that the angle has *positive* measure, at most 180°. Thus, if an angle is indicated as in Figure 19, we infer that the angle has positive measure, about 130° in Figure 19. In other words, with no indication of the initial and terminal sides, or the amount of rotation involved, we return to the attitude of elementary geometry and take the angle's measure to be positive or zero and at most 180°. Thus, in any triangle, each angle will be considered to have a positive measure.

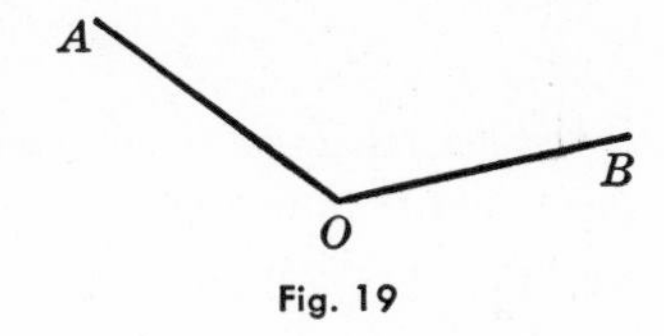

Fig. 19

Note 1. We have agreed to use a symbol such as 45° for the *value* of a certain angle. However, we do not refer to 45° as a *number*. We recognize "45°" as an abbreviation for the phrase "45 *degrees*," where the *number* involved is 45 and the symbol "°" shows that the unit of measurement is *one degree*.*

18. Standard position of an angle

We shall say that an angle θ is in its *standard position on a coordinate system* if the vertex of θ is at the origin and the initial side of θ lies on the positive part of the horizontal axis.

Illustration 1. To place 240° in standard position in Figure 20, imagine rotating OX about O through 240° counterclockwise to find the terminal side: $\gamma = 240°$. Similarly, we place $\alpha = -60°$ and $\theta = 30°$ in standard positions.

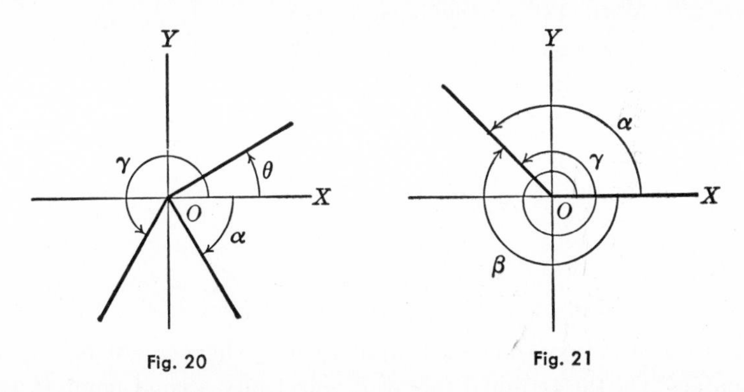

Fig. 20 Fig. 21

* Symbols for measures such as 45°, 6′, meaning 6 feet, etc., sometimes have been called *denominate numbers*. We shall not use such terminology, in order to avoid confusion with the proper use of the word *number*.

To state that an angle θ is *in a certain quadrant* will mean that the terminal side of θ falls *inside* that quadrant when θ is in its standard position. If the terminal side of θ falls *on a coordinate axis*, then θ is not said to lie in any quadrant, but is called a **quadrantal angle.**

ILLUSTRATION 2. In Figure 20, θ is in quadrant I and γ is in quadrant III. Angles between $-180°$ and $-270°$ are in quadrant II. Obtuse angles lie in quadrant II. Examples of quadrantal angles are $0°$, $90°$, $360°$, $-90°$, $-180°$.

Two or more angles are said to be **coterminal** if their terminal sides coincide after the angles are placed in their standard positions.

ILLUSTRATION 3. In Figure 21 on page 31, α, β, and γ are coterminal.

EXERCISE 7

Sketch the angle in standard position and indicate the angle by an arrow. Give two coterminal angles, one positive and one negative, and indicate them by arrows.

1. 45°.	**2.** 90°.	**3.** 120°.	**4.** − 210°.	**5.** − 60°.
6. 150°.	**7.** − 270°.	**8.** − 315°.	**9.** − 180°.	**10.** − 90°.
11. 270°.	**12.** 420°.	**13.** 495°.	**14.** − 390°.	**15.** 0°.
16. 135°.	**17.** − 225°.	**18.** 870°.	**19.** 1050°.	**20.** − 1200°.

19. Trigonometric functions of an angle

Let θ be a variable whose domain D consists of all angles. Thus, at the moment, the *system of measurement* to be used for angles is *not involved.* Each value of θ in D is just a geometric entity called an *angle.* For any angle θ, let it be placed in its standard position on a coordinate system, as in Figure 22, where a *single unit is used for the scales on the coordinate axes and for distance measured in any direction in the plane.** Let $P:(x, y)$ be any point other than the origin, O, on the terminal side of θ, as in Figure 22. With AP perpendicular to OX, we have a right triangle OAP, called a **reference triangle** for θ, in which OA and AP are *directed segments,* where $OA = x$, $AP = y$, and $OP = r$. The *radius vector,* r, of P is taken as *positive,* for all angles θ. Then, we form the ratios

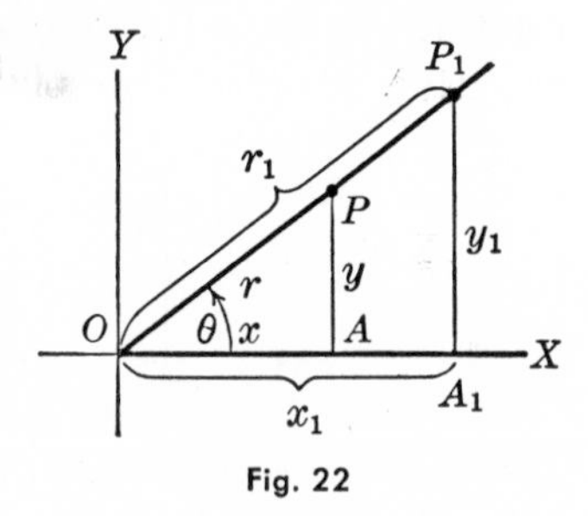

Fig. 22

$$\frac{AP}{OP} \text{ or } \frac{y}{r}, \quad \frac{OA}{OP} \text{ or } \frac{x}{r}, \quad \frac{y}{x}, \quad \frac{x}{y}, \quad \frac{r}{x}, \quad \frac{r}{y}, \tag{1}$$

omitting those fractions for quadrantal angles where $x = 0$ or $y = 0$ in a denominator. On the terminal side of θ, select any second point $P_1:(x_1, y_1)$,

* This agreement will hold, except where otherwise stated, when we make use of a coordinate system.

not O, with radius vector r_1. Then, new ratios (1) formed with x_1, y_1, and r_1 are equal to the ratios formed with x, y, and r. For instance, since the directed distances OA and OA_1 have the same sign, by properties of the similar triangles OAP and OA_1P_1 we obtain

$$\frac{x}{r} = \frac{OA}{OP} = \frac{OA_1}{OP_1} = \frac{x_1}{r_1}; \quad \frac{y}{x} = \frac{y_1}{x_1}; \textit{ etc.}$$

Thus, the values of the ratios in (1) depend *only on the position of the terminal side of* θ and not on the particular point P used to find x, y, and r. Hence, *corresponding to each angle* θ (with certain exceptions for quadrantal angles to be noted later) *there exists a unique value for each of the six ratios in* (1). Thus, each ratio defines a *function of* θ, called a *trigonometric function* of θ, where the *domain* of the function consists of *angles* θ, and the *range* of the function consists of *real numbers.* For any angle θ, the values of these functions are defined below, where x, y, and r are illustrated in Figure 23. We *name* and *read* the functions as at the left in (2) below, and *abbreviate* as at the right in (2).

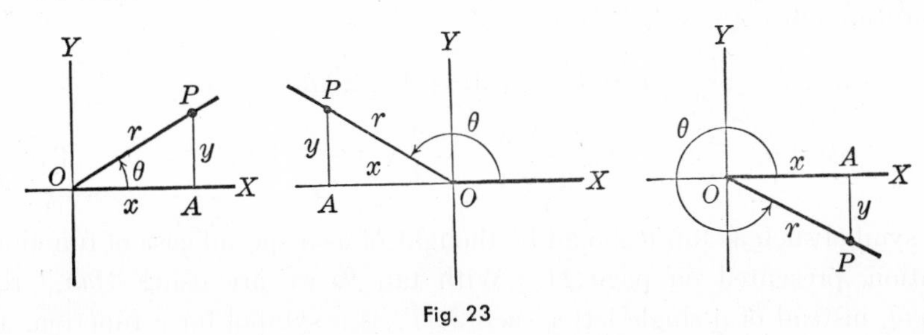

Fig. 23

DEFINITION I. *Place angle* θ *in standard position on a coordinate system. Choose any point P, not the origin, on the terminal side of* θ; *let the coordinates and radius vector of P be* (x, y) *and* r, *respectively.* Then,

$$\left.\begin{aligned}
\textit{sine } \theta &= \frac{\textit{ordinate of P}}{\textit{radius vector of P}}, \quad \textit{or} \quad \mathbf{sin}\ \theta = \frac{y}{r};\\
\textit{cosine } \theta &= \frac{\textit{abscissa of P}}{\textit{radius vector of P}}, \quad \textit{or} \quad \mathbf{cos}\ \theta = \frac{x}{r};\\
\textit{tangent } \theta &= \frac{\textit{ordinate of P}}{\textit{abscissa of P}}, \quad \textit{or} \quad \mathbf{tan}\ \theta = \frac{y}{x};\\
\textit{cotangent } \theta &= \frac{\textit{abscissa of P}}{\textit{ordinate of P}}, \quad \textit{or} \quad \mathbf{cot}\ \theta = \frac{x}{y};\\
\textit{secant } \theta &= \frac{\textit{radius vector of P}}{\textit{abscissa of P}}, \quad \textit{or} \quad \mathbf{sec}\ \theta = \frac{r}{x};\\
\textit{cosecant } \theta &= \frac{\textit{radius vector of P}}{\textit{ordinate of P}}, \quad \textit{or} \quad \mathbf{csc}\ \theta = \frac{r}{y}.
\end{aligned}\right\} \quad (2)$$

Since Definition I involves only the terminal side of θ, **if two angles are coterminal then their trigonometric functions are equal.**

ILLUSTRATION 1. Since 30° and 390° are coterminal, $\cos 30° = \cos 390°$.

EXAMPLE 1. Find the *functions* * (meaning the *values of the functions*) of an angle θ if its terminal side in standard position passes through $P{:}(3, -4)$.

SOLUTION. A reference triangle for θ is shown in Figure 24. We select P with $x = 3$ and $y = -4$; then $r = \sqrt{3^2 + (-4)^2} = 5$. Hence, from (2),

$$\sin\theta = -\tfrac{4}{5};\quad \cos\theta = \tfrac{3}{5};\quad \tan\theta = -\tfrac{4}{3};$$
$$\csc\theta = -\tfrac{5}{4};\quad \sec\theta = \tfrac{5}{3};\quad \cot\theta = -\tfrac{3}{4}.$$

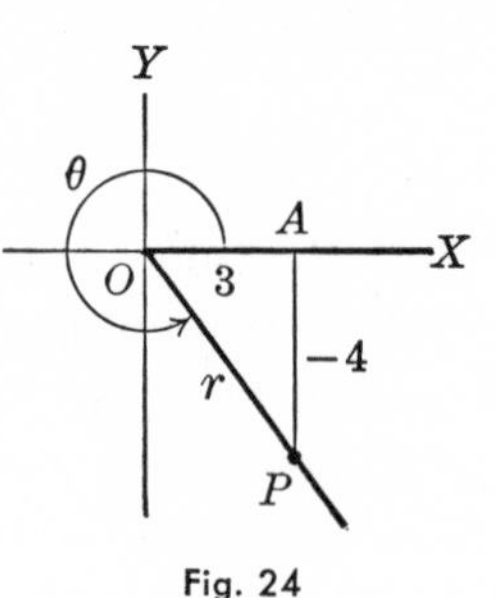

Fig. 24

Note 1. To find r when x and y are given, from page 15 we recall

$$r^2 = x^2 + y^2; \qquad r = \sqrt{x^2 + y^2}. \tag{3}$$

ILLUSTRATION 2. If the terminal side of an angle θ in its standard position passes through $P{:}(-\sqrt{3}, 1)$, then

$$r = \sqrt{(-\sqrt{3})^2 + 1} = 2, \textit{ and}$$

$$\sec\theta = \frac{2}{-\sqrt{3}} = -\frac{2}{\sqrt{3}}\cdot\frac{\sqrt{3}}{\sqrt{3}} = -\frac{2}{3}\sqrt{3} = -1.155. \qquad \text{(Table I)}$$

A symbol such as $\tan\theta$ should be thought of as a special case of functional notation, presented on page 24. With $\tan\theta$, we are using "*tan*," read *tangent*, instead of a single letter such as T, as a symbol for a function, and write simply $\tan\theta$ in place of $\tan(\theta)$, which would be the natural consequence of the notation on page 24. Thus, in (2), we have formulas defining the *values of the six trigonometric functions*, the sine and cosine functions, the tangent and cotangent functions, and the secant and cosecant functions. We have used θ in (2) as the *independent variable*, whose domain is *all angles* (with a few exceptions mentioned later for certain functions); the *range* for each trigonometric function consists of real numbers.

20. Equations and inequalities involving trigonometric functions

On page 9, we defined the notion of a *solution* for an equation or inequality in a variable x, with its domain thought of as consisting of numbers. We now take over all terminology for equations and inequalities from Section 6 on page 9 with the domain of any variable now consisting of *angles*. Thus, from page 9, a **trigonometric identity** in a variable angle θ is *an equation in θ which is satisfied by* **all values of θ** *in its domain.*

* Until otherwise indicated, in any reference to a *function* or to a *trigonometric function* of an angle, we shall mean one of the fundamental functions of Definition I.

From (2) on page 33, we observe that each of the following equations is an identity, because it is a true statement for each value * of θ for which both functions in the equation are defined.

$$\left.\begin{aligned} \sin\theta &= \frac{1}{\csc\theta}, \quad \textit{or} \quad \csc\theta = \frac{1}{\sin\theta}; \\ \cos\theta &= \frac{1}{\sec\theta}, \quad \textit{or} \quad \sec\theta = \frac{1}{\cos\theta}; \\ \tan\theta &= \frac{1}{\cot\theta}, \quad \textit{or} \quad \cot\theta = \frac{1}{\tan\theta}. \end{aligned}\right\} \tag{1}$$

ILLUSTRATION 1. If $\sin\theta \neq 0$, $\dfrac{1}{\sin\theta} = \dfrac{1}{\frac{y}{r}} = \dfrac{r}{y}$, *or* $\dfrac{1}{\sin\theta} = \csc\theta.$

We verify the signs of the values of the trigonometric functions of θ for angles θ in the various quadrants, as indicated in Figure 25. For θ in any quadrant, $\sin\theta$ and $\csc\theta$ have the same sign because $\sin\theta = 1/\csc\theta$; $\tan\theta$ and $\cot\theta$ have the same sign; $\cos\theta$ and $\sec\theta$ have the same sign. Thus, if we remember the signs of $\sin\theta$, $\cos\theta$, and $\tan\theta$ for angles θ in any quadrant, the signs of the other functions can be specified immediately.

EXAMPLE 1. Determine the signs of the values of the trigonometric functions of θ for angles θ in quadrant II.

SOLUTION. If θ is in quadrant II, then $x < 0$, $y > 0$, and $r > 0$ in Definition I. Hence, regarding only signs,

$$\sin\theta = \frac{y}{r} = \frac{+}{+} = +;$$

$$\cos\theta = \frac{x}{r} = \frac{-}{+} = -;$$

$$\tan\theta = \frac{y}{x} = \frac{+}{-} = -.$$

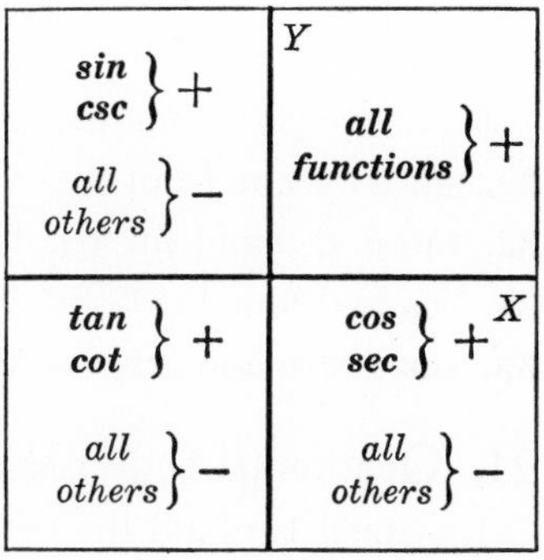

	Y
sin, *csc* } + ; *all others* } −	*all functions* } +
tan, *cot* } + ; *all others* } −	*cos*, *sec* } + ; *all others* } − X

Fig. 25

EXAMPLE 2. If $\sin\theta > 0$ and $\cot\theta < 0$, in what quadrant does θ lie?

SOLUTION. Since $\sin\theta > 0$, θ is in quadrant I or quadrant II. Since $\cot\theta < 0$, θ is in quadrant II or quadrant IV. Hence, θ is in quadrant II.

In Figure 23 on page 33 for any angle θ, neither $|OA|$ nor $|AP|$ is greater than OP. Hence, the absolute value of x or of y *cannot exceed* r, and the absolute value of x/r or of y/r *cannot exceed* 1. That is,

$$|\sin\theta| \leqq 1; \qquad |\cos\theta| \leqq 1. \tag{2}$$

* In the case of $\tan\theta$, $\cot\theta$, $\sec\theta$, and $\csc\theta$, "*all values of* θ" always will mean "*all for which the function is defined.*"

Later, we shall see that the *range* of the functions sin θ and cos θ consists of *all numbers from* -1 *to* $+1$, *including* ± 1. Similarly, the absolute value of r/x or of r/y *cannot be smaller than* 1, or

$$|\sec \theta| \geqq 1; \qquad |\csc \theta| \geqq 1. \qquad (3)$$

Later, we shall see that the range of the functions sec θ and csc θ consists of *all numbers with absolute values greater than or equal to* 1.

EXERCISE 8

Find the trigonometric functions of the angle θ if the terminal side of θ, in its standard position, passes through the given point on a coordinate system.

1. (4, 3). **2.** (5, 12). **3.** (7, 24). **4.** (12, − 5).
5. (− 3, − 2). **6.** (− 24, 7). **7.** (− 15, 8). **8.** (− 8, − 15).
9. (6, − 8). **10.** (− 1, 1). **11.** $(1, -\sqrt{3})$. **12.** $(\sqrt{3}, 1)$.
13. (0, 4). **14.** (4, − 5). **15.** (0, − 2). **16.** (2, − 3).
17. (− 1, − 1). **18.** (5, 0). **19.** (− 3, 5). **20.** (− 2, 0).

21. Verify the signs in Figure 25 for quadrant III; quadrant IV.

Give the value of another function of the angle whose function value is given.

22. $\tan \theta = \frac{3}{7}$. **23.** $\cos \alpha = \frac{4}{9}$. **24.** $\cot \beta = \frac{5}{2}$. **25.** $\sec \gamma = \frac{7}{3}$.

Under the given condition, in which quadrants may θ lie?

26. $\sin \theta < 0$. **27.** $\tan \theta < 0$. **28.** $\sec \theta > 0$. **29.** $\cot \theta > 0$.

Under the given conditions, in which quadrant must θ lie?

30. $\sin \theta < 0$ and $\tan \theta > 0$. **31.** $\cos \theta < 0$ and $\sin \theta > 0$.
32. $\tan \theta < 0$ and $\sin \theta < 0$. **33.** $\sec \theta < 0$ and $\tan \theta > 0$.
34. $\cos \theta < 0$ and $\cot \theta < 0$. **35.** $\csc \theta > 0$ and $\cot \theta < 0$.
36. $\cos \theta < 0$ and $\tan \theta > 0$. **37.** $\sin \theta < 0$ and $\cos \theta < 0$.

21. Quadrantal angles and other special angles

EXAMPLE 1. Find the trigonometric functions of 180°.

SOLUTION. 1. Draw 180° in standard position, as in Figure 26. The ordinate of any point on the terminal side is zero.

2. Choose P as $(-3, 0)$. Then $r = OP = 3$. On substituting $x = -3$, $y = 0$, and $r = 3$ in (2) on page 33, we obtain

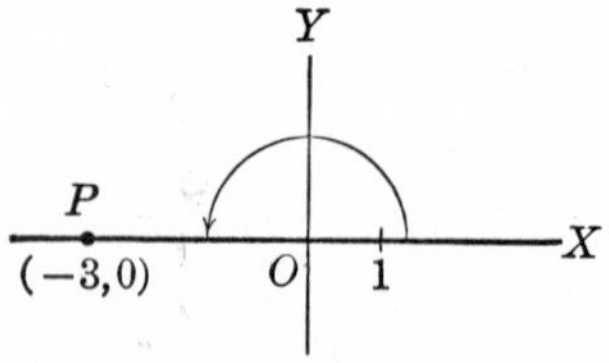

$$\tan 180° = \frac{0}{-3} = 0; \quad \sec 180° = \frac{3}{-3} = -1;$$

$$\sin 180° = \frac{0}{3} = 0; \quad \cos 180° = \frac{-3}{3} = -1.$$

Fig. 26

Since $y = 0$, r/y and x/y are meaningless because *division by zero has no meaning.* Therefore, **180° has no cosecant and no cotangent.**

If θ is any quadrantal angle, so that its terminal side falls on a coordinate axis, either $\cot\theta$ and $\csc\theta$, or $\tan\theta$ and $\sec\theta$, are *undefined* for the reason just met in discussing cot 180° and csc 180°. From Example 1 and later problems, a complete list of the undefined function values of angles from 0° to 360°, inclusive, is as follows:

$$\text{UNDEFINED FUNCTION VALUES}\begin{cases}\cot 0^\circ;\quad \tan 90^\circ;\quad \cot 180^\circ;\quad \tan 270^\circ;\quad \cot 360^\circ;\\ \csc 0^\circ;\quad \sec 90^\circ;\quad \csc 180^\circ;\quad \sec 270^\circ;\quad \csc 360^\circ.\end{cases} \tag{1}$$

We reserve this matter of undefined values for later discussion.

EXAMPLE 2. Find the trigonometric functions of 45°.

SOLUTION. Figure 27 shows the angle 45° in its standard position. The reference triangle AOP is *isosceles* with $\overline{OA} = \overline{AP}$. Hence, we may choose P with $x = 1$ and $y = 1$; then $r = \sqrt{2}$ and, from page 33,

$$\sin 45^\circ = \frac{1}{\sqrt{2}} = \frac{1}{\sqrt{2}}\cdot\frac{\sqrt{2}}{\sqrt{2}} = \frac{1}{2}\sqrt{2};$$

$$\sec 45^\circ = \frac{\sqrt{2}}{1} = \sqrt{2};\ \textit{etc.}$$

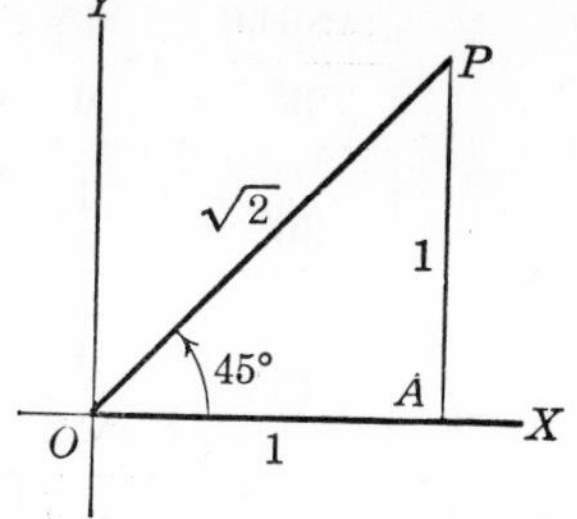

Fig. 27

The student should memorize $\triangle OAP$.

Note 1. In the equilateral triangle ABD of Figure 28, drop a perpendicular BC to AD, obtaining two right triangles with the acute angles 30° and 60°. If we let $AB = BD = AD = 2$, then $AC = 1$ and

$$\overline{BC}^2 + \overline{AC}^2 = \overline{AB}^2 \quad or$$
$$\overline{BC}^2 = \overline{AB}^2 - \overline{AC}^2 = 4 - 1 = 3.$$

Thus, $BC = \sqrt{3}$. Hence, as a *standard right triangle with the acute angles* 30° *and* 60°, we may use triangle ABC with sides 1, 2, and $\sqrt{3}$.

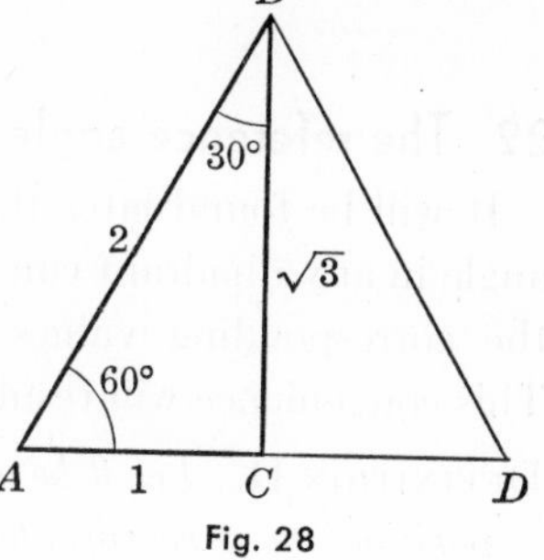

Fig. 28

ILLUSTRATION 1. To obtain the trigonometric functions of 30°, after placing the angle in its standard position in Figure 29 on page 38, we choose P on the terminal side so that $OP = 2$. Then, the reference triangle OAP has the acute angles 30° and 60°, and the sides 1, 2, and $\sqrt{3}$; we find

$$\sin 30^\circ = \frac{1}{2};\quad \tan 30^\circ = \frac{1}{\sqrt{3}} = \frac{1}{\sqrt{3}}\cdot\frac{\sqrt{3}}{\sqrt{3}} = \frac{1}{3}\sqrt{3};\ \textit{etc.}$$

To obtain the trigonometric functions of 60° by use of Figure 30 on page 38, we choose P so that $OP = 2$ and again the reference triangle has the acute angles 30° and 60°, and sides 1, 2, and $\sqrt{3}$. The student should verify all entries in the following table.

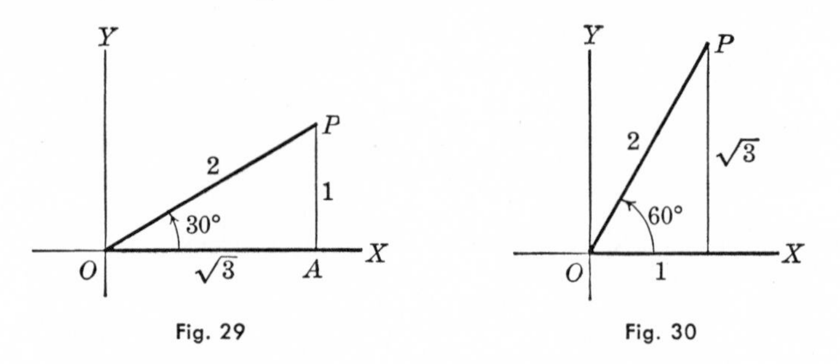

Fig. 29 Fig. 30

ANGLE	SIN	COS	TAN	COT	SEC	CSC
0°	0	1	0	*none*	1	*none*
30°	$\frac{1}{2}$	$\frac{\sqrt{3}}{2}$	$\frac{1}{\sqrt{3}}$	$\sqrt{3}$	$\frac{2}{\sqrt{3}}$	2
45°	$\frac{1}{\sqrt{2}}$	$\frac{1}{\sqrt{2}}$	1	1	$\sqrt{2}$	$\sqrt{2}$
60°	$\frac{\sqrt{3}}{2}$	$\frac{1}{2}$	$\sqrt{3}$	$\frac{1}{\sqrt{3}}$	2	$\frac{2}{\sqrt{3}}$
90°	1	0	*none*	0	*none*	1

22. The reference angle for a given angle

It will be found later that the values of the trigonometric functions of an angle in any quadrant can be obtained if we have means available for finding the corresponding values of the trigonometric functions of acute angles. This convenience will result from use of a *reference angle*, described as follows.

Definition II. *Let θ be an angle in any quadrant, and consider θ in standard position on a coordinate system. Then, the* **reference angle** *for θ is the acute angle α between the terminal side of θ and the horizontal coordinate axis.*

Illustration 1. If $\theta = 120°$, as in Figure 31, then the reference angle is $\alpha = 60°$.

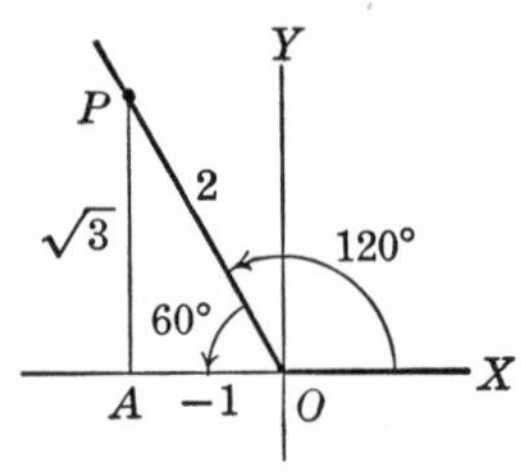

Fig. 31

If the reference angle for an angle θ is 30°, 45°, or 60°, any reference triangle for obtaining the values of the trigonometric functions of θ can be given the dimensions used in obtaining the trigonometric functions of 30°, 45°, or 60°, respectively.

ILLUSTRATION 2. If $\theta = 225°$, the reference angle is 45°, in Figure 32, and triangle AOP has the sides 1, 1, and $\sqrt{2}$; P is $(-1, -1)$. Then,

$$\sin 225° = \frac{-1}{\sqrt{2}} = -\frac{1}{2}\sqrt{2}; \qquad \tan 225° = \frac{-1}{-1} = 1; \ etc.$$

For $\theta = 120°$ in Figure 31 on page 38, and $\theta = -150°$ in Figure 33, $OP = 2$ and the reference triangles have the sides 1, 2, and $\sqrt{3}$; then

$$\tan 120° = \frac{\sqrt{3}}{-1} = -\sqrt{3}; \qquad \cos(-150°) = \frac{-\sqrt{3}}{2} = -\frac{1}{2}\sqrt{3}; \ etc.$$

On account of the similarity of the reference triangles for 45° and 225°, any trigonometric function of 225° differs *at most in sign* from the same function of 45°. Likewise, the trigonometric functions of 120° and of $-150°$ *differ at most in signs* from the corresponding functions of their reference angles 60° and 30°, respectively.

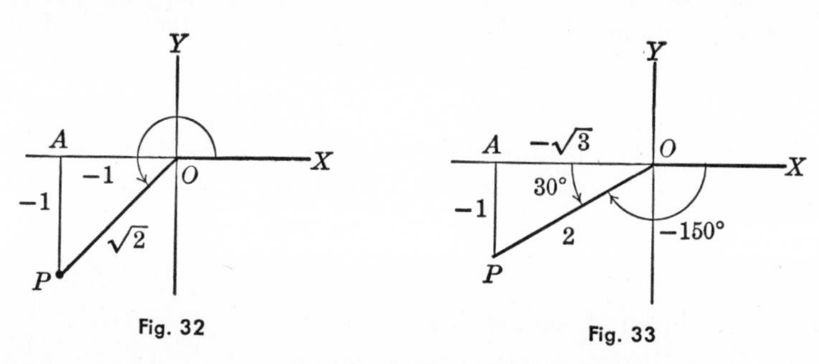

Fig. 32 Fig. 33

In Illustration 2 we met special cases of the theorem that *the value of any trigonometric function of an angle θ differs at most in sign from the same function of the reference angle for θ.* We shall prove this theorem on page 47.

EXERCISE 9

Place the angle in its standard position on a coordinate system and find the trigonometric functions of the angle. Rationalize any radical denominator and compute by use of Table I, *if necessary.*

1. 0°. **2.** 90°. **3.** 30°. **4.** 60°. **5.** 135°.
6. 120°. **7.** 150°. **8.** 270°. **9.** 360°. **10.** 315°.
11. 330°. **12.** 240°. **13.** $-90°$. **14.** $-180°$. **15.** $-45°$.
16. $-60°$. **17.** $-135°$. **18.** 225°. **19.** 390°. **20.** 405°.
21. 585°. **22.** 495°. **23.** 540°. **24.** 480°. **25.** $-495°$.

26. Give all angles θ between $-360°$ and 360° such that the functions of θ are numerically equal to the corresponding functions of 45°; 30°; 60°.

27. Give all angles θ between $-720°$ and 720° for which (*a*) $\tan\theta$ is not defined; (*b*) $\sec\theta$ is not defined; (*c*) $\csc\theta$ and $\cot\theta$ are not defined.

23. The fundamental identities

By use of Definition I on page 33, we proved that the reciprocal identities (1) below are true for all angles θ for which no denominator is zero. Similarly, we shall prove the identities (2) and (3).

$$\csc \theta = \frac{1}{\sin \theta}; \qquad \sec \theta = \frac{1}{\cos \theta}; \qquad \cot \theta = \frac{1}{\tan \theta}. \tag{1}$$

$$\tan \theta = \frac{\sin \theta}{\cos \theta}; \qquad \cot \theta = \frac{\cos \theta}{\sin \theta}. \tag{2}$$

$$\sin^2 \theta + \cos^2 \theta = 1; \quad \tan^2 \theta + 1 = \sec^2 \theta; \quad 1 + \cot^2 \theta = \csc^2 \theta. \tag{3}$$

Note 1. To indicate a power of a value of a trigonometric function, we place the exponent between the function's name and the angle. An exception is made in case the exponent is -1; thus, we write $(\sin \theta)^{-1}$, and not $\sin^{-1} \theta$, to mean $1/\sin \theta$.

Proof of (2). Let θ be any angle whose terminal side is not vertical when θ is placed in its standard position on a coordinate system. Then, in Definition I on page 33, $x \neq 0$ and hence $\cos \theta \neq 0$, so that

$$\frac{\sin \theta}{\cos \theta} = \frac{\frac{y}{r}}{\frac{x}{r}} = \frac{y}{r} \cdot \frac{r}{x} = \frac{y}{x} = \tan \theta.$$

Similarly, $\cot \theta = \cos \theta / \sin \theta$ if θ is any angle for which $\sin \theta \neq 0$.

Proof of (3). From (3) on page 34,
$$x^2 + y^2 = r^2. \tag{4}$$

On dividing both sides of (4) by r^2, we obtain

$$\frac{y^2}{r^2} + \frac{x^2}{r^2} = 1, \quad \text{or} \quad \sin^2 \theta + \cos^2 \theta = 1.$$

Similarly, on dividing both sides of (4) in turn by x^2 when $x \neq 0$, and by y^2 when $y \neq 0$, we obtain the other equations in (3).

Slight modifications of identities (1), (2), and (3) should be recognized.

ILLUSTRATION 1. From (1), $\sin \theta = \dfrac{1}{\csc \theta}$.

From (2), $\quad \sin \theta = \cos \theta \tan \theta; \quad \cos \theta = \sin \theta \cot \theta.$

From (3), $\quad \sin^2 \theta = 1 - \cos^2 \theta; \quad \cos \theta = \pm \sqrt{1 - \sin^2 \theta}.$

From (1), $\quad \tan \theta \cot \theta = 1.$

24. Construction of an angle if the value of one of its functions is known

At present, suppose that the domain of the variable angle θ consists only of angles which are *not quadrantal.* Then, we shall meet illustrations of the following facts, with θ in its standard position on a coordinate system.

$$\left\{\begin{array}{l}\textit{If the value of } \textbf{just one trigonometric function} \textit{ of } \theta \textit{ and its } \textbf{quad-}\\ \textbf{rant} \textit{ are given, there exists } \textbf{just one location for the terminal side}\\ \textit{of } \theta\textit{, and thus } \textbf{just one solution} \textit{ for } \theta \textit{ between } 0^\circ \textit{ and } 360^\circ.\end{array}\right\} \quad (1)$$

$$\left\{\begin{array}{l}\textit{If merely the value of } \textbf{one trigonometric function} \textit{ of } \theta \textit{ is given,}\\ \textit{there exist } \textbf{two corresponding locations for the terminal}\\ \textbf{side} \textit{ of } \theta\textit{, and thus } \textbf{two solutions} \textit{ for } \theta \textit{ between } 0^\circ \textit{ and } 360^\circ.\end{array}\right\} \quad (2)$$

EXAMPLE 1. If θ is in quadrant II and $\sin\theta = \frac{3}{5}$, construct the terminal side of θ in its standard position on a coordinate system and find the values of all other trigonometric functions of θ.

SOLUTION. 1. From page 33, if θ is the desired angle, and $P:(x, y)$ is a point on the terminal side of θ in its standard position, then

$$\sin\theta = \frac{y}{r} = \frac{3}{5}. \quad (3)$$

Hence, one pair of values of y and r is $(y = 3, r = 5)$. We sketch the terminal side of θ roughly to scale in Figure 34, and indicate any corresponding angle θ.

2. From $r^2 = x^2 + y^2$,

$$x^2 = r^2 - y^2 = 25 - 9 = 16; \qquad x = \pm 4.$$

Since P is in quadrant II, the abscissa of P is $x = -4$. Then, from Definition I on page 33, with $x = -4$, $y = 3$, and $r = 5$, we have $\cos\theta = -\frac{4}{5}$, $\tan\theta = -\frac{3}{4}$, etc.

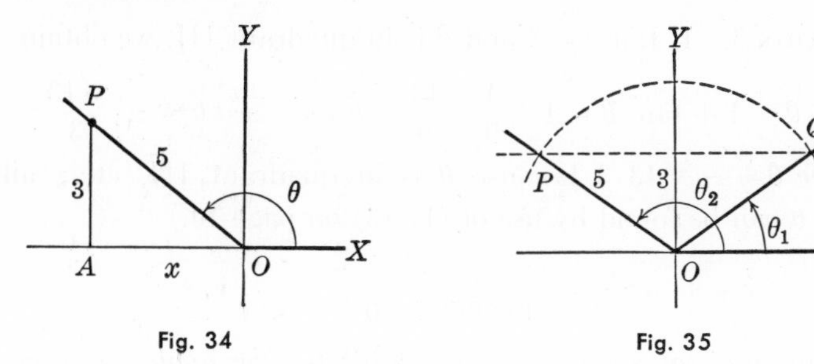

Fig. 34 Fig. 35

Comment. In Example 1, we dealt with the simple *trigonometric equation* $\sin\theta = \frac{3}{5}$. As yet, we are unable to find the values of θ which are solutions of the equation. However, in Example 1, we constructed the terminal side of any solution θ lying in quadrant II. An accurate figure was not needed in obtaining the values of the functions of the solution θ. If it is desired to construct OP accurately, as in Figure 35, draw a circle of radius 5 with center at O; construct the line $y = 3$, intersecting the circle at P in quadrant II and at Q in quadrant I. Then, $\sin\theta = \frac{3}{5}$ if θ has either OP or OQ as the terminal side. In Example 1, we use OP.

ILLUSTRATION 1. Without knowing the quadrant for θ, if we are given $\sin\theta = \frac{3}{5}$, then Figure 35 shows that there are two possible solutions for θ on the range $0° < \theta < 360°$, approximately $\theta_1 = 40°$ and $\theta_2 = 140°$.

ILLUSTRATION 2. If $\tan\theta = \frac{2}{3}$ and $\sin\theta < 0$, then θ lies in quadrant III. In the notation of page 33, we use $\frac{2}{3} = y/x$, and obtain $P:(x = -3, y = -2)$ as a corresponding point in quadrant III on the terminal side of θ. Then, we may construct this side, obtain $r = \sqrt{9+4} = \sqrt{13}$, and finally write all functions of θ by use of Definition I.

The fundamental identities of page 40 can be used to solve Example 1 without a figure. It is useful to carry out a few solutions by this method.

EXAMPLE 2. Solve Example 1 by use of the fundamental identities (1), (2), and (3) on page 40.

SOLUTION. With $\sin\theta = \frac{3}{5}$ and θ in quadrant II, first we obtain

$$\csc\theta = \frac{1}{\sin\theta} = \frac{5}{3}.$$

From $\sin^2\theta + \cos^2\theta = 1$,

$$\tfrac{9}{25} + \cos^2\theta = 1; \quad \cos^2\theta = \tfrac{16}{25}; \quad \cos\theta = \pm\tfrac{4}{5}.$$

Since θ is in quadrant II, we select $\cos\theta = -\frac{4}{5}$. Then, from (1) and (2) on page 40,

$$\sec\theta = \frac{1}{\cos\theta} = -\frac{5}{4}; \quad \tan\theta = \frac{\sin\theta}{\cos\theta} = \frac{\frac{3}{5}}{-\frac{4}{5}} = -\frac{3}{4}; \quad \cot\theta = \frac{1}{\tan\theta} = -\frac{4}{3}.$$

ILLUSTRATION 3. If $\tan\theta = \frac{2}{3}$ and θ is in quadrant III, we obtain

$$\sec^2\theta = 1 + \tan^2\theta = 1 + \frac{4}{9} = \frac{13}{9}; \quad \textit{hence} \quad \sec\theta = \pm\frac{\sqrt{13}}{3};$$

we select $\sec\theta = -\sqrt{13}/3$ because θ is in quadrant III, etc.; all other functions of θ can be found by use of (1)–(3) on page 40.

EXERCISE 10

The Roman numeral specifies the quadrant for the angle θ. Construct a corresponding angle θ on the range $0° < \theta < 360°$ accurately in standard position on a coordinate system, and find the unknown functions of θ. Do not use the fundamental identities of page 40 in the first ten problems. Thereafter, use the identities either partially or for the whole solution.

1. $\tan\theta = \frac{5}{12}$; θ in (I).
2. $\cot\theta = -\frac{4}{3}$; θ in (II).
3. $\sin\theta = \frac{4}{5}$; θ in (II).
4. $\cos\theta = \frac{5}{13}$; θ in (IV).
5. $\csc\theta = \frac{5}{3}$; θ in (I).
6. $\sec\theta = \frac{13}{12}$; θ in (I).
7. $\cot\theta = \frac{12}{5}$; θ in (III).
8. $\sin\theta = -\frac{15}{17}$; θ in (IV).
9. $\cos\theta = -\frac{15}{17}$; θ in (II).
10. $\tan\theta = -\frac{7}{24}$; θ in (II).

11. $\tan\theta = 1$; θ in (III). **12.** $\sin\theta = \frac{2}{3}$; θ in (I).

13. $\sec\theta = \frac{4}{3}$; θ in (IV). **14.** $\csc\theta = -\frac{5}{2}$; θ in (III).

15. θ is an acute angle and $\cos\theta = \frac{4}{5}$.

16. θ is an acute angle and $\sec\theta = \frac{25}{7}$.

17. θ is an obtuse angle and $\cot\theta = -\frac{8}{15}$.

18. θ is an obtuse angle and $\tan\theta = -\frac{24}{7}$.

Construct all angles θ between 0° and 360° in standard positions corresponding to the data. Estimate the values of θ with a protractor. Then, find all functions of each angle by use of fundamental identities.

19. $\tan\theta = \frac{2}{3}$. **20.** $\sin\theta = \frac{2}{5}$. **21.** $\cos\theta = -\frac{2}{3}$. **22.** $\cot\theta = -\frac{5}{2}$.

By recalling a fundamental identity, write a proper right-hand member involving only one function or one number.

23. $\dfrac{1}{\cot\theta} = ?$ **24.** $\dfrac{1}{\sec\theta} = ?$ **25.** $\dfrac{1}{\csc\theta} = ?$

26. $\cos\theta\sec\theta = ?$ **27.** $\tan\theta\cot\theta = ?$ **28.** $\sin\theta\csc\theta = ?$

29. $1 - \sin^2\theta = ?$ **30.** $\sec^2\theta - 1 = ?$ **31.** $\csc^2\theta - 1 = ?$

32. $1 - \cos^2\theta = ?$ **33.** $1 + \cot^2\theta = ?$ **34.** $\sec^2\theta - \tan^2\theta = ?$

35. Compute $3\tan\theta\,(2\cot\theta + 1 - \sec^2\theta)$ if $\tan\theta = 2$.

36. Compute $3\cot^2\theta\,(\sin\theta + \csc\theta)$ if $\sin\theta = \frac{1}{4}$.

37. Compute $\tan\theta\,(\sin\theta - 1)$ if $\cos\theta = \frac{2}{3}$ and θ is in quadrant (IV).

Express each trigonometric function of the angle x in terms of the given function value by use of fundamental identities.

38. $\tan x$. **39.** $\sin x$. **40.** $\cos x$. **41.** $\sec x$. **42.** $\csc x$.

HINT for Problem 38. $\cot x = \dfrac{1}{\tan x}$; $\sec x = \pm\sqrt{1 + \tan^2 x}$; etc.

25. Trigonometric functions of acute angles

Any acute angle α can be thought of as one of the angles of an associated right triangle. This fact permits us to prove special formulas for the functions of α involving the sides of the triangle.

Let triangle ABC in Figure 36 on page 44 be a right triangle with the 90° angle at C, and with α and β as the acute angles at A and B, respectively. Let a, b, and c be the sides (or *lengths* of the sides) of triangle ABC opposite A, B, and C, respectively. Hereafter, in any typical right triangle, we shall assume that the preceding notation is in use. By the Pythagorean theorem,

$$c^2 = a^2 + b^2. \tag{1}$$

Let α be any acute angle, and let $\triangle ABC$ in Figure 36 be any right triangle having α as the angle at A. Then, to place α in standard position on a coordinate system as in Figure 37, we locate $\triangle ABC$ with A at the origin, C on the positive ray of the x-axis, and B above OX. In the terminology of page 32, $\triangle ABC$ becomes a *reference triangle* for α; B is a point on the terminal side of α with coordinates $(x = b, y = a)$ and radius vector $r = \overline{AB} = c$. We shall refer to a as the *side opposite* α, b as the *side adjacent* to α, and c as the *hypotenuse*. Then, with $x = b$, $y = a$, and $r = c$ in the definitions on page 33, we obtain

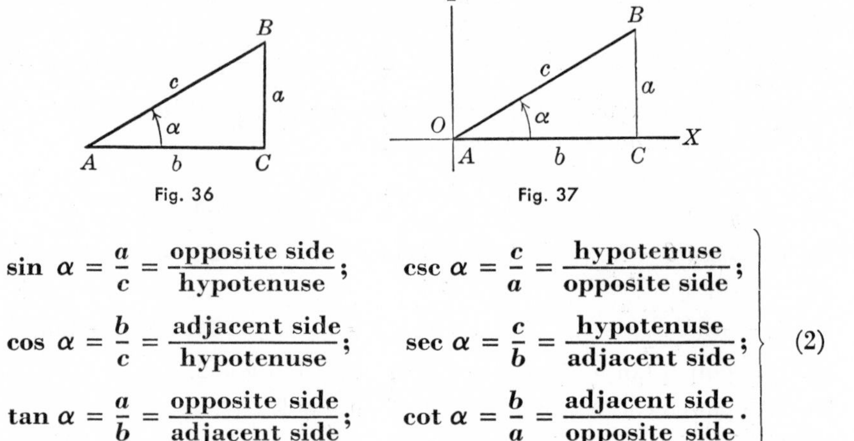

Fig. 36 Fig. 37

$$\left.\begin{aligned} \sin\alpha &= \frac{a}{c} = \frac{\text{opposite side}}{\text{hypotenuse}}; & \csc\alpha &= \frac{c}{a} = \frac{\text{hypotenuse}}{\text{opposite side}};\\ \cos\alpha &= \frac{b}{c} = \frac{\text{adjacent side}}{\text{hypotenuse}}; & \sec\alpha &= \frac{c}{b} = \frac{\text{hypotenuse}}{\text{adjacent side}};\\ \tan\alpha &= \frac{a}{b} = \frac{\text{opposite side}}{\text{adjacent side}}; & \cot\alpha &= \frac{b}{a} = \frac{\text{adjacent side}}{\text{opposite side}}. \end{aligned}\right\} \quad (2)$$

Thus, in (2), by use of the fundamental definitions on page 33, we have proved the following result, which emphatically applies *only to acute angles.*

$$\left\{\begin{array}{l}\textit{If an acute angle } \alpha \textit{ is located as an angle in a right triangle,}\\ \textit{without using a coordinate system we can express the functions}\\ \textit{of } \alpha \textit{ as quotients of the lengths of sides of the triangle, as in (2).}\end{array}\right\} \quad (3)$$

ILLUSTRATION 1. From Figure 38,

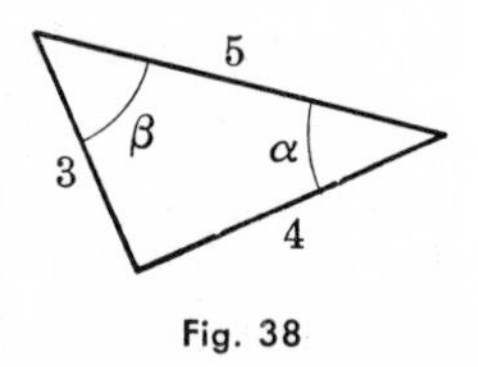

Fig. 38

$\sin\alpha = \frac{3}{5}$; $\cos\alpha = \frac{4}{5}$; $\tan\alpha = \frac{3}{4}$;
$\csc\alpha = \frac{5}{3}$; $\sec\alpha = \frac{5}{4}$; $\cot\alpha = \frac{4}{3}$;
$\sin\beta = \frac{4}{5}$; $\cos\beta = \frac{3}{5}$; $\tan\beta = \frac{4}{3}$;
$\csc\beta = \frac{5}{4}$; $\sec\beta = \frac{5}{3}$; $\cot\beta = \frac{3}{4}$.

EXAMPLE 1. Construct the acute angle α approximately and find $\cos\alpha$ and $\tan\alpha$, if $\sin\alpha = \frac{3}{4}$.

SOLUTION. In equations (2), $\sin\alpha = a/c$. In Figure 39, we indicate a right triangle (which need not be drawn accurately to scale) with $a = 3$ and $c = 4$. Then, $b^2 = c^2 - a^2$, or $b^2 = 7$; $b = \sqrt{7}$. Thus,

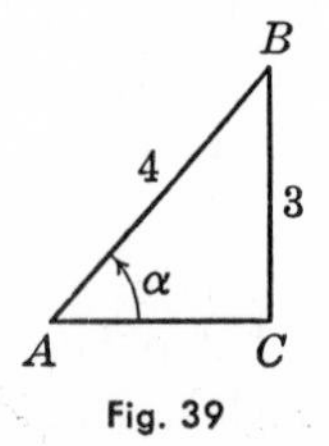

Fig. 39

$$\cos\alpha = \frac{\sqrt{7}}{4}; \qquad \tan\alpha = \frac{3}{\sqrt{7}} = \frac{3}{7}\sqrt{7}.$$

ILLUSTRATION 2. In Figures 40 and 41, we may read off the functions of 30°, 45°, and 60°.

If α and β are acute angles and $\alpha + \beta = 90°$, then α and β are said to be *complementary;* either is called the *complement* of the other angle.

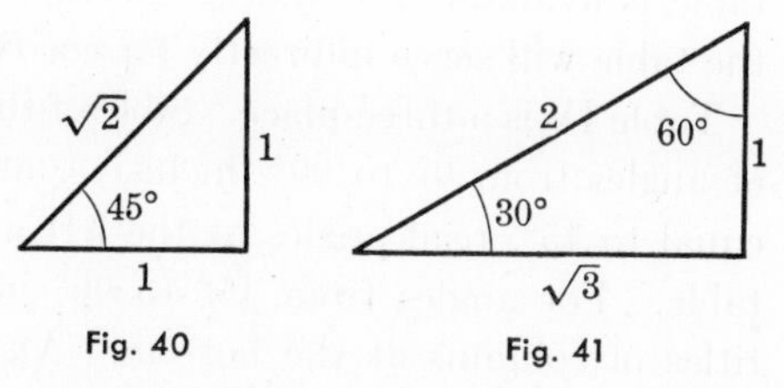

Fig. 40 Fig. 41

ILLUSTRATION 3. The complement of 35° is (90° − 35°) or 55°.

If α and β are the acute angles of a right triangle ABC, then α and β are complementary, and $\beta = 90° - \alpha$. From Figure 42, side a is *opposite* α and *adjacent* to β. Hence, from (2) on page 44,

$$\sin \alpha = \frac{a}{c} = \cos \beta; \qquad \cos \alpha = \frac{b}{c} = \sin \beta;$$

$$\tan \alpha = \cot \beta; \qquad \cot \alpha = \tan \beta;$$

$$\sec \alpha = \csc \beta; \qquad \csc \alpha = \sec \beta.$$

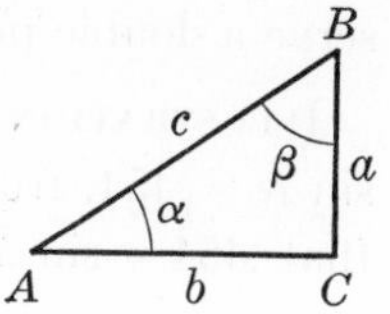

Fig. 42

On using $\beta = 90° - \alpha$, the preceding results become

$$\left.\begin{array}{ll} \sin \alpha = \cos (90° - \alpha); & \sec \alpha = \csc (90° - \alpha); \\ \cos \alpha = \sin (90° - \alpha); & \csc \alpha = \sec (90° - \alpha); \\ \tan \alpha = \cot (90° - \alpha); & \cot \alpha = \tan (90° - \alpha). \end{array}\right\} \qquad (4)$$

Thus, we have proved that equations (4) are *identities*, if the domain of α consists of *all acute angles*. On page 55, we shall prove that the equations are identities also when the domain of the variable α consists of *all angles* (with the usual exceptions for the tangent, cotangent, secant, and cosecant).

The trigonometric functions may be grouped as follows: *sine* and **co***sine;* *tangent* and **co***tangent;* *secant* and **co***secant.* In each pair, either function may be referred to as the **co***function* of the other one. Then, (4) states that *any function of an acute angle α is equal to the cofunction of the complement of α.* We call (4) the *cofunction identities.*

ILLUSTRATION 4. sin 33° = cos 57°. tan 29° = cot 61°. csc 15° = sec 75°.

Note 1. In the Middle Ages, it was customary at first to refer to the *cosine*, in Latin, as *complementi sinus*, meaning the sine of the complement. Eventually, *complementi sinus* was abbreviated to *cosinus.*

26. A three-place trigonometric table

In general, any value of a trigonometric function is an endless * decimal. By advanced methods, the functions of any angle can be computed to as many decimal places as desired. We shall learn later how the values of the trigonometric functions for an angle θ in any quadrant can be expressed

* See page 68.

in terms of the function values for an acute reference angle, α. Hence, if a table is available for finding the function values for angles from 0° to 90°, the table will serve indirectly for corresponding angles of any size.

Table IV is a three-place * table of the values of the trigonometric functions of angles from 0° to 90°, inclusive, at intervals of 1°. For angles at most equal to 45°, read angles at the left and titles of columns at the top in the table. For angles from 45° to 90° inclusive, read angles at the right and titles of columns at the bottom. At present we disregard the reference to radian measure in Table IV.

Each entry in the function columns of Table IV is a function of some angle and, also, is the cofunction of the complementary angle, on account of the identities (4) on page 45. Thus, those identities make each entry in Table IV serve a double purpose.

ILLUSTRATION 1. From Table IV, $\tan 57° = 1.540$. If α is acute and $\sin \alpha = .454$, from the column in Table IV headed sine at the top, we read that $.454 = \sin 27°$, and hence $\alpha = 27°$.

EXERCISE 11

Construct the acute angle α and find the values of all functions of α.

1. $\tan \alpha = \frac{3}{4}$. **2.** $\sin \alpha = \frac{4}{5}$. **3.** $\cos \alpha = \frac{7}{25}$. **4.** $\sec \alpha = \frac{17}{8}$.

5. $\cos \alpha = \frac{15}{17}$. **6.** $\cot \alpha = \frac{12}{5}$. **7.** $\csc \alpha = \frac{3}{2}$. **8.** $\cos \alpha = \frac{1}{3}$.

9. From Figures 40 and 41, page 45, find the functions of 30°, 45°, and 60°.

Express each function value as a function value for the complementary angle. Also, obtain the function value from Table IV.

10. sin 20°. **11.** cos 15°. **12.** tan 49°. **13.** cot 38°.

14. sec 41°. **15.** csc 12°. **16.** sec 81°. **17.** tan 39°.

18. sec 85°. **19.** sin 67°. **20.** cot 67°. **21.** sin 82°.

22. By use of a protractor, construct on cross-section paper a right triangle of generous dimensions with 35° as one acute angle. Then, by finding quotients of the measured lengths of the sides of the triangle, find the functions of 35° and 55° approximately to one decimal place.

23. In a standard right triangle ABC, observe that $a < c$ and $b < c$. What facts does this recall about $\sin \alpha$, $\cos \alpha$, $\sec \alpha$, and $\csc \alpha$?

24. In the triangle ABC of Problem 23, what is true about sides a and b if (1) $\alpha = 45°$; (2) $\alpha < 45°$; (3) $\alpha > 45°$? In each case, also state corresponding facts about $\tan \alpha$ and $\cot \alpha$.

25. Prove that the equation $\sin 2\theta = 2 \sin \theta$ is **NOT** an identity.

26. Prove that the equation $\tan 3\theta = 3 \tan \theta$ is **NOT** an identity.

27. Prove that the equation $\sin (\alpha + \beta) = \sin \alpha + \sin \beta$ is **NOT** an identity.

* That is, most of the values are given accurately to at least three significant digits. See pages 68 and 69 if desired at this time.

27. Graphical reduction to acute angles

From page 38, we recall the notion of an acute *reference angle*, α, for an angle θ of any size in any quadrant. Various reference angles are exhibited in Figure 43. From other figures, the student may verify the following facts.

$$\textit{θ between } 90° \textit{ and } 180°; \textit{ reference angle is } \boldsymbol{\alpha = 180° - \theta}. \tag{1}$$

$$\textit{θ between } 180° \textit{ and } 270°; \textit{ reference angle is } \boldsymbol{\alpha = \theta - 180°}. \tag{2}$$

$$\textit{θ between } 270° \textit{ and } 360°; \textit{ reference angle is } \boldsymbol{\alpha = 360° - \theta}. \tag{3}$$

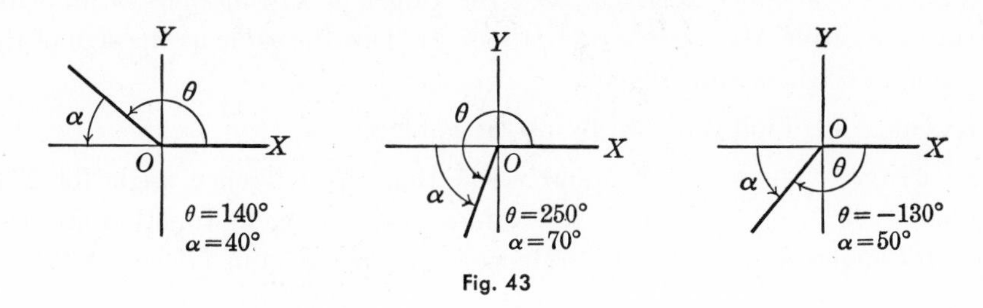

Fig. 43

Theorem I. *The value of any trigonometric function of an angle θ in any quadrant is numerically equal to the value of the same-named function of the reference angle, α, for θ. That is,*

$$\textbf{(any function of } \theta) = \pm \textbf{ (same function of reference angle } \alpha), \tag{4}$$

with "+" or "−" according as the function of θ is positive or negative.

Illustration 1. To find tan 140°, notice that $\alpha = 40°$ in Figure 43. Also, the tangent is negative in quadrant II. Hence, from (4) and Table IV for acute angles,

$$\tan 140° = -\tan 40° = -.839.$$

Illustration 2. The reference angle for 315° is 45° and tan 315° is negative, while cos 315° is positive. Hence, from (4),

$$\tan 315° = -\tan 45° = -1; \quad \cos 315° = +\cos 45° = \tfrac{1}{2}\sqrt{2}.$$

Proof of Theorem I. 1. Place θ in its standard position on a coordinate system, as in Figure 44; the reference angle for θ is the acute angle α of the reference $\triangle AOP$.

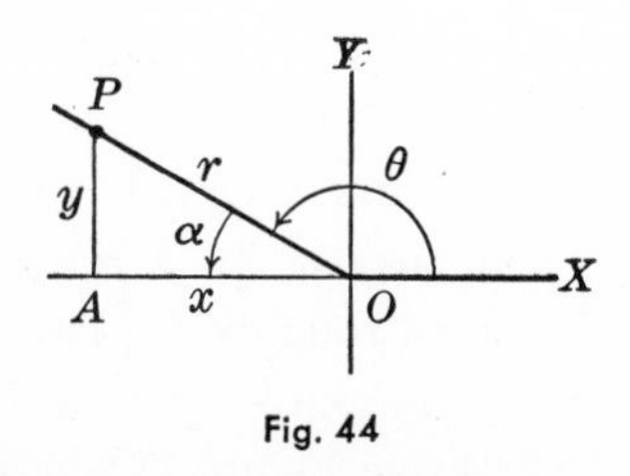

Fig. 44

2. Let the positive numbers $\overline{OA}$ and $\overline{AP}$ be the *lengths* of OA and AP. Then, $x = \pm\overline{OA}$ and $y = \pm\overline{AP}$, where the sign "+" or "−" in each case depends on the signs of x and y in the quadrant where P is located.

3. In $\triangle AOP$, $\overline{AP}$ and $\overline{OA}$ are the *lengths* of the sides opposite and adjacent

to α, and $r = \overline{OP}$. Then, we obtain the functions of α by use of page 44, and the functions of θ from definitions on page 33:

$$\sin \alpha = \frac{\overline{AP}}{r}; \qquad \sin \theta = \frac{y}{r} = \pm \frac{\overline{AP}}{r} = \pm \sin \alpha.$$

$$\tan \alpha = \frac{\overline{AP}}{\overline{OA}}; \qquad \tan \theta = \frac{y}{x} = \frac{\pm \overline{AP}}{\pm \overline{OA}} = \pm \tan \alpha.$$

Similarly, the value of each function of θ differs from the value of the same function of α at most in sign. Since the values of all functions of an acute angle are positive, the sign, $+$ or $-$, to use in (4) is the same as the sign of the function of θ which is involved.

EXAMPLE 1. Find tan 283° by use of Table IV.

SOLUTION. The student should verify that the reference angle for 283° is (360° − 283°) or 77°. Also, the values of the tangent function are negative for angles in quadrant IV. Hence, $\tan 283° = -\tan 77° = -4.331$.

ILLUSTRATION 3. Since $398° = 360° + 38°$, the angles 398° and 38° are coterminal and hence have the same values for their trigonometric functions. Also, we observe that 38° is the reference angle for 398°. From either viewpoint, $\sin 398° = \sin 38°$.

Note 1. For a quadrantal angle θ, we may call 0° or 90° the reference angle for θ according as its terminal side, in standard position, falls on the *horizontal* or *vertical* coordinate axis. Then, (4) holds for quadrantal angles as well as all other angles. However, this fact is seldom used because it is easy to memorize the functions of quadrantal angles.

Note 2. Instead of (4), we can say that the *absolute value* of any trigonometric function of θ is equal to the same-named function of the acute reference angle for θ. Thus, $|\sin \theta| = \sin \alpha$, etc.

We can use Theorem I, without drawing a coordinate system, to find the values of all functions of a particular angle θ if just *one function* of θ and its *quadrant* are given. We obtain the results by first finding the functions of the reference angle for θ from a right triangle.

EXAMPLE 2. Find $\sin \theta$ in case $\cos \theta = -\frac{2}{3}$ and θ is in quadrant III.

SOLUTION. 1. Let α be the reference angle for θ. Then, $\cos \alpha = \frac{2}{3}$. A right $\triangle ABC$ with α as one angle is shown roughly to scale in Figure 45; the value of a was computed: $a = \sqrt{9 - 4} = \sqrt{5}$.

2. From Figure 45, $\sin \alpha = \frac{1}{3}\sqrt{5}$. From Theorem I, we have $|\sin \theta| = \sin \alpha$; also, $\sin \theta < 0$. Hence, we obtain $\sin \theta = -\frac{1}{3}\sqrt{5}$.

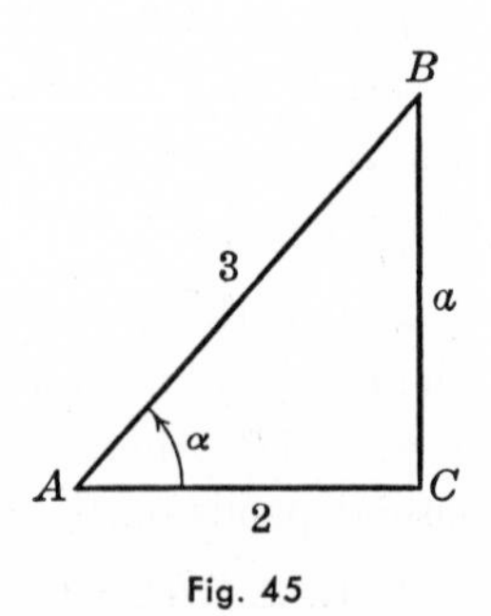

Fig. 45

EXERCISE 12

Sketch the angle in standard position and find the reference angle.

1. 121°. **2.** 203°. **3.** 267°. **4.** − 210°. **5.** 470°.

By use of a reference angle, find each function value. Give the result in exact form if the reference angle is 30°, 45°, *or* 60°, *and otherwise use Table* IV.

6. tan 115°.	**7.** cot 142°.	**8.** sin 208°.	**9.** cos 225°.
10. sec 330°.	**11.** csc 340°.	**12.** sin 394°.	**13.** cot 326°.
14. cos 117°.	**15.** cot 153°.	**16.** cot 210°.	**17.** sin 120°.
18. sin (− 25°).	**19.** tan (− 52°).	**20.** cos (− 75°).	**21.** sec (− 80°).
22. cot (− 130°).	**23.** sec (− 120°).	**24.** sin (− 210°).	**25.** csc (− 230°).
26. sin 250°.	**27.** sec 305°.	**28.** tan 216°.	**29.** cos 93°.
30. sin (− 200°).	**31.** tan (− 302°).	**32.** sec 420°.	**33.** cos 495°.
34. sin 530°.	**35.** cot 844°.	**36.** sec (− 403°).	**37.** cos 907°.

38. By placing each angle in standard position on a coordinate system as on page 33, obtain the values of all functions which exist for 0°, 90°, 180°, and 270°, to fill in a table with a row for each angle.

39. By reference to a coterminal angle in the table for Problem 38, read off the values of all trigonometric functions which exist for 360°; 540°; − 180°; − 270°; − 90°; − 720°; 450°; 630°.

40. Prove that each of the following equations is **NOT** an identity:

$$\cos(-\theta) = -\cos\theta;\quad \tan(-\theta) = \tan\theta;\quad \tan(\theta+\gamma) = \tan\theta + \tan\gamma.$$

By use of a right triangle corresponding to the reference angle, find the values of all functions of the angle θ *satisfying the conditions.*

41. $\tan\theta = -\frac{3}{5}$; θ in (II). **42.** $\sin\theta = -\frac{3}{4}$; θ in (IV).

43. $\cos\theta = -\frac{4}{7}$; θ in (II). **44.** $\cot\theta = \frac{5}{2}$; θ in (III).

28. Geometric representation of sin θ and cos θ

Let θ be any angle, and suppose that it is placed in standard position on a coordinate system, as in Figure 46, where a circle of radius 1 is constructed with the origin as center. Let $P:(x, y)$ be the intersection of the terminal side of θ and the circle. Then, we have

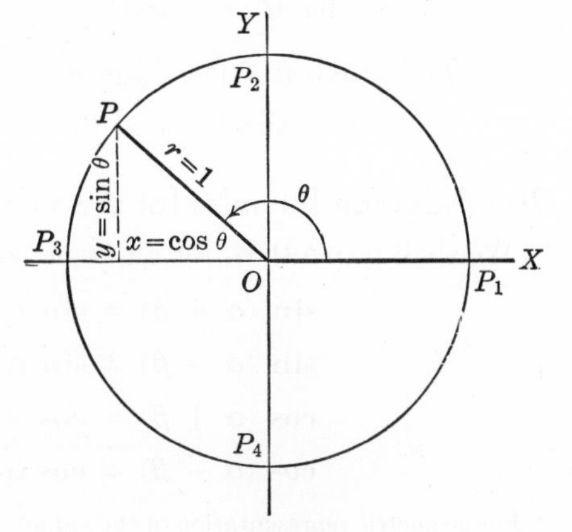

Fig. 46

$$r = OP = 1;$$

$$\sin\theta = \frac{y}{r} = \frac{y}{1} = y;\qquad \cos\theta = \frac{x}{1} = x.$$

That is, for any angle θ, the *ordinate* of P is $\sin\theta$ and the *abscissa* of P is $\cos\theta$.

If a variable angle θ changes continuously from $\theta = 0°$ to $\theta = 360°$, the corresponding variation in $\sin \theta$ or $\cos \theta$ can be learned by use of the geometric interpretation of $\sin \theta$ and $\cos \theta$ in Figure 46. Thus, if θ increases from 0° to 90°, point P of Figure 46 moves on the circle from P_1 to P_2, while $\sin \theta$ increases from 0 to 1. If θ increases from 90° to 270°, then P moves from P_2 to P_4, and $\sin \theta$ decreases from $+1$ to -1. If θ increases from 270° to 360°, then P moves from P_4 to P_1, and $\sin \theta$ increases from -1 to zero. Thus, $\sin \theta$ takes on as its value all numbers from -1 to $+1$, inclusive, as θ varies from 0° to 360°. Moreover, for any value of $\theta < 0°$ or $\theta > 360°$, $\sin \theta$ has one of the values met when $0° \leqq \theta \leqq 360°$. Hence, the **range of the sine function** is the set of *all numbers from* -1 *to* $+1$, *inclusive.* Similarly, the student should discuss the variation of $\cos \theta$ as θ changes continuously from 0° to 360°. The conclusion will be reached that the **range of the cosine function** also is the set of *all numbers from* -1 *to* $+1$, *inclusive.**

29. An auxiliary result

Let θ be any angle, positive, negative, or zero, with vertex O, initial side OB, and terminal side OC, where $OB = 1$ and $OC = 1$. Then, if triangle OBC is completed, as in Figure 47, we shall prove that

$$\overline{BC}^2 = 2 - 2 \cos \theta. \qquad (1)$$

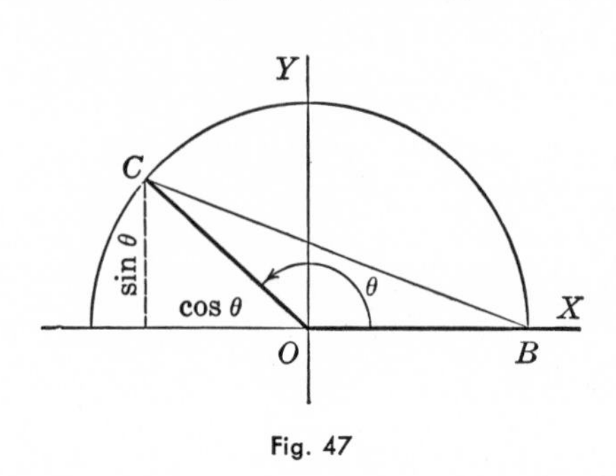

Fig. 47

Proof. 1. Place θ in standard position on a coordinate system, as in Figure 47, with B on the x-axis in the positive direction from O. Then, from Figure 46 on page 49, the coordinates of C are $(\cos \theta, \sin \theta)$, and the coordinates of B are $(1, 0)$, for any angle θ.

2. By the distance formula, page 14,

$$\overline{BC}^2 = (\cos \theta - 1)^2 + (\sin \theta - 0)^2 = \cos^2 \theta - 2 \cos \theta + 1 + \sin^2 \theta$$
$$= 1 + (\sin^2 \theta + \cos^2 \theta) - 2 \cos \theta = 2 - 2 \cos \theta.$$

30. Addition formulas for the sine and cosine

We shall prove that, for all angles α and β,

$$\sin (\alpha + \beta) = \sin \alpha \cos \beta + \cos \alpha \sin \beta; \qquad (1)$$

$$\sin (\alpha - \beta) = \sin \alpha \cos \beta - \cos \alpha \sin \beta; \qquad (2)$$

$$\cos (\alpha + \beta) = \cos \alpha \cos \beta - \sin \alpha \sin \beta; \qquad (3)$$

$$\cos (\alpha - \beta) = \cos \alpha \cos \beta + \sin \alpha \sin \beta. \qquad (4)$$

* For geometric representation of the values of the tangent, cotangent, secant, and cosecant as directed line segments, see Note 3 in the Appendix.

We refer to identities (1) and (3) as *addition formulas;* later we shall see that (2) and (4) are special cases of (1) and (3), respectively, or vice versa.

Proof of (4). 1. For any angles α and β, let $\phi = \alpha - \beta$. Then, $\alpha = \phi + \beta$. Place β in standard position on a coordinate system, as in Figure 48, with initial side OM and terminal side OC, where $\overline{OM} = \overline{OC} = 1$. The semicircle in Figure 48 has radius 1 and center at O. Rotate OC through the angle ϕ to form $\alpha = \phi + \beta$, with OB as the terminal side of α and $OB = 1$. Then, α also is in standard position.

2. From Figure 46 on page 49, the coordinates of C are $(\cos \beta, \sin \beta)$, and of B are $(\cos \alpha, \sin \alpha)$. By use of the distance formula of page 14,

$$\overline{BC}^2 = (\cos \alpha - \cos \beta)^2 + (\sin \alpha - \sin \beta)^2$$

$$= (\cos^2 \alpha + \sin^2 \alpha) + (\cos^2 \beta + \sin^2 \beta) - 2(\cos \alpha \cos \beta + \sin \alpha \sin \beta). \quad (5)$$

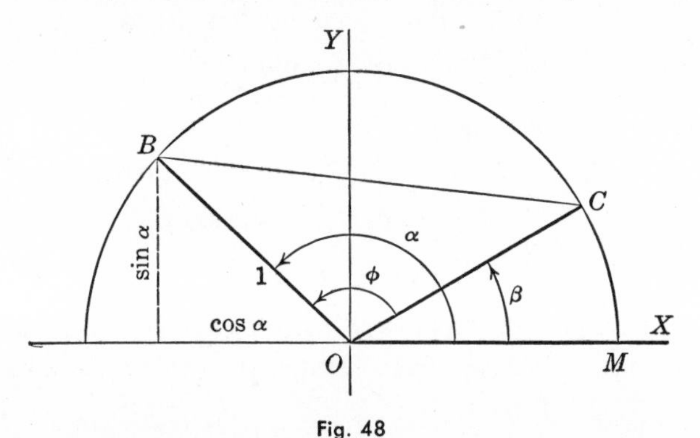

Fig. 48

From (1) of Section 29 on page 50, and (5), we then obtain (4):

$$2 - 2 \cos \phi = 2 - 2(\cos \alpha \cos \beta + \sin \alpha \sin \beta), \text{ or}$$

$$\cos \phi = \cos (\alpha - \beta) = \cos \alpha \cos \beta + \sin \alpha \sin \beta.$$

By use of (4), we shall prove the following identities, which are involved in proving (1).

$$\sin (-\theta) = -\sin \theta; \quad \cos (-\theta) = \cos \theta. \quad (6)$$

$$\sin (90° - \theta) = \cos \theta; \quad \cos (90° - \theta) = \sin \theta. \quad (7)$$

Proof of **cos (– θ) = cos θ.** From (4) with $\alpha = 0°$ and $\beta = \theta$,

$$\cos (0° - \theta) = \cos (-\theta) = \cos 0° \cos \theta + \sin 0° \sin \theta = \cos \theta,$$

because $\cos 0° = 1$ and $\sin 0° = 0$.

Proof of **cos (90° – θ) = sin θ.** From (4) with $\alpha = 90°$ and $\beta = \theta$,

$$\cos (90° - \theta) = \cos 90° \cos \theta + \sin 90° \sin \theta = \sin \theta,$$

because $\cos 90° = 0$ and $\sin 90° = 1$.

Proof of **sin (90° − θ) = cos θ.** In cos (90° − θ) = sin θ, when θ is replaced by (90° − θ) on both sides, we obtain

$$\cos[90° - (90° - \theta)] = \sin(90° - \theta), \quad or \quad \cos\theta = \sin(90° - \theta).$$

Proof of **sin (− θ) = − sin θ.** From cos (90° − θ) = sin θ with θ replaced by − θ, we obtain

$$\sin(-\theta) = \cos[90° - (-\theta)] = \cos[\theta - (-90°)]. \tag{8}$$

On using (4) with $\alpha = \theta$ and $\beta = -90°$ in (8), we find

$$\sin(-\theta) = \cos\theta\cos(-90°) + \sin\theta\sin(-90°) = -\sin\theta,$$

because $\cos(-90°) = 0$ and $\sin(-90°) = -1$. Thus, we have proved identities (6) and (7).

Proof of (1). By use of $\sin\theta = \cos(90° - \theta)$ with $\theta = \alpha + \beta$, and then from (4) with α replaced by $(90° - \alpha)$, we obtain

$$\begin{aligned}\sin(\alpha+\beta) &= \cos[90° - (\alpha+\beta)] = \cos[(90° - \alpha) - \beta]\\ &= \cos(90° - \alpha)\cos\beta + \sin(90° - \alpha)\sin\beta\\ &= \sin\alpha\cos\beta + \cos\alpha\sin\beta,\end{aligned}$$

where we used (7) with $\theta = \alpha$. Hence, (1) is true.

Proof of (2) *and* (3). If we replace β by $-\beta$, and use (6), then (1) yields (2) and (4) becomes (3). Thus, from (1) and then (6),

$$\begin{aligned}\sin[\alpha + (-\beta)] &= \sin\alpha\cos(-\beta) + \cos\alpha\sin(-\beta)\\ &= \sin\alpha\cos\beta - \cos\alpha\sin\beta.\end{aligned}$$

EXAMPLE 1. Find sin 135° and cos 135° by using 90° and 45°.

SOLUTION. From (1) with $\alpha = 90°$ and $\beta = 45°$,

$$\sin 135° = \sin 90°\cos 45° + \cos 90°\sin 45° = \cos 45° = \tfrac{1}{2}\sqrt{2},$$

because $\sin 90° = 1$ and $\cos 90° = 0$. Similarly, from (3), $\cos 135° = -\frac{1}{2}\sqrt{2}$.

EXAMPLE 2. Find $\sin(\alpha + \beta)$ if $\sin\alpha = \frac{3}{5}$, $\cos\beta = -\frac{5}{13}$, α is in quadrant I, and β is in quadrant II.

SOLUTION. Figure 49 shows a possible illustration of β, where the reference $\triangle OMN$ has $\overline{ON} = 13$, $\overline{OM} = 5$, and therefore $\overline{MN} = 12$, by the Pythagorean theorem. Then $\sin\beta = \frac{12}{13}$. Similarly, from a reference triangle with sides 3, 4, and 5, $\cos\alpha = \frac{4}{5}$. Hence, (1) gives

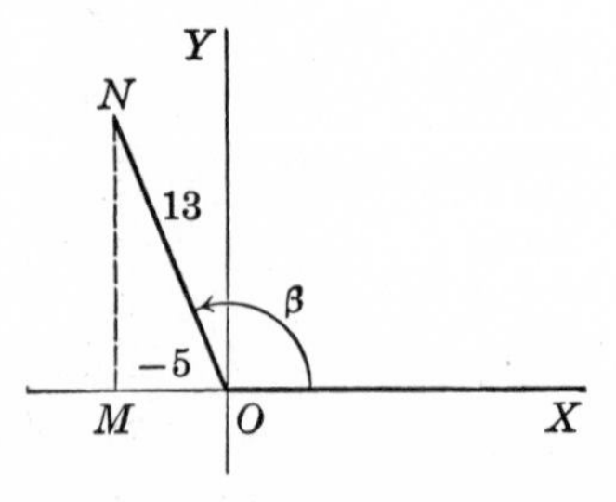

Fig. 49

$$\sin(\alpha+\beta) = \tfrac{3}{5}(-\tfrac{5}{13}) + \tfrac{4}{5}(\tfrac{12}{13}) = \tfrac{33}{65}.$$

EXERCISE 13

Express the angle as a sum or difference and solve by use of (1)–(4) *on page* 50.

1. Find sin 225° and cos 225° by using functions of 180° and 45°.
2. Find sin 210° and cos 210° by using functions of 180° and 30°.
3. Find sin 315° and cos 315° by using functions of 360° and 45°.
4. Find sin 150° and cos 150° by using functions of 180° and 30°.
5. Find sin 180° and cos 180° by using functions of 240° and 60°.
6. Find sin 45° and cos 45° by using functions of 180° and 135°.
7. Find sin 75° and cos 75° by using functions of 135° and 60°.

Find the sine and cosine of the angle without using a table.

8. 105°. **9.** 165°. **10.** 195°. **11.** 285°. **12.** 225°.

Without use of tables, find the sine and cosine, and then the tangent and cotangent of $(\alpha + \beta)$ *and of* $(\alpha - \beta)$.

13. $\sin \alpha = \frac{4}{5}$, α in quadrant I; $\cos \beta = -\frac{12}{13}$, β in quadrant II.
14. $\sin \alpha = \frac{24}{25}$, α in quadrant II; $\cos \beta = \frac{5}{13}$, β in quadrant IV.
15. $\sin \alpha = \frac{5}{13}$, α in quadrant II; $\cos \beta = -\frac{24}{25}$, β in quadrant III.
16. $\sin \alpha = -\frac{8}{17}$, α in quadrant III; $\sin \beta = -\frac{24}{25}$, β in quadrant IV.

Expand by use of (1)–(4) *on page* 50 *and insert known function values.*

17. $\sin (30° + \theta)$. **18.** $\cos (45° - \alpha)$. **19.** $\sin (60° + \theta)$.
20. $\sin (90° + \theta)$. **21.** $\cos (90° + \theta)$. **22.** $\sin (\theta - 90°)$.
23. $\sin (270° - \theta)$. **24.** $\sin (180° + \theta)$. **25.** $\cos (\theta - 270°)$.
26. $\cos (\theta - 180°)$. **27.** $\sin (\theta - 450°)$. **28.** $\sin (-90° - \theta)$.

Prove that the equation is ***NOT*** *an identity in the angles* α *and* β.

29. $\sin (\alpha - \beta) = \sin \alpha - \sin \beta$. **30.** $\cos (\alpha - \beta) = \cos \alpha - \cos \beta$.

31. Periodicity of the trigonometric functions

Let f be a function whose domain consists of all numbers x in a certain set D. Suppose that p is a positive constant such that

$$f(x + p) = f(x) \text{ at all admissible values of } x. \tag{1}$$

Then, we say that f is **periodic** and has p as a **period.** This means that values of f repeat at intervals of length p in the values of x. Then

$$f(x + 2p) = f[(x + p) + p] = f(x + p) = f(x),$$

so that $2p$ also is seen to be a period for f. Similarly, $3p$, $4p$, or in general np is a period for f, with n as any positive integer. If f is periodic, the *smallest number* p which is a period for f is called **THE period** for f. On replacing x in (1) by $(x - p)$, we obtain $f[(x - p) + p] = f(x - p)$, or

$$f(x) = f(x - p) \text{ at all values of } x. \tag{2}$$

ILLUSTRATION 1. Let the function $f(x)$ have the graph shown in Figure 50, where a semicircle of radius 2 is repeated above the x-axis endlessly to the left and the right. Then, from this graph of $y = f(x)$, we see that f is periodic with the period 4, because $f(x + 4) = f(x)$ at all values of x. For instance,

$$f(0) = 2 = f(\pm 4) = f(\pm 8) = etc.; \quad f(2) = 0 = f(-2) = f(6) = etc.$$

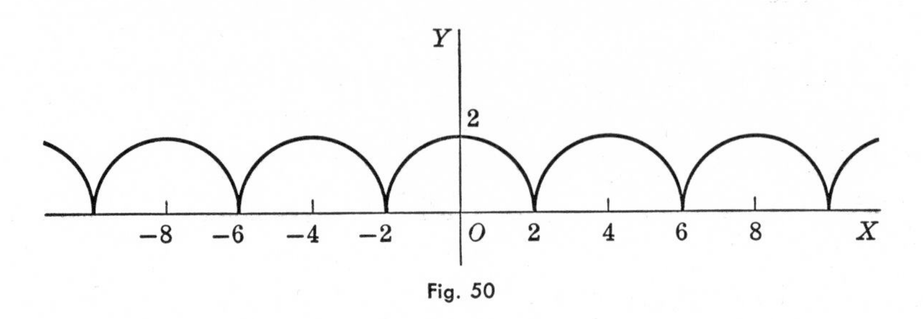

Fig. 50

The definition of periodicity summarized in (1) extends naturally to a function $f(\theta)$ where θ represents the measure of an angle.

THEOREM II. *Each trigonometric function of an angle θ is periodic and has* 360°, *or one complete rotation, as a period. That is, for all values of θ,**

$$[\textbf{any function of } (\theta + 360°)] = (\textbf{same function of } \theta); \tag{3}$$

$$[\textbf{any function of } (\theta - 360°)] = (\textbf{same function of } \theta). \tag{4}$$

Proof. For every value of θ, the angles θ, $(\theta + 360°)$, and $(\theta - 360°)$ are coterminal. Since coterminal angles have identical trigonometric functions, equations (3) and (4) are true for all values of θ, and hence are identities.

Note 1. In illustrative Example 1 on page 128, and Problem 33 on page 129, it is proved that the *smallest* period of the functions $\tan\theta$ and $\cot\theta$ is 180°, and of $\sin\theta$, $\cos\theta$, $\sec\theta$, and $\csc\theta$ is 360°.

Equation (3) abbreviates six identities,

$$\sin(\theta + 360°) = \sin\theta, \quad \cos(\theta + 360°) = \cos\theta, \quad \cdots, \quad \csc(\theta + 360°) = \csc\theta.$$

ILLUSTRATION 2. From (3) and (4), the values of $\sin\theta$ repeat at intervals of 360° in the values of θ if we increase or decrease θ. Thus, $\sin\theta$ repeats the value $\sin 30° = \frac{1}{2}$ at intervals of 360°:

$$\tfrac{1}{2} = \sin 30° = \sin(30° \pm 360°) = \sin(30° \pm 720°) = etc.$$

Identities (3) and (4) are equivalent, although in different notation. Thus, either (3) or (4) states that *if two angles differ by* 360°, *the values of corresponding functions of the two angles are equal.*

* With the usual proviso that, when the tangent, cotangent, secant, or cosecant is involved, the equation does not hold true for any quadrantal value of θ for which the function is not defined.

32. Reduction formulas

Simple relations exist between the values of the trigonometric functions of any two angles whose sum or whose difference is an integral multiple of 90°. In (1) below, the multiple of 90° is $0 \cdot 90°$; in (2), the multiple is $1 \cdot 90°$; in (3), the multiple is $\pm 2 \cdot 90°$. Identities of this variety are called *reduction formulas.* The periodicity identities of Section 31 are reduction formulas.

Any reduction formula involving the sine or cosine functions can be proved by use of (1)–(4) on page 50. The following reduction formulas are so useful that they deserve being memorized; some of them were met in proving (1)–(4) of page 50.

$$\sin(-\theta) = -\sin\theta; \quad \cos(-\theta) = \cos\theta; \quad \tan(-\theta) = -\tan\theta. \tag{1}$$

$$[\text{any trig. function of } (90° - \theta)] = (\text{cofunction of } \theta). \tag{2}$$

$$\tan(\theta \pm 180°) = \tan\theta; \qquad \cot(\theta \pm 180°) = \cot\theta. \tag{3}$$

$$\sin(180° - \theta) = \sin\theta; \qquad \cos(180° - \theta) = -\cos\theta. \tag{4}$$

We call (2) the **cofunction identities.** Identities (3) state that the tangent and cotangent functions are periodic with the period 180°, as well as the larger period 360° which is common to all trigonometric functions.

ILLUSTRATION 1. In Section 30, we proved the identities involving the sine and cosine in (1). Then, from the fundamental identities of page 40, we obtain

$$\tan(-\theta) = \frac{\sin(-\theta)}{\cos(-\theta)} = \frac{-\sin\theta}{\cos\theta} = -\tan\theta.$$

From (1), by taking reciprocals, we may write

$$\csc(-\theta) = \frac{1}{\sin(-\theta)} = \frac{1}{-\sin\theta} = -\frac{1}{\sin\theta} = -\csc\theta.$$

In the same manner, by use of (1) and by taking reciprocals, the student should obtain

$$\sec(-\theta) = \sec\theta; \qquad \cot(-\theta) = -\cot\theta.$$

Similarly, for any set of reduction formulas, if we obtain those involving the sines and cosines, we can prove the corresponding formulas for the other functions by use of fundamental identities.

ILLUSTRATION 2. In Section 30, we proved (2) for $\sin(90° - \theta)$ and $\cos(90° - \theta)$ on the left. Hence, we obtain

$$\tan(90° - \theta) = \frac{\sin(90° - \theta)}{\cos(90° - \theta)} = \frac{\cos\theta}{\sin\theta} = \cot\theta.$$

Then, on taking reciprocals as in Illustration 1, we could show that (2) holds for $\cot(90° - \theta)$, $\sec(90° - \theta)$, and $\csc(90° - \theta)$.

ILLUSTRATION 3. By use of the addition formula for the sine function, with $\sin 180° = 0$ and $\cos 180° = -1$,

$$\sin(\theta + 180°) = \sin\theta\cos 180° + \cos\theta\sin 180° = -\sin\theta.$$

Similarly, $\cos(\theta + 180°) = -\cos\theta$. Hence,

$$\tan(\theta + 180°) = \frac{\sin(\theta + 180°)}{\cos(\theta + 180°)} = \frac{-\sin\theta}{-\cos\theta} = \tan\theta. \tag{5}$$

Then, $\cot(\theta + 180°) = \cot\theta$. Identities (3) for $(\theta - 180°)$ can be proved by use of the results for $(\theta + 180°)$, and (4) on page 54. Thus,

$$\cot\theta = \cot(\theta + 180°) = \cot[(\theta + 180°) - 360°] = \cot(\theta - 180°).$$

ILLUSTRATION 4. If θ is an acute angle, the *supplement* of θ is $(180° - \theta)$. Thus, (4) gives the sine and cosine of the supplement of θ in terms of $\sin\theta$ and $\cos\theta$, respectively. The student should prove (4) for any angle θ by use of (2) and (4) on page 50.

All reduction formulas are special cases of the following general identity, which can be proved by use of the addition formulas for the sine and cosine and the fundamental identities, as in Illustration 3. In (6), n represents any integer, 0, positive, or negative.

$$\left\{\begin{matrix}\textbf{Any trigonometric} \\ \textbf{function of } (\pm\boldsymbol{\theta} + \boldsymbol{n}\cdot\textbf{90°})\end{matrix}\right\} = \left\{\begin{matrix}\pm\ (\textbf{same function of } \boldsymbol{\theta}),\ \boldsymbol{n}\ \textbf{even;} \\ \pm\ (\textbf{cofunction of } \boldsymbol{\theta}),\ \boldsymbol{n}\ \textbf{odd.}\end{matrix}\right\} \tag{6}$$

In (6), for any specified function on the left-hand side, and any integer n, just one sign, $+$ or $-$, applies on the right, with the *same sign involved for all values of* θ. Thus, we find that, for all values of θ,

$$\sin(270° + \theta) = -\cos\theta; \qquad \cos(270° + \theta) = \sin\theta. \tag{7}$$

A general proof of (6) is suggested in the next exercise. For any particular angle $(\pm\theta + n\cdot 90°)$, the identities obtainable from (6) can be proved as in Illustration 3.

ILLUSTRATION 5. To prove (7), we use (1) and (3) of page 50 with $\alpha = 270°$ and $\beta = \theta$:

$$\sin(270° + \theta) = \sin 270°\cos\theta + \cos 270°\sin\theta = -\cos\theta,$$

because $\sin 270° = -1$ and $\cos 270° = 0$. Similarly, the student should obtain $\cos(270° + \theta) = \sin\theta$. Then, by use of the fundamental identities,

$$\tan(270° + \theta) = \frac{\sin(270° + \theta)}{\cos(270° + \theta)} = \frac{-\cos\theta}{\sin\theta} = -\cot\theta.$$

Hereafter, unless otherwise specified, we shall use (6) without proof in any special case.

EXAMPLE 1. Express $\cot (270° - \theta)$ in terms of a function of θ.

SOLUTION. 1. From (6), since $270° = 3 \cdot 90°$, we have

$$\cot (270° - \theta) = \pm \tan \theta, \tag{8}$$

where the sign $\pm$ is independent of the value of θ.

2. To determine the sign on the right in (8), let θ be thought of as an acute angle. Then, $(270° - \theta)$ is an angle in quadrant III, and $\cot (270° - \theta) > 0$; since $\tan \theta > 0$ when θ is acute, we must use "+" on the right in (8) to make the right-hand side positive. Hence, when θ is acute, and therefore for *all* admissible values of θ, we have $\cot (270° - \theta) = \tan \theta$.

SUMMARY. *To obtain any particular reduction formula, use* (6) *with an ambiguous sign. Then, determine the proper sign by checking signs on the two sides for the case where θ is acute.*

By use of the periodicity of the trigonometric functions and (1), any trigonometric function of an angle θ of any magnitude, positive or negative, can be expressed as a function of a *nonnegative angle* less than 360°. Then, by use of an acute reference angle, the function of θ can be expressed as a function of an acute angle, in two ways if (2) is used.

ILLUSTRATION 6. To find $\tan (-1257°)$, notice that $1257° = 1080° + 177°$. Then, by (1) and the periodicity of the tangent function,

$$\tan (-1257°) = -\tan 1257° = -\tan (3 \cdot 360° + 177°) = -\tan 177°.$$

The acute reference angle for 177° is 3°; $\tan 177° = -\tan 3°$. Hence,

$$\tan (-1257°) = -(-\tan 3°) = \tan 3° = .052 \qquad \text{(Table IV)}$$

$$= \cot 87° = .052. \qquad \text{[Using (2)]}$$

EXERCISE 14

Prove the reduction formulas for the specified function values.

1. $\sin (270° - \theta)$. **2.** $\cos (\theta - 270°)$. **3.** $\cos (\theta - 180°)$.
4. $\sin (\theta - 90°)$. **5.** $\cos (\theta + 90°)$. **6.** $\sin (450° + \theta)$.
7. $\sin (\theta - 180°)$. **8.** $\cos (\theta + 540°)$. **9.** $\sin (\theta - 270°)$.

By use of addition formulas, prove the reduction formulas for the sine and cosine of the specified angle, and then obtain the reduction formulas for all other functions of the angle by use of the fundamental identities.

10. $(\theta - 90°)$. **11.** $(270° - \theta)$. **12.** $(540° - \theta)$. **13.** $(\theta + 90°)$.
14. $(\theta + 270°)$. **15.** $(450° - \theta)$. **16.** $(\theta + 450°)$. **17.** $(630° - \theta)$.

Express the function value in terms of the value of a function of θ.

18. $\cot (180° + \theta)$. **19.** $\sin (270° + \theta)$. **20.** $\cos (270° - \theta)$.
21. $\tan (270° - \theta)$. **22.** $\csc (180° + \theta)$. **23.** $\tan (360° + \theta)$.

24. $\sin(\theta - 720°)$. 25. $\sec(270° + \theta)$. 26. $\csc(360° - \theta)$.
27. $\sec(-\theta)$. 28. $\cos(450° + \theta)$. 29. $\sin(-270° + \theta)$.
30. $\tan(270° - \theta)$. 31. $\cot(540° + \theta)$. 32. $\tan(\theta - 540°)$.
33. $\csc(\theta - 360°)$. 34. $\cot(-180° + \theta)$. 35. $\sec(90° + \theta)$.

Sketch the angle roughly in standard position on a coordinate system, and express the sine, cosine, and tangent of the angle in terms of a trigonometric function value for a positive angle at most 45°. *Use the cofunction relations.*

36. 47°. 37. 63°. 38. 129°. 39. 147°. 40. 218°.
41. 176°. 42. 243°. 43. 284°. 44. 304°. 45. 352°.
46. − 37°. 47. − 56°. 48. − 124°. 49. − 256°. 50. − 310°.
51. 305°. 52. 487°. 53. − 247°. 54. − 849°. 55. − 283°.

★56. Prove (6) on page 56 for the cases of the sine and cosine on the left, if n is an even integer. Then, prove (6) for the tangent on the left.

HINT. If n is an even integer, $\sin n \cdot 90° = 0$ and $\cos n \cdot 90° = \pm 1$.

★57. Repeat Problem 56 for the case where n is odd.

33. Graphs of the sine and cosine, in degree measure

In Definition I on page 33, as emphasized on page 33, the domain of each of the trigonometric functions is a set of *geometrical objects*, called *angles*. Sometimes, with this viewpoint, Definition I is said to describe the *geometric trigonometric functions*.

In the definition of the graph of a function on page 20, both the *domain* and the *range* of the function were sets of *numbers*. We desire to obtain this situation for the trigonometric functions, in order to consider their graphs. Hence, we depart from the viewpoint of Definition I, and shall refer to each trigonometric function as having a domain consisting of *real numbers*, which are the *measures of angles*, at present *measured in degrees*.

ILLUSTRATION 1. Let f be a function whose domain is the set, D, of all real numbers and whose value at any point x of D is $f(x) = \sin x°$. Thus, $f(2) = \sin 2° = .035$, by Table IV; $f(90) = \sin 90° = 1$.

When we refer to the graphs of the trigonometric functions in degree measure, we shall be speaking of the graphs of the functions $\sin x°$, $\cos x°$, $\tan x°$, $\cot x°$, $\sec x°$, and $\csc x°$, where the independent variable is x, and the range for x is *all real numbers* for which the functions are defined. We shall call these functions a variety of *analytic trigonometric functions*, or *trigonometric functions of numbers*.

The graph of the function $\sin x°$ is the graph of the equation $y = \sin x°$. We make up the entries in the following table, with x ranging from 0 to 90, by use of Table IV or from memory about the convenient angles 0°, 30°, 45°, 60°, and 90°. Then we choose other values of x so that the acute reference angles for $x°$ are those just used. Thus, corresponding to 75°, we have $\sin 105° = \sin 75° = .97$; $\sin (180° + 75°) = \sin 255° = -\sin 75° = -.97$; *etc.*

x	0	30	45	60	75	90	105	120	135	150	180
$y = \sin x°$	0	.50	.71	.87	.97	1.00	.97	.87	.71	.50	0
x	180	210	225	240	255	270	285	300	315	330	360
$y = \sin x°$	0	− .50	− .71	− .87	− .97	− 1.00	− .97	− .87	− .71	− .50	0

The points (x, y) from the table were used to obtain the graph in Figure 51. The scale units on the coordinate axes were chosen unequal in order to obtain

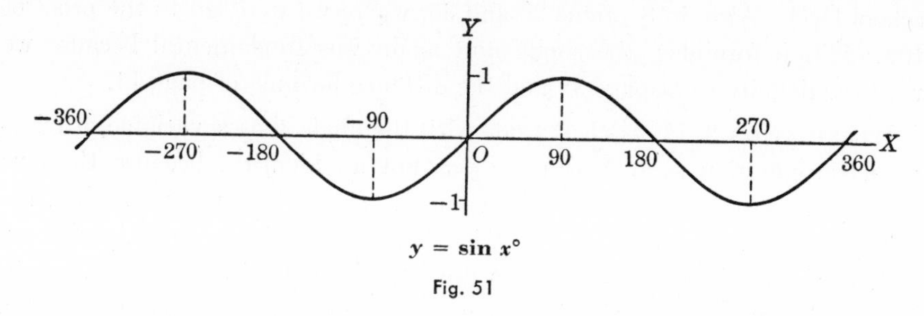

$y = \sin x°$

Fig. 51

a graceful curve showing the major features of the sine function clearly. The complete graph consists of this wave and its endless repetitions on both sides, because $\sin x°$ is a periodic function with the period 360. That is,

$$\sin (x \pm 360)° = \sin (x° \pm 360°) = \sin x°.$$

Thus, to plot the point (x, y) on the graph where $x = -330$, we use the ordinate where $x = 30$, because $-330° + 360° = 30°$, and hence $\sin (-330°) = \sin 30°$. The graph of $y = \cos x°$ can be obtained similarly, as given in Figure 52.

The identity $\sin (x° + 90°) = \cos x°$ states that *the cosine of any angle is the same as the sine of an angle which is 90° greater.* Therefore, if we shift the graph of $\sin x°$ to the left, through a distance equal to 90 on the horizontal scale, we obtain the graph of $\cos x°$, as in Figure 52.

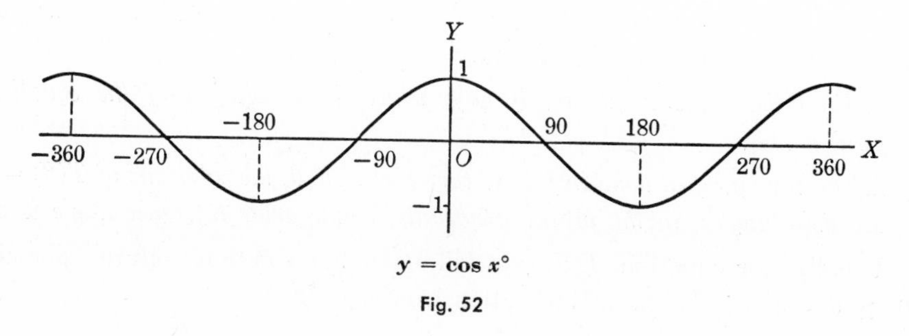

$y = \cos x°$

Fig. 52

ILLUSTRATION 2. In Figure 51 on page 59, if x varies from $x = 0$ to $x = 90$, the graph *rises*, or $\sin x°$ *increases* from 0 to 1. If x varies from 90 to 270, the graph *falls*, or $\sin x°$ *decreases* from 1 to -1; etc.

Note 1. On page 23, we noticed that, in drawing the graph of a function $y = f(x)$ in an xy-plane, as a rule there is *no necessity for choosing equal scale units on the coordinate axes.* This fact was recognized in the construction of Figures 51 and 52. However, in the definition of the trigonometric functions on page 33, and in the proof of the distance formula on page 14, the use of a *single unit of length* in the whole plane was a fundamental feature. The preceding fact is true because, on those pages, we used *distance in any direction* with the basis provided by Euclidean geometry as met at the high school level. Also, in Sections 29 and 30, where we were led to the proof of the addition formulas, the single unit again was fundamental because we used the definitions of page 33 and the distance formula of page 14.

ILLUSTRATION 3. It is clear that, with the angle θ as a variable, a trigonometric equation such as $\sin \theta = \frac{1}{2}$ is not an identity, because the sine function does not always have the value $\frac{1}{2}$. Hence, we propose finding the solutions of the equation on a restricted domain for θ, say on the domain $-360° < \theta < 360°$. To solve $\sin \theta = \frac{1}{2}$, we recall the sines of convenient angles and the signs of the sine function in the various quadrants. We see that θ must be in quadrant I or quadrant II. Hence, on the domain $-360° < \theta < 360°$, the solutions of $\sin \theta = \frac{1}{2}$ are, first, 30° and 150°, and then the coterminal angles θ such that $-360° < \theta < 0°$, or $-210°$ and $-330°$. Thus, we have four solutions: 30°, 150°, $-210°$, and $-330°$. In Figure 51 on page 59, if the student draws the line $y = \frac{1}{2}$, it will intersect the graph of $y = \sin x°$ at four points, where x has the values -210, -330, 30, and 150, corresponding to the values of θ above. From the periodicity of $\sin \theta$, all solutions of $\sin \theta = \frac{1}{2}$, with no limitation on the size of θ, are of the following forms where n may be any integer, positive, negative, or zero:

$$\theta = 30° + n(360°) \quad \textit{and} \quad \theta = 150° + n(360°).$$

Let T represent any trigonometric function of an angle θ, and consider solving a trigonometric equation $T(\theta) = b$, where b is a known constant. Let α be the acute reference angle for θ. Then, $T(\alpha) = |b|$. Hence, to solve $T(\theta) = b$, we proceed as follows.

1. *Find the acute angle, α, if any, which is a solution of the equation $T(\alpha) = |b|$.*

2. *On any specified domain for the variable angle θ, the solutions of $T(\theta) = b$ are those angles, in the proper quadrants, whose acute reference angle is α.*

Usually, an equation $T(\theta) = b$ will have *two* solutions on the domain $0° \leqq \theta < 360°$, as seen in Illustration 1 on page 42.

ILLUSTRATION 4. To find all solutions of $\sin\theta = -\frac{1}{2}\sqrt{3}$ on the range $0° \leqq \theta < 360°$, let α be the acute reference angle for θ. Then, $\sin\alpha = |-\frac{1}{2}\sqrt{3}|$, or $\sin\alpha = \frac{1}{2}\sqrt{3}$; hence $\alpha = 60°$. Since θ is in quadrant III or quadrant IV because $\sin\theta < 0$, we obtain the solutions $\theta = 180° + 60°$ and $\theta = 360° - 60°$, or 240° and 300°.

EXERCISE 15

Graph the functions in an xy-plane. For the x and y scales, make the distance for 180 *units on the x-axis about three times the unit distance on the y-axis.*

1. The function $\sin x°$, for $-180 \leqq x \leqq 540$.

2. The function $\cos x°$, for $270 \leqq x \leqq 450$.

Note 1. To appreciate the effect of coordinate scale units in graphing, make a rough graph of $y = \sin x°$ with the unit on the x-axis one third of the unit on the y-axis, for the domain $0 \leqq x \leqq 90$.

3. By inspection of a graph, describe the variation of each of the functions $\sin\theta$ and $\cos\theta$ as the angle θ changes continuously from $-180°$ to 360°.

Graph each of the equations on the domain $0 \leqq x \leqq 360$, *by use of just quadrantal angles* $x°$. *Make gracefully rounded curves.*

4. $y = 2\sin x°$. **5.** $y = -2\sin x°$. **6.** $y = 3\cos x°$.

Find all solutions for the angle θ *on the domain* $-360° \leqq \theta \leqq 360°$.

7. $\sin\theta = 1$. **8.** $\cos\theta = -1$. **9.** $\cos\theta = 0$. **10.** $\cos\theta = \frac{1}{2}$.

11. $\sin\theta = 0$. **12.** $\sin\theta = -1$. **13.** $\cos\theta = -\frac{1}{2}$.

14. $\sin\theta = -\frac{1}{2}$. **15.** $\cos\theta = \frac{1}{2}\sqrt{2}$. **16.** $\sin\theta = \frac{1}{2}\sqrt{2}$.

17. $\sin\theta = \frac{1}{2}\sqrt{3}$. **18.** $\cos\theta = \frac{1}{2}\sqrt{3}$. **19.** $\sin\theta = -\frac{1}{2}\sqrt{2}$.

20. $\cos\theta = -\frac{1}{2}\sqrt{2}$. **21.** $\cos\theta = -\frac{1}{2}\sqrt{3}$. **22.** $\sin\theta = \frac{1}{2}$.

23. In the artillery service of the armed forces, angles frequently are measured in **mils,** where (1600 *mils*) = 90°. Let g be a function whose domain is the set D of all real numbers and whose value at any point x in D is $g(x) = \sin x^{(m)}$, where $x^{(m)}$ means x *mils*. Let $f(x) = \sin x°$. Find $g(800)$; $f(800)$; $f(320)$; $g(320)$. Are f and g the same function?

★**24.** Write expressions for all solutions in Problems 15 and 19.

34. Variation of tan θ and sec θ

Suppose that $0° \leqq \theta < 90°$, and that θ is placed in standard position on a coordinate system, as in Figure 53, where $P{:}(x, y)$ is chosen on the terminal side of θ so that $x = 1$. Then, from page 33,

$$\tan\theta = \frac{y}{x} = \frac{y}{1} = y; \qquad \sec\theta = \frac{r}{x} = r.$$

Or, the ordinate of P is equal to $\tan\theta$ and $r = \sec\theta$.

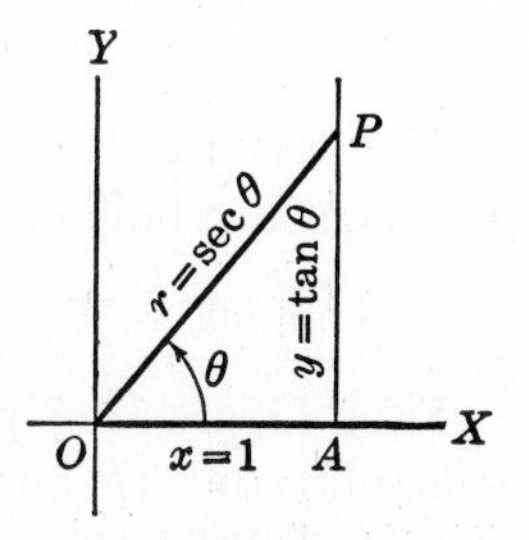

Fig. 53

If θ increases steadily from $0°$ and approaches $90°$ as a limit, then the corresponding point P in Figure 53 moves upward beyond all bounds; the ordinate, $\tan\theta$, of P increases from 0 through all positive values. Hence, $\tan\theta$ becomes greater than any specified number, however large, for all values of θ sufficiently near $90°$. We summarize this by saying that **tan θ becomes positively infinite, or approaches + ∞** (read *plus infinity*), *as the acute angle θ approaches* $90°$ *as a limit.* Figure 53 does not apply when $\theta = 90°$, and we recall that $\tan 90°$ does not exist because y/x is not defined if $x = 0$. Similar statements can be made about $\sec\theta$, or r in Figure 53, as $\theta \rightarrow 90°$ (where "$\rightarrow$" is read *approaches*). Thus, **sec θ becomes positively infinite** *as the acute angle* $\theta \rightarrow 90°$.

In Figure 54 for $\theta > 90°$, we choose $P:(x, y)$ so that $x = -1$. Then, from page 33,

$$\tan\theta = \frac{y}{x} = \frac{y}{-1} = -y, \quad or \quad y = -\tan\theta;$$

$$\sec\theta = \frac{r}{-1} = -r, \quad or \quad r = -\sec\theta.$$

If θ decreases steadily from $180°$ and approaches $90°$ as a limit, then the absolute value of $\tan\theta$, and of $\sec\theta$, or the lengths of AP and OP, become positively infinite. That is, $\tan\theta$ and $\sec\theta$ become *negatively infinite* as the obtuse angle $\theta \rightarrow 90°$.

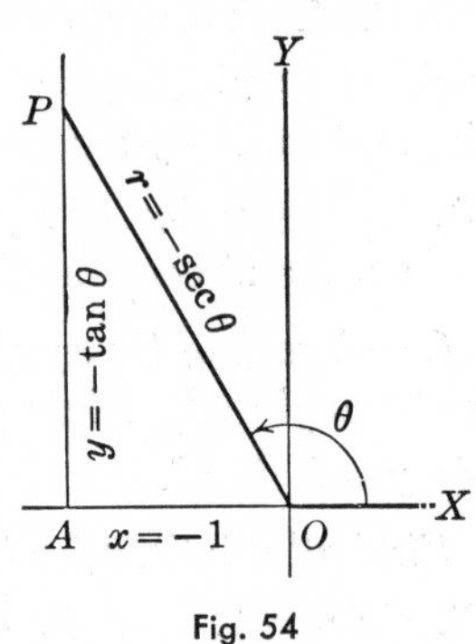

Fig. 54

In summary, we write

$$\textbf{tan } 90° \textbf{ is infinite;} \qquad \textbf{sec } 90° \textbf{ is infinite.} \tag{1}$$

Statements (1) abbreviate the following information:

1. *There is no tangent (and no secant) for* $90°$.

2. *The absolute value of* $\tan\theta$ *(and of* $\sec\theta$*) becomes greater than any number, however large, for all values of θ sufficiently near* $90°$, *or*

$$\lim_{\theta\rightarrow 90°} |\tan\theta| = \infty; \qquad \lim_{\theta\rightarrow 90°} |\sec\theta| = \infty. \tag{2}$$

In (2), we read "*the limit of* $|\tan\theta|$ *is infinity as* $\theta \rightarrow 90°$," etc. Similarly,

$$\left\{\begin{array}{l}\tan\theta \textit{ and } \sec\theta \textit{ are infinite if } \theta \textit{ is any angle whose} \\ \textit{terminal side in standard position is } \textbf{vertical.}\end{array}\right\} \tag{3}$$

ILLUSTRATION 1. From (3), $\tan 270°$ and $\sec 270°$ are infinite. By use of trigonometric tables not in this text, we find

$$\tan 89° = 57; \quad \tan 89° 59' = 3438; \quad \tan 89° 59' 59'' = 206{,}265.$$

From Figure 53 on page 61, where $0° \leqq \theta < 90°$, $\tan\theta$ takes on *all positive values* because AP increases from $AP = 0$, when $\theta = 0°$, through all positive values as $\theta \rightarrow 90°$; also, from Figure 54, where $90° < \theta \leqq 180°$, $\tan\theta$

takes on all negative values. This range of values, which consists *of all real numbers*, is repeated if $180° \leqq \theta < 360°$, with $\theta = 270°$ omitted. Similarly, $\sec \theta$ takes on all values greater than or equal to 1 if $0° \leqq \theta < 90°$, and all values less than or equal to -1 if $90° < \theta \leqq 180°$.

SUMMARY. *For the* **tangent** *and* **secant functions.** *Their* **domain** *consists of all angles θ where the terminal side of θ, in standard position in a coordinate plane,* **does not fall on the vertical axis.** *The* **range of the tangent function** *consists of all real numbers. The* **range of the secant function** *consists of all numbers with absolute value at least* 1. *Thus,* $\tan \theta$ *and* $\sec \theta$ *assume all values such that*

$$-\infty < \tan \theta < +\infty \quad \textit{and} \quad |\sec \theta| \geqq 1. \tag{4}$$

35. Variation of cot θ and csc θ

From Definition I on page 33, we recall that $\cot \theta$ and $\csc \theta$ do not exist when $y = 0$, which occurs when the terminal side of θ is *horizontal* on page 33. For other values of θ, from (1) and (2) on page 40,

$$\cot \theta = \frac{\cos \theta}{\sin \theta} \quad \textit{and} \quad \csc \theta = \frac{1}{\sin \theta}. \tag{1}$$

If $\theta \to 0°$, or $\theta \to 180°$, etc., then $|\sin \theta| \to 0$ and $|\cos \theta| \to 1$. Hence, the absolute value of each fraction in (1) grows large without bound, or $|\cot \theta| \to \infty$ and $|\csc \theta| \to \infty$ as $\theta \to 0°$, or as $\theta \to 180°$, etc. In particular, we arrive at the following conclusions:

$$\textbf{cot } 0° \textbf{ is infinite,} \quad \textit{and} \quad \textbf{csc } 0° \textbf{ is infinite,} \textit{ or} \tag{2}$$

$$\lim_{\theta \to 0°} |\cot \theta| = \infty; \qquad \lim_{\theta \to 0°} |\csc \theta| = \infty. \tag{3}$$

Our general reasoning justifies the statement that

$$\left\{\begin{matrix} \cot \theta \textit{ and } \csc \theta \textit{ are infinite if } \theta \textit{ is any angle whose} \\ \textit{terminal side in standard position is } \textbf{horizontal.} \end{matrix}\right\} \tag{4}$$

Moreover, as $|\sin \theta|$ *decreases* from 1 to 0, the *reciprocal* of $|\sin \theta|$, or $|\csc \theta|$, *increases from* 1 *through all values greater than* 1. Similarly, since the range of $\tan \theta$ consists of *all real numbers*, it follows that the range of $1/\tan \theta$, or $\cot \theta$, likewise consists of *all real numbers.*

SUMMARY. *For the* **cotangent** *and* **cosecant functions.** *Their* **domain** *consists of all angles θ where the terminal side* **does not fall on the horizontal axis** *when θ is in its standard position in a coordinate plane. The* **range of the cotangent function** *consists of all real numbers. The* **range of the cosecant function** *consists of all numbers with absolute value at least* 1. *Thus,* $\cot \theta$ *and* $\csc \theta$ *assume all values such that*

$$-\infty < \cot \theta < +\infty \quad \textit{and} \quad |\csc \theta| \geqq 1. \tag{5}$$

36. Graphs of the tangent and cotangent, in degree measure

Let x be a variable with the range D consisting of *all real numbers*. Then the *analytic* trigonometric functions $\tan x°$, $\cot x°$, $\sec x°$, and $\csc x°$ are defined for all x in the domain D, except for certain values of x for each function, where $x°$ is quadrantal. To graph the functions $\tan x°$ and $\cot x°$ in an xy-plane, we graph the equations $y = \tan x°$ and $y = \cot x°$, respectively. Each of these functions is periodic with the period 180, because

$$\tan\,(x + 180)° = \tan\,(x° + 180°) = \tan x°; \tag{1}$$

$$\cot\,(x + 180)° = \cot\,(x° + 180°) = \cot x°. \tag{2}$$

Hence, the complete graph of $y = \tan x°$ consists of the piece from $x = 90$ to $x = 270$ in Figure 55, and endless repetitions of this piece to the left and the right. Similarly, the graph of $y = \cot x°$ consists of the piece for $0 < x < 180$ and endless repetitions of this piece to the left and the right in Figure 56.

ILLUSTRATION 1. The graph of $y = \tan x°$ was constructed by use of the following table. The scale units on the coordinate axes in Figure 55 were chosen unequal. First, points were plotted from the table. Then, points on

x	0	15	30	45	60	75	78	90
$y = \tan x°$	0	.3	.6	1.0	1.7	3.7	4.7	∞
x	180	165	150	135	120	105	102	90
$y = \tan x°$	0	− .3	− .6	− 1.0	− 1.7	− 3.7	− 4.7	∞

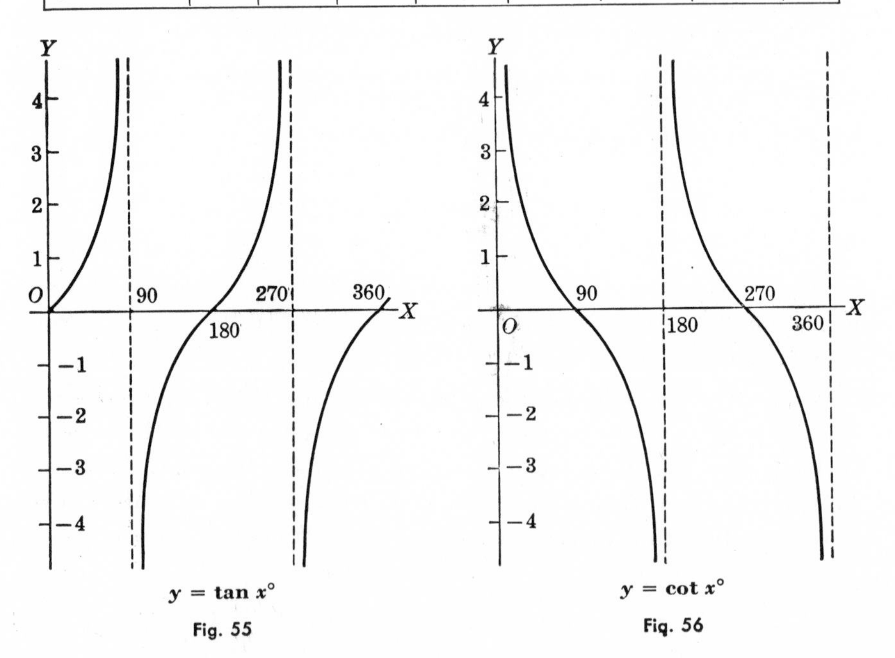

Fig. 55

Fig. 56

the range $180 \leqq x < 360$ were plotted by use of the periodicity identity in (1). Thus, since $(x = 30, y = .6)$ is a point from the table, we find $(x = 30 + 180, y = .6)$ as a point on the graph. In Figure 55, the vertical broken lines are called **asymptotes,** and have the equations $x = 90$ and $x = 270$, respectively. The graph does not meet the line $x = 90$ because the angle 90° has no tangent. If $x \to 90$, from either side, the corresponding point $P:(x, y)$ on the graph recedes from the x-axis beyond all bounds because the absolute value of y grows large without bound, or

$$\lim_{x\to 90} |\tan x^\circ| = \infty. \qquad (3)$$

We can approach as closely as we desire to the asymptote $x = 90$, but never reach it, by receding sufficiently far from the x-axis on the graph. To construct Figure 55, the asymptotes were drawn first as guide lines. Then, the branches of the graph were drawn with the objective of making the curves approach the asymptotes smoothly. The entry ∞ for $x = 90$ in the table is just an abbreviated reminder of (3). The graph of $y = \cot x^\circ$ in Figure 56 was constructed similarly. The asymptotes are the lines $x = 0$, $x = 180$, and $x = 360$, because of (4) of Section 35 on page 63.

37. Graphs of the secant and cosecant, in degree measure

Graphs of the functions $\sec x^\circ$ and $\csc x^\circ$ are shown in Figures 57–58. Each graph has a vertical asymptote corresponding to each value of x for which the function is undefined. Thus, the graph of $y = \csc x^\circ$ has the vertical

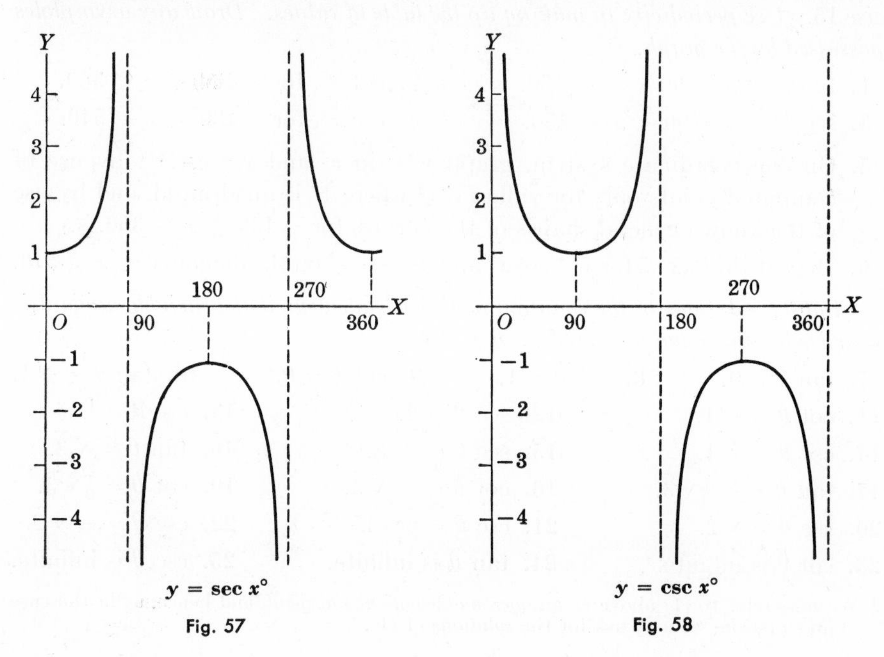

Fig. 57

Fig. 58

lines $x = 0$, $x = 180$, and $x = 360$ as asymptotes because each of csc 0°, csc 180°, and csc 360° is infinite.

Example 1. Describe the variation of sec $x°$ on the range $0 \leqq x \leqq 360$.

Solution. From Figure 57, if x increases continuously from 0 to 90, the graph rises, or sec $x°$ increases from 1 to plus infinity $(+\infty)$; as x increases from 90 to 180, the graph rises, or sec $x°$ increases from $-\infty$ to -1; as x increases from 180 to 270, sec $x°$ decreases from -1 to $-\infty$; as x increases from 270 to 360, sec $x°$ decreases from $+\infty$ to 1.

Illustration 1. The only solution of the equation $\tan \theta = 1$ on the domain 0° to 90° is $\theta = 45°$. Therefore, since $\tan \theta$ has 180° as a period, the solutions of $\tan \theta = 1$ on the domain 0° to 360° are $\theta = 45°$ and $\theta = 225°$, where we were aided by Figure 55 on page 64 in our decision.

Example 2. Find all values of θ on the domain $-360°$ to $+360°$ for which

$$\sec \theta \text{ is infinite.*} \qquad (1)$$

Solution. From Figure 52 on page 59, $\cos \theta = 0$ when $\theta = -270°$, $-90°$, 90°, and 270°. Since $\sec \theta = 1/\cos \theta$, statement (1) is satisfied when θ is $-270°$, $-90°$, 90°, and 270°, where we verify that $x = 90$ and $x = 270$ are the equations of the asymptotes in Figure 57.

EXERCISE 16

Graph the function in an xy-plane, with units on the axes chosen as in Exercise 15. Use periodicity in making up the table of values. Draw any asymptotes possessed by the graph.

1. tan $x°$, for $-90 < x < 450$.
2. cot $x°$, for $-180 < x < 360$.
3. sec $x°$, for $-90 < x < 450$.
4. csc $x°$, for $-180 < x < 540$.

5. On one coordinate system, graph $y = \sin x°$ and $y = \csc x°$, by use of computed points only for values of x where $x°$ is quadrantal, and by use of the known general shapes of the curves, for $-180 \leqq x \leqq 360$.

6. Repeat Problem 5 for $y = \cos x°$ and $y = \sec x°$ on the domain $0 < x < 540$.

Find the solutions of the equation or verbal statement if the variable angle θ is restricted to the domain $-360° < \theta < 360°$.

7. $\tan \theta = 0$.
8. $\cot \theta = 1$.
9. $\cot \theta = 0$.
10. $\tan \theta = -1$.
11. $\cot \theta = -1$.
12. $\sec \theta = 2$.
13. $\csc \theta = 1$.
14. $\csc \theta = -1$.
15. $\sec \theta = -1$.
16. $\tan \theta = \sqrt{3}$.
17. $\tan \theta = -\frac{1}{3}\sqrt{3}$.
18. $\cot \theta = -\sqrt{3}$.
19. $\cot \theta = \frac{1}{3}\sqrt{3}$.
20. $\sec \theta = \sqrt{2}$.
21. $\csc \theta = \frac{2}{3}\sqrt{3}$.
22. $\csc \theta = -\sqrt{2}$.
23. $\cot \theta$ is infinite.
24. $\tan \theta$ is infinite.
25. $\csc \theta$ is infinite.

* We may refer to (1) above as an *open mathematical statement*, and hence, as in the case of an equation, we may ask for the *solutions* of (1).

EXERCISE 17

REVIEW OF CHAPTER 2

1. Specify two negative and two positive angles coterminal with 231°.

2. Prove that $\sin 4\theta = 4 \sin \theta$ is **NOT** an identity and is consistent.

Solve by use of Definition I *on page* 33, *with the angle in standard position.*

3. Obtain the trigonometric functions of 330°; 225°; 540°; 630°.

4. Find the trigonometric functions of angle θ if its terminal side in standard position on an xy-plane passes through the point $(3, -7)$.

5. If $\sin \theta > 0$ and $\tan \theta < 0$, in what quadrant does θ lie?

6. By use of a right triangle, obtain all of the trigonometric functions of the acute angle α in case $\tan \alpha = \frac{2}{5}$; $\sin \alpha = \frac{3}{5}$; $\sec \alpha = \frac{4}{3}$.

By use of Table IV, *obtain the function value.*

7. sin 57°. **8.** cot 39°. **9.** cos 231°. **10.** sec 298°.

11. tan 127°. **12.** sin (− 192°). **13.** cos (− 200°). **14.** csc (− 310°).

15. Explain verbally what is meant by the statement "tan (− 90°) *is infinite.*"

16. If θ is a solution of the equation $\sin \theta = -\frac{8}{17}$, construct all possible positions for the terminal side of angle θ in standard position in an xy-plane, and obtain all trigonometric functions of θ for each possibility.

17. By use of the fundamental identities, without a figure, obtain the values of all trigonometric functions of an angle θ for which (a) $\tan \theta = 2$ and θ is in quadrant III; (b) $\sin \theta = -\frac{1}{3}$ and θ is in quadrant IV.

18. Prove the reduction formulas for the trigonometric functions of $(270° - \theta)$ by use of the addition formulas and fundamental identities.

By use of the reduction formula (6) *on page* 56 *or periodicity identities, without proof, express the specified function value in terms of a value of a trigonometric function of the angle* θ.

19. $\sin (180° - \theta)$. **20.** $\tan (630° + \theta)$. **21.** $\csc (360° - \theta)$.

22. $\cot (\theta + 540°)$. **23.** $\cos (90° + \theta)$. **24.** $\sec (270° - \theta)$.

25. Graph the functions $\sin x°$ and $\csc x°$ on the same coordinate system by use of the values of the functions, or asymptotes, corresponding to just quadrantal angles, for x on the interval $180 \leqq x \leqq 720$.

26. Repeat Problem 25 for $\cos x°$ and $\sec x°$ with $-270 \leqq x \leqq 90$.

27. Graph the function $\tan x°$ on the interval $-270 \leqq x \leqq 270$.

Find all solutions of the statement, on the interval $-180° \leqq \theta < 360°$.

28. $\sin \theta = -\frac{1}{2}$. **29.** $\cos \theta = -\frac{1}{2}\sqrt{3}$. **30.** $\tan \theta = \sqrt{3}$.

31. $\cot \theta$ is infinite. **32.** $\sec \theta$ is infinite. **33.** $\tan \theta$ is infinite.

34. $\sin \theta = \frac{1}{2}\sqrt{2}$. **35.** $\cot \theta = -\frac{1}{3}\sqrt{3}$. **36.** $\sec \theta = \frac{1}{2}$.

Graph the equation for x *on the interval* $-180 \leqq x \leqq 360$.

37. $y = -3 \sin x°$. **38.** $y = \frac{1}{2} \cos x°$. **39.** $y = \frac{1}{3} \tan x°$.

3

SOLUTION OF RIGHT TRIANGLES

38. Significant digits

At present, assume that any number is written in decimal notation, where we visualize an *endless sequence of decimal places* in the number. A *terminating decimal* is one with an endless sequence of zeros to the right of a certain decimal place. An *endless decimal* is one which does not terminate.

ILLUSTRATION 1. 35.673, or 35.673000 · · ·, is a terminating decimal. The constant $\pi = 3.141593 \cdots$ is an endless, nonrepeating decimal.

In any number N, let us read its digits from left to right. Then, by definition, the **significant digits** or **figures** of N are its digits, in sequence, starting with the first one not zero and ending with the last one definitely specified. Notice that this definition does not involve any reference to the position of the decimal point in N. Usually we do not mention *final zeros* at the right in referring to the significant digits of N, except when it is the approximate value of some item of data.

ILLUSTRATION 2. The significant digits of 410.58 or of .0041058 are (4, 1, 0, 5, 8).

If T is the *true value*, and A is an *approximate value* of a quantity, we agree to call $|A - T|$ the **error** * of A.

ILLUSTRATION 3. If $T = 35.62$, and if $A = 35.60$ is an approximation to T, then the error of A is $|35.60 - 35.62|$ or .02.

The significant digits in an approximate value A should indicate the maximum possible error of A. This error is understood to be *at most one half of a unit in the last significant place in* A or, which is the same, *not more than* 5 *units in the next place to the right.*

* Sometimes, the error is defined as $(A - T)$, which thus is positive, negative, or zero. Then, a positive error means that $A > T$. Also, the error sometimes is defined as $(T - A)$, which reverses the preceding inequality. This lack of uniformity, and the frequent use of $|A - T|$ as the error, causes us to adopt this meaning.

ILLUSTRATION 4. If a surveyor measures a distance as 256.8 yards, he should mean that the error is at most .05 yard and that the true result lies between 256.75 and 256.85, inclusive, since the error might be .05.

In referring to the significant digits of an *approximate* value A, *it is essential to mention all final zeros designated in* A.

ILLUSTRATION 5. To state that a measured weight is 35.60 pounds should mean that the true weight differs from 35.60 pounds by at most .005 pound. To state that the weight is 35.6 pounds should mean that the true weight differs from this by at most .05 pound.

For abbreviation, or to indicate how many digits in a large number are significant, we may write a number N in the following form, sometimes called the **scientific notation** for a number:

Express the number N *as the product of an integral power of* 10 *and a number equal to or greater than* 1 *but less than* 10, *with as many significant digits as are justified by the data.*

ILLUSTRATION 6.

$$385{,}720 = 3.8572(100{,}000) = 3.8572(10^5).$$

$$.000'000'368 = 3.68(.000'000'1) = 3.68(10^{-7}).$$

ILLUSTRATION 7. If 5,630,000 is an approximate value, its appearance fails to show how many zeros are significant. If five digits are significant, we write $5.6300(10^6)$, and if just three are significant, $5.63(10^6)$.

39. Accuracy of computation

In referring to a *place* in a number, we shall mean any place where a significant digit stands. In referring to a *decimal place*, the word *decimal* will be used explicitly.

To round off N to k figures, or to write a k-place approximation for N, means to write an approximate value with k significant digits so that the error of this value is not more than one half of a unit in the kth place, or 5 units in the first neglected place. This leads to the following routine.

SUMMARY. **To round off a number** N *to* k *places, drop off the part of* N *beyond the* kth *place (filling in zeros if necessary to the left of the decimal point) and then proceed as follows.*

1. *Leave the digit of* N *in the* kth *place* **unchanged** *or* **increase it by 1,** *according as the omitted part of* N *is* **less than** *or* **greater than 5 units** *in the* $(k+1)$th *place.*

2. *If the omitted part is exactly* 5 *units in the* $(k+1)$th *place,* **increase the digit** *in the* kth *place by* 1 *or* **leave the digit unchanged,** *with the object of making* **the final choice an even digit.***

* This agreement could be replaced by various similar and equally justified rules.

ILLUSTRATION 1. The seven-place approximation to π is 3.141593. On rounding off to five places, we obtain $\pi = 3.1416$; the four-place approximation is $\pi = 3.142$. In rounding off 315.475 to five places, with equal justification we could specify 315.47 or 315.48; in accordance with (2) in the Summary we choose 315.48.

By illustrations, we can verify that the following rules do not *underestimate* the accuracy of computation. On the other hand, we admit that the rules sometimes *overestimate* the accuracy. However, we shall assume that a result obtained by these rules will have a negligible error in the last significant place which is specified.

I. *In adding approximate values, round off the result in the first place where the last significant digit of any given value is found.*

II. *In multiplying or dividing approximate values, round off the result to the smallest number of significant digits found in any given value.*

ILLUSTRATION 2. Let $a = 35.64$, $b = 342.72$, and $c = .03147$ be approximate values. Then, $a + b + c$ is not reliable beyond the *second* decimal place because a and b are subject to an unknown error which may be as large as 5 units in the third decimal place. Hence, we write

$$a + b + c = 378.39147 = 378.39, \textit{ approximately.}$$

ILLUSTRATION 3. If $x = 31.27$ and $y = .021$ are approximate values, by Rule II we take $xy = .66$, because y has only two significant digits:

$$xy = 31.27(.021) = .65667 = .66, \textit{ approximately.}$$

To avoid unnecessary work in multiplying, it is sensible to retain only two places beyond those to which the result will be rounded off by Rule II.

ILLUSTRATION 4. If a surveyor measures a rectangular field as 385.6′ by 432.4′, it would be unjustified to write that the area is $(385.6)(432.4) = 166{,}733.44$ square feet. For, an error of .05 foot in either dimension would cause an error of about 20 square feet in the area. By Rule II, a justified result would be that the area is 166,700 square feet, to the nearest 100 square feet, or $1.667(10^5)$ square feet.

In problems where approximate values enter, or where approximate results are obtained from exact data, the results should be rounded off so as to avoid giving a false appearance of accuracy. No hard and fast rules for such rounding off should be adopted, and the final decision as to the accuracy of a result should be made only after a careful examination of the details of the solution. *Until otherwise stated in this text, we shall assume that the data in any problem are* **exact,** *and we shall compute our results as accurately as is justified by the means at our disposal.* Later, we shall introduce agreements about approximate data.

EXERCISE 18

Express as a power of 10.

1. 10,000,000. **2.** 100,000. **3.** .0001. **4.** .01. **5.** 1.

Round off, first to five and then to three significant digits.

6. 13.24683. **7.** .2123589. **8.** 215.634. **9.** .00215388.
10. 6.312162. **11.** .0493576. **12.** 1,593,485. **13.** 612,915.

Write the number in ordinary decimal form.

14. $2.63(10^3)$. **15.** $1.598(10^7)$. **16.** $3.4153(10^{-3})$. **17.** $8.195(10^{-6})$.

Write as the product of a power of 10 *and a number between* 1 *and* 10.

18. 2,567,000. **19.** 89,315,000. **20.** .0000578. **21.** .00000364.

If the measured length of a rod is given as the specified number of inches, tell between what two values, inclusive, the true length lies.

22. 238. **23.** 238.3. **24.** 238.0. **25.** 42.16. **26.** 21.60.

Assume that the numbers are approximate data. Find their sum and their product, and express the results without false accuracy.

27. 21.65 and .0324. **28.** .024512 and 2.15. **29.** 2.8 and .3167.

30. The measured dimensions of a field are 238.7 feet and 58.4 feet. Find the perimeter and the area of the field.

Write the number as the product of an integral power of ten and a number between 1 *and* 10 *under the assumption, first, that there are just five significant digits and, second, that there are just three significant digits.*

31. 8,426,000. **32.** 290,000. **33.** 42,700,000. **34.** 629,000,000.

40. A four-place trigonometric table

Unless otherwise stated, any angle to which we refer in this chapter will be acute. It will be useful to keep in mind the following facts about the values of the trigonometric functions of acute angles. These facts can be checked by use of the graphs in Chapter 2, or by reference to the special formulas for the trigonometric functions of an acute angle on page 44.

If the acute angle α *increases, then* $\sin \alpha$ *and* $\tan \alpha$ *increase while* $\cos \alpha$ *and* $\cot \alpha$ *decrease.*

Since $\sec \alpha = 1/\cos \alpha$ and $\csc \alpha = 1/\sin \alpha$, the preceding statement shows that $\sec \alpha$ *increases* and $\csc \alpha$ *decreases* if α increases.

$$\tan 45° = \cot 45° = 1.$$

When $\alpha < 45°$, $\tan \alpha < 1$ *and* $\cot \alpha > 1$.

When $\alpha > 45°$, $\tan \alpha > 1$ *and* $\cot \alpha < 1$.

Table VII is a four-place table of the trigonometric functions of acute angles at intervals of $10'$. Each entry in Table VII has been rounded off in the last significant place, leaving four significant digits except in a few entries. For angles at most equal to 45°, read angles at the left and titles of columns at the top in the main part of each page of the table. For angles greater than 45°, read titles at the bottom and angles at the right.

ILLUSTRATION 1. To find cot 5° 30′, look in the left-hand angle columns for 5° 30′: $\cot 5° 30' = 10.39$. To find sin 77° 20′, look for 77° 20′ in the right-hand angle columns: $\sin 77° 20' = .9757$.

Each entry in the function columns of Table VII is a function value for some angle and, also, is the value of the *cofunction* for the *complementary angle*, on account of the cofunction identities on page 45.

ILLUSTRATION 2. We read in Table VII that

$$.9757 = \sin 77° 20' = \cos 12° 40'.$$

EXAMPLE 1. From Table VII, find the acute angle α if $\cos \alpha = .4173$.

SOLUTION. We look for .4173 in the cosine columns in Table VII. We find .4173 on page 15 in the column with cosine at the bottom; hence we read that

$$.4173 = \cos 65° 20', \quad \textit{or} \quad \alpha = 65° 20'.$$

41. Interpolation in a four-place trigonometric table

With the assistance of a method called **interpolation** by the **principle of proportional parts,** we shall use Table VII for angles not tabulated there. In this method, it is assumed that, *for small changes in an angle α, the corresponding changes in the value of any one of the functions of α are proportional to the changes in α.* This assumption, which is only approximately true, leads to results which are sufficiently accurate for practical purposes.

EXAMPLE 1. By use of Table VII, find sin 27° 43′.

SOLUTION. 1. We see that 27° 43′ is **bracketed** * by 27° 40′ and 27° 50′, whose trigonometric functions are in the table.

2. By the principle of proportional parts, an increase of 3′ in the angle 27° 40′ should cause 3/10 as much change in the sine as is caused by an increase of 10′. Or, in the following table, with d expressed in units in the 4th decimal place, to the nearest unit $d = 8$. Hence,

$$\mathbf{\sin 27° 43' = .4643 + .0008 = .4651.} \qquad (1)$$

10	3	*From table:*	$\sin 27° 40' = .4643$	d	26	$\frac{d}{26} = \frac{3}{10}$;
			$\sin 27° 43' = ?$			
		From table:	$\sin 27° 50' = .4669$			$d = .3(26) = 7.8.$

* That is, 27° 43′ is *between* the table angles 27° 40′ and 27° 50′.

Comment. 1. We call .0008 the *proportional part* of the *tabular difference.* In passing from .4643 to .4669 there is an *increase* of .0026; hence, in the interpolation, we *added* .0008.

2. We changed from .00078 to .0008 in accordance with Rule I on page 70, because the table entries are accurate only to four decimal places.

EXAMPLE 2. Find csc 19° 27′ from Table VII.

SOLUTION. 1. 19° 27′ is 7/10 of the way from 19° 20′ to 19° 30′.

10 ↓	7 ↓	*From table:*	csc 19° 20′ = 3.021	d ↓	25 ↓	$\frac{d}{25} = \frac{7}{10}$;
			csc 19° 27′ = ?			
		From table:	csc 19° 30′ = 2.996			$d = .7(25) = 17.5.$

2. We can find .7(25) = 17.5 in the auxiliary column of tenths of 25 on page 15 in Table VII. Since there is a *decrease* of .025 in passing from 3.021 to 2.996, we *subtract* d from 3.021. We could choose $d = 17$ or $d = 18$. In interpolation, whenever such ambiguity is met, we agree to make that choice which gives **an even last digit in the final result.** Hence, at present, we use $d = 17$:

$$\textbf{csc 19° 27′ = 3.021 − .017 = 3.004.}$$

Comment. For a different solution, we could observe that 19° 27′ is 3/10 of the way from 19° 30′ to 19° 20′. Then, since csc 19° 20′ is *greater* than csc 19° 30′, we would *add* 3/10 of the tabular difference to csc 19° 30′ in order to obtain csc 19° 27′:

$$\csc 19° 27' = 2.996 + .3(.025) = 2.996 + .0075 = 3.004.$$

EXAMPLE 3. Find α if $\sin \alpha = .9254$.

Solution. In the sine column of Table VII, we search for the entries which *bracket* .9254; we find .9250 = sin 67° 40′ and .9261 = sin 67° 50′. Hence, α lies between 67° 40′ and 67° 50′. In the following table, x is the unknown number of minutes in the difference between α and 67° 40′. By the *principle of proportional parts*, $(x/10) = (4/11)$.

11 ↓	4 ↓	.9250 = sin 67° 40′	x ↓	10 ↓	$\frac{x}{10} = \frac{4}{11}$; $x = \frac{4}{11}(10)$;
		.9254 = sin α			
		.9261 = sin 67° 50′			$\frac{4}{11} = .36 = .4$, *to nearest tenth;*

$$\boldsymbol{\alpha = 67° 40' + .4(10') = 67° 44'.}$$

Comment. 1. When using Table VII to find an unknown angle, we agree to state the result to the *nearest minute*, because such accuracy but no greater refinement is justified. Hence, in Example 3, we computed 4/11 to the *nearest tenth* because we were to multiply by 10′.

2. To gain speed, we could obtain $\frac{4}{11} = .4$ by merely inspecting the tenths of 11 in the column of proportional parts in Table VII. We read the following results:

$$.3(11) = 3.3, \quad \text{or} \quad \frac{3.3}{11} = .3; \qquad .4(11) = 4.4, \quad \text{or} \quad \frac{4.4}{11} = .4.$$

Since 4 is nearer to 4.4 than to 3.3, we decide that 4/11 is nearer to .4 than to .3.

EXAMPLE 4. Find α if $\cot \alpha = 1.387$.

SOLUTION. Since $\cot \alpha > 1$, we have $\alpha < 45°$. Hence, we look in the columns of Table VII labeled *cotangent* at the *top*, and find the entries 1.393 and 1.385 which *bracket* 1.387. Since 1.387 is 6/8 of the way from 1.393 to 1.385, we assume that α is 6/8 of the way from 35° 40′ to 35° 50′.

$$8\left[\begin{array}{l} 6\left[\begin{array}{l} 1.393 = \cot 35°\,40' \\ 1.387 = \cot \alpha \end{array}\right] x \\ 1.385 = \cot 35°\,50' \end{array}\right] 10 \qquad \begin{array}{r} \frac{6}{8} = .75 = .8, \textit{ approximately}, \\ x = .8(10) = 8. \\ \alpha = 35°\,40' + .8(10') = 35°\,48'. \end{array}$$

EXERCISE 19

Find each function value by use of Table VII.

1. sin 12°.	**2.** tan 33°.	**3.** cot 58°.	**4.** sec 64°.
5. csc 73°.	**6.** cos 9° 20′.	**7.** sin 13° 30′.	**8.** tan 53° 40′.
9. cot 85° 20′.	**10.** csc 73° 50′.	**11.** sec 18° 10′.	**12.** sin 42° 40′.

Find the acute angle α by use of Table VII *to satisfy the equation.*

13. $\tan \alpha = .4074$.	**14.** $\sin \alpha = .1016$.	**15.** $\sec \alpha = 1.167$.
16. $\cot \alpha = 1.621$.	**17.** $\cos \alpha = .9261$.	**18.** $\csc \alpha = 4.134$.
19. $\csc \alpha = 1.033$.	**20.** $\tan \alpha = 1.437$.	**21.** $\cos \alpha = .3035$.

Find each function value by interpolation in Table VII.

22. tan 4° 43′.	**23.** tan 5° 17′.	**24.** sin 46° 52′.	**25.** sin 47° 46′.
26. cot 27° 4′.	**27.** cos 33° 15′.	**28.** cos 24° 44′.	**29.** cot 32° 38′.
30. sin 14° 24′.	**31.** tan 32° 36′.	**32.** sec 45° 27′.	**33.** csc 56° 46′.
34. sin 80° 17′.	**35.** sin 28° 5′.	**36.** csc 65° 39′.	**37.** sec 53° 13′.
38. cot 77° 16′.	**39.** cos 28° 19′.	**40.** sin 1° 11′.	**41.** tan 6° 23′.

Find the acute angle α by interpolation in Table VII *to satisfy the equation.*

42. $\tan \alpha = .0831$.	**43.** $\sin \alpha = .4955$.	**44.** $\sin \alpha = .3812$.
45. $\sec \alpha = 1.128$.	**46.** $\cos \alpha = .9381$.	**47.** $\cot \alpha = 1.558$.
48. $\sec \alpha = 1.506$.	**49.** $\tan \alpha = 1.031$.	**50.** $\csc \alpha = 1.265$.
51. $\sin \alpha = .7967$.	**52.** $\cos \alpha = .7037$.	**53.** $\tan \alpha = 1.322$.
54. $\sec \alpha = 1.183$.	**55.** $\cos \alpha = .9987$.	**56.** $\sec \alpha = 1.568$.

Find the acute angle α, without interpolation, to the nearest 10′ *by inspection of Table* VII, *to satisfy the equation.*

57. $\sin \alpha = .2231$. **58.** $\tan \alpha = 7.703$. **59.** $\cot \alpha = 4.671$.

60. $\cos \alpha = .3437$. **61.** $\sin \alpha = .6773$. **62.** $\csc \alpha = 1.230$.

63. $\tan \alpha = .8352$. **64.** $\sin \alpha = .6993$. **65.** $\cos \alpha = .2175$.

42. Five-place values of the trigonometric functions

By means of Table XI, without interpolation, values of the trigonometric functions of an acute angle α can be found correct to five decimal places if α is expressed to the nearest minute. If a function of α is given, without interpolation the value of α to the nearest minute can be found from Table XI. By use of interpolation, we can employ Table XI with angles expressed to the nearest tenth of a minute.

ILLUSTRATION 1. If $\sin \alpha = .03914$, from the sine column for 2° in Table XI, we find that $\alpha = 2° 15'$ to the nearest minute. By interpolation, we then obtain

$$\alpha = 2° 14' + \tfrac{17}{29}(1') = 2° 14' + .6' = 2° 14.6'.$$

EXERCISE 20

Find each function value, or angle α to the nearest minute, by inspection of Table XI.

1. $\cos 5° 27'$. **2.** $\csc 72° 18'$. **3.** $\sin 43° 51'$. **4.** $\tan 28° 17'$.

5. $\sin \alpha = .29245$. **6.** $\cot \alpha = 6.9592$. **7.** $\cos \alpha = .68125$.

★*By use of interpolation in Table* XI, *find each function value, or the unknown acute angle α.*

8. $\sin 32° 13.6'$. **9.** $\cos 81° 28.6'$. **10.** $\cot 43° 36.2'$.

11. $\tan 34° 32.3'$. **12.** $\sec 15° 8.2'$. **13.** $\tan 20° 18.7'$.

★**14–16.** Find α to the nearest tenth of a minute by interpolation in Table XI, in Problems 5–7, respectively.

43. Solution of a right triangle

A right triangle has six parts, consisting of *three sides* and *three angles*, one of which is 90°. In the standard right triangle *ABC*, as in Figure 59, we let α and β be the acute angles (or their measures). We let *a* and *b* be the *lengths* of the sides opposite α and β, respectively, and let *c* be the *length* of the hypotenuse. Also, for abbreviation, we shall use *a*, *b*, and *c* as symbols for the sides themselves. By means of trigonometry, if *two sides*, or *an acute angle and a side*, of $\triangle ABC$ are given,* we can compute the unknown parts. This computation is called

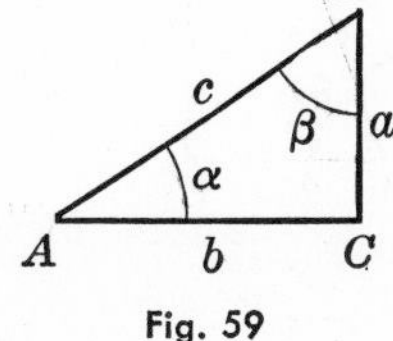

Fig. 59

* Recall that it is possible then to construct the triangle by plane geometry.

the *solution of the triangle.* Recall the following formulas for $\triangle ABC$ in Figure 59 on page 75.

$$a^2 + b^2 = c^2. \qquad (1) \qquad\qquad \alpha + \beta = 90°. \qquad (2)$$

$$\sin \alpha = \frac{a}{c} = \cos \beta. \qquad (3) \qquad\qquad \cos \alpha = \frac{b}{c} = \sin \beta. \qquad (4)$$

$$\tan \alpha = \frac{a}{b} = \cot \beta. \qquad (5) \qquad\qquad \cot \alpha = \frac{b}{a} = \tan \beta. \qquad (6)$$

$$\sec \alpha = \frac{c}{b} = \csc \beta. \qquad (7) \qquad\qquad \csc \alpha = \frac{c}{a} = \sec \beta. \qquad (8)$$

From (3) and (4) we obtain the following useful formulas:

$$a = c \sin \alpha; \qquad b = c \cos \alpha; \qquad (9)$$

or, *the leg opposite* α *is equal to the hypotenuse times* $\sin \alpha$, *and the leg adjacent to* α *is equal to the hypotenuse times* $\cos \alpha$. We shall avoid (1) until we use logarithms. As an aid to accuracy, we usually employ (3) or (4) in preference to (7) or (8) in finding angles. Formulas (7) and (8) are useful in avoiding division when finding c.

To solve a right triangle with given data, first sketch the triangle roughly to scale. Then, outline the formulas to be used; for any unknown part, if possible, choose a formula involving it *but no other unknown part.* Also, if convenient, use a formula *avoiding division.* To check the results roughly, compare them with the preliminary sketch. For a more refined check, substitute *from the results and the data in any one of* (3) *to* (8) *not used in the solution*, and compute both sides of the formula for comparison. In results, round off lengths, quotients, and products to four significant digits and angles to minutes if four-place tables are used.

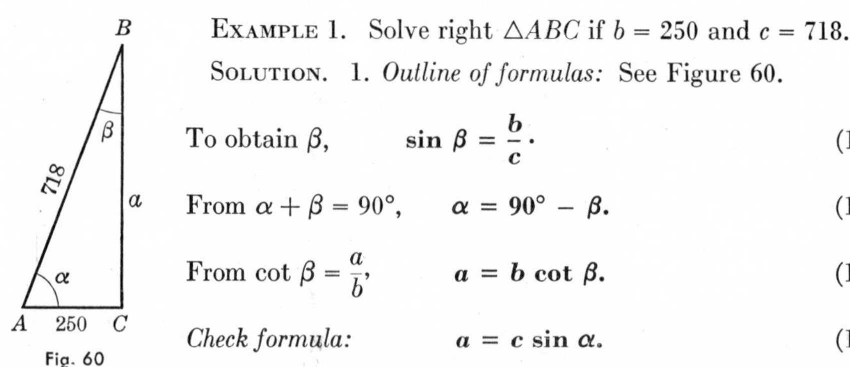

Fig. 60

EXAMPLE 1. Solve right $\triangle ABC$ if $b = 250$ and $c = 718$.

SOLUTION. 1. *Outline of formulas:* See Figure 60.

To obtain β, $$\sin \beta = \frac{b}{c}. \qquad (10)$$

From $\alpha + \beta = 90°$, $$\alpha = 90° - \beta. \qquad (11)$$

From $\cot \beta = \frac{a}{b}$, $$a = b \cot \beta. \qquad (12)$$

Check formula: $$a = c \sin \alpha. \qquad (13)$$

2. *Computation.* $$\sin \beta = \frac{250}{718} = .3482.$$

By interpolation in Table VII, $\beta = 20° 23'$.

Hence, $\alpha = 90° - 20° 23' = 69° 37'$.

From (12) and Table VII,

$$a = 250 \cot 20° 23' = 250(2.692) = 673.0.$$

3. *Check.* $c \sin \alpha = 718 \sin 69° 37' = 718(.9374) = 673.1$. Since $a = 673.0$, the check is satisfactory; the difference between 673.1 and 673.0 could be due to errors introduced by rounding off in computation.

Comment. Even with absolutely correct computation, a greater discrepancy than just observed will sometimes be met in checking.

EXAMPLE 2. Solve right $\triangle ABC$ if $a = 30.5$ and $\beta = 32° 10'$.

OUTLINE OF SOLUTION. Since $\alpha + \beta = 90°$, $\boldsymbol{\alpha = 90° - \beta}$.

From $\frac{b}{a} = \tan \beta$, $\boldsymbol{b = a \tan \beta}$.

From $\frac{c}{a} = \sec \beta$, $\boldsymbol{c = a \sec \beta}$.

Check formula: $\boldsymbol{b = c \cos \alpha}$.

EXERCISE 21

With the given data, solve right $\triangle ABC$ by use of Table VII.

1. $\alpha = 23° 30'$; $a = 50$.
2. $b = 75$; $\alpha = 68° 40'$.
3. $c = 125$; $\beta = 13° 20'$.
4. $c = 15$; $\alpha = 56° 30'$.
5. $a = 400$; $b = 446$.
6. $c = 7.5$; $b = 5.083$.
7. $a = 85.22$; $b = 65$.
8. $c = 1.4$; $\alpha = 16° 13'$.
9. $a = .518$; $c = 1.16$.
10. $b = .48$; $c = .97$.
11. $a = 2.3$; $b = 1.25$.
12. $a = .262$; $c = .43$.
13. $b = .425$; $c = .73$.
14. $a = 25.4$; $b = 89.6$.
15. $b = .013$; $\alpha = 52° 11'$.
16. $b = .38$; $\beta = 48° 1'$.
17. $c = 1.6$; $\alpha = 80° 12'$.
18. $a = 1625$; $b = 2950$.
19. $b = 4500$; $c = 8600$.
20. $b = .135$; $\beta = 79° 28'$.

21–30. Solve Problems 11–20, respectively, by use of Table XI *without interpolation*, rounding off angles to the nearest minute and sides to four significant digits. Use of Table XI as specified gives about the same accuracy as is obtainable by interpolation in Table VII.

★*Solve by use of Table* XI, *obtaining angles to tenths of a minute and sides to five significant digits.*

31. $a = 35$; $\beta = 68° 43.3'$.
32. $b = 14$; $\beta = 47° 28.7'$.
33. $c = 13.6$; $\alpha = 74° 14.3'$.
34. $c = .88$; $\beta = 26° 41.6'$.
35. Solve Problem 9.
36. Solve Problem 11.

44. Applications of right triangles

In any geometrical application of trigonometry, it is advisable to perform the following actions before computing.

1. *Construct a figure roughly to scale for the data.*
2. *Introduce single letters to represent unknown angles or lengths.*
3. *Outline the solution by specifying triangles or formulas to use; solve each formula for the quantity to be obtained from it.*

In either diagram in Figure 61, O is a point from which we sight an object at C, and OH is a horizontal line in the same vertical plane as C. Then, the acute angle COH between the line of sight to C and the horizontal line is called the *angle of elevation* of C or the *angle of depression* of C, as seen from O, according as C is *above* O or *below* O.

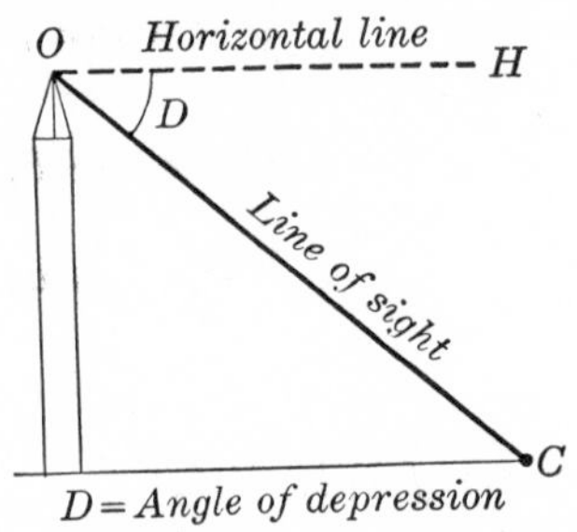

Fig. 61

EXAMPLE 1. From a cliff 700 feet above a plane, the angle of depression of a church is 38° 27′. Find the horizontal distance from the cliff to the church.

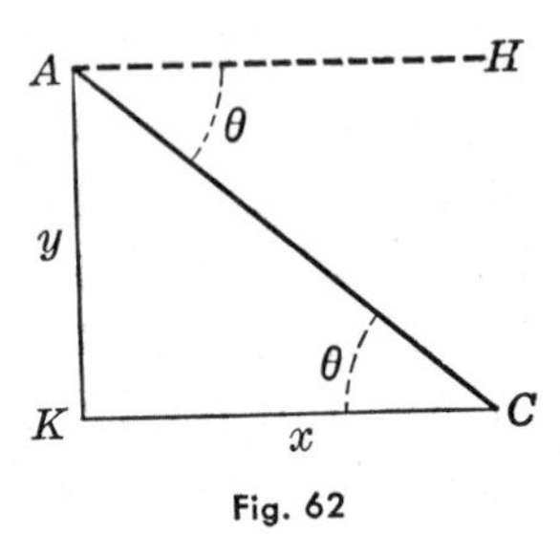

Fig. 62

OUTLINE OF SOLUTION. 1. In Figure 62, C represents the church. The angle of depression is $\angle CAH$, or θ. We desire to find $x = KC$.

2. In right $\triangle AKC$, $y = 700$ and $\theta = 38° 27'$.

3. From $\cot \theta = x/y$, $\qquad x = y \cot \theta.$

EXERCISE 22

Solve by use of four-place tables except where use of Table XI without interpolation is requested.

1. Find the length of the horizontal shadow of a man 6 feet tall when the angle of elevation of the sun is 75° 36′.
2. How tall is a chimney whose horizontal shadow is 90 feet long when the angle of elevation of the sun is 67° 42′?
3. A guy wire 35 feet long is stretched from level ground to the top of a pole 25 feet high. Find the angle between the pole and the wire.

4. From a mountaintop 4000 feet above a fort, the angle of depression of the fort is 16° 45′. Find the air-line distance from the mountaintop to the fort.

5. How high does an airplane rise in flying 4000 feet upward along a straight path inclined 28° 47′ from the horizontal?

6. From an airplane flying 7000 feet above the ground, the angle of depression of a landing field is 19° 32′. Find the air-line distance from the plane to the field. Use Table XI.

7. Find the height of the Empire State Building in New York City if the angle of elevation of its top is 61° 37′ when seen from a point on the street level 675.4 feet from the building.

8. An inclined ramp into a garage is 260 feet long and rises 76 feet. Find the inclination of the ramp from the horizontal.

9. The largest tree in California is the General Sherman tree in the Sequoia National Park. At a point 185 feet from the tree, at the same elevation as its foot, the angle of elevation of the top of the tree is 55° 49′. How tall is the tree?

10. In flying upward for 1260 yards along a straight inclined path, an airplane rises 156 yards. Find the climbing angle.

11. A spy arranges to show a light at an oil tank 250 feet above water level near an ocean beach. An observer 10 feet above water level on an enemy submarine finds that the angle of elevation of the light is 3° 27′. Find the line-of-sight distance from the submarine's guns to the tank.

12. A painter desires to reach a window 40 feet above the ground. Find the length of the shortest ladder he can use if it must not incline more than 78° from the horizontal.

13. On a 3% railroad grade, at what angle are the rails inclined to the horizontal, and how far does one rise in traveling upward 9000 feet measured along the rails? Use Table XI. (The tracks rise 3 feet for each 100 feet of horizontal distance gained.)

14. If the grade of a railroad is 6.75%, how far must one travel along the rails to rise 500 feet? Use Table XI.

15. From a cliff 150 feet above a lake, we see a boat sailing directly toward us. The angle of depression of the boat is seen to be 5° 7′, and then later is 11° 18′. Find the distance the boat sailed between these observations. Use Table XI.

16. From a mountaintop 5000 feet above a horizontal plane, we observe two villages in the plane due east of us, whose angles of depression are 8° 38′ and 5° 46′. How far apart are the villages? Use Table XI.

17. A gun G shoots at T at a range of 5400 yards, and the shot hits at S so that $\angle TGS = 3°$. Assume that $\angle GTS = 90°$. How far from T is S? Use Table XI.

4

LOGARITHMS

45. Irrational numbers as exponents

The student has met the definition of a^x, where $a \neq 0$ and x is any rational number.* In a^x, we call a the **base** and x the **exponent**; a^x itself is referred to as the xth **power** of the base a. In obtaining a^x, we speak of *raising a to the xth power*. If $x = p/q$, where p and q are integers with $q > 0$, then

$$a^{\frac{p}{q}} = \sqrt[q]{a^p}. \tag{1}$$

A logical foundation for the use of irrational numbers as exponents is beyond the scope of this text. In such a foundation, it is learned that major difficulties arise if the base is *negative*. Hence, we proceed with the understanding that the base is *positive*. Then, we shall assume the fact that a^x has meaning when x is a real number, *rational* or *irrational*, and that the following laws apply when the exponents are real numbers.

In multiplication: $$a^x a^y = a^{x+y}. \tag{2}$$

In division: $$\frac{a^x}{a^z} = a^{x-z}. \tag{3}$$

In raising to a power: $$(a^x)^y = a^{xy}. \tag{4}$$

ILLUSTRATION 1. The student may use his intuition safely in connection with the symbol $10^{\sqrt{2}} = 10^{1.414\cdots}$, where the exponent is irrational. Closer and closer approximations to $10^{\sqrt{2}}$ are obtained if the successive decimal approximations to $\sqrt{2}$ are used as exponents. That is, $10^{\sqrt{2}}$ can be approximated as closely as we please if we proceed far enough out in the sequence

$$10^1,\ 10^{1.4},\ 10^{1.41},\ 10^{1.414},\ \cdots,$$

where all exponents are rational numbers. Thus, $1.41 = \dfrac{141}{100}$; $1.414 = \dfrac{1414}{1000}$.

* See Note 1 in the Appendix.

46. The exponential function

If a is a positive constant, let $F(x) = a^x$, where the domain of the variable x consists of *all real numbers*. Then, we call F the *exponential function* with a as the *base*. On account of later applications, we assume now that $a > 1$. A graph of $y = a^x$ is shown in Figure 63, for the special case $a = 2$. The graph was drawn by use of the following table of values. Thus, $2^0 = 1$; $2^{-1} = \frac{1}{2}$;

x	...	-3	-2	-1	0	1	2	3	...
$y = 2^x$	...	$\frac{1}{8}$	$\frac{1}{4}$	$\frac{1}{2}$	1	2	4	8	...

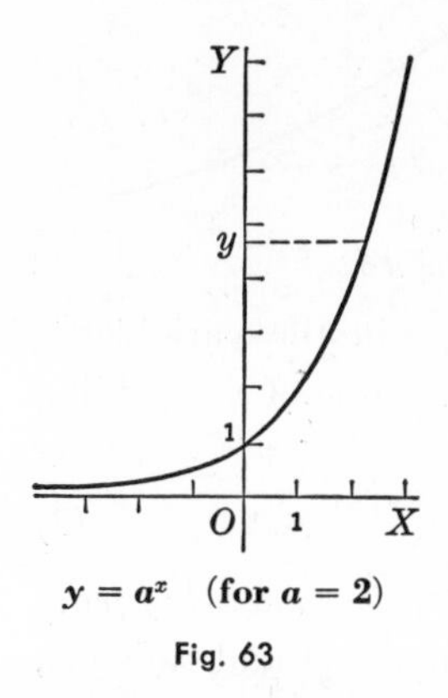

$y = a^x$ (for $a = 2$)

Fig. 63

$2^{-2} = 1/2^2 = \frac{1}{4}$; etc. On the basis of numerical intuition, aided by the preceding table and Figure 63, we now accept the following facts concerning a^x, if $a > 1$.

$$a^x \textit{ steadily increases as } x \textit{ increases.} \tag{1}$$

$$\textit{If } x \to +\infty, \textit{ then } a^x \to +\infty. \tag{2}$$

$$\textit{If } x \to -\infty, \textit{ then } a^x \to 0. \tag{3}$$

From (1), the graph of $y = a^x$ continually *rises* if we move on the graph from left to right. From (3), the graph approaches the x-axis as $x \to -\infty$, or the x-axis is an *asymptote* of the graph. In Figure 63, we see that a perpendicular to the y-axis, at any point where $y > 0$, cuts the graph at *just one point*. Thus, a^x takes on as its value, just once, each positive number y. Hence, *the* **range** *of the exponential function a^x consists of all positive numbers.*

47. The general notion of an inverse function

Consider a function f of the independent variable x, and let $y = f(x)$. Suppose that the domain, D, of f is the interval $a \leqq x \leqq b$ and the range, R, of f is the interval $c \leqq y \leqq d$. Then, by Definition III on page 19, to each number x in D there corresponds just one number y in R. Now, suppose also that, *to each number y in R, there corresponds just one number x*, as in (1):

$$\left\{\begin{array}{l}\textit{For each value of } x \textit{ on the interval}^{*}\ a \leqq x \leqq b, \textit{ the equation} \\ y = f(x) \textit{ defines a single value } y \textit{ on the interval}^{*}\ c \leqq y \leqq d. \\ \textit{And, for each value of } y \textit{ on this interval, there exists} \\ \textit{just one value of } x \textit{ on } a \leqq x \leqq b \textit{ satisfying } y = f(x).\end{array}\right\} \tag{1}$$

Statements (1) are true, for instance, if the value of $f(x)$ *increases steadily* (or *decreases steadily*) if x changes continuously from $x = a$ to $x = b$. With moderate modifications, the preceding sentence states the situation which

* We allow either interval to extend to either $+\infty$ or $-\infty$. Thus, the domain of x might be all real numbers, that is, all x such that $-\infty < x < +\infty$.

exists whenever (1) is true. Hence, the student may base his intuitions for the remainder of our present discussion on the inference that (1) is equivalent to an assumption that *the graph of the equation* $y = f(x)$ *has the appearance shown in Figure* 64 *or in Figure* 65.

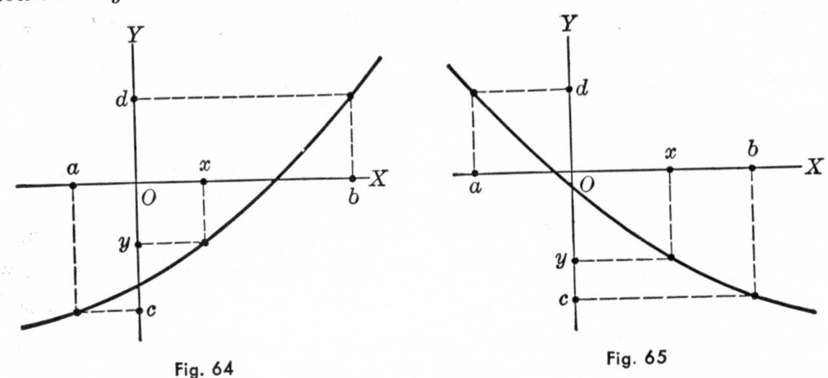

Fig. 64 Fig. 65

With f satisfying (1), consider the equation $y = f(x)$ in the variables x and y. For each value of y, let $g(y)$ represent the single value of x satisfying $y = f(x)$. Thus, we meet a *function* g such that

$$y = f(x) \quad \textit{is equivalent to} \quad x = g(y). \tag{2}$$

Each of the equations $y = f(x)$ and $x = g(y)$ is satisfied by *the same set of pairs of numbers* (x, y). In (2), f is a function with the domain D and range R, whereas R is the domain and D is the range for g. We call g the **inverse** of the function f, and f the inverse of g. *Jointly*, we call f and g *inverse functions.* On account of (2), the graphs of the equations $y = f(x)$ and $x = g(y)$ on the same xy-plane are *identical.*

Illustration 1. Let y be the function of x defined by $y = 3x + 7$. Then, $x = \frac{1}{3}y - \frac{7}{3}$. In this case, with the notation of (2), $f(x) = 3x + 7$ and $g(y) = \frac{1}{3}y - \frac{7}{3}$. The graph of either $y = f(x)$ or $x = g(y)$ in this case would be the line which is the graph of $y = 3x + 7$.

★Illustration 2. Let us call N^{-1}, or $1/N$, the *inverse of* N, for a present analogy. Then, we verify that "*the inverse of the inverse*" of N is N, *or* $[1 \div 1/N] = N$. A somewhat similar situation arises from (2). Since $x = g(y)$ is the solution of $y = f(x)$, we have $f(g(y)) = y$, or the value of "*the inverse function, f, of its inverse function, g,*" at any value of y is y. Similarly, $g(f(x)) = x$. Thus, in a symbolic sense, the *composite function* $f(g)$, as an operator on y, *leaves* y *unchanged*, or g acts like a *reciprocal* of f as applied to y.

48. The inverse of the exponential function

If $F(x) = a^x$ with $a > 1$, the graph of $y = F(x)$ in Figure 63 on page 81, for x on the domain $-\infty < x < \infty$, is of the same general nature as the curve in Figure 64 on page 82. Hence, from Section 47, the equation $y = F(x)$ *defines x as a function, G, of y, where* **G is the inverse of the exponential function F.** Also, the equations $y = F(x)$ and $x = G(y)$ are *equivalent.* We call G the **logarithm function** *to the base a*, and write

$$G(y) = \log_a y, \qquad (1)$$

where we read "$\log_a$" as "*logarithm to the base a*," and "$\log_a y$" as "*logarithm to the base a of y.*" In (1), we have introduced "$\log_a$" as a substitute for "G." Since F and G are inverse functions,

$$y = a^x \quad \textit{is equivalent to} \quad x = \log_a y. \qquad (2)$$

From Figure 63 on page 81, the *domain* of the function $\log_a$ consists of *all* $y > 0$, and the *range* of values of $\log_a$ is the set of *all real numbers x.*

The graph of each of the equations of (2) is in Figure 63 on page 81, but the coordinate axes are not oriented as usual for the graph of a function with the values $\log_a y$, where y is the *independent variable.* Hence, to graph the function $\log_a$ in normal orientation, we first interchange x and y in (2):

$$y = \log_a x \quad \textit{is equivalent to} \quad x = a^y. \qquad (3)$$

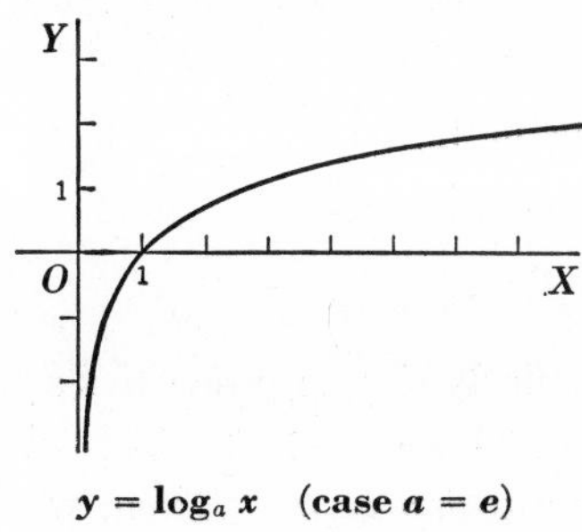

$y = \log_a x$ (case $a = e$)

Fig. 66

Then, with any particular value of a, we use $x = a^y$ to compute representative solutions (x, y) of (3). If $a = 2$, we obtain solutions by merely interchanging the labels x and y for the rows in the table on page 81. For any base a, the following skeleton table is useful in sketching a graph of $y = \log_a x$ quickly. Figure 66 shows the graph of $y = \log_e x$, or of $x = e^y$, where $e = 2.718281828 \cdots$, which is an irrational number (not a repeating decimal) of great importance in calculus and more advanced fields of mathematics.

$x =$	$0 \leftarrow x$	1	a	$x \rightarrow +\infty$
$y = \log_a x$	$-\infty \leftarrow y$	0	1	$y \rightarrow +\infty$

The fact that "$x \rightarrow 0$ *as* $y \rightarrow -\infty$" is equivalent to (3) on page 81 with x replaced by y, and shows that *the line $x = 0$*, or the y-axis, is an *asymptote* of the graph in Figure 66. This graph helps us remember the following facts:

1. *If $G(x) = \log_a x$, where $a > 1$, the* **domain** *of G consists of all $x > 0$, and the* **range** *of G is the set of all real numbers.*
2. *If* $0 < x < 1$, *then* $\log_a x < 0$, *and* $\log_a 1 = 0$.
3. *If* $x \rightarrow +\infty$, *then* $\log_a x \rightarrow +\infty$; *if* $x \rightarrow 0$, *then* $\log_a x \rightarrow -\infty$.

EXAMPLE 1. If $f(x) = 3^x$, graph f. Also, on a different sheet of paper, graph the function $\log_3 x$.

OUTLINE OF SOLUTION. 1. Let $y = 3^x$ and compute solutions (x, y) on the interval $-3 \leqq x \leqq 2$. Use a whole sheet of coordinate paper with the x-axis *near the bottom* and the y-axis about one third of the width from the right-hand edge of the sheet. Extend the graph to show its approach to the asymptote, which is the line $y = 0$.

2. To graph $y = \log_3 x$, first write the equivalent equation $x = 3^y$. Obtain solutions (x, y) by interchanging x and y in the solutions for Part 1. Place the vertical axis *near the left-hand edge* and the horizontal axis about one third of the way from the top of the sheet to the bottom.

Note 1. In this text, the most useful value of the base a in a^x and in $\log_a x$ is $a = 10$. In calculus, the most useful value is $a = e = 2.71828 \cdots$. We could give a discussion of $\log_a x$ for $0 < a < 1$ similar to that for $a > 1$.

ILLUSTRATION 1. Functions whose values are given by $a^{f(x)}$, where f is a function of x, also are called exponential functions, and have wide applications. For instance, if $F(x) = 10^{x^2}$, then F is called an exponential function. To distinguish such a function from the function K where $K(x) = a^x$, we sometimes call K a *simple* exponential function.

★*Note 2.* The constant e is defined as the following limit:

$$e = \lim_{h \to 0} (1 + h)^{\frac{1}{h}}.$$

In calculus, the function e^x is found to have particularly simple properties as compared to the function a^x for all other values $a \neq 1$ with $a > 0$. Instead of $\log_e x$, many texts use "**ln x**," read "*natural logarithm of x*." Then, we note that

$$y = e^x \quad \textit{is equivalent to} \quad x = \ln y. \tag{4}$$

Sometimes the functions e^x and $\ln y$ are called the *standard* exponential and logarithm functions. With an interchange of x and y, from (4) we have

$$y = \ln x \quad \textit{is equivalent to} \quad x = e^y. \tag{5}$$

A graph of $y = \ln x$ is shown in Figure 66 on page 83.

EXERCISE 23

1. Obtain the graphs as requested in Example 1 above.

Graph the function f with the specified values by use of just a few representative ordered pairs $[x, f(x)]$. If a logarithm is involved, use the equivalence (3) of page 83 to compute pairs $[x, f(x)]$.

2. $f(x) = 4^x$. **3.** $f(x) = \log_4 x$. **4.** $f(x) = 10^x$. **5.** $f(x) = \log_{10} x$.

★*Graph the equation. Where x^2 is involved, give a rounded appearance to the graph near the point where $x = 0$. In computing solutions (x, y), arrange to have the exponents as integers.*

6. $y = 2^{-x}$. **7.** $y = 10^{-x}$. **8.** $y = 3^{-x}$. **9.** $y = .5^{-x}$.

10. $y = 3^{-\frac{1}{2}x^2}$. **11.** $y = 2^{-\frac{1}{4}x^2}$. **12.** $y = 10^{-\frac{1}{2}x^2}$.

★*Note 1.* In Problem 10, $y = 3^{-\frac{1}{2}x^2}$ is an approximation to $y = e^{-\frac{1}{2}x^2}$, which is of great importance in mathematical statistics.

49. Basis for the use of the logarithm function in computation

We verify that the following definition of the symbol $\log_a x$ is equivalent to our introduction of the logarithm function $y = \log_a x$ as the inverse of the function $x = a^y$.

DEFINITION I. *If $a > 0$, $a \neq 1$ and $x > 0$, the* **logarithm of x to the base a,** *written* **$\log_a x$,** *is the* **exponent,** *y, of the power of the base which is equal to x. Thus,*

$$\mathbf{y = \log_a x} \quad \textit{is equivalent to} \quad \mathbf{x = a^y}. \tag{1}$$

We emphasize again that the *domain* of x in (1) consists of *all positive numbers;* thus, $\log_a x$ is **NOT** defined if $x \leqq 0$. And, the *domain* of y is the set of *all real numbers.* In (1), we call "$y = \log_a x$" the *logarithmic form* and "$x = a^y$" the *equivalent exponential form.* If one form is given, the other form can be written immediately by use of (1). For brevity hereafter, we shall frequently speak simply of "*a logarithm,*" meaning "*the value of the logarithm function at some number in its domain.*"

ILLUSTRATION 1. If $N = 4^5$, then 5 is the logarithm of N to the base 4.

ILLUSTRATION 2. "$\log_2 64$" is read "*the logarithm of 64 to the base 2*";

$$\textit{since} \quad 64 = 2^6, \quad \log_2 64 = 6.$$

ILLUSTRATION 3. Since $\quad \sqrt[3]{5} = 5^{\frac{1}{3}}, \qquad \log_5 \sqrt[3]{5} = \frac{1}{3} = .333 \cdots.$

ILLUSTRATION 4. Since $\quad \dfrac{1}{8} = \dfrac{1}{2^3} = 2^{-3}, \qquad \log_2 \dfrac{1}{8} = -3.$

ILLUSTRATION 5. If $\log_b 16 = 4$, then $b^4 = 16$; $b = \sqrt[4]{16} = 2$.

ILLUSTRATION 6. If $\log_a 2 = -\frac{1}{3}$, then $a^{-\frac{1}{3}} = 2$. Hence,

$$\frac{1}{a^{\frac{1}{3}}} = 2; \quad a^{\frac{1}{3}} = \frac{1}{2}; \quad a = \left(\frac{1}{2}\right)^3 = \frac{1}{8}.$$

ILLUSTRATION 7. If $\log_{10} N = -4$, then $N = 10^{-4} = .0001$.

We shall find that, by use of logarithms, we may accomplish the operations of multiplication, division, and raising to powers (or extraction of roots), by use of the simpler operations of addition, subtraction, and multiplication, respectively. The preceding facts are arrived at by use of properties of logarithms which are proved in the next section.

ILLUSTRATION 8. It is useful to write the equivalent equations (1) with various choices for the letters representing variables. Thus, from (1), for any numbers $N > 0$ and $M > 0$,

$$x = \log_a N \quad \textit{is equivalent to} \quad N = a^x. \tag{2}$$

$$z = \log_a M \quad \textit{is equivalent to} \quad M = a^z. \tag{3}$$

We shall frequently use the notation of (2). From (1) or (2), we have the catch phrase that *logarithms are exponents.*

For any base a, we have $a^0 = 1$ and $a^1 = a$. Hence, from (1) or (2),

$$\log_a 1 = 0; \qquad \log_a a = 1. \tag{4}$$

Note 1. In future discussion, frequently it will be useful for the student to make a rough sketch of the graph of $y = \log_a x$, as on page 83, by use of (4) and the fact that when $a > 1$, $\log_a x \to -\infty$ *as* $x \to 0$.

EXAMPLE 1. Find $\log_5 125$.

SOLUTION. Let $y = \log_5 125$. From (2), $5^y = 125$. Since $125 = 5^3$, we have $5^y = 5^3$. Hence, $y = 3$; or $\log_5 125 = 3$.

Note 2. We do not use $a = 1$ as a base for logarithms because every power of 1 is 1, and hence no number except 1 could have a logarithm to the base 1.

EXERCISE 24

Write a logarithmic equation equivalent to the exponential form.

1. $N = 2^6$. **2.** $N = 10^4$. **3.** $x = 5^{-2}$. **4.** $N = 10^{-\frac{1}{2}}$.
5. $H = 4^{\frac{1}{3}}$. **6.** $K = 10^{\frac{5}{3}}$. **7.** $x = 10^{.35}$. **8.** $32 = 2^5$.
9. $625 = 5^4$. **10.** $\frac{1}{49} = 7^{-2}$. **11.** $\frac{1}{27} = 3^{-3}$. **12.** $.0001 = 10^{-4}$.

Find the number whose logarithm is given.

13. $\log_6 N = 2$. **14.** $\log_2 N = 3$. **15.** $\log_{10} N = 4$.
16. $\log_7 M = 2$. **17.** $\log_5 M = 3$. **18.** $\log_{10} K = 0$.
19. $\log_{15} K = 1$. **20.** $\log_{10} N = 1$. **21.** $\log_5 N = -1$.
22. $\log_{10} M = -2$. **23.** $\log_b M = 1$. **24.** $\log_{11} N = -2$.
25. $\log_9 N = \frac{1}{2}$. **26.** $\log_{64} N = \frac{1}{3}$. **27.** $\log_{216} N = -\frac{1}{3}$.
28. $\log_4 N = \frac{3}{2}$. **29.** $\log_{27} N = \frac{2}{3}$. **30.** $\log_8 N = \frac{5}{3}$.

Find the following logarithms.

31. $\log_9 81$. **32.** $\log_5 25$. **33.** $\log_3 81$. **34.** $\log_9 3$.
35. $\log_{10} 100$. **36.** $\log_{10} 1000$. **37.** $\log_3 243$. **38.** $\log_{11} 121$.
39. $\log_{16} 4$. **40.** $\log_{100} 10$. **41.** $\log_7 \frac{1}{7}$. **42.** $\log_4 \frac{1}{4}$.
43. $\log_3 \frac{1}{27}$. **44.** $\log_2 \frac{1}{16}$. **45.** $\log_{10} .001$. **46.** $\log_{10} .0001$.

Find a, N, or x, whichever is not given.

47. $\log_a 8 = 2.$ **48.** $\log_a 64 = 3.$ **49.** $\log_a 10{,}000 = 4.$
50. $\log_a 10{,}000 = 2.$ **51.** $\log_a 5 = \frac{1}{2}.$ **52.** $\log_a 4 = \frac{1}{3}.$
53. $\log_6 N = 3.$ **54.** $\log_{10} N = -3.$ **55.** $\log_{49} N = \frac{3}{2}.$
56. $\log_{16} N = \frac{3}{4}.$ **57.** $\log_{27} N = -\frac{4}{3}.$ **58.** $\log_a 4 = -\frac{2}{3}.$
59. $\log_{256} 16 = x.$ **60.** $\log_5 625 = x.$ **61.** $\log_{10} x = -\frac{1}{2}.$

50. Some properties of logarithms

PROPERTY I. *The logarithm of a product is equal to the sum of the logarithms of the factors; for instance,*

$$\log_a MN = \log_a M + \log_a N. \tag{1}$$

ILLUSTRATION 1. $\log_{10} 897(596) = \log_{10} 897 + \log_{10} 596.$

Proof of (1). Let $x = \log_a M$ and $y = \log_a N$. Then,*

$$M = a^x \quad \textit{and} \quad N = a^y. \qquad \text{(Definition of the logarithm function)}$$

$$MN = a^x a^y = a^{x+y}. \qquad \text{(A law of exponents)}$$

Therefore, by the definition of the logarithm function, we obtain the result stated in (1):

$$\log_a MN = x + y = \log_a M + \log_a N.$$

Note 1. By use of (1) we can prove Property I for a product of any number of factors. Thus, since $MNP = (MN)(P)$,

$$\log_a MNP = \log_a MN + \log_a P = \log_a M + \log_a N + \log_a P.$$

PROPERTY II. *The logarithm of a quotient is equal to the logarithm of the dividend minus the logarithm of the divisor:*

$$\log_a \frac{M}{N} = \log_a M - \log_a N. \tag{2}$$

ILLUSTRATION 2. $\log_{10} \frac{89}{57} = \log_{10} 89 - \log_{10} 57.$

Proof of (2). Let $\log_a M = x$ and $\log_a N = y$. Then,

$$\frac{M}{N} = \frac{a^x}{a^y} = a^{x-y}. \qquad \text{(A law of exponents)}$$

Hence, by the definition of the logarithm function, we obtain (2):

$$\log_a \frac{M}{N} = x - y = \log_a M - \log_a N.$$

* In a reference to the definition of the logarithm function, the most direct contact with our present notation is in the equivalence statement (2) on page 86.

ILLUSTRATION 3. By use of (1) and (2),

$$\log_a \frac{MK}{N} = \log_a MK - \log_a N = \log_a M + \log_a K - \log_a N.$$

PROPERTY III. *The logarithm of the* kth *power of a number* N *is equal to* k *times the logarithm of* N:

$$\log_a N^k = k \log_a N. \tag{3}$$

ILLUSTRATION 4. $\log_a 7^5 = 5 \log_a 7.$ $\log_a \sqrt[4]{3} = \log_a 3^{\frac{1}{4}} = \frac{1}{4} \log_a 3.$

Proof of (3). Let $x = \log_a N$. Then, $N = a^x$ and

$$N^k = (a^x)^k = a^{kx}. \qquad \text{(A law of exponents)}$$

Hence, by the definition of the logarithm function, we obtain (3):

$$\log_a N^k = kx = k \log_a N.$$

Since $\sqrt[h]{N} = N^{\frac{1}{h}}$, by use of (3) with $k = 1/h$ we obtain

$$\log_a \sqrt[h]{N} = \frac{1}{h} \log_a N. \tag{4}$$

ILLUSTRATION 5. $\log_a \sqrt{N} = \frac{1}{2} \log_a N;$ $\log_a \sqrt[3]{25} = \frac{1}{3} \log_a 25.$

Logarithms to the base 10 are called **common logarithms** and are the most useful variety for computational purposes. Hereafter, unless otherwise stated, when we mention a *logarithm* we shall mean a *common* logarithm. For abbreviation, we shall write merely $\log N$, instead of $\log_{10} N$, for the common logarithm of N. We read "$\log N$" simply as "*the logarithm of* N." With 10 as the base for $\log N$, the equivalence statement (2) on page 86 becomes

$$x = \log N \quad \textit{is equivalent to} \quad N = 10^x. \tag{5}$$

The following common logarithms, obtained from (5), will be useful later.

$N =$	.0001	.001	.01	.1	1	10	100	1000	10,000	100,000
$\log N =$	-4	-3	-2	-1	0	1	2	3	4	5

ILLUSTRATION 6. If we are given $\log 3 = .4771$, then by use of Properties I, II, and III we obtain the following results:

$$\log 300 = \log 3(100) = \log 3 + \log 100 = .4771 + 2 = 2.4771;$$

$$\log .003 = \log \frac{3}{1000} = \log 3 - \log 1000 = .4771 - 3 = -2.5229;$$

$$\log \sqrt[4]{3} = \log 3^{\frac{1}{4}} = \frac{1}{4} \log 3 = \frac{1}{4}(.4771) = .1193.$$

EXERCISE 25

Find the logarithm of each number by use of the following logarithms.

$\log 2 = .3010;\ \log 3 = .4771;\ \log 7 = .8451;\ \log 17 = 1.2304.$

1. 14. **2.** 51. **3.** 30. **4.** 170. **5.** 21. **6.** 42.
7. $\frac{7}{2}$. **8.** $\frac{17}{3}$. **9.** $\frac{3}{7}$. **10.** $\frac{10}{3}$. **11.** $\frac{17}{14}$. **12.** .7.
13. 200. **14.** $\frac{34}{3}$. **15.** $\frac{2}{21}$. **16.** $\frac{100}{17}$. **17.** $\frac{100}{21}$. **18.** 49.
19. 32. **20.** 81. **21.** $\sqrt{3}$. **22.** $\sqrt{14}$. **23.** $\sqrt{\frac{7}{3}}$. **24.** $\sqrt[3]{\frac{2}{17}}$.

51. Characteristic and mantissa

Every number, and hence *every value of the logarithm function*, can be written as the sum of *an integer and a decimal* which is *positive or zero* and *less than* 1. When $\log N$ is written in this way, we call the integer the *characteristic* and the decimal the *mantissa* of $\log N$.

$$\mathbf{\log N = (an\ integer) + (a\ decimal, \geqq 0, < 1);}$$
$$\mathbf{\log N = characteristic + mantissa.} \qquad (1)$$

Illustration 1. If $\log N = 4.6832 = 4 + .6832$, then .6832 is the mantissa and 4 is the characteristic of $\log N$.

Illustration 2. The following logarithms were obtained by later methods.

	Logarithm	Characteristic	Mantissa
log 300 = 2.4771	= 2 + .4771	2	.4771
log 50 = 1.6990	= 1 + .6990	1	.6990
log .001 = − 3	= − 3 + .0000	− 3	.0000
log 6.5 = 0.8129	= 0 + .8129	0	.8129
log .0385 = − 1.4145	= − 2 + .5855	− 2	.5855
log .005 = − 2.3010	= − 3 + .6990	− 3	.6990

Illustration 3. All numbers whose logarithms are given below have the same significant digits (3, 8, 0, 4). To obtain the logarithms, log 3.804 was found from a table to be discussed later; the other logarithms were obtained then by the use of Properties I and II of Section 50.

$$\log 380.4 = \log 100(3.804) = \log 100 + \log 3.804 = 2 + \mathbf{.5802};$$
$$\log 38.04 = \log 10(3.804) = \log 10 + \log 3.804 = 1 + \mathbf{.5802};$$
$$\log 3.804 = .5802 = 0 + \mathbf{.5802};$$
$$\log .3804 = \log \frac{3.804}{10} = \log 3.804 - \log 10 = -1 + \mathbf{.5802};$$
$$\log .03804 = \log \frac{3.804}{100} = \log 3.804 - \log 100 = -2 + \mathbf{.5802}.$$

Similarly, if N is *any* number whose significant digits are (3, 8, 0, 4), then N is equal to 3.804 multiplied, or else divided, by a positive integral power of 10; hence, it follows as before that .5802 is the mantissa of $\log N$.

With a change only in the mantissa involved, the reasoning in Illustration 3 could be repeated with negligible alteration for any specified sequence of significant digits. We shall accept these remarks as sufficient proof for the following result.

THEOREM I. *The mantissa of* $\log N$ *depends only on the sequence of significant digits in* N. *That is,* **if two numbers differ only in the position of the decimal point, their logarithms have the same mantissa.**

In (1), let $M =$ mantissa and $C =$ characteristic. We have $0 \leqq M < 1$, and C is an integer. If $C \geqq 0$, then $(C + M)$ is positive. If $C = -1$, or if C is *any other negative integer*, then $C + M < 0$ because $M < 1$. Hence

$$\left\{\begin{array}{l}\textbf{log } N \textbf{ is negative } \textit{if and only if the} \\ \textbf{characteristic of log } N \textbf{ is negative.}\end{array}\right\} \tag{2}$$

ILLUSTRATION 4. If $\log N = -3.75$, then $\log N$ lies between -4 and -3. Hence, $\log N = -4 + (a\ fraction)$. To find the fraction, subtract: $4 - 3.75 = .25$. Hence, $\log N = -3.75 = -4 + .25$; the mantissa is .25.

From the graph of $y = \log_a x$ in Figure 66 on page 83, we recall that, for *any* base a, $\log_a x$ *increases steadily as* x *increases.* Hence, with $a = 10$ as at present, if M, N, and K are positive numbers,

$$\log M < \log N < \log K \quad \textit{if and only if} \quad M < N < K. \tag{3}$$

From our knowledge of the logarithms of powers of 10, as on page 88, by use of (3) we can determine the *characteristics* of logarithms. In doing this, we shall make use of the following fact, where h is an integer and the number L is subject to the specified condition:

$$\textit{if } h \leqq L < h + 1, \quad \textit{then} \quad L = h + M \quad \textit{where} \quad 0 \leqq M < 1. \tag{4}$$

ILLUSTRATION 5. To find the characteristic of log 380.4, we notice that

$$100 < 380.4 < 1000, \quad \textit{or} \quad 10^2 < 380.4 < 10^3. \tag{5}$$

Hence, $\quad \log 10^2 < \log 380.4 < \log 10^3, \quad \textit{or} \quad 2 < \log 380.4 < 3. \qquad (6)$

Therefore, $\log 380.4 = 2 + M$, where $0 < M < 1$. Or, by definition, the characteristic of log 380.4 is 2.

In Illustration 3, we met special cases of the results of the following theorems which enable us to find the characteristic of $\log N$, for an assigned number N, by mere inspection of N. The method of Illustration 5 can be used to prove the theorems, as outlined later.

THEOREM II. **When $N > 1$,** *the characteristic of* $\log N$ *is an integer, positive or zero, which is* **one less than the number of digits in N to the left of the decimal point.**

THEOREM III. **If $N < 1$,** *the characteristic of* $\log N$ *is a negative integer;* **if the first significant digit of N is in the kth decimal place, then $-k$ is the characteristic of $\log N$.**

ILLUSTRATION 6. By Theorem III, the characteristic of log .00039 is -4 because "3" is in the 4th decimal place. By Theorem II, the characteristic of log 1578.6 is 3.

For convenience in computation, **if the characteristic of $\log N$ is negative, $-k$, change it to the equivalent value**

$$[(10 - k) - 10], \quad or \quad [(20 - k) - 20], \text{ etc.}$$

ILLUSTRATION 7. Given that $\log .000843 = -4 + .9258$, we write

$$\log .000843 = -4 + .9258 = (6 - 10) + .9258 = 6.9258 - 10.$$

The characteristics of the following logarithms are obtained by use of Theorem III; the mantissas are identical, by Theorem I.

1ST SIGNIF. DIGIT IN	ILLUSTRATION	LOG N | STANDARD FORM
1st *decimal place*	$N = .843$	$-1 + .9258 = 9.9258 - 10$
2d *decimal place*	$N = .0843$	$-2 + .9258 = 8.9258 - 10$
6th *decimal place*	$N = .00000843$	$-6 + .9258 = 4.9258 - 10$

★*Note 1.* To prove Theorems II and III, we first remark that the characteristic of $\log N$ is h if and only if $h \leqq \log N < h + 1$. Since $h = \log 10^h$ and $h + 1 = \log 10^{h+1}$, on account of (3) we obtain

$$h \leqq \log N < h + 1 \quad \textit{is equivalent to} \quad 10^h \leqq N < 10^{h+1}. \tag{7}$$

If $h \geqq 0$, condition (7) is equivalent to the statement that *the first significant digit of N occurs in the* $(h + 1)$th *place to the left of the decimal point.* Thus, $10^2 \leqq 450 < 10^3$, and "4" occurs in the 3d place to the left of the decimal point. If $h < 0$, let $h = -k$. Then, (7) is equivalent to $10^{-k} \leqq N < 10^{-k+1}$, which means that *the first significant digit of N occurs in the* kth *decimal place.* For instance,

$$.001 < .0045 < .01, \textit{ or}$$

$$10^{-3} < .0045 < 10^{-2},$$

and the 1st significant digit of .0045 occurs in the 3d decimal place. The preceding remarks lead to the summarizing rules stated in Theorems II and III.

52. A four-place table of logarithms

Mantissas can be computed by advanced methods and, usually, are endless decimals. Computed mantissas are found in tables of logarithms, also called *tables of mantissas.*

ILLUSTRATION 1. The mantissa for log 10705 is .029586671630457, to fifteen decimal places.

Table V gives the mantissa of log N correct to four decimal places, if N has at most three significant digits aside from additional zeros at the right. A decimal point is understood at the left of each mantissa in the table. If N lies between 1 and 10, the characteristic of log N is *zero*, so that log N is *the same as its mantissa.* Hence, a four-place table of mantissas also is a table of *the actual four-place logarithms of all numbers with at most three significant digits from* $N = 1.00$ *to* $N = 9.99$. If $N \geqq 10$ or $N < 1$, we supply the characteristic of log N by use of Theorems II and III of Section 51.

EXAMPLE 1. Find log .0316 from Table V.

SOLUTION. 1. *To obtain the mantissa:* find "31" in the column headed N in the table; in the row for "31," read the entry in the column headed "6." The mantissa is .4997.

2. By Theorem III, the characteristic of log .0316 is -2, or $(8 - 10)$:

$$\log .0316 = -2 + .4997 = 8.4997 - 10.$$

ILLUSTRATION 2. From Table V and Theorem II, log 31,600 = 4.4997.

EXAMPLE 2. Find N if $\log N = 7.6064 - 10$.

SOLUTION. 1. *To find the significant digits of* N*:* the mantissa of log N is .6064; this is found in Table V as the mantissa for the digits "404."

2. *To locate the decimal point in* N*:* the characteristic of log N is $(7 - 10)$, or -3; hence, by Theorem III, $N = .00404$.

ILLUSTRATION 3. If $\log N = 3.6064$, the characteristic is 3 and, by Theorem II, N has 4 digits to the left of the decimal point: the mantissa is the same as in Example 2. Hence, $N = 4040$.

DEFINITION II. *To say that* N *is the* **antilogarithm** *of* L *means that* $\log N = L$, *or* $N = 10^L$, *and we write* $N =$ **antilog** L.

ILLUSTRATION 4. Since log 1000 = 3, then 1000 = antilog 3.

ILLUSTRATION 5. In Example 2 we found *antilog* $(7.6064 - 10) = .00404$.

53. A five-place table of logarithms

Table VIII gives the mantissa of log N correct to five decimal places if N is any number with at most four significant digits aside from additional zeros at the right. A five-place table of mantissas also is a table of the actual logarithms of all numbers with at most four significant digits, from $N = 1.000$ to $N = 9.999$.

EXAMPLE 1. Find log 31,680 from Table VIII.

SOLUTION. 1. In the row of 316, in the column headed by 8 on page 22, we find *079; the asterisk (*) means that the first two digits are 50, instead of 49 as at the beginning of the row. The mantissa is .50079.

2. The characteristic of the desired logarithm is 4. Hence,

$$\log 31{,}680 = 4.50079.$$

EXERCISE 26*

The given number is the logarithm of some number N. State the characteristic and the mantissa of log N.

1. 3.5217. **2.** 25.3189. **3.** $-$ 2.450. **4.** 6.3159 $-$ 10.
5. $-$ 3.1582. **6.** $-$ .6354. **7.** 5.2891 $-$ 10. **8.** 9.1346 $-$ 10.

Write the following negative logarithms in standard form.

9. $-2 + .1356$. **10.** $.2341 - 3$. **11.** $.5268 - 4$. **12.** -5.3214.

State the characteristic of the logarithm of each number.

13. 41,356. **14.** 249. **15.** .000047. **16.** .0036. **17.** .000007.

Use Table V *to find the four-place logarithm of the number.*

18. 35.6. **19.** 124. **20.** 8950. **21.** .261. **22.** .495.
23. .0562. **24.** .00008. **25.** 20,900. **26.** .000419. **27.** .909.
28. .0861. **29.** 15,200. **30.** .000643. **31.** .0000219. **32.** 256,000.

Find the antilogarithm of the given logarithm by use of Table V.

33. 2.1335. **34.** 3.5263. **35.** 9.7185 $-$ 10. **36.** 7.4183 $-$ 10.
37. 1.7459. **38.** 0.2148. **39.** 8.5752 $-$ 10. **40.** 4.2945 $-$ 10.
41. 0.5198. **42.** 6.3096. **43.** 7.4669 $-$ 10. **44.** 9.3201 $-$ 10.
45. 7.5172. **46.** 1.2304. **47.** 6.6325 $-$ 10. **48.** 2.4955 $-$ 10.

49. Find N if (*a*) $\log N = -3.6021$; (*b*) $\log N = 7.6021 - 10$.

50. Find N if (*a*) $\log N = 3 - 2.3979$; (*b*) $\log N = 8.3979 - 10$.

Find the five-place logarithm of each number by use of Table VIII.

51. 198.7. **52.** 18.56. **53.** 1.389. **54.** 2.633. **55.** .01118.
56. .2866. **57.** .2563. **58.** .0146. **59.** 59,600. **60.** 69,990.

Find the antilogarithm of each logarithm by use of Table VIII.

61. 1.25115. **62.** 0.66058. **63.** 9.42716 $-$ 10. **64.** 6.55630 $-$ 10.
65. 2.47305. **66.** 5.83052. **67.** 8.58726 $-$ 10. **68.** 5.68124 $-$ 10.

* The major emphasis will be given to use of four-place logarithms. The methods are presented so that they carry over without alteration in principles to the use of five-place logarithms. The use of five-place tables in exercises will be subject to the decision of the teacher.

54. Interpolation in a four-place table of logarithms

Interpolation in a table of mantissas is based on the assumption that, *for small changes in* N, *the corresponding changes in* log N *are proportional to the changes in* N. This **principle of proportional parts** is merely a useful approximation to the truth.

We agree that, when a mantissa is found by interpolation from a table, we shall express the result *only to the number of decimal places given in table entries.* Also, in finding N by interpolation in a table of mantissas when log N is given, we agree to specify just **four** or just **five** significant digits according as we are using a **four-place** or a **five-place** table.

In using a four-place table of logarithms, it is convenient to act as if each number N whose logarithm is mentioned has *just four significant digits,* perhaps including one or more zeros at the right. Thus, we attach one or more final zeros to the significant part of N if it has *less* than four significant digits. Or we *round off* N to four significant digits if N initially has more than four-place accuracy. We then think of each entry in Table V as the mantissa for the logarithm of a number N with *four* significant digits, obtained by attaching a final zero to the part arising in the table.

EXAMPLE 1. Find log 13.86 by interpolation in Table V.

SOLUTION. Since 13.86 has four significant digits, with the 4th not zero, the mantissa for log 13.86 cannot be read directly from the table. In the following table, log 13.80 and log 13.90 are obtained from Table V. The equation for x is a consequence of the principle of proportional parts.

$$.10\left[\;.06\left[\begin{array}{l}\log 13.80 = 1.1399\\ \log 13.86 = \;\;?\end{array}\right]x\;\right.\begin{array}{l}\\ \log 13.90 = 1.1430\end{array}\Bigg]\,31$$

Tabular difference *is* .0031.

$$\frac{x}{31} = \frac{.06}{.10}; \quad x = \frac{6}{10}(31).$$

$x = .6(31) = 18.6 = 19,$ *approximately;*

log 13.86 = 1.1399 + .0019 = 1.1418.

Comment. We found .6(31) = 18.6 in the column of *proportional parts.*

ILLUSTRATION 1. To find log .002913 from Table V:

$$10\left[\;3\left[\begin{array}{l}2910\text{: } \textit{mantissa is } .4639\\ 2913\text{: } \textit{mantissa is } \;?\end{array}\right]x\;\right.\begin{array}{l}\\ 2920\text{: } \textit{mantissa is } .4654\end{array}\Bigg]\,15$$

Tabular difference *is* $.4654 - .4639 = .0015.$

$x = .3(15) = 4.5,$ or 5.

Hence, the mantissa for 2913 *is* **.4639 + .0005 = .4644.**

By Theorem III, **log .002913 = − 3 + .4644 = 7.4644 − 10.**

We used .3(15) as 5, instead of 4, in agreement with paragraph (2) of the solution of Example 2 on page 73.

EXAMPLE 2. Find N from Table V if $\log N = 1.6187$.

SOLUTION. 1. The mantissa .6187 is not in Table V but is *bracketed* by the consecutive entries .6180 and .6191, the mantissas for 415 and 416.

2. Since .6187 is $\frac{7}{11}$ of the way from .6180 to .6191, we assume that N is $\frac{7}{11}$ of the way from 41.50 to 41.60. Thus, in the following table,

$$\frac{x}{.10} = \frac{7}{11}, \quad or \quad x = \frac{7}{11}(.10).$$

11	7	$1.6180 = \log 41.50$	x	$41.60 - 41.50 = .10.$
		$1.6187 = \log N$	.10	$x = \frac{7}{11}(.10) = .064$, *or*
		$1.6191 = \log 41.60$		*approximately* .06.

$$N = 41.50 + \tfrac{7}{11}(.10) = \mathbf{41.50 + .06 = 41.56.}$$

ILLUSTRATION 2. To find N if $\log N = 6.1053 - 10$:

34	15	.1038, *mantissa for* 1270	x	$\frac{15}{34} = .4.$ *Hence,*
		.1053, *mantissa for* ?	10	$x = .4(10) = 4.$
		.1072, *mantissa for* 1280		$1270 + 4 = 1274.$

Hence, .1053 *is the mantissa for* 1274 *and* N = **.0001274.**

Comment. We obtain $\frac{15}{34} = .4$, approximately, by inspection of the tenths of 34 in the columns of proportional parts. We read

$$13.6 = .4(34) \quad or \quad \frac{13.6}{34} = .4, \quad and \quad \frac{17}{34} = .5.$$

Since 15 is nearer to 13.6 than to 17, then $\frac{15}{34}$ is nearer to .4 than to .5.

Suppose that a number N is written in the *scientific notation* $N = P(10^k)$, where k is an integer and $1 \leqq P < 10$. Then

$$\log N = \log P + \log 10^k = k + \log P,$$

where $0 \leqq \log P < 1$ because $1 \leqq P < 10$. Thus, with N written in the scientific notation, k is the *characteristic* and $\log P$ is the *mantissa* for $\log N$.

ILLUSTRATION 3. If $\log N = 9.7419$, and if we use the form $N = P(10^k)$, we have $k = 9$ and $\log P = 0.7419$. Hence,

$$P = 5.520; \quad N = 5.520(10^9). \qquad \textit{(Four digits significant.)}$$

★55. Interpolation in a five-place table of logarithms

In using a five-place table of logarithms, it is convenient to act as if each number N whose logarithm is to be mentioned has *just five significant digits*, perhaps including one or more zeros at the right. Thus, we attach one or more final zeros to the significant part of N if it has *less* than five significant digits. Or we *round off* N to five significant digits if N initially has more than five-place accuracy. We then think of each entry in Table VIII as the mantissa for the logarithm of a number N with *five* significant digits, obtained by attaching a final zero to the significant part arising in the table.

EXAMPLE 1. Find log .0012397 by use of Table VIII.

SOLUTION. Notice that .0012397 is *bracketed* by .0012390 and .0012400; the mantissas for their logarithms are obtained directly from Table VIII.

$$10\left[\;7\left[\begin{array}{l}12390\text{: } \textit{mantissa is } .09307\\ 12397\text{: } \textit{mantissa is } \quad ?\\ 12400\text{: } \textit{mantissa is } .09342\end{array}\right]x\;\right]35$$

Tabular difference is .00035.

$$\frac{x}{35}=\frac{7}{10}; \quad x=\frac{7}{10}(35).$$

$x = .7(35) = 24.5 = 25$, *approximately;*

log .0012397 = − 3 + .09307 + .00025 = 7.09332 − 10.

EXAMPLE 2. Find antilog 2.40971 by use of Table VIII.

SOLUTION. 1. Let $N =$ antilog 2.40971. Then, log $N = 2.40971$. The mantissa is .40971, which is *bracketed* by the mantissas .40960 and .40976 in Table VIII, corresponding to 25680 and 25690.

$$16\left[\;11\left[\begin{array}{l}.40960\text{, } \textit{mantissa for } 25680\\ .40971\text{, } \textit{mantissa for } \quad ?\\ .40976\text{, } \textit{mantissa for } 25690\end{array}\right]x\;\right]10$$

$\frac{11}{16} = .7$, *to nearest tenth;*

$x = .7(10) = 7.$

$25680 + 7 = 25687.$

The characteristic of log N *is* 2; **antilog 2.40971 = 256.87.**

Comment. We obtained $\frac{11}{16} = .7$ in the column of proportional parts.

EXERCISE 27

Find the four-place logarithm of the number from Table V.

1. 1923. **2.** 2725. **3.** 5815. **4.** 12.76.
5. 9.436. **6.** .1787. **7.** .7094. **8.** .003196.
9. .005135. **10.** .0001245. **11.** .0002007. **12.** $2.456(10^5)$.
13. 80,090. **14.** 204,600. **15.** 3.126. **16.** 1.573.
17. 25,780. **18.** $2.643(10^6)$. **19.** $6.214(10^{-3})$. **20.** $5.439(10^{-5})$.

Find the antilogarithm of the four-place logarithm, from Table V.

21. 1.6553. **22.** 2.3468. **23.** 9.0226 − 10. **24.** 8.1691 − 10.
25. 0.5510. **26.** 1.3754. **27.** 8.6432 − 10. **28.** 0.5309.
29. 2.0360. **30.** 7.4483 − 10. **31.** 6.0211 − 10. **32.** 2.0493.
33. 5.9367 − 10. **34.** 6.3194. **35.** 7.0364. **36.** 0.2779.
37. 3.3614. **38.** 2.8547. **39.** 9.9546 − 10. **40.** 9.9990 − 10.
41. 0.9871. **42.** 6.2338 − 10. **43.** 1.5648. **44.** 3.1542 − 10.

★*Find the five-place logarithm of each number from Table* VIII.

45. 18,563. **46.** 21.285. **47.** 4.7178. **48.** .89316. **49.** 61.597.
50. 25,632. **51.** .30129. **52.** 31.648. **53.** .75362. **54.** .071384.
55. 5.3217. **56.** .042087. **57.** .073563. **58.** 53.193. **59.** 896,910.
60. .0040063. **61.** .00078651. **62.** 966,910. **63.** $6.1324(10^{-12})$.
64. .0062873. **65.** $1.3006(10^{6})$. **66.** .00041569. **67.** $5.0006(10^{8})$.

★*Find the antilogarithm of each five-place logarithm by use of Table* VIII.

68. 2.21388. **69.** 9.65328 − 10. **70.** 9.00858 − 10. **71.** 6.03271.
72. 3.21631. **73.** 8.12277 − 10. **74.** 3.33412 − 10. **75.** 5.45698.
76. 1.33740. **77.** 7.94014 − 10. **78.** 6.24049 − 10. **79.** 0.97035.
80. 2.05297. **81.** 9.77817 − 10. **82.** 8.73168 − 20. **83.** 0.28779.

56. Computation of products and quotients

Until otherwise specified, we shall assume that the data of any given problem are *exact.* Under this assumption, the accuracy of a product, quotient, or power computed by use of logarithms depends on the number of places in the table being used. The result frequently is subject to an unavoidable error which usually is at most a few units in the last significant place given by interpolation. Hence, as a rule, we should compute with at least *five-place* logarithms to obtain *four-place accuracy,* and with at least *four-place* logarithms to obtain *three-place accuracy.* Usually, in any result, we shall give *all digits obtainable by interpolation* in the specified table.

EXAMPLE 1. Compute .0631(7.208)(.5127) by use of Table V.

SOLUTION. Let P represent the product. We find the logarithms of the factors from Table V, add to obtain log P, and then finally obtain P from Table V. The computing form, given in blackface type, was made up completely as *the first step in the solution.*

$$\begin{aligned} \textbf{log .0631} &= 8.8000 - 10 && \text{(Table V)} \\ \textbf{log 7.208} &= 0.8578 && \text{(Table V)} \\ \textbf{log .5127} &= 9.7099 - 10 && \text{(Table V)} \\ \hline (\textbf{\textit{add}})\ \textbf{log}\ \boldsymbol{P} &= 19.3677 - 20 = 9.3677 - 10. \end{aligned}$$

Hence, $\boldsymbol{P}$ **=** .2332. [= antilog (9.3677 − 10), Table V]

Note 1. It is essential to become familiar with rounding off data, if necessary, to that number of significant digits which should be used with a *given table of logarithms.* Retention of more digits does not increase accuracy.

EXAMPLE 2. Compute $q = \dfrac{431.91}{15.6873}$ by use of Table V.

SOLUTION. 1. By Property II, on page 87, log q is equal to *the logarithm of the numerator minus the logarithm of the denominator.*

2. Before computing, we *round off* each given number to *four* significant digits because we are using a four-place table.

$$\begin{array}{rll} \textbf{log 431.9} = 2.6354 & & \text{(Table V)} \\ (-)\ \textbf{log 15.69} = 1.1956 & & \text{(Table V)} \\ \hline \textbf{log } \boldsymbol{q} = 1.4398. & \textbf{Hence, } \boldsymbol{q} = 27.53. & \text{(Table V)} \end{array}$$

EXAMPLE 3. Compute $q = \dfrac{257}{8956}$ by use of Table V.

SOLUTION.

$$\begin{array}{rcl} \textbf{log 257} = 2.4099 & = & 12.4099 - 10 \\ (-)\ \textbf{log 8956} = 3.9521 & = & 3.9521 \\ \hline \textbf{log } \boldsymbol{q} = \quad ? & = & 8.4578 - 10; \quad \boldsymbol{q} = .02869. \end{array}$$

Comment. We saw that log q would be *negative* because log 8956 is *greater* than log 257. In order that log q should appear immediately in the *standard form for a negative logarithm,* we changed log 257 by adding 10 and then subtracting 10 to compensate for the first change. Actually,

$$\log q = 2.4099 - 3.9521 = -1.5422 = 8.4578 - 10.$$

Whenever it is necessary to subtract a logarithm from a smaller one in computing a quotient, add 10 to the characteristic of the smaller logarithm and then subtract 10 to compensate for the change.

EXAMPLE 4. Compute $q = \dfrac{(4.803)(269.9)(1.636)}{(7880)(253.6)}$.

INCOMPLETE SOLUTION. We make a **computing form,** to subtract the logarithm of the denominator from the logarithm of the numerator.

$$\begin{array}{r} (+)\left\{\begin{array}{l}\textbf{log 4.803} = \\ \textbf{log 269.9} = \\ \textbf{log 1.636} = \end{array}\right. \\ \hline \textbf{log numer.} = \\ (-)\ \textbf{log denom.} = \\ \hline \textbf{log } \boldsymbol{q} = \end{array} \qquad \begin{array}{r} (+)\left\{\begin{array}{l}\textbf{log 7880} = \\ \textbf{log 253.6} = \end{array}\right. \\ \hline \textbf{log denom.} = \\ \\ \\ \textbf{Hence, } \boldsymbol{q} = \end{array}$$

EXAMPLE 5. Compute the reciprocal of 189 by use of Table V.

SOLUTION. Let $R = 1/189$.

$$\begin{array}{rcl} \textbf{log 1} = 0.0000 & = & 10.0000 - 10 \\ (-)\ \textbf{log 189} = 2.2765 & = & 2.2765 \\ \hline \textbf{log } \boldsymbol{R} = \quad ? & = & 7.7235 - 10. \end{array}$$

$$\textbf{Hence, } \boldsymbol{R} = .005290.$$

Comment. In writing any approximate value, indicate all final zeros which are significant. In $R = .005290$ in Example 5, the final zero was essential.

★57. Cologarithms

The logarithm of the *reciprocal* of N, that is, the logarithm of $1/N$, is called the *cologarithm* of N and is written **colog N.** Since $\log 1 = 0$,

$$\textbf{colog}\ N = \log \frac{1}{N} = 0 - \log N. \tag{1}$$

ILLUSTRATION 1. $\text{Colog } .031 = \log \dfrac{1}{.031}$:

$$\begin{array}{rl} \log 1 = & 10.0000 - 10 \\ (-)\ \log .031 = & 8.4914 - 10 \\ \hline \text{colog } .031 = & 1.5086. \end{array}$$

The positive part of colog N can be obtained quickly by inspection of log N: *subtract each digit (except the last at the right) in the positive part of* log N *from* 9, *and subtract the last digit from* 10.

EXAMPLE 1. Compute $q = \dfrac{16.083 \times 256}{47 \times .0158}$ by use of cologarithms.

SOLUTION. To *divide* by N is the same as to *multiply* by $1/N$. Hence, instead of *subtracting the logarithm* of each factor of the denominator, we *add the cologarithm* of the factor:

$$q = \frac{16.083 \times 256}{47 \times .0158} = (16.083 \times 256)\left(\frac{1}{47}\right)\left(\frac{1}{.0158}\right).$$

$$\begin{array}{rl} \log 16.08 = & 1.2063 \\ \log 256 = & 2.4082 \end{array}$$

$\log 47 = 1.6721$; **hence,** $\qquad \text{colog } 47 = 8.3279 - 10$

$\log .0158 = 8.1987 - 10$; **hence,** $\qquad \text{colog } .0158 = 1.8013$

$$\begin{array}{rl} \hline (\textit{add})\ \log q = & 13.7437 - 10 \\ = & 3.7437. \\ q = & 5542. \end{array}$$

Note 1. Use cologarithms only as directed by the instructor.

EXERCISE 28

Compute with four-place or five-place logarithms, as the instructor directs.

1. $31.57 \times .789$. **2.** $925.6 \times .137$. **3.** $.8475 \times .0937$.

4. $.0179 \times .356413$.* **5.** $925.618 \times .000217$.* **6.** $3.41379 \times .0142$.

7. $(-84.75)(.00368)(.02458)$. **8.** $(-16.8)(-136.943)(-.00038)$.

HINT. Only *positive* numbers have *real* logarithms. First compute as if all factors were positive; then determine the sign by inspection.

* Before finding the logarithm of a number N, we *round off N to four or to five significant digits* according as we are using *four*-place or *five*-place logarithms.

9. $\frac{675}{13.21}$. 10. $\frac{568.5}{23.14}$. 11. $\frac{728.72}{895}$. 12. $\frac{753.166}{9273.8}$.

13. $\frac{.0894}{.6358}$. 14. $\frac{.0421}{.53908}$. 15. $\frac{1}{325.932}$. 16. $\frac{1}{100{,}935}$.

17. $\frac{16.083 \times 256}{47 \times .0158}$. 18. $\frac{.42173 \times .217}{.3852 \times .956}$. 19. $\frac{9.32 \times 531}{.8319 \times .5685}$.

20. $\frac{5.4171 \times .429}{18.1167 \times 37}$. 21. $\frac{1}{.53819 \times .0673}$. 22. $\frac{1}{.00073 \times .965}$.

23. $\frac{(-.29)(.038)(-.0065)}{(-1006.332)(2.71)}$. 24. $\frac{5.6(-3.9078)(-.00031)}{(132)(-1.93)}$.

Compute the reciprocal of the number.

25. 63283. **26.** .00382. **27.** .02567. **28.** .0683(.52831).

29. (*a*) Compute 652(735); (*b*) compute (log 652)(log 735).

30. (*a*) Compute .351 ÷ 625; (*b*) compute (log .351) ÷ (log 625).

31. Find the logarithms of 3.1570, 3.1569, 3.1568, 3.1567, 3.1566 from Table VIII and round off each result to four decimal places. Then, obtain log 3.157 from Table V. The similarity of the results shows the sense involved in the footnote for Problem 4.

32. By use of Table VIII, compute $10^{3.61738}$; $10^{-2.31462}$.

58. Computation of powers and roots

We recall the following results, where k may be any real number and h is a positive integer:

$$\log N^k = k \log N; \tag{1}$$

since $\sqrt[h]{N} = N^{\frac{1}{h}}$,

$$\log \sqrt[h]{N} = \frac{\log N}{h}. \tag{2}$$

EXAMPLE 1. Compute $(.3156)^4$ by use of Table V.

SOLUTION.

$$\log (.3156)^4 = 4 \log (.3156) = 4(9.4991 - 10).$$

$$\log (.3156)^4 = 37.9964 - 40 = 7.9964 - 10.$$

$$\text{Therefore, } (.3156)^4 = .009918.$$

EXAMPLE 2. Compute $\sqrt[6]{.08351}$ by use of Table V.

SOLUTION. By (2), $\log \sqrt[6]{N} = \frac{1}{6} \log N$.

$$\log \sqrt[6]{.08351} = \frac{\log .08351}{6} = \frac{8.9218 - 10}{6};$$

$$\log \sqrt[6]{.08351} = \frac{58.9218 - 60}{6} = 9.8203 - 10. \tag{3}$$

$$\text{Therefore, } \sqrt[6]{.08351} = .6611.$$

Comment. Before dividing a negative logarithm by a positive integer, usually it is best to write the logarithm in such a way that *the negative part after division will be* -10. Thus, in (3), we altered $(8.9218 - 10)$ by *subtracting* 50 from -10 to make it -60, and by *adding* 50 to 8.9218 to compensate for the subtraction; the result after division by 6 is in the standard form for a negative logarithm.

EXAMPLE 3. Compute $34.62^{-\frac{3}{2}}$ by use of Table V.

SOLUTION. We recall that $a^{-n} = 1/a^n$. Let $q = (34.62)^{-\frac{3}{2}} = \dfrac{1}{(34.62)^{\frac{3}{2}}}$.

We use (1) with $k = \frac{3}{2}$ in obtaining the logarithm of the denominator. To keep control of accuracy in the last place, we first multiply by 3 and then divide by 2, in obtaining $\frac{3}{2}(\log 34.62)$.

$$\log 34.62 = 1.5393 \qquad 3 \log 34.62 = 4.6179$$

$$\begin{aligned} \log 1 &= 0.0000 = 10.0000 - 10 \\ \tfrac{1}{2}(3 \log 34.62) &= 2.3090 = 2.3090 \qquad (-) \\ \hline \log q &= \qquad\quad\;\; = 7.6910 - 10 \\ q &= .004909. \end{aligned}$$

EXERCISE 29

Compute by use of four-place or five-place logarithms.

1. $(17.5)^3$. **2.** $(.837)^5$. **3.** $(.0315)^3$. **4.** $(3.1279)^4$.
5. $(1.9572)^6$. **6.** $(.0715)^3$. **7.** $\sqrt{531.2}$. **8.** $\sqrt[3]{2795}$.
9. $\sqrt[4]{861}$. **10.** $\sqrt[5]{34168}$. **11.** $\sqrt[3]{.857}$. **12.** $\sqrt[5]{.0797}$.
13. $\sqrt[4]{.03107}$. **14.** $\sqrt[6]{.0001}$. **15.** $(.0138273)^{\frac{1}{2}}$. **16.** $(143.54)^{\frac{3}{4}}$.
17. $(.0057)^{\frac{2}{5}}$. **18.** $(.821)^{\frac{5}{3}}$. **19.** $(139)^{-2}$. **20.** $(26.812)^{-3}$.
21. $(.925)^{-2}$. **22.** $(1.06)^{-1}$. **23.** $(1.03)^{-5}$. **24.** $(.003156)^{-\frac{2}{3}}$.

59. Problems in computation

EXAMPLE 1. Compute $q = \left(\dfrac{(.5831)^3}{65.3\sqrt{146}}\right)^{\frac{2}{5}}$ by use of Table V.

SOLUTION. 1. Let F represent the fraction. Then $\log q = \frac{2}{5} \log F$.

2. Notice that $\log (.5831)^3 = 3 \log .5831$; $\log \sqrt{146} = \frac{1}{2} \log 146$.

$$(+)\begin{cases} \log 65.3 = 1.8149 \\ \tfrac{1}{2} \log 146 = 1.0822 \end{cases} \qquad \log \text{denom.} = 2.8971.$$

$$\begin{aligned} \log .5831 &= 9.7658 - 10 \\ \log 146 &= 2.1644 \\ \hline 3 \log .5831 &= 9.2974 - 10 \\ (-)\ \log \text{denom.} &= 2.8971 \\ \hline \log F &= 6.4003 - 10; \quad 2 \log F = 2.8006 - 10 = 42.8006 - 50. \end{aligned}$$

$$\log q = \frac{2 \log F}{5} = \frac{42.8006 - 50}{5} = 8.5601 - 10; \quad q = .03632.$$

It is important to realize that the properties of logarithms offer no assistance in the computation of a sum or difference, except perhaps in the auxiliary computation of individual terms.

ILLUSTRATION 1. To compute $q = \dfrac{\sqrt{896} + 5.672}{532 - (15.31)^2}$, we would first compute $\sqrt{896}$ and $(15.31)^2$ by logarithms, then insert the results in the fraction, and finally compute it by logarithms.

Note 1. Logarithms were invented by a Scotsman, JOHN NAPIER, Laird of Merchiston (1550–1617). His logarithms were not defined as exponents of powers of a base. Common logarithms were invented by an Englishman, HENRY BRIGGS (1556–1631), who was aided by Napier.

MISCELLANEOUS EXERCISE 30

Compute by use of four-place or five-place logarithms.

1. $5.713(2.56)^3$.
2. $.165\sqrt{9.13497}$.
3. $.0956(13.217)^2$.
4. $73.14\sqrt{.981358}$.
5. $(14.6)^2\sqrt[3]{.085}$.
6. $(3.456)^{-3}\sqrt[3]{.7316}$.
7. $\dfrac{758.32}{(46.3)^3}$.
8. $\dfrac{.0198}{(3.8262)^2}$.
9. $\dfrac{.03156(75.31)}{221.38(.3561)^2}$.
10. $\sqrt{\dfrac{89.1}{163(.62)}}$.
11. $\sqrt[3]{\dfrac{47.5317}{.031(.964)}}$.
12. $\dfrac{\sqrt[3]{-463.192}}{\sqrt{16.3144}}$.
13. $10^{.723}(8.52)$.
14. $\dfrac{10^{-1.42}\sqrt{.387}}{57(8.64)^2}$.
15. $\left(\dfrac{16.7(.58)^2}{65.1314}\right)^{\frac{2}{3}}$.
16. $(71.38)^{.85}$.
17. $(57.2)^{-.32}$.
18. $(.0895)^{.36}$.

HINT for Problem 17. $-.32 \log 57.2 = -.5624 = 9.4376 - 10.$

19. $\dfrac{3 + \log 75}{\log 63.6}$.
20. $\dfrac{\log .95 - 20}{658}$.
21. $\dfrac{753 \log 8}{\log .189}$.
22. If n is a positive integer, *the* **geometric mean** *of n numbers* is defined as the *nth root of their product.* Thus the geometric mean of M, N, R is $\sqrt[3]{MNR}$. Find the geometric mean of (a) 138, 395, 426, 537, 612; (b) .00138, .19276, .08356, .0131.

★23. Compute $(1.03)^{100}$ entirely by use of five-place logarithms. Then, compute by using log 1.03 from Table XVI, and Table VIII to finish.

★*Compute the amount A in the formula of compound interest $A = P(1 + r)^k$ for the given data, with Table* XVI *used to obtain* $\log (1 + r)$, *and five-place logarithms used otherwise.*

24. $P = \$265;\ k = 30;\ r = .02.$
25. $P = \$2358;\ k = 47;\ r = .04.$
26. If a body has fallen s feet from rest in a vacuum near the earth's surface, the speed v of the body in feet per second is given by $v^2 = 2gs$ where $g = 32.16$, approximately. Find the speed of a body which has fallen 1740 feet.

27. The time t in seconds for one oscillation of a simple pendulum, whose length is l centimeters, is given by $t = \pi\sqrt{l/g}$, where $g = 980$. Find t for a pendulum with length 95.8 centimeters.

If a, b, and c are the lengths of the sides of a triangle, it is proved on page 177 *that A, the area of the triangle, is given by*

$$A = \sqrt{S(S-a)(S-b)(S-c)}, \quad \textit{where} \quad S = \tfrac{1}{2}(a+b+c).$$

Find the area if the sides have the given lengths, in inches.

28. 268.39; 154.32; 264.93.

29. 1.3584; .9863; 1.321.

★60. Exponential and logarithmic equations

A *logarithmic equation* is one in which there appears the logarithm of some expression involving the variables.

EXAMPLE 1. Solve for x: $\log x + \log \dfrac{2x}{5} = 6.$

SOLUTION. $\log x + \log 2 + \log x - \log 5 = 6.$

$$2 \log x = 6 + \log 5 - \log 2 = 6.3980. \qquad \text{(Table V)}$$

$$\log x = 3.1990; \quad x = \text{antilog } 3.1990 = 1581. \qquad \text{(Table V)}$$

An equation in a variable x which appears in an exponent is called an *exponential equation.* Sometimes, an exponential equation can be solved by equating the logarithms of the members of the equation.

EXAMPLE 2. Solve $16^x = 74$.

SOLUTION. Equate the logarithms of the two sides: $x \log 16 = \log 74$;

$$x = \frac{\log 74}{\log 16} = \frac{1.8692}{1.2041}. \qquad \begin{array}{r} \log 1.869 = 0.2716 \\ (-)\ \log 1.204 = 0.0806 \\ \hline \log x = 0.1910; \end{array} \quad \textit{hence} \quad x = 1.552.$$

★61. Logarithms to various bases

The base 10 is convenient for logarithms when they are being used to simplify computation. The only other base which is used appreciably is the irrational number $\boldsymbol{e = 2.71828 \cdots}$. Logarithms to the base e are called **natural logarithms,** and are indispensable, for noncomputational purposes, in calculus and other parts of advanced mathematics.

Recall that the equations $N = a^x$ and $x = \log_a N$ are equivalent. Hence, if N and a are given, we can find $\log_a N$ by solving the exponential equation $N = a^x$ by use of *common* logarithms.

EXAMPLE 1. Find $\log_e 35$. Check with Table XIV.

SOLUTION. Let $x = \log_e 35$; then, $35 = e^x$. On taking the common logarithms of both sides we obtain $x \log_{10} e = \log_{10} 35$. Then,

$$x = \frac{\log_{10} 35}{\log_{10} e} = \frac{1.5441}{0.4343}; \qquad \begin{array}{rl} \log 1.544 = & 10.1886 - 10 \\ (-) \log .4343 = & 9.6378 - 10 \\ \hline \log x = & 0.5508. \end{array}$$

$$x = 3.555 = \log_e 35.$$

To check with Table XIV, use $35 = 10(3.5)$, where $\log_e 10$ and $\log_e 3.5$ are found in the table.

THEOREM IV. *If a and b are any two bases for logarithms, then*

$$\log_a N = (\log_a b)(\log_b N). \qquad (1)$$

Proof. Let $y = \log_b N$; then $\qquad N = b^y. \qquad (2)$

Hence, $\qquad \log_a N = \log_a b^y = y \log_a b = (\log_a b)(\log_b N).$

The number $\log_a b$ is called the **modulus** of the system of base a with respect to the system of base b. Given a table of logarithms to the base b, we could form a table of logarithms to the base a by multiplying each entry of the given table by $\log_a b$.

★EXERCISE 31

Solve for x by use of four-place or five-place logarithms.

1. $12^x = 31.$ **2.** $46^x = 975.$ **3.** $.69^x = 85.$ **4.** $5^{2x} = 64.$

5. $4^{3x} = 17.$ **6.** $.09^x = .15.$ **7.** $.85^x = .45.$ **8.** $3^x = 28(4^x).$

9. $2^x = 3^x(17).$ **10.** $27^{x^2} = 67.$ **11.** $(1.03)^{-x} = .475.$ **12.** $(1.02)^{-x} = .642.$

13. $\log x^2 - \log (2x/5) = 7.58.$ **14.** $\log 3x^2 + \log (5/x) = 4.725.$

Find each logarithm by use of Table V *or Table* VIII. *Check each natural logarithm by use of Table* XIV.

15. $\log_{12} 100.$ **16.** $\log_{15} 33.$ **17.** $\log_e 75.$ **18.** $\log_e 1360.$ **19.** $\log_5 .097.$

20. By use of Table XIV, find $\log_e 4.37$; $\log_e 43.7$; $\log_e 437$. Notice that, although 4.37, 43.7, and 437 differ only in the position of the decimal point, their natural logarithms do *not* differ only by integers. The fact thus illustrated, as compared to Theorem I on page 90, causes common logarithms to be preferred over natural logarithms for computation.

21. A given radioactive substance decomposes at such a rate that, if B is the initial number of atoms of the substance and N is the number remaining at the end of t hours, then $N = Be^{-kt}$, where k is a constant and $e = 2.71828 \cdots$. Given that, out of 21,000 atoms, 14,500 remain at the end of $\frac{1}{2}$ hour, (*a*) find k; (*b*) find when only $\frac{1}{2}$ of the atoms will remain.

22. The intensity, I, of a beam of light after passing through t centimeters of a liquid which absorbs light, is given by $I = Ae^{-kt}$, where A is the intensity of the light when it enters the liquid, $e = 2.71828 \cdots$, and k is a constant for any given liquid. If $k = .12526$, find how many centimeters of the liquid are sufficient to reduce the intensity of a beam by 75%.

5

APPLICATIONS OF RIGHT TRIANGLES

62. Logarithms of trigonometric function values

Frequently, in computation involving products or quotients of trigonometric function values, Table VI makes it unnecessary to use Table VII, and Table IX makes it unnecessary to use Table XI.

EXAMPLE 1. Compute 156 sin 21° 10′ by four-place logarithms, from Tables V and VI.

SOLUTION. In Table VI we find **log sin** 21° 10′, *the logarithm of* sin 21° 10′. Frequently, we prefer to read "log sin 21° 10′" briefly *as it is written:* "*log, sine,* 21° 10′."

$$\begin{array}{rll} \log 156 &= 2.1931 & \text{(Table V)} \\ (+)\ \log \sin 21^\circ 10' &= 9.5576 - 10 & \text{(Table VI)} \\ \hline \log 156 \sin 21^\circ 10' &= 1.7507. & \end{array}$$

Hence, 156 sin 21° 10′ = 56.32, where we found antilog 1.7507 by interpolation in Table V.

The sine or cosine of any angle between 0° and 90°, or the tangent of any angle between 0° and 45°, or the cotangent of any angle between 45° and 90° is *not zero* and is *less than* 1. Therefore, the logarithms of these function values have *negative* characteristics. To abbreviate, Tables VI and IX omit "− 10" belonging with each of these logarithms which are tabulated. Hence, **in using the columns labeled log sin, log cos, and log tan for 0° to 45°, we subtract 10 from each given entry.** To abbreviate the tables, we omit the logarithms of secants and cosecants. Hence, before computing a trigonometric expression by use of logarithms, if the *secant* or *cosecant* of an angle occurs as a factor, we change this function value to the *reciprocal* of the *cosine* or *sine*, respectively, of the angle.

Sometimes the values of trigonometric functions are referred to as **natural function values,** to emphasize the distinction between them and *their logarithms.* Thus, we call Table VII a table of the values of the *natural trigonometric functions.*

EXAMPLE 2. Find log tan 29° 27′ by use of Table VI.

SOLUTION. 29° 27′ is 7/10 of the way from 29° 20′ to 29° 30′. See page 10 of the tables. We omit "– 10" until the end of the solution. By the principle of proportional parts, with d as the unknown increment for the mantissa in the following table,

$$\frac{d}{29} = \frac{7}{10} \quad or \quad d = .7(29) = 20.$$

log tan 29° 20′ → 9.7497	d	29	$d = .7(29) = 20.$
log tan 29° 27′ → ?			$9.7497 + .0020 = 9.7517.$
log tan 29° 30′ → 9.7526			**log tan 29° 27′ = 9.7517 – 10.**

Note 1. Recall that $\tan \alpha = \dfrac{1}{\cot \alpha}$ and hence

$$\log \tan \alpha = \log 1 - \log \cot \alpha = 0 - \log \cot \alpha = - \log \cot \alpha.$$

Therefore, any change in log tan α corresponds to a change of *equal numerical value, but opposite sign,* in log cot α. Hence, in Tables VI and IX, the column "*c d*" gives the *common differences* for the columns *log tan* and *log cot.*

EXAMPLE 3. Find the acute angle α if log sin α = 8.7808 – 10.

SOLUTION. Since the characteristic is (8 – 10) or – 2, sin α is a small decimal. Hence, α is near 0°, and we commence looking for 8.7808 on page 6 in Table VI. The bracketing entries are 8.7645 and 8.7857 in the column headed "L Sin" at the top, where the tabular difference is 212, in the 4th decimal place. Since the partial difference, as in the table below, is

$$7808 - 7645 = 163 \quad and \quad \frac{163}{212} = .8, \; approximately,$$

angle α is taken .8 of the way from 3° 20′ to 3° 30′. The auxiliary column of tenths of 212 was used to obtain $\frac{163}{212}$ = .8, approximately.

212	163	8.7645 → 3° 20′	x	10	$\frac{163}{212} = .8,$ *to nearest tenth.*
		8.7808 → α			$x = .8(10) = 8.$
		8.7857 → 3° 30′			**α = 3° 20′ + 8′ = 3° 28′.**

EXAMPLE 4. Compute 2753 sin 293° 28′.

PARTIAL SOLUTION. The reference angle for 293° 28′ is 66° 32′, and the values of the sine function are negative in quadrant IV. Hence,

$$2753 \sin 293° \, 28' = - 2753 \sin 66° \, 32'. \tag{1}$$

Then, we would compute p = 2753 sin 66° 32′ by use of Tables V and VI, or VIII and IX. The desired result is $- p$.

★ILLUSTRATION 1. By use of Table IX, we find that

$$\log \cot 69° \, 32.3' = 9.57197 - .3(.00039) - 10 = 9.57185 - 10.$$

★ILLUSTRATION 2. By use of Table IX, if $\log \cos \alpha = 9.43254 - 10$ and α is acute, then α is $\frac{24}{45}$ of the way from 74° 17′ to 74° 18′, or

$$\alpha = 74° \, 17' + \tfrac{24}{45}(1') = 74° \, 17' + .5' = 74° \, 17.5'.$$

If the logarithm of some function of an unknown angle α is given, we find α by use of the four-place Table VI or five-place Table IX according as the given logarithm is specified to *four* or to *five* decimal places, respectively. Then, we agree to state the resulting value of α as follows:

To the nearest minute if four-place Table VI *is used.*

To the nearest tenth of a minute if five-place Table IX *is used.*

EXERCISE 32

1. (*a*) Find sin 12° 20′ from Table VII. (*b*) Find the logarithm of the result of Part (*a*) from Table V. (*c*) Find log sin 12° 20′ from Table VI.

Find the four-place logarithm of the function value, or find the acute angle α, *from Table* VI.

2. cot 55° 40′. **3.** sin 78° 37′. **4.** cos 45° 18′. **5.** sin 53° 24′.
6. tan 23° 26′. **7.** cos 63° 13′. **8.** sin 26° 42′. **9.** tan 32° 57′.
10. sin 16° 18′. **11.** cot 23° 51′. **12.** cos 15° 19′. **13.** cot 79° 16′.

14. $\log \cot \alpha = 9.9595 - 10$.
15. $\log \tan \alpha = 0.3141$.
16. $\log \cos \alpha = 9.4113 - 10$.
17. $\log \sin \alpha = 9.5470 - 10$.
18. $\log \sin \alpha = 9.9349 - 10$.
19. $\log \tan \alpha = 9.4201 - 10$.
20. $\log \cos \alpha = 8.9850 - 10$.
21. $\log \cot \alpha = 9.2931 - 10$.

22. Find from Table VII: sec 143° 17′; sin 133° 26′; cos 156° 12′.

Compute by use of four-place logarithms.

23. .4314/tan 303° 36′.
24. 31.47 cos 313° 10′.
25. .0937 cos 158° 10′.
26. 1.630/cot 112° 50′.
27. .1342 tan 118° 20′.
28. 152.3 cos 426° 15′.

★*Find the five-place logarithm of the function value, or find the acute angle* α, *from Table* IX *by interpolation.*

29. sin 17° 23.6′. **30.** cot 56° 8.1′. **31.** tan 46° 0.7′.
32. tan 27° 39.7′. **33.** sin 38° 23.7′. **34.** cot 38° 19′ 26″.
35. cot 22° 33.3′. **36.** cos 62° 33.7′. **37.** sin 54° 31′ 29″.

38. $\log \tan \alpha = 0.86333$.
39. $\log \cos \alpha = 9.52714 - 10$.
40. $\log \tan \alpha = 9.48750 - 10$.
41. $\log \tan \alpha = 9.59743 - 10$.
42. $\log \sin \alpha = 9.38941 - 10$.
43. $\log \sin \alpha = 9.19516 - 10$.

63. Logarithmic solution of right triangles

For right $\triangle ABC$ of Figure 67, we recall the following formulas from page 76.

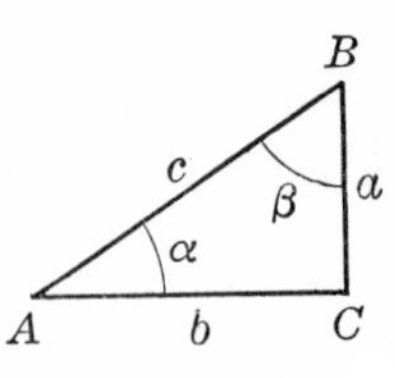

Fig. 67

(1) $a^2 + b^2 = c^2$. (2) $\alpha + \beta = 90°$.

(3) $\tan\alpha = \dfrac{a}{b} = \cot\beta$. (4) $\cot\alpha = \dfrac{b}{a} = \tan\beta$.

(5) $\sin\alpha = \dfrac{a}{c} = \cos\beta$. (6) $\cos\alpha = \dfrac{b}{c} = \sin\beta$.

We may alter (1) by writing $a^2 = c^2 - b^2$ and $b^2 = c^2 - a^2$. Then, we obtain $a^2 = (c - b)(c + b)$ and $b^2 = (c - a)(c + a)$, or

$$a = \sqrt{(c - b)(c + b)}; \qquad b = \sqrt{(c - a)(c + a)}. \tag{7}$$

Sometimes it is desirable to use (1) or (7) to find an unknown side when two sides are given. In such a case, logarithms or Table XII should be employed to compute squares or square roots. However, it is suggested that (1) and (7) be reserved for use as check formulas.

Different methods of solution may yield slightly different results, because of interpolation and rounding off in tables.

EXAMPLE 1. Solve right $\triangle ABC$ if $a = 135.1$ and $c = 367.2$.

SOLUTION. We arrange the computing form, which is given in boldface type, *before looking up any logarithms*. We use four-place logarithms.

Formulas	*Computation*
	Data: $a = 135.1$, $c = 367.2$.
$\sin\alpha = \dfrac{a}{c}$.	$\log a = 2.1306$ (Table V) $(-)\ \log c = 2.5649$ (Table V) $\log\sin\alpha = 9.5657 - 10$ $\alpha = 21°\ 35'$. (Table VI)
$\cos\alpha = \dfrac{b}{c}$, *or* $b = c\cos\alpha$.	$\log c = 2.5649$ (Above) $(+)\ \log\cos\alpha = 9.9684 - 10$ (Table VI) $\log b = 2.5333$; $b = 341.4$. (Table V)
$\beta = 90° - \alpha$.	$\beta = 90° - 21°\ 35' = 68°\ 25'$.
Summary:	$\alpha = 21°\ 35'$, $\beta = 68°\ 25'$, $b = 341.4$.

Check. $a = \sqrt{(c - b)(c + b)}$, *or* $\log a = \frac{1}{2}\log[(c - b)(c + b)]$.

$c - b = 25.8$ $\qquad \log(c - b) = 1.4116$

$c + b = 708.6$ $\qquad (+)\ \log(c + b) = 2.8504$

$\log[(c - b)(c + b)] = 4.2620$.

$\log a = 2.1306 \longrightarrow \longleftarrow \frac{1}{2}\log[(c - b)(c + b)] = 2.1310$.

Comment. The check is satisfactory. The difference (2.1310 − 2.1306), or .0004, could result from an error of less than one unit in the *fourth* significant digit of b, because this would affect the *third* digit of $(c - b)$.

EXAMPLE 2. By use of four-place logarithms, solve right $\triangle ABC$ if $a = .8421$ and $\alpha = 27° 39.7'$. (α must be rounded off as below.)

SOLUTION. The student should check the following solution by use of (1).

Formulas	*Computation*
	Data: $a = .8421$; $\alpha = 27° 40'$.
$\beta = 90° - \alpha$.	$\beta = 90° - 27° 40' = 62° 20'$.
$\frac{b}{a} = \cot \alpha$, *or* $b = a \cot \alpha$.	$\log a = 9.9254 - 10$ (Table V) (+) $\log \cot \alpha = 0.2804$ (Table VI) $\log b = 0.2058$; $b = 1.606$.
$\frac{a}{c} = \sin \alpha$, *or* $c = \frac{a}{\sin \alpha}$.	$\log a = 9.9254 - 10$ (−) $\log \sin \alpha = 9.6668 - 10$ $\log c = 0.2586$; $c = 1.814$.
Summary:	$\beta = 62° 20'$, $b = 1.606$, $c = 1.814$.

EXERCISE 33

Solve by use of four-place or five-place logarithms, as directed by the instructor, in this exercise.

Solve right $\triangle ABC$ with the given data. Check the solution.

1. $a = 15.7$; $\alpha = 36° 20'$.
2. $c = .943$; $\beta = 62° 40'$.
3. $a = .3590$; $b = .6611$.
4. $a = 23.18$; $\beta = 47° 17'$.
5. $c = .685$; $\alpha = 29° 43'$.
6. $c = .3675$; $a = .1943$.
7. $a = .5731$; $b = .6298$.
8. $\alpha = 25° 8'$; $c = 37.857$.
9. $\alpha = 31° 24.7'$; $a = 1.6315$.
10. $a = 2.1523$; $b = 4.1392$.
11. $c = 915.62$; $b = 411.37$.
12. $\alpha = 68° 39'14''$; $c = 1000.3$.
13. $\beta = 43° 17' 34''$; $a = 42.930$.
14. $\alpha = 53° 22.6'$; $b = 93.142$.

★*An isosceles $\triangle ABK$ has its equal angles at A and B, and angle γ at K. Find the unknown sides or angles of the triangle under the given conditions. (Divide the triangle into two right triangles by dropping a perpendicular to AB from K, as in Figure* 68.)

15. $\gamma = 68° 20'$; $\overline{AK} = 456$.
16. $\overline{AB} = .63284$; $\overline{AK} = .83172$.

Fig. 68

Note 1. In any $\triangle ABC$, as in Figure 69, let α, β, and γ be the angles at A, B, and C, and let a, b, and c be the lengths of the sides opposite A, B, and C, respectively. If we are given *two sides and one angle* or *two angles and one side* of the triangle, we can find its unknown parts by solving two right triangles. To obtain them, we drop a perpendicular from an end point of a known side to the opposite side.

★*Solve $\triangle ABC$ with the given data. That is, find any unknown sides and angles of the triangle.*

17. $\begin{cases} b = 275, \\ \alpha = 46° 26', \\ \gamma = 103° 54'. \end{cases}$ **18.** $\begin{cases} c = .9438, \\ \alpha = 43° 18', \\ \gamma = 61° 44'. \end{cases}$

19. $\begin{cases} c = 68.452, \\ b = 31.267, \\ \alpha = 28° 15.6'. \end{cases}$ **20.** $\begin{cases} a = 14.56, \\ b = 19.37, \\ \beta = 110° 50'. \end{cases}$

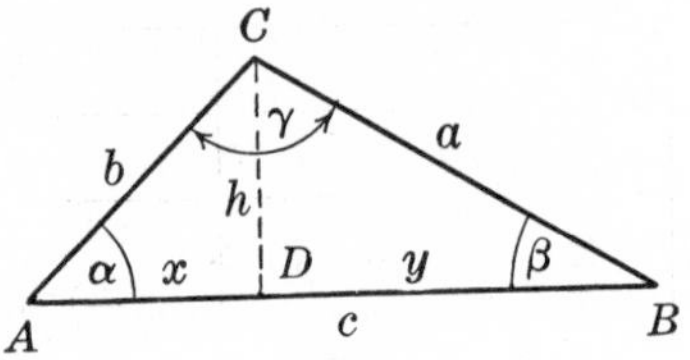

Fig. 69

64. Problems with approximate data

In computation in this book up to the present time, the emphasis has been placed on computing with *all the accuracy obtainable from our tables,* under the assumption that *the data are exact.* Now we consider computation where the given numbers are only *approximate values* of corresponding quantities. Then, we ask the following questions: (*a*) *With what refinement should computation be performed when the data are known to have only a specified degree of accuracy?* (*b*) *To what stage of accuracy should the final results be specified?* No hard and fast rules should be followed in answering (*a*) and (*b*) in any problem. However, the following agreements are satisfactory for problems of the types which the student is likely to meet.

1. *In data concerning triangles, it is roughly true that three-place, four-place, and five-place accuracy in the lengths of sides corresponds to accuracy to the nearest* 10′, 1′, *and* .1′, *respectively, in the angles.*

2. *In computing, use four-place or five-place tables according as the data are accurate to three or to four places.*

3. *Round off final results to the same number of places as given in the data, or possibly to a smaller number of places, depending on the method used.*

In stating that certain data have *four-place accuracy,* for instance, we shall mean that the angular data are accurate to the nearest *minute,* and the lengths to *four significant digits.* Rule 2 is a suggestion to carry *at least one protective place* beyond the stage to which final results will be rounded off.

Hereafter in this book, assume that the data in any applied problem *stated in words* are *not exact* but are the result of measurement, with accuracy limited to the significant places in given numbers. Answers will be rounded off to a number of places which appear reasonably justified by the data.

65. Projections

In a given plane, let OL be a given line and let CD be any line segment. Then, if A and B are the feet of the perpendiculars from C and D to OL, we call AB the *projection* of CD on OL. * If OL and CD (possibly extended) form an acute angle α, as in Figure 70, we construct ECH parallel to OL and obtain triangle CHD. Then, we observe that $CH = AB$ and

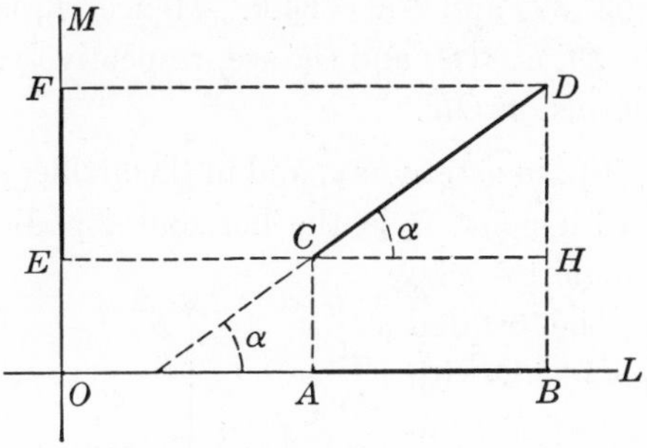

$$\frac{CH}{CD} = \frac{AB}{CD} = \cos \alpha, \text{ or}$$

$$\boldsymbol{AB = CD \cdot \cos \alpha.} \qquad (1)$$

Fig. 70

If OM is perpendicular to OL in Figure 70, the projection of CD on OM is EF. Then, in triangle CHD, $HD = EF$ and

$$\boldsymbol{EF = CD \cdot \sin \alpha.} \qquad (2)$$

Thus, *the projection of CD on OL is equal to $CD \cdot \cos \alpha$, and the projection of CD on a line perpendicular to OL is equal to $CD \cdot \sin \alpha$*, where α is the acute angle formed by OL and CD. Formulas (1) and (2) remain true with $\alpha = 0°$ if CD is parallel to OL, and with $\alpha = 90°$ if CD is perpendicular to OL.

ILLUSTRATION 1. If a train travels 3000 feet along a straight grade inclined 2° 37′ from the horizontal, the horizontal and vertical projections of the path of the train are 3000 cos 2° 37′ and 3000 sin 2° 37′, respectively.

66. Bearing angle and azimuth

In a horizontal plane, let any direction be represented by a directed line segment or arrow radiating from some fixed point O, as in Figure 71. Frequently, a direction is called a **bearing,** and it may be described by stating the angle, acute or 0°, made by it with the *north* or *south* direction. This angle will be called the **bearing angle** for the given direction.

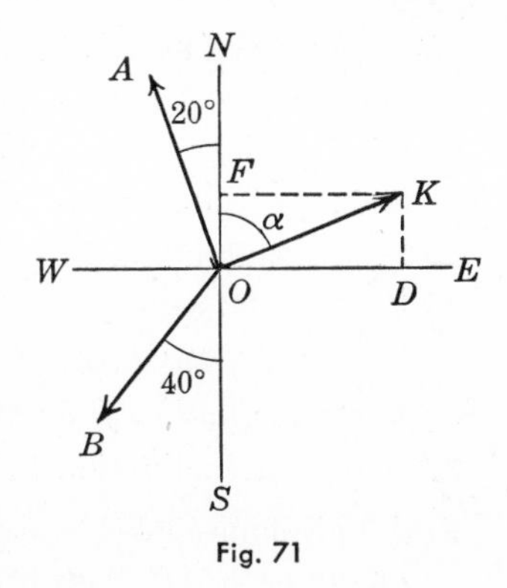

Fig. 71

ILLUSTRATION 1. In Figure 71, the bearing of OA is 20° west of north, abbreviated $N\,20°\,W$. The bearing of OB is $S\,40°\,W$. To describe the bearing of a line, we first write the letter N (or S), then the bearing angle between the given line and ON (or OS), and finally write E or W to show on which side the given direction falls.

* If CD is a directed line segment, then AB is understood to be directed, from A to B.

EXAMPLE 1. Find the bearing and distance of K as seen from O, if K is 30.6 miles north and 78.3 miles east of O.

SOLUTION. 1. In Figure 71, page 111, $FK \perp ON$; $OF = 30.6$; $FK = 78.3$.

2. In $\triangle OFK$, $\tan \alpha = \frac{78.3}{30.6}$; $\frac{OF}{OK} = \cos \alpha$, *or* $OK = \frac{OF}{\cos \alpha}$.

By use of four-place logarithms, $\alpha = 68° 39'$ and $OK = 84.0$. Hence, K is 84.0 miles from O in the direction $N\ 68° 39'\ E$. OD and OF are, respectively, the *east* and *north projections*, or *components*, of OK.

In the navigation of an airplane or a ship, in astronomy, and in the artillery service, the direction from a point G to a point B in the horizontal plane frequently is described by telling the angle through which a line GN pointing north must be rotated (*clockwise*) toward the east in order to coincide with GB. This angle is called the **azimuth** of B from G, or the azimuth of GB, and is an angle β, called nonnegative, such that $0° \leqq \beta < 360°$. Frequently, to find the azimuth of a specified direction, we shall first find its bearing angle.

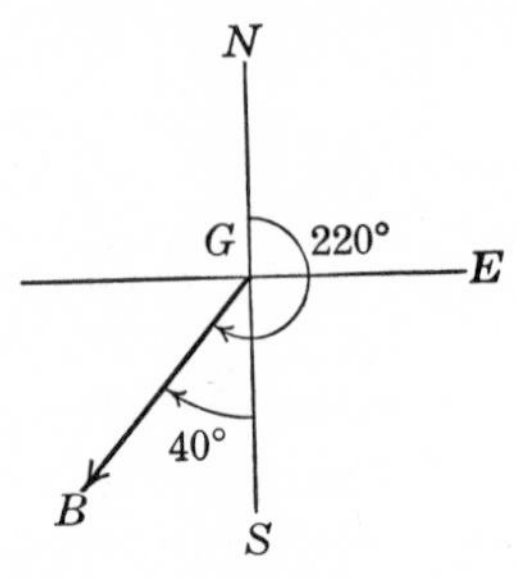

Fig. 72

ILLUSTRATION 2. In Figure 72, the azimuth of GB is 220°. The bearing of GB is $S\ 40°\ W$.

In any problem which refers to the flight of an airplane or the sailing of a ship, we shall assume that the motion is along paths consisting of one or more straight-line segments in a *horizontal plane*, unless otherwise specified. Thus, we shall be dealing with a navigation problem in **plane sailing.** Similar examples are met in **plane surveying,** where the surveyor is assumed to work in a horizontal plane, except as points may be elevated above or below it.

EXERCISE 34

Solve by use of logarithms except as directed.

1. From the top row in a football stadium, 85 feet above the ground, the angle of depression of the center of the field is 32° 10′. Find the air-line distance from the top row to the center of the field.
2. Find the area of a parallelogram whose sides are 150.6 feet and 235.3 feet long, if one angle is 127° 46′.

Find the horizontal and vertical projections of line segment AB with the given length and inclination from the horizontal.

3. 137.5 ft.; inclination 17° 18′.
4. .1638 ft.; inclination 49° 7′.
5. An airplane makes a straight ascent from A to B. Find the inclination of the path AB from the horizontal if its horizontal and vertical projections are 1780 feet and 2360 feet, respectively.

Find the azimuth of a direction having the given bearing.

6. $S\ 20°\ E$. **7.** $N\ 39°\ W$. **8.** $N\ 53°\ E$. **9.** $S\ 72°\ 13'\ W$.

10. In planning a straight railroad grade to rise 75 feet, it is decided to incline the tracks 4° 32′ from the horizontal. Find the horizontal projection of the grade, and its length.

11. How far north or south, and how far east or west is M from P if M is 385 miles from P in the direction $N\ 43°\ 20'\ W$?

Find the distance MP, and the bearing and azimuth of MP.

12. M is 58.9 miles north and 32.7 miles east of P.

13. P is 138 miles north and 289 miles east of M.

14. A battery of artillery emplaced at B is ordered to fire at a target T which is 6480 yards west and 5720 yards north of B. Find the range, bearing, and azimuth of T from B.

15. The *pitch* of a gable roof is defined as the *height* of its peak above the eaves *divided by* the roof's *width*. Find the pitch of a roof 45.7 feet wide whose peak is 17.6 feet above the lowest point (the eaves). Also, find the angle at which a side of the gable is inclined from the horizontal.

16. A porch, whose roof is 10.6 feet above the ground, projects 15.3 feet from the wall of a house. Find the length of the shortest ladder which would reach over the porch to a window 55.6 feet above the ground.

17. A regular octagon is inscribed in a circle whose radius is 36.8 feet. Find the length of a side of the octagon and the radius of its inscribed circle.

HINT. The radii to the end points of a side create an isosceles triangle.

18. Each side of a regular hexagon (six sides) is 50.8 inches long. Find the radii of its inscribed and circumscribed circles.

19. A tower stands on a cliff 653 feet above a horizontal plane. From a point A in the plane, the angles of elevation of the top and the bottom of the tower are 47° 28′ and 43° 36′. How high is the tower?

An airplane flies or a ship sails from A to B and the navigator then heads for C. Find the distance and azimuth of C from B for the given data.

★20. $AB = 120$ mi., $N\ 27°\ 16'\ E$; C is 257 mi. east and 55 mi. north of A.

★21. $AB = 250$ mi., $S\ 57°\ 40'\ W$; C is 350 mi. west and 30 mi. north of A.

★22. From two points 835.7 yards apart on a horizontal road running due east from a mountain, the angles of elevation of its top are, respectively, 43° 27′ and 30° 18′. How high above the road is the mountaintop?

HINT. 1. In Figure 73, we desire h; a, α, and β are given. We find

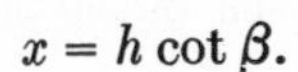

$$x = h \cot \beta.$$

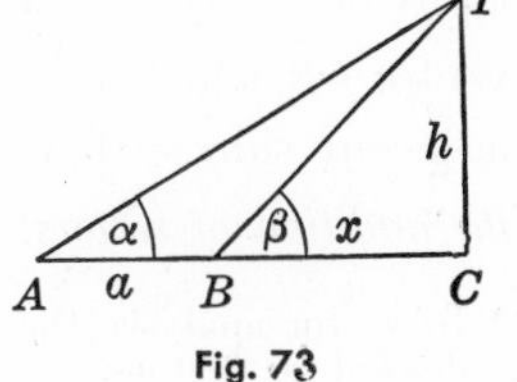

Fig. 73

2. From $\triangle ACT$, $\cot \alpha = AC/h$, or

$$a + x = h \cot \alpha.$$

3. Solve for h. The equations involve two unknowns, x and h, but the value of x is not needed. Use Table XI.

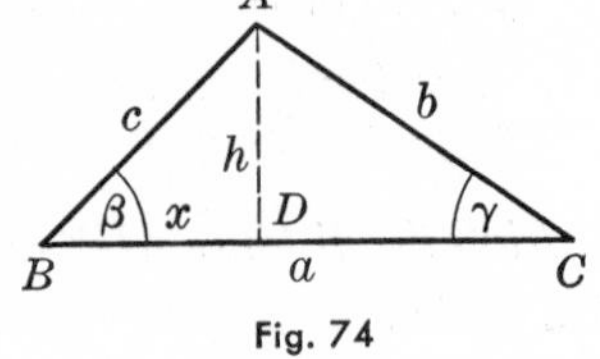

Fig. 74

★**23.** In Figure 74, suppose that side a and angles β and γ are given. If h is the length of the altitude from A to BC, prove that

$$h = \frac{a}{\cot \beta + \cot \gamma}.$$

67. Vectors

A directed line segment or arrow, such as $\overrightarrow{OR}$ in Figure 75, may be called a **stroke.** The measure of the length of $\overrightarrow{OR}$ in some linear unit is called the *magnitude* of $\overrightarrow{OR}$ and is denoted sometimes by $|\overrightarrow{OR}|$. Thus, a stroke $\overrightarrow{OR}$ has a *direction*, a *magnitude*, an *initial point* O, and a *terminal point* R. Now, consider a given set of strokes, all in a certain plane, or perhaps in space of three dimensions. Then, the strokes are called **vectors** if they combine in accordance with certain agreements, where the rules essential for our purposes are met in the following discussion. At present, any vectors which we consider simultaneously will be in the same plane. In such a case, the vectors are said to be **coplanar.**

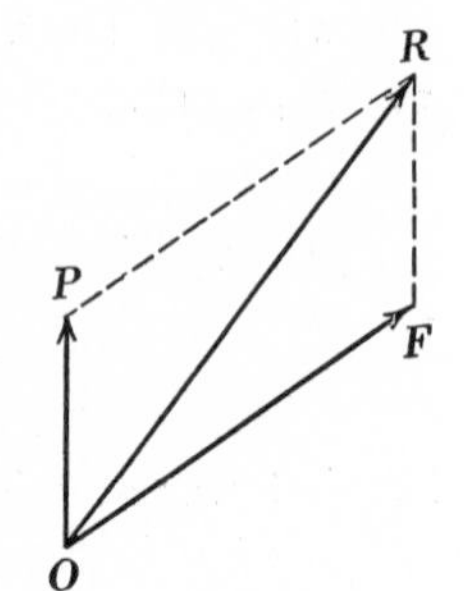

Fig. 75

Two vectors are said to be *equal* if they have the same direction and magnitude, regardless of their locations. Thus, *if a vector is moved without altering its direction and magnitude, the vector is considered unaltered.* The *zero vector* is defined as one having the magnitude zero and *any* direction.

Let two vectors $\overrightarrow{OF}$ and $\overrightarrow{OP}$ be given, and let them be drawn with a common initial point O, as in Figure 75. Then, we define the *sum,** or the **resultant,** of $\overrightarrow{OP}$ and $\overrightarrow{OF}$ as a vector $\overrightarrow{OR}$ where R is located as follows: *Place the initial point, O, of $\overrightarrow{OF}$ on the terminal point, P, of $\overrightarrow{OP}$, giving PR.* When OP and OF do not have the same or opposite directions, the preceding construction is equivalent to the following description: *The resultant of $\overrightarrow{OP}$ and $\overrightarrow{OF}$* is the vector $\overrightarrow{OR}$ which is the diagonal of the parallelogram having $\overrightarrow{OP}$ and $\overrightarrow{OF}$ as adjacent sides. This definition is referred to as the *parallelogram law for the addition of vectors.* We call $\overrightarrow{OP}$ and $\overrightarrow{OF}$ the *components of $\overrightarrow{OR}$* along the

* In vector analysis, the operation of subtraction, and various notions of products are defined for vectors.

lines of the corresponding sides of the parallelogram. The sum of two vectors of the same magnitude but opposite directions is seen to be the zero vector.

ILLUSTRATION 1. Any force, velocity, or acceleration, as defined in physics, possesses a direction and a magnitude, and hence can be represented geometrically by a properly directed stroke, with the measure of its length in some linear unit equal to the measure of the physical quantity in some physical unit. In Figure 75, let $\overrightarrow{OF}$ and $\overrightarrow{OP}$ represent any two forces pulling (or *acting*) simultaneously on an object at O. Then, in physics it is found that the combined effect of forces $\overrightarrow{OF}$ and $\overrightarrow{OP}$ is the same as the effect of the single **resultant force** represented by the *resultant vector* $\overrightarrow{OR}$. This fact is referred to as the *parallelogram law for the composition of forces.* If $\overrightarrow{OF}$ and $\overrightarrow{OP}$ represent velocities simultaneously imposed on an object at O, the resultant velocity is represented by $\overrightarrow{OR}$. Thus, velocities and, similarly, accelerations also obey the parallelogram law in composition. Hence, we are justified in representing sets of forces, or velocities, or accelerations as vectors.

Any physical quantity with the property just mentioned for forces, velocities, and accelerations is referred to as a **vector quantity.** In contrast, if a symbol or quantity merely has a *value* (with no direction characteristic), we sometimes call it a **scalar.**

The components of a vector $\overrightarrow{OR}$ along two perpendicular lines ON and OE are the vectors obtained by projecting $\overrightarrow{OR}$ on ON and OE. In Figure 76, the magnitudes of the components are

$$\overline{OB} = \overline{OR} \cos \beta; \qquad \overline{OD} = \overline{OR} \sin \beta.$$

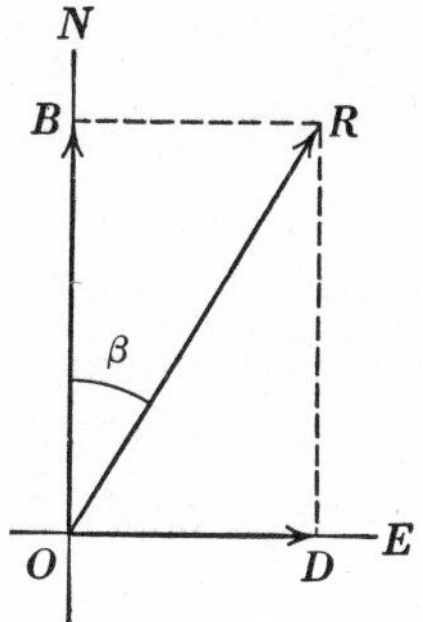

Fig. 76

The vector $\overrightarrow{OR}$ is the resultant of its components $\overrightarrow{OB}$ and $\overrightarrow{OD}$. In finding $\overrightarrow{OB}$ and $\overrightarrow{OD}$ in Figure 76, we say that we have *resolved* the given vector into *components.*

ILLUSTRATION 2. In Figure 76, let $\overrightarrow{OR}$ represent a force of 150 pounds acting in the direction $N\,31°\,E$; the bearing angle is $\beta = 31°$.

$$OB = 150 \cos 31° = 129; \quad OD = 150 \sin 31° = 77.$$

The north component of the given force is 129 pounds; the east component is 77 pounds.

Note 1. If the *weight* of an object is w pounds, the attraction of gravity on it is a vertical *force* of w pounds acting at the object's center of gravity.

Note 2. The direction in which the nose of an airplane or the prow of a ship is pointed in its motion is called the *heading.* The direction of the motion relative to the ground is called the *course* of the airplane or ship.

EXAMPLE 1. An airplane is headed east with an airspeed of 240 miles per hour. A north wind is blowing with a speed of 40 miles per hour. Find the airplane's groundspeed per hour and course.

SOLUTION. 1. In Figure 77, $\overrightarrow{OH}$ represents the wind velocity, with which the air moves. The airplane's velocity *in the moving air* is represented by $\overrightarrow{OP}$, called the *airspeed vector*, whose magnitude * is the *airspeed*. The airplane's ground velocity (relative to the ground) is represented by $\overrightarrow{OG}$, the resultant of $\overrightarrow{OH}$ and $\overrightarrow{OP}$. We call $\overrightarrow{OG}$ the *groundspeed vector;* its magnitude is the groundspeed; the *azimuth* of $\overrightarrow{OG}$ is called the *course* of the airplane.

2. In $\triangle OPG$, $OP = 240$ and $PG = 40$; on solving, we find $\delta = 9° \ 28'$ and $OG = 243$. The groundspeed is 243 miles and the course is azimuth 99° 28′.

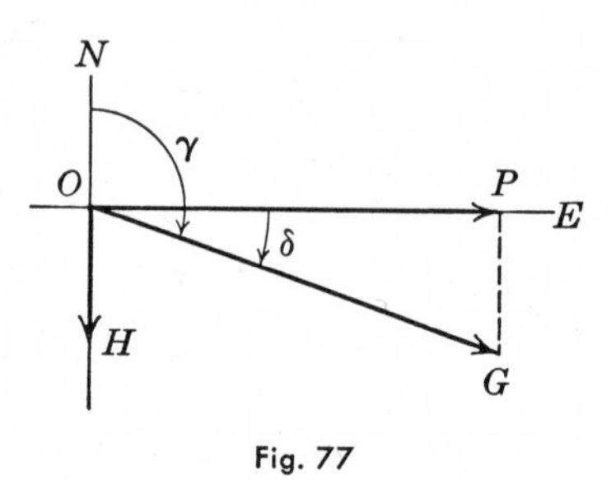

Fig. 77

Comment. The smallest angle, positive or 0°, between the *heading* and *course* of an airplane is called the *drift angle.* It is 9° 28′ in Example 1; the wind blows the airplane 9° 28′ *off its heading.*

EXAMPLE 2. Find the force which is just sufficient to keep a 1000-pound weight from sliding down a plane inclined 47° to the horizontal, under the assumption that there is no friction.

SOLUTION. 1. The attraction of gravity on the weight A, in Figure 78, is a vertical force $\overrightarrow{AW}$, of 1000 pounds. We resolve $\overrightarrow{AW}$ into two perpendicular components, $\overrightarrow{AK}$ acting along the plane and $\overrightarrow{AH}$ perpendicular to the plane. Force $\overrightarrow{AH}$ creates pressure on the plane and is counteracted by its supports. Force $\overrightarrow{AK}$ acts to move the weight A downward. Hence, we must apply force $\overrightarrow{AF}$ equal in magnitude to $\overrightarrow{AK}$ and opposite in direction.

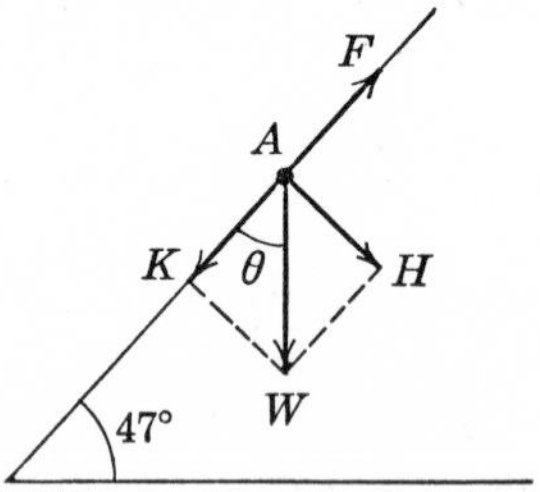

2. In $\triangle KAW$, $\theta = 43°$ and $AW = 1000$. Thus we obtain

$$AK = 1000 \cos 43° = 731.4.$$

Fig. 78

Hence, a force of 731.4 lb. would hold the weight steady. Any greater force would move the weight upward. The favorable difference between 1000 and 731.4 shows the advantage of the inclined ramp. A force slightly greater than 1000 lb. is necessary to raise the weight vertically.

* The *magnitude* of any *velocity* is called *speed.*

EXERCISE 35

Find the horizontal and vertical components of the force.

1. 153.8 lb. acting downward at inclination of 56° 34′ from horizontal.

2. 2183 lb. acting downward at inclination of 36° 33′ from horizontal.

Find the north or south and east or west components of the force or velocity.

3. 42.65 lb. force acting *S* 31° 10′ *W*. **4.** 1329 lb. force acting *N* 31° 37′ *W*.

5. Groundspeed of 300 miles per hour with azimuth 160°.

6. Groundspeed of 150 miles per hour with azimuth 250°.

A body is acted upon by the given forces simultaneously. Find the magnitude of the resultant force and its direction.

7. 162 lb. north; 53.7 lb. east. **8.** 638 lb. south; 217 lb. west.

For the given wind velocity, find the groundspeed, course, and drift angle for the airplane. All speeds are "per hour."

9. Wind blowing 30 miles from west: airspeed 200 miles north.

10. Wind blowing 25 miles from east; airspeed 220 miles south.

11. A ship is headed east at 18 miles per hour relative to the water. An ocean current is carrying the water south at 3 miles per hour. Find the course of the ship and its speed with respect to the ocean floor.

12. A 150-pound shell for a battery of artillery is dragged up a runway inclined 42° to the horizontal. Find the pressure of the shell against the runway and the force required to drag the shell.

13. A truck weighing 6875 pounds moves up a bridge inclined 7° 32′ from the horizontal. Find the pressure of the truck against the bridge.

14. An automobile weighing 2600 pounds stands on a hill inclined 25° 36′ from the horizontal. How large a force must be counteracted by the brakes of the automobile to prevent it from rolling downhill?

15. A guy wire 78 feet long runs from the top of a telegraph pole 56 feet high to the ground and pulls with a force of 290 pounds. What vertical force does the wire exert as added pressure of the pole against the ground?

16. What force must be exerted to drag a 150-pound weight up a slope which inclines 25° from the horizontal?

17. Find the largest weight which a man can drag up a slope inclined 35° from the horizontal, if he is able to pull with a force of 125 pounds.

18. At what speed with respect to the water should a ship head south in order to sail in the direction with azimuth 168° 26′, if the ship is in a current flowing east at the rate of 5 miles per hour?

★*Find the magnitude and direction of the resultant of the given forces acting simultaneously on an object.*

19. 50 lb. acting *N* 21° 16′ *E*; 150 lb. acting *N* 49° 28′ *W*.

20. 57.3 lb. acting *N* 21° 10′ *E*; 158 lb. acting *N* 49° 20′ *E*.

6

TRIGONOMETRIC FUNCTIONS OF NUMBERS

68. Radian measure for angles

On page 30, to define 1° as an angular unit for measuring rotation, we considered a central angle in a circle. We shall define a new unit of angular measurement, called a *radian*, in a similar fashion.

DEFINITION I. *One* **radian** *is the measure of a positive angle for which, if its vertex is at the center of a circle, rotation of the initial side to the terminal side will sweep out on the circumference an arc whose length is the radius of the circle.*

Thus, a central angle of one radian in a circle *intercepts* on the circumference an arc whose length is the radius of the circle.

ILLUSTRATION 1. In Figure 79, the measure of angle BOC is one radian, and the length of the intercepted arc BC is r.

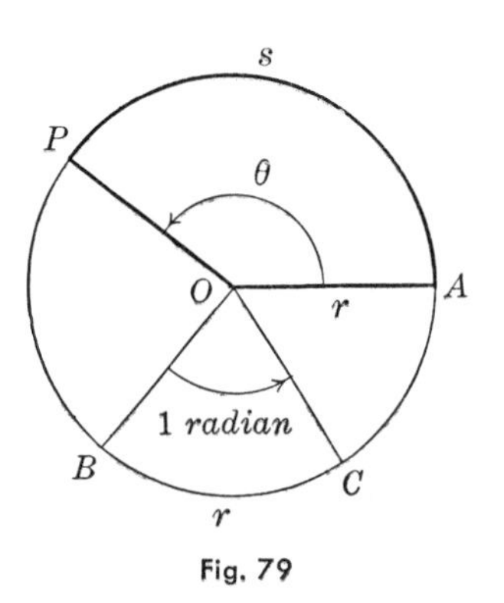

Fig. 79

Let K be the measure in radians of the angle generated by revolving OB of Figure 79 about O through a complete revolution, counterclockwise. We recall that the measures of central angles in a circle are proportional to the lengths of the arcs intercepted by the angles on the circumference. The angle K intercepts the whole circumference, of length $2\pi r$, and 1 radian intercepts BC, of length r. Hence,

$$\frac{K}{1} = \frac{2\pi r}{r}, \quad or \quad K = 2\pi. \tag{1}$$

That is, the measure of the complete (counterclockwise) angle about a point is 2π radians. Since this angle also has the measure 360°,

$$360° = (2\pi \text{ radians}), \; or \tag{2}$$

$$\mathbf{180° = (\pi \text{ radians}).} \tag{3}$$

Notice that (2) and (3), and similar equalities below, are *not equations* in the usual sense of expressing the equality of *two numbers*. Thus, (2) is just a convenient abbreviation for "*an angle of* 360° *also has the measure* 2π *radians.*" On dividing both sides of (3) first by 180, and second by π, we obtain

$$1^\circ = \left(\frac{\pi}{180}\ \textbf{radians}\right) = \textbf{.0174533 radian, } \textit{approximately;} \tag{4}$$

$$(\textbf{1 radian}) = \frac{180^\circ}{\pi} = \textbf{57.2958}^\circ\textbf{, } \textit{approximately.} \tag{5}$$

From (4) and (5), respectively, we arrive at the following rules:

$$\left\{\begin{array}{l}\textit{To change degree measure to radian measure,}\\ \textit{multiply the number of degrees by } \boldsymbol{\pi/180}.\end{array}\right\} \tag{6}$$

$$\left\{\begin{array}{l}\textit{To change radian measure to degree measure,}\\ \textit{multiply the number of radians by } \boldsymbol{180/\pi}.\end{array}\right\} \tag{7}$$

Instead of (6), frequently it is useful to recall (3), and notice that *any multiple of* 180° *is the same multiple of* π *radians.**

Illustration 2. $30^\circ = \frac{1}{6}(180^\circ) = (\frac{1}{6}\pi\ \textit{radians})$;

$$45^\circ = \tfrac{1}{4}(180^\circ) = (\tfrac{1}{4}\pi\ \textit{radians}); \qquad 60^\circ = (\tfrac{1}{3}\pi\ \textit{radians});$$

$$90^\circ = \tfrac{1}{2}(180^\circ) = (\tfrac{1}{2}\pi\ \textit{radians}) = (1.5708\ \textit{radians}).$$

From (7), $(3.2\ \textit{radians}) = 3.2\,\frac{180^\circ}{\pi} = \frac{(3.2)(180^\circ)}{3.1416} = 183.35^\circ$, *by logarithms.*

Illustration 3. To change 143° 27′ to radians, first express 27′ as a decimal part of 1° and multiply by $\pi/180$ with the aid of logarithms. Thus,

$$27' = \tfrac{27}{60}(1^\circ) = .45^\circ;$$

$$143.45^\circ = \left[\frac{(143.45)(\pi)}{180}\ \textit{rad.}\right] = \left[\frac{(143.45)(3.1416)}{180}\ \textit{rad.}\right] = [2.5037\ \textit{rad.}].$$

69. Relation between arc, angle, and radius

In a circle of radius r, in Figure 79 on page 118, let s represent the length of the arc intercepted on the circumference by a positive central angle of θ radians. Since 1 radian at the center intercepts an arc whose length is r, then θ radians intercept an arc whose length is $\theta \cdot r$. That is,

$$\boldsymbol{s = r\theta;} \tag{1}$$

$$\textbf{arc} = \textbf{(radius)} \times \textbf{(angle, in radians).} \tag{2}$$

Illustration 1. If $r = 25$ feet and $s = 75$ feet, $\theta = \frac{s}{r} = \frac{75}{25} = 3$ *radians.*

* See Note 4 of the Appendix for an introduction to **mil measure** for angles, which is used in military service.

Example 1. Find the length of the arc intercepted by a central angle of 35° in a circle whose radius is 20 feet.

Solution. 1. Let θ be the radian measure of 35°:

$$\theta = 35 \cdot \frac{\pi}{180} = \frac{7\pi}{36} \text{ } radian.$$

2. Since $r = 20$,

$$s = r\theta = 20 \cdot \frac{7\pi}{36} = \frac{35\pi}{9}, \quad or \quad s = 12.2 \text{ ft.}$$

Note 1. Example 1 can also be solved by use of a simple proportion, without use of radian measure. Thus, $s : 2\pi r = 35° : 360°$.

70. Linear and angular speed

Consider an object P which is moving with uniform speed on the circumference of a circle with center O and radius r. Let v represent the length of arc traversed by P in one unit of time. Then v is the **linear speed** of P. In Figure 80, let ω be the absolute value of the measure of the angle through which the line OP turns in one unit of time. Then, we call ω the **angular speed** of P with respect to O. If ω is expressed in radian measure, from (1) of Section 69 we obtain

$$v = r\omega. \tag{1}$$

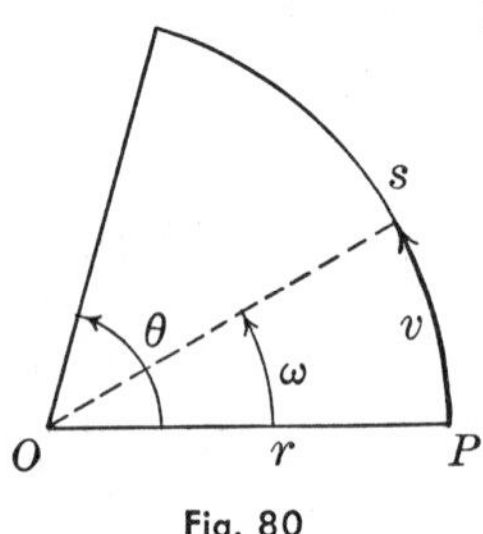

Fig. 80

If, in t units of time, P moves over an arc of length s and OP revolves through an angle with positive measure, θ, then

$$s = vt; \qquad \theta = \omega t. \tag{2}$$

Any circular motion which we shall consider will be at uniform speed.

Example 1. A belt passes over the rim of a flywheel 30 inches in diameter. Find the speed of the belt if it drives the wheel at the rate of 5 revolutions per second.

Solution. 1. The belt moves with the same speed as a point on the rim.

2. One revolution is 2π radians; hence, $\omega = (5 \times 2\pi) = (10\pi$ *rad. per sec.*).

3. From (1), the belt speed is

$$v = 15(10\pi) = 150\pi = 471.2 \text{ in. per sec.}$$

EXERCISE 36

Express the angle as a multiple of π radians.

1. 30°. **2.** 45°. **3.** 60°. **4.** 36°. **5.** 120°.

6. 135°. **7.** 150°. **8.** 720°. **9.** – 90°. **10.** – 180°.

11. 240°. **12.** 270°. **13.** 300°. **14.** – 315°. **15.** 450°.

Given the radian measure of an angle, change to degree measure.

16. $\frac{\pi}{6}$. **17.** $\frac{\pi}{3}$. **18.** $\frac{3\pi}{4}$. **19.** $\frac{\pi}{9}$. **20.** $\frac{5\pi}{6}$.

21. $\frac{7\pi}{6}$. **22.** $\frac{7\pi}{4}$. **23.** $\frac{4\pi}{3}$. **24.** $\frac{5\pi}{12}$. **25.** $\frac{7\pi}{15}$.

26. 3π. **27.** 2. **28.** 4. **29.** 2.5. **30.** 3.6.

Let all angles in the following problems have positive measure. Construct the angle approximately to scale.

31. 3 rad. **32.** 2 rad. **33.** .1 rad. **34.** 1.5 rad.

35. In a triangle, one angle is 36° and another is $\frac{2}{3}\pi$ radians. Find the third angle in radians.

36. Through how many radians does the hour hand of a clock revolve in 40 minutes?

37. Through how many radians does the minute hand of a clock revolve in 25 minutes?

Express in radians, using Table V in the computation.

38. 38° 21′. **39.** 123° 50′. **40.** 273° 45′. **41.** 183° 18′.

By use of $s = r\theta$, find whichever of (r, s, θ) is not given, to three significant digits, where θ is the measure of an angle in radians, at the center of a circle of radius r. In any problem, α represents the degree measure of θ radians.

42. $r = 10$ ft.; $\theta = 2.3$. **43.** $r = 450$ ft.; $\theta = 5.7$.

44. $\theta = \frac{7}{6}\pi$; $s = 125$ in. **45.** $\theta = 6.8$; $s = 50.6$ in.

46. $\alpha = 120°$; $s = 375$ in. **47.** $\alpha = 340°$; $r = 50$ ft.

48. $s = 175$ in.; $r = 4$ ft. **49.** $s = 2500$ ft.; $r = .75$ mi.

50. On a circle, if an arc 30 feet long is intercepted by an angle of 2 radians at the center, find the radius of the circle.

51. In a circle 16 inches in diameter, how long an arc is intercepted on the circumference by an angle of 2.4 radians at the center?

52. A railroad curve, in the form of an arc of a circle, is 850 yards long. If the radius of the circle is 950 yards, find the angle in degrees through which a train turns in going around the curve.

53. If a flywheel is 4 feet in diameter, find the speed of a belt which drives the wheel at 400 revolutions per minute.

54. If a flywheel is 3 feet in diameter and if a belt over the wheel is traveling at 3000 feet per minute, find the revolutions of the wheel per minute.

55. Find the radius of a flywheel if it is turned at 1250 revolutions per minute by a belt over the rim with a speed of 60 feet per second.

56. Assume that the earth is a sphere with a radius of 4000 miles which revolves on its axis once in 24 hours. Disregarding the other motions of the earth, find the linear speed per second of a point on the equator.

71. Trigonometric functions of angles, with radian measure

Hereafter, when no unit is indicated in giving the measure of an angle, **we agree that the unit of measurement is a radian.** Frequently, then, we shall let the value of an angle in radians be used as a symbol for the angle. Thus, we may refer to *the angle* x, meaning an angle whose measure is x radians.

Illustration 1. The "*cosine of* π *radians*" is denoted by $\cos \pi$. Since (π *radians*) $= 180°$, $\cos \pi = -1$. From Table XIII, $\sin 1.18 = .92461$. From Table IV, 33° has the measure .576 radian; hence $\tan .576 = .649$.

All of the trigonometric identities in Chapter 2, where θ, α, β, or some other letter represented an angle involved, now may be interpreted as identities where the symbol for the angle is understood to be its value in radian measure. Any statement of a property of the trigonometric functions involving remarks about a multiple of 90° implies a corresponding statement involving a multiple of $\frac{1}{2}\pi$ radians. In particular, if x represents an angle with measure x radians, the reduction formulas of pages 54–56, in radian measure, are as follows:

$$[\text{any trig. function of } (x \pm 2\pi)] = (\text{same function of } x); \tag{1}$$

$$\tan (x \pm \pi) = \tan x; \qquad \cot (x \pm \pi) = \cot x; \tag{2}$$

$$[\text{any trig. function of } (\tfrac{1}{2}\pi - x)] = (\text{cofunction of } x); \tag{3}$$

$$\sin (-x) = -\sin x; \quad \cos (-x) = \cos x; \quad \tan (-x) = -\tan x; \tag{4}$$

$$\sin (\pi - x) = \sin x; \qquad \cos (\pi - x) = -\cos x; \tag{5}$$

$$\left[\text{any trig. func. of } \left(n\cdot\frac{\pi}{2} \pm x\right)\right] = \begin{cases} \pm\ (\text{same func. of } x),\ n \text{ even}; \\ \pm\ (\text{cofunc. of } x),\ n \text{ odd}. \end{cases} \tag{6}$$

Illustration 2. By (1) each trigonometric function has the period 2π and, by (2), $\tan x$ and $\cot x$ have the smaller period π. Thus, by (1), $\sin (x \pm 2\pi) = \sin x$.

Example 1. Express $\csc (\pi - \theta)$ and $\tan (\frac{3}{2}\pi + \theta)$ as functions of θ by use of identity (6).

Solution. 1. Since $\pi = 2(\frac{1}{2}\pi)$, from (6) for *n even* we obtain the following result, where we must still choose the proper sign:

$$\csc (\pi - \theta) = \pm \csc \theta. \tag{7}$$

If θ is acute, then $(\pi - \theta)$ is an angle in quadrant II, where the cosecant is positive. Hence, to make the right-hand side positive in (7) we need the plus sign: $\csc (\pi - \theta) = +\csc \theta$.

2. From (6) for n odd, $\tan (\frac{3}{2}\pi + \theta) = \pm \cot \theta$. If θ is acute, $(\frac{3}{2}\pi + \theta)$ is an angle in quadrant IV where the tangent is negative. Hence, we obtain $\tan (\frac{3}{2}\pi + \theta) = -\cot \theta$.

ILLUSTRATION 3. Since Table XIII extends only through an angle of 1.60 radians, for larger angles we must use reduction formulas or acute reference angles before referring to Table XIII. To obtain cos 3.59, we recall $\pi = 3.14$, and $3.59 - 3.14 = .45$:

$$\cos 3.59 = \cos (\pi + .45) = -\cos .45 = -.90045. \qquad \text{(Table XIII)}$$

Thus, we recognized .45 radian as the *reference angle* for 3.59 radians. Or, we used the *reduction formula* $\cos (\pi + x) = -\cos x$ with $x = .45$.

With the numbers x and y representing angles whose measures are x and y radians, respectively, the addition formulas of page 50 become

$$\sin (x + y) = \sin x \cos y + \cos x \sin y; \qquad (8)$$

$$\cos (x + y) = \cos x \cos y - \sin x \sin y; \qquad (9)$$

$$\sin (x - y) = \sin x \cos y - \cos x \sin y; \qquad (10)$$

$$\cos (x - y) = \cos x \cos y + \sin x \sin y. \qquad (11)$$

ILLUSTRATION 4. From (8), $\sin (\frac{3}{2}\pi + x) = \sin \frac{3}{2}\pi \cos x + \cos \frac{3}{2}\pi \sin x$, or

$$\sin (\tfrac{3}{2}\pi + x) = (-1) \cos x + (0) \sin x = -\cos x.$$

In calculus, for convenience in various important classes of operations where trigonometric functions are met, it becomes imperative that any angle involved should be measured in *radians*. Hence, since this text is designed for students who are preparing for calculus, **we shall use radian measure for angles exclusively hereafter,** except where occasional use of degree measure clarifies the content, and except when we solve triangles.

EXERCISE 37

1. Without using a trigonometric table, make up a table showing the exact values of all trigonometric functions (which exist) for the angles 0, $\frac{1}{6}\pi$, $\frac{1}{4}\pi$, $\frac{1}{3}\pi$, $\frac{1}{2}\pi$, $\frac{2}{3}\pi$, $\frac{3}{4}\pi$, $\frac{5}{6}\pi$, π, $\frac{7}{6}\pi$, $\frac{5}{4}\pi$, $\frac{4}{3}\pi$, $\frac{3}{2}\pi$, $\frac{5}{3}\pi$, $\frac{7}{4}\pi$, $\frac{11}{6}\pi$, and 2π.

By use of Table IV, *find the radian measure of the angle.*

2. 37°. **3.** 77°. **4.** 53°. **5.** 98°. **6.** 238°. **7.** 329°.

HINT for Problem 5. 98° = 90° + 8°; add $\frac{1}{2}\pi$ or 1.571 to the value for 8°.

Find the function value by use of Table XIII.

8. sin 1.35. **9.** cos .84. **10.** tan 1.02. **11.** sin 1.47.
12. cot 4.29. **13.** sin 2.64. **14.** cos 5.23. **15.** tan 3.79.

Apply the addition formulas (8)–(11) *above to obtain the reduction formula for the given function value.*

16. $\sin (\pi + x)$. **17.** $\cos (\pi - x)$. **18.** $\sin (x - \frac{3}{2}\pi)$.
19. $\cos (x - \frac{3}{2}\pi)$. **20.** $\sin (x - \frac{1}{2}\pi)$. **21.** $\cos (x - \frac{1}{2}\pi)$.
22. $\sin (x + \frac{5}{2}\pi)$. **23.** $\cos (x + \frac{5}{2}\pi)$. **24.** $\sin (x - \frac{5}{2}\pi)$.

Express each function value in terms of the value of a trigonometric function of x, by use of (1)–(6) *on page* 122.

25. $\tan(2\pi - x)$.
26. $\sin(x - 2\pi)$.
27. $\cot(x - \pi)$.
28. $\tan(\frac{1}{2}\pi - x)$.
29. $\cos(\frac{1}{2}\pi - x)$.
30. $\sec(\frac{1}{2}\pi - x)$.
31. $\sec(-x)$.
32. $\csc(-x)$.
33. $\cot(-x)$.
34. $\tan(\pi + x)$.
35. $\sin(\pi + x)$.
36. $\tan(3\pi + x)$.
37. $\sin(x - 4\pi)$.
38. $\cos(x + 3\pi)$.
39. $\tan(\frac{3}{2}\pi - x)$.
40. $\tan(\frac{5}{2}\pi + x)$.
41. $\sec(\frac{1}{2}\pi + x)$.
42. $\sin(\frac{1}{2}\pi + x)$.
43. $\cos(x - \frac{5}{2}\pi)$.
44. $\cot(x - \frac{5}{2}\pi)$.
45. $\sin(x - \frac{3}{2}\pi)$.
46. $\tan(3\pi - x)$.
47. $\sin(x - \frac{7}{2}\pi)$.
48. $\sec(\frac{3}{2}\pi - x)$.

72. The standard trigonometric functions of numbers

From Definition I on page 33, we refer to $\sin x$ as the (*geometrical*) sine of *the angle x radians*, and "x" in $\sin x$ is a symbol for this *angle*. With an altered viewpoint, let us say that, *for every number x, a corresponding number* "$\sin x$" *has been defined*. Thus, we have pairs of numbers, $(x, \sin x)$. *These pairs form a function*, to be called the **standard analytic sine function,** whose domain is the set, D, of all real numbers x, and whose value $\sin x$ is *the sine of x radians*. Similarly, we have the other analytic trigonometric functions $\cos x$, $\tan x$, $\cot x$, $\sec x$, and $\csc x$, each having the domain * D.

Hereafter *in this text and in the whole of calculus*, except when otherwise specified, a *trigonometric function* means one of the *standard functions*. The *value* of any one of these for any number x in D is the value of the *same-named geometric function of the angle x radians*. Hence, any property or identity known for the geometric functions translates into a property for the standard functions. Whenever useful, we may alter our viewpoint about the meaning of the independent variable x and, for instance, reinterpret the symbol for the standard function $\sin x$ as the geometric sine of the angle x radians. However, in dealing with a standard function such as $\sin x$, usually there will be no necessity for thinking of any angle x; only the *values* of $\sin x$, *for all real numbers x*, will be of importance.

ILLUSTRATION 1. From (1) on page 122, the standard trigonometric functions are periodic with the period 2π; $\tan x$ and $\cot x$ have the smaller period π. Thus, $\sin(x + 2\pi) = \sin x$; $\tan(x + \pi) = \tan x$.

In connection with the standard trigonometric functions, we shall say that the independent variable x *lies on an interval in quadrant* I, II, III, or IV if *the angle x radians is in that quadrant.*

ILLUSTRATION 2. If x is on an interval in quadrant III, then $\tan x > 0$ and $\sin x < 0$. For instance, $\sin \frac{5}{4}\pi < 0$.

* With the usual omissions when x radians is a quadrantal angle.

The standard trigonometric functions are called **trigonometric functions of numbers** because the domain of the functions consists of *real numbers*, x, and *not of angles* as on page 33. We introduced other trigonometric functions of numbers, based on degree measure, on page 58.*

In dealing with the values of the standard trigonometric functions at a particular value of the independent variable x, we define the **reference number** for x to be that number w such that w radians is the reference angle for x radians.

ILLUSTRATION 3. With $x = \frac{3}{4}\pi$, the reference number for x is $\frac{1}{4}\pi$. Thus, each trigonometric function of $\frac{3}{4}\pi$ is numerically equal to the corresponding function of $\frac{1}{4}\pi$.

73. Graphs of the standard trigonometric functions

In calculus and related fields, the graphs of the trigonometric functions usually are made subject to the following agreements, which we adopt: †

I. *To graph a trigonometric function means to graph one of the* **standard functions** *of Section* 72.

II. *A single unit is used for measuring all distances in the coordinate plane; in particular, then, the unit distance is the same on the two axes.*

EXAMPLE 1. Graph the function sin x on the range $0 \leqq x \leqq \pi$.

SOLUTION. We graph the equation $y = \sin x$. We use Table IV, with x interpreted as the measure of an angle in *radians*. On the interval $0 \leqq x \leqq \frac{1}{2}\pi = 1.57$, we take the convenient multiples of π, and just one other value (equivalent to 75°); then we obtain sin x from Table IV or from memory. By use of the identity $\sin(\pi - x) = \sin x$, or from memory of convenient values, we find values of sin x for x on the interval $\frac{1}{2}\pi \leqq x \leqq \pi$. The decimal values of x for the multiples of π can be computed by use of $\pi = 3.142$, or can be read from Table IV. In the table below, γ is the degree measure of x radians. The table was the basis for Figure 81 on page 126.

γ	0°	30°	45°	60°	75°	90°	105°	120°	135°	150°	180°
$x =$	0	$\frac{1}{6}\pi$	$\frac{1}{4}\pi$	$\frac{1}{3}\pi$	$\frac{5}{12}\pi$	$\frac{1}{2}\pi$	$\frac{7}{12}\pi$	$\frac{2}{3}\pi$	$\frac{3}{4}\pi$	$\frac{5}{6}\pi$	π
$x =$	0	.52	.79	1.05	1.31	1.57	1.83	2.09	2.36	2.62	3.14
$y = \sin x$	0	.50	.71	.87	.97	1.00	.97	.87	.71	.50	0

* In this text, we first introduced the trigonometric functions of *angles* in Section 19 on page 32. Then, in the present section we have made the transition to the trigonometric functions of *numbers*. This sequence of ideas can be reversed. That is, we could first introduce trigonometric functions of *numbers, without mentioning or thinking about associated angles*, and later make a transition to the familiar functions of *angles*. This attitude is adopted in the so-called **winding process** in Note 3 of the Appendix.

† The student must not infer that graphs based on degree measure are of no importance. However, they are ruled out frequently in calculus.

Comment. To graph $y = \sin x$ quickly, memory of $\sin \frac{1}{6}\pi = \sin \frac{5}{6}\pi = \frac{1}{2}$, $\sin 0 = \sin \pi = 0$, and $\sin \frac{1}{2}\pi = 1$, and recollection of the rounded appearance of the graph near $x = \frac{1}{2}\pi$ should give a near duplicate of Figure 81. Then, we recall the reduction formula

$$\sin (\pi + x) = - \sin x. \tag{1}$$

This result shows that the graph of $y = \sin x$ on the interval $\pi \leqq x \leqq 2\pi$ is obtainable by translating the curve of Figure 81 to the *right* for a distance of π units and then **reflecting** * *the curve in the x-axis.* Or, the student might

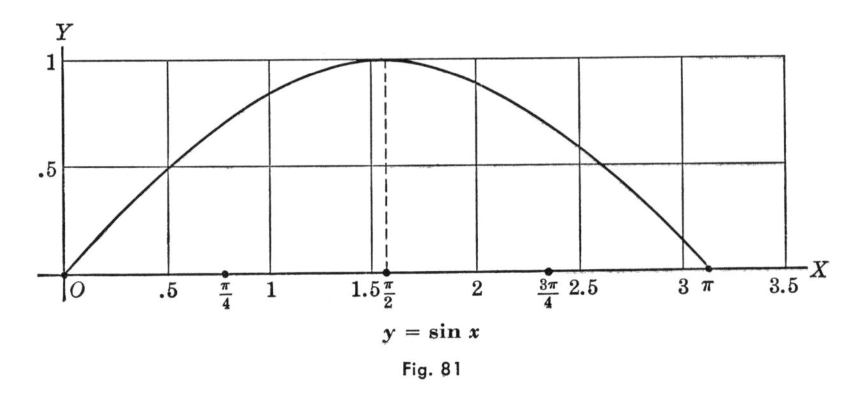

$y = \sin x$

Fig. 81

prefer to prepare a table of values for $y = \sin x$ by listing $\sin x$ for x having the values $0, \frac{1}{6}\pi, \frac{1}{2}\pi, \frac{5}{6}\pi, \pi, \frac{7}{6}\pi, \frac{3}{2}\pi, \frac{11}{6}\pi$, and 2π. The function $\sin x$ is periodic with the period 2π, or $\sin (x + 2\pi) = \sin x$ is an identity. Hence, the graph of $y = \sin x$ consists of the wave for $0 \leqq x \leqq 2\pi$ repeated endlessly to the left and the right, as shown for $- 2\pi \leqq x \leqq 2\pi$ in Figure 82.

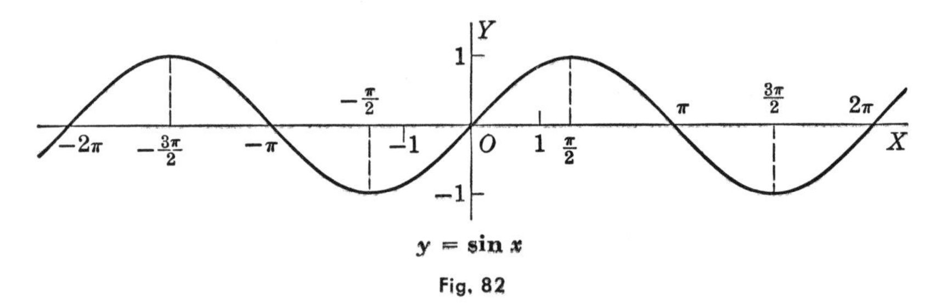

$y = \sin x$

Fig. 82

Illustration 1. To graph the function $\cos x$, or the equation $y = \cos x$, recall the identity $\cos x = \sin (x + \frac{1}{2}\pi)$. Hence, for any value of x, $\cos x$ is equal to the value of the sine function at the point $(x + \frac{1}{2}\pi)$, which is $\frac{1}{2}\pi$ units to the *right*. That is, *if the graph of* $\sin x$ *is shifted* $\frac{1}{2}\pi$ *units to the*

* The **reflection** of a curve *in the x-axis* is obtained on replacing each point (x, y) on the curve by the point $(x, - y)$, symmetrical to (x, y) with respect to the x-axis. The reflection can be thought of as if the given curve were *reflected downward in water* where the water level is at the x-axis.

left, we obtain the graph of $\cos x$, as shown in Figure 83. Or the student may prefer to list the few values of $\cos x$ in the following table, as a basis for drawing the graph.

x	0	$\frac{1}{2}\pi$	π	$\frac{3}{2}\pi$	2π
$y = \cos x$	1	0	-1	0	1

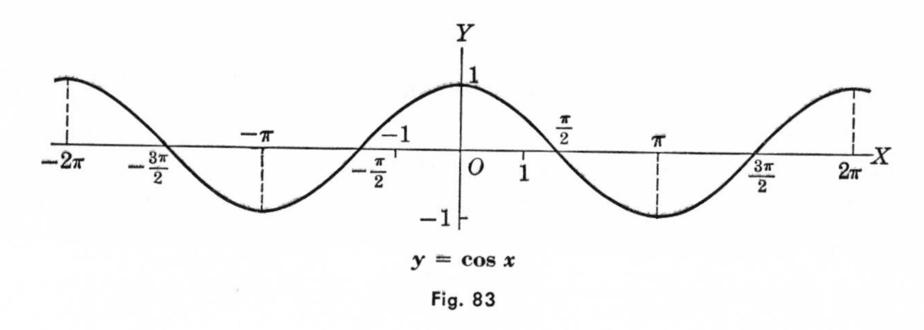

$y = \cos x$

Fig. 83

Illustration 2. To graph the equation $y = \tan x$, we recall that $\tan x$ is infinite when x is $-\frac{1}{2}\pi$, $\frac{1}{2}\pi$, $\frac{3}{2}\pi$, etc., and $\tan x = 0$ when $x = 0$, π, 2π, etc. Also, $\tan x$ is a *periodic* function with the *period* π. The following values of $\tan x$, and its asymptotes, which are the lines $x = -\frac{1}{2}\pi$ and $x = \frac{1}{2}\pi$, were the basis for the typical piece of the graph in Figure 84. Similarly, we obtain

x	$-\frac{1}{2}\pi$	$-\frac{1}{4}\pi$	0	$\frac{1}{4}\pi$	$\frac{1}{2}\pi$
$y = \tan x$	∞	-1	0	1	∞

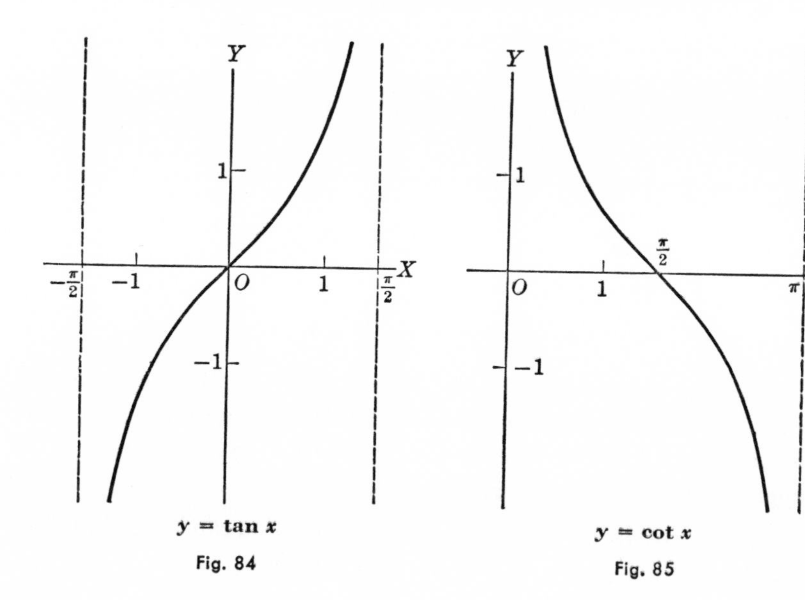

$y = \tan x$

Fig. 84

$y = \cot x$

Fig. 85

a typical piece of the graph of the function $\cot x$ in Figure 85 on page 127 from a brief table and two asymptotes, which are the lines $x = 0$ and $x = \pi$. A piece of the graph of the function $\sec x$ would be produced by use of the following table of values and two asymptotes, which are the lines $x = -\frac{1}{2}\pi$ and $x = \frac{1}{2}\pi$. Similar remarks apply for the graph of the function $\csc x$.

x	$-\frac{1}{2}\pi$	$-\frac{1}{3}\pi$	0	$\frac{1}{3}\pi$	$\frac{1}{2}\pi$
$y = \sec x$	∞	2	1	2	∞

The graphs of the trigonometric functions are useful in solving simple trigonometric equations.

ILLUSTRATION 3. To solve the equation $\sin x = 0$, recall Figure 82 on page 126. The values of x on the interval $-2\pi \leqq x \leqq 2\pi$ for which $\sin x = 0$, or the *solutions* of this equation on the specified interval, are the x-intercepts of the graph in Figure 82, or -2π, $-\pi$, 0, π, and 2π.

ILLUSTRATION 4. To solve $\cos x = -\frac{1}{2}\sqrt{3}$, for all values of x on the interval $-2\pi \leqq x \leqq 2\pi$, we recall that $\cos \frac{1}{6}\pi = \frac{1}{2}\sqrt{3}$, and $\cos x$ is *negative* if x is on an interval in quadrant II or quadrant III. Hence, with $\frac{1}{6}\pi$ as the *reference number* for x, the solutions of $\cos x = -\frac{1}{2}\sqrt{3}$ are $(\pi - \frac{1}{6}\pi)$ or $\frac{5}{6}\pi$, $\frac{7}{6}\pi$, $-\frac{5}{6}\pi$, and $-\frac{7}{6}\pi$. These are the values of x at the points where the horizontal line $y = -\frac{1}{2}\sqrt{3}$ would intersect the graph of $y = \cos x$ in Figure 83 on page 127. The student should sketch the line $y = -\frac{1}{2}\sqrt{3}$ lightly with a pencil in Figure 83 to check the preceding statements. The remarks preceding Illustration 1 on page 42 should be reviewed at this time.

EXAMPLE 1. Prove that 2π is the smallest period (understood to be *positive*) of the function $f(x) = \sin x$, and that the same fact is true for the functions $\cos x$, $\csc x$, and $\sec x$.

PARTIAL SOLUTION. 1. If the function $f(x)$ is periodic with p as a period, then $f(x \pm p) = f(x)$ at all values of x.

2. Let p be any period of f. Then,

$$f(x - p) = f(x), \quad \textit{or} \quad \sin(x - p) = \sin x. \tag{2}$$

In (2), let $x = \frac{1}{2}\pi$. Then, we obtain

$$\sin(\tfrac{1}{2}\pi - p) = \sin \tfrac{1}{2}\pi = 1. \tag{3}$$

But, by the cofunction identities, $\sin(\frac{1}{2}\pi - p) = \cos p$. Hence, from (3), $\cos p = 1$. The smallest positive solution of this equation for p is $p = 2\pi$, and this fact proves the desired result for the function $\sin x$. A similar proof would apply for the function $\cos x$.

Comment. The result just proved for the sine function can be used to show that 2π is the smallest period for the cosecant function.

EXERCISE 38

Draw graphs for the standard trigonometric functions over the indicated intervals of values of the independent variable. Use relatively few plotted points but obtain smooth graphs and draw any asymptotes which exist.

1. $y = \sin x$; $x = -2\pi$ to $x = 2\pi$. **2.** $y = \cos x$; $x = -\frac{3}{2}\pi$ to $x = \frac{5}{2}\pi$.

3. $y = \tan x$; $x = -\frac{1}{2}\pi$ to $x = \frac{5}{2}\pi$. **4.** $y = \cot x$; $x = -\pi$ to $x = 2\pi$.

5. $y = \sec x$; $x = -\frac{1}{2}\pi$ to $x = \frac{5}{2}\pi$. **6.** $y = \csc x$; $x = -\pi$ to $x = 2\pi$.

Write the equation of each asymptote possessed by the graph of the equation on the interval $-\pi \leqq x \leqq 3\pi$.

7. $y = \tan x$. **8.** $y = \cot x$. **9.** $y = \sec x$. **10.** $y = \csc x$.

Find all solutions of the equation with the variable x restricted to the interval $-2\pi \leqq x \leqq 2\pi$.

11. $\sin x = 0$. **12.** $\cos x = 0$. **13.** $\tan x = 0$. **14.** $\cot x = 0$.

15. $\sec x = 0$. **16.** $\csc x = 0$. **17.** $\sin x = -1$. **18.** $\cos x = -1$.

19. $\tan x = 1$. **20.** $\cot x = -1$. **21.** $\sec x = 1$. **22.** $\csc x = -1$.

23. $\sin x = -\frac{1}{2}$. **24.** $\cos x = \frac{1}{2}\sqrt{3}$. **25.** $\tan x = -\sqrt{3}$.

26. $\csc x = 2$. **27.** $\cos x = -\frac{1}{2}$. **28.** $\sin x = -\frac{1}{2}\sqrt{3}$.

29. $\sin x = \frac{1}{2}\sqrt{2}$. **30.** $\cos x = \frac{1}{2}\sqrt{2}$. **31.** $\tan x = \frac{1}{3}\sqrt{3}$.

32. For what values of x on the interval $-\pi \leqq x \leqq 3\pi$ is the statement true? (*a*) $\tan x$ is infinite. (*b*) $\cot x$ is infinite. (*c*) $\sec x$ is infinite.

★**33.** Prove that π is the smallest period of the functions $\tan x$ and $\cot x$.

★**34.** Complete the solution of Example 1 on page 128 for the functions $\cos x$, $\sec x$, and $\csc x$.

74. Graphs of composite trigonometric functions

From page 34, we recall that an expression like $\sin x$ is a special case of the common functional notation, such as $f(x)$, with "sin" playing the role of f. Then, in $\sin x$, on replacing x by a value of any function of x, such as $g(x)$, we obtain $\sin g(x)$, which is the value of the standard sine function of $g(x)$. We may call the resulting function $\sin g(x)$ a *composite* trigonometric function, but the name is not important at this point.

EXAMPLE 1. Graph the function $\sin 3x$ from $x = 0$ to $x = 2\pi$.

SOLUTION. 1. We desire the graph of $y = \sin 3x$. If x increases from 0 to 2π, then $3x$ increases from 0 to 6π, and thus $\sin 3x$ passes through all values taken on by $\sin \alpha$ if α ranges from 0 to 6π. Thus, on the interval from $x = 0$ to $x = 2\pi$, the graph of $y = \sin 3x$ will consist of *three* sine waves, whereas the graph of $y = \sin x$ would consist of just *one* wave. The *amplitude* (maximum ordinate) of the wave for $\sin 3x$ is the same as for $\sin x$.

2. The x-intercepts of the graph are the values of x which satisfy the equation $\sin 3x = 0$; its solutions for $3x$ on the range 0 to 6π are

$$3x = 0,\ \pi,\ 2\pi,\ 3\pi,\ 4\pi,\ 5\pi,\ \textit{and}\ 6\pi;\ \textit{hence},$$

$$x = 0,\ \tfrac{1}{3}\pi,\ \tfrac{2}{3}\pi,\ \pi,\ \tfrac{4}{3}\pi,\ \tfrac{5}{3}\pi,\ \textit{and}\ 2\pi. \tag{1}$$

The values in (1) are the x-intercepts of the full-line curve which is shown in Figure 86.

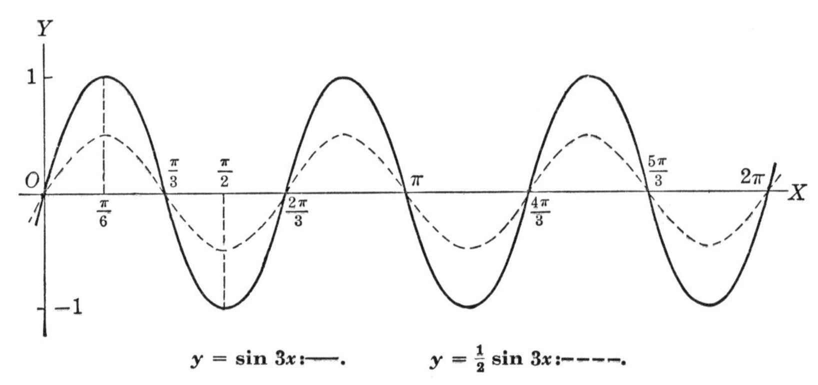

Fig. 86

3. The *maximum* value of y occurs when $\sin 3x = 1$; the solutions of this equation for $3x$ on the range 0 to 6π are

$$3x = \tfrac{1}{2}\pi,\ (2\pi + \tfrac{1}{2}\pi)\ \textit{or}\ \tfrac{5}{2}\pi,\ \textit{and}\ \tfrac{9}{2}\pi;\quad \textit{or}\quad x = \tfrac{1}{6}\pi,\ \tfrac{5}{6}\pi,\ \textit{and}\ \tfrac{3}{2}\pi. \tag{2}$$

Similarly, $y = -1$ when $\sin 3x = -1$, or when $x = \frac{1}{2}\pi$, $\frac{7}{6}\pi$, and $\frac{11}{6}\pi$.

4. The points (x, y) corresponding to the values of x found in Steps 2 and 3 were the basis for the graph of $y = \sin 3x$ in Figure 86.

Comment. Since the function $\sin\theta$ has the period 2π,

$$\sin 3x = \sin(3x + 2\pi) = \sin 3(x + \tfrac{2}{3}\pi).$$

Or, the function $\sin 3x$ is periodic with the period $2\pi/3$. This corresponds to the fact that there are three complete waves in Figure 86. Similarly, if n is any positive number, the functions $\sin nx$, $\cos nx$, $\sec nx$, and $\csc nx$ are periodic with the period $2\pi/n$. The functions $\tan nx$ and $\cot nx$ are periodic with the period π/n because the functions $\tan\theta$ and $\cot\theta$ have the period π.

Illustration 1. The graph of $y = \frac{1}{2}\sin 3x$ is the broken-line curve in Figure 86 where each wave has one half of the amplitude of the wave for $y = \sin 3x$.

75. Addition of ordinates

Let g, h, and F be functions with the same domain, D, and suppose that $F(x) = h(x) + g(x)$ for all numbers x in D. In some cases it may be desirable to graph F by first graphing h and g separately on one coordinate system. Then, to obtain the point on the graph of F, for any value of x, we may *add geometrically* (by use of dividers or a ruler) *the ordinates of the graphs of f and g at this value of x.* When this is done, we say that the graph of F is obtained by *addition* (or *composition*) of ordinates.

EXAMPLE 1. Graph the function $(\sin x + \cos x)$.

SOLUTION. 1. We wish the graph of $y = \sin x + \cos x$. Let $y_1 = \sin x$ and $y_2 = \cos x$; the graphs of these equations are shown in Figure 87.

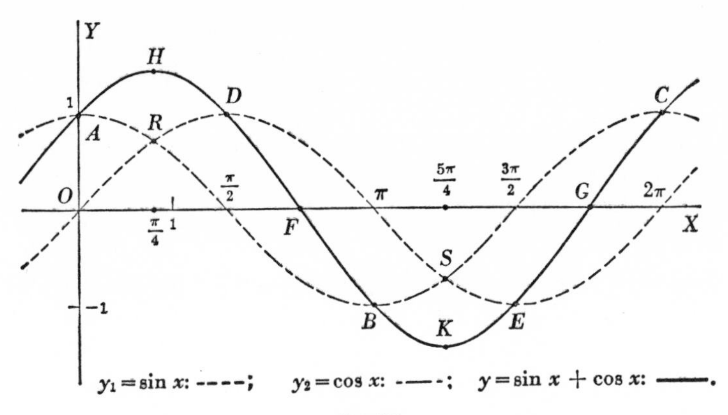

Fig. 87

2. At any value of x, we have $y = y_1 + y_2$. Hence, at any value of x, we may add the corresponding ordinates y_1 and y_2 to obtain y.

3. If $y_1 = 0$, then $y = y_2$; this gives A, B, C on the desired graph; D and E are obtained where $y_2 = 0$. If $y_1 = -y_2$, then $y = 0$; this gives F and G. Other ordinates were added. The graph is the full-line curve in Figure 87.

★76. General sine waves

EXAMPLE 1. Express the function $f(x) = \sin x + \cos x$ of Example 1 above in the form $f(x) = H \sin (x + \alpha)$ where $H > 0$ and $|\alpha| < \pi$.

SOLUTION. 1. We desire H and α so that

$$\sin x + \cos x = H \sin (x + \alpha) = (H \cos \alpha) \sin x + (H \sin \alpha) \cos x, \quad (1)$$

where we used the addition formula (8) of page 123. From (1),

$$H \cos \alpha = 1 \quad \textit{and} \quad H \sin \alpha = 1. \quad (2)$$

From (2), $$H^2 \sin^2 \alpha + H^2 \cos^2 \alpha = 2, \quad \textit{or} \quad H^2 = 2.$$

Thus, we take $H = \sqrt{2}$.

2. From (2), $\sin \alpha = \frac{1}{2}\sqrt{2}$ and $\cos \alpha = \frac{1}{2}\sqrt{2}$. Hence, we take $\alpha = \frac{1}{4}\pi$ and $H = \sqrt{2}$ to satisfy (1). Then we obtain $f(x) = \sqrt{2} \sin (x + \frac{1}{4}\pi)$.

Comment. Also, we could have obtained the form $f(x) = \sqrt{2} \cos (x - \frac{1}{4}\pi)$.

From Example 1, we note that the graph of the function in Figure 87 on page 131 is the graph of $y = \sqrt{2} \sin (x + \frac{1}{4}\pi)$, which is a sine wave with amplitude (maximum ordinate) $\sqrt{2}$, period 2π, and an x-intercept at $x = -\frac{1}{4}\pi$. The graph could be obtained by shifting (translating) the graph of $y = \sqrt{2} \sin x$ through the horizontal distance $\frac{1}{4}\pi$ to the *left*, because the value of $\sin (x + \frac{1}{4}\pi)$ for any x is the value of $\sin \theta$ at the point $\theta = x + \frac{1}{4}\pi$, which is $\frac{1}{4}\pi$ units to the *right*.

Now, consider any function $f(x) = H \sin (ax + k)$, where we arrange to have $H > 0$ and $a > 0$. With $\alpha = k/a$, we obtain $f(x) = H \sin a(x + \alpha)$. We call the graph of f a *sine wave* with amplitude H. Since $a\alpha = k$, and

$$f\left(x + \frac{2\pi}{a}\right) = H \sin a\left(x + \frac{2\pi}{a} + \alpha\right) = H \sin [a(x + \alpha) + 2\pi], \text{ or}$$

$$f\left(x + \frac{2\pi}{a}\right) = H \sin a(x + \alpha), \quad \textit{we have} \quad f\left(x + \frac{2\pi}{a}\right) = f(x),$$

at all values of x. Hence, f has the *period* $2\pi/a$. The graph of the equation $y = f(x)$ can be thought of as the graph of the *simple sine wave* $H \sin ax$, shifted α units to the *left* in the xy-plane. Hence, we refer to k as the **phase constant** for f. In Example 1, we found a phase constant $\frac{1}{4}\pi$. By the method of Example 1, any function of the form $f(x) = b \sin ax + c \cos ax$ with * $a > 0$ and $b^2 + c^2 \neq 0$ can be expressed in the form $f(x) = H \sin a(x + \alpha)$ or $f(x) = H \cos a(x + \alpha)$, as we please, with $H > 0$ and $|a\alpha| \leqq \pi$. Hence, the graph of f is a sine wave.

EXERCISE 39

Graph each equation on the interval $0 \leqq x \leqq 2\pi$.

1. $y = 3 \sin x$. **2.** $y = -2 \cos x$. **3.** $y = \sin 2x$. **4.** $y = \cos 3x$.
5. $y = \cot 3x$. **6.** $y = \tan 2x$. **7.** $y = \sec 2x$. **8.** $y = \csc 3x$.
9. $y = -3 \sin x$. **10.** $y = -\sin 3x$. **11.** $y = \sin \frac{1}{2}x$.
12. $y = \cos \frac{1}{3}x$. **13.** $y = \cos x + \sin 2x$. **14.** $y = \sin x - \cos x$.
15. $y = \cos 2x + \sin x$. **16.** $y = \sin 2x + \cos 2x$. **17.** $y = \cot x + \cos x$.
18. $y = x + \sin x$. **19.** $y = x + \cos x$. **20.** $y = 2x - \sin x$.

★*For the function f whose value for any real number x is given by the indicated expression, write* $f(x)$ *in the form* $H \sin a(x + \alpha)$ *and then draw the graph of the function f by use of the new form, without adding ordinates. Also, tell the period of f.*

21. $2 \sin x + 2\sqrt{3} \cos x$. **22.** $5 \sin 2x - 5 \cos 2x$.
23. $3 \sin \frac{1}{2}x - 3\sqrt{3} \cos \frac{1}{2}x$. **24.** $-4 \sin 3x - 4 \cos 3x$.

* If $a < 0$, we use $\sin (-\theta) = -\sin \theta$ and $\cos (-\theta) = \cos \theta$ to obtain a new form with $a > 0$.

7

APPLICATIONS OF FUNDAMENTAL IDENTITIES

77. Review of the fundamental identities

From page 40, we have the following fundamental identities, where the functions may be thought of either as the standard trigonometric functions of numbers or as the geometric trigonometric functions of angles. That is, as desired, we may consider θ either as a symbol for an *angle*, or as a *number symbol.*

$$\csc \theta = \frac{1}{\sin \theta}; \qquad \sec \theta = \frac{1}{\cos \theta}; \qquad \cot \theta = \frac{1}{\tan \theta}. \tag{1}$$

$$\tan \theta = \frac{\sin \theta}{\cos \theta}; \qquad \cot \theta = \frac{\cos \theta}{\sin \theta}. \tag{2}$$

$$\sin^2 \theta + \cos^2 \theta = 1; \quad \tan^2 \theta + 1 = \sec^2 \theta; \quad 1 + \cot^2 \theta = \csc^2 \theta. \tag{3}$$

From (1) and (2), the values of all trigonometric functions of θ are expressible in terms of $\sin \theta$ and $\cos \theta$ without introducing radicals.

ILLUSTRATION 1. On using (1) and (2), we obtain *

$$\frac{\tan \theta + \cot \theta}{\tan \theta - \cot \theta} = \frac{\dfrac{\sin \theta}{\cos \theta} + \dfrac{\cos \theta}{\sin \theta}}{\dfrac{\sin \theta}{\cos \theta} - \dfrac{\cos \theta}{\sin \theta}} = \frac{\dfrac{\sin^2 \theta + \cos^2 \theta}{\sin \theta \cos \theta}}{\dfrac{\sin^2 \theta - \cos^2 \theta}{\sin \theta \cos \theta}}$$

$$= \frac{1}{\sin \theta \cos \theta} \cdot \frac{\sin \theta \cos \theta}{\sin^2 \theta - \cos^2 \theta} = \frac{1}{\sin^2 \theta - \cos^2 \theta}.$$

78. Proofs of identities

In applications of trigonometry in later mathematics, it is sometimes necessary to prove that a given trigonometric equation is an *identity*. On

* It will be assumed hereafter (usually without remarks) that the independent variables are restricted to values for which *no denominator is zero*, and for which *all function values exist*, in any equation which is considered.

account of the nature of the applications, Method I of the following Summary will be emphasized. Also, a method not in this Summary will be met later in this section.

SUMMARY. *Methods for proving that an equation is an identity.*

I. *Leave one side unaltered, and change the appearance of the other side to the same form as the first side.*

II. *Alter the appearance of both sides independently until they are exhibited in identical form.*

EXAMPLE 1. Prove that the equation is an identity:

$$\tan\theta + 2\cot\theta = \frac{\sin^2\theta + 2\cos^2\theta}{\sin\theta\cos\theta}. \tag{1}$$

SOLUTION. We decide to leave the right-hand side unaltered. Since it involves only $\sin\theta$ and $\cos\theta$, we express the left-hand side in terms of $\sin\theta$ and $\cos\theta$, by use of (2) in Section 77.

$$\tan\theta + 2\cot\theta = \frac{\sin\theta}{\cos\theta} + \frac{2\cos\theta}{\sin\theta} = \frac{\sin^2\theta + 2\cos^2\theta}{\sin\theta\cos\theta}.$$

Hence, (1) is true for all values of θ for which $\sin\theta\cos\theta \neq 0$, and hence is an identity. Notice that the solution used Method I of the Summary.

EXAMPLE 2. Prove that the equation is an identity:

$$\tan x + \cot x = \frac{\csc x}{\cos x}. \tag{2}$$

SOLUTION *by Method* II. We shall operate on both sides of (2), to change them to the same form. In the details below, a double line is drawn separating the two sides, and thus emphasizing that their equality is not being assumed while we are trying to prove it.

$\tan x + \cot x = \dfrac{\sin x}{\cos x} + \dfrac{\cos x}{\sin x}$	$\dfrac{\csc x}{\cos x} = \csc x \cdot \dfrac{1}{\cos x}$
$= \dfrac{\sin^2 x + \cos^2 x}{\sin x\cos x} = \dfrac{1}{\sin x\cos x}.$	$= \dfrac{1}{\sin x}\cdot\dfrac{1}{\cos x} = \dfrac{1}{\sin x\cos x}.$

Hence, each side of (2) is equal to $1/(\sin x\cos x)$, and the two sides of (2) have the same value for every value of x where $\sin x\cos x \neq 0$.

EXAMPLE 3. Prove that the equation is an identity:

$$\frac{1 + \cos x}{\sin x} = \frac{\sin x}{1 - \cos x}. \tag{3}$$

SOLUTION. 1. We wish to prove that (3) is true for all values of x where $\sin x \neq 0$ and $1 - \cos x \neq 0$.

2. **IF** (3) **is true** at any value of x, we obtain a true statement on multiplying both sides by $(\sin x)(1 - \cos x)$, which gives

$$1 - \cos^2 x = \sin^2 x. \tag{4}$$

We know that (4) **IS TRUE** for all values of x because $\sin^2 x + \cos^2 x = 1$ is an identity.

3. To arrive at (3), we now start with (4). Since (4) is true for all values of x, on dividing both sides of (4) by $(1 - \cos x)$ and by $\sin x$, which are not zero in either case, we know that the resulting equation is true for all values of x. This division gives

$$\frac{1 + \cos x}{\sin x} = \frac{\sin x}{1 - \cos x}; \quad \textit{hence, (3) is an identity.}$$

In the preceding solution, we illustrated a third method, as follows, for proving an identity.

1. *Assume that the conjectured identity is true and manipulate it until an obvious identity is obtained.*

2. *Start anew with the obvious identity and prove that, from it, the conjectured identity can be obtained* **by reversal of the previous steps.**

We emphasize that Part 1 of the method by itself does *not* constitute a proof. A by-product of the method is that, if Part 1 does not lead to an identity, we may obtain some equation which we recognize as a conditional equation. Then, we might conclude that the conjectured identity is a conditional equation, and incidentally have a means for its solution.

EXAMPLE 4. Prove that the equation is an identity, if the domain of x consists of all values of x where $\sec x + \tan x > 0$.

$$\sqrt{\frac{\sec x - \tan x}{\sec x + \tan x}} = \frac{1}{\sec x + \tan x}. \tag{5}$$

SOLUTION. We leave the right-hand side unaltered, and rationalize the denominator on the left by multiplying both numerator and denominator by $(\sec x + \tan x)$ under the radical:

$$\sqrt{\frac{\sec x - \tan x}{\sec x + \tan x}} = \sqrt{\frac{\sec x - \tan x}{\sec x + \tan x} \cdot \frac{\sec x + \tan x}{\sec x + \tan x}} = \sqrt{\frac{\sec^2 x - \tan^2 x}{(\sec x + \tan x)^2}}$$

[using (3) on page 133] $\quad = \dfrac{1}{\sec x + \tan x}$, because * $\sec x + \tan x > 0$.

Comment. As a rule, in any equation involving a radical, as in Example 4, we shall assume that the variables are restricted to a domain where any

* If $H > 0$, recall from page 207 that $\sqrt{H}$ represents the positive square root of H. If $a \geq 0$, then $\sqrt{a^2} = a$. If $a < 0$, then $\sqrt{a^2} = -a$.

factor removed from under the radical is *positive.* This will avoid the ambiguous sign $\pm$ on many occasions. Thus, in Example 4, we restrict x so that $\sec x + \tan x > 0$. If $\sec x + \tan x < 0$, a minus sign should precede the right-hand side in (5), or we should use the absolute value of the right-hand side to cover all possibilities.

The following suggestions are useful in proving identities.

a. *If possible, avoid using formulas involving radicals.*

b. *Perhaps express all function values in terms of sines and cosines.*

c. *If one side of the identity involves just one function, perhaps express everything on the other side in terms of values of this function.*

EXERCISE 40

Prove that the equation is an identity by use of the fundamental identities.

1. $\cos\alpha\csc\alpha = \cot\alpha$.

2. $\sin\theta\sec\theta = \tan\theta$.

3. $\cos^2\theta - \sin^2\theta = 2\cos^2\theta - 1$.

4. $\cos^2\theta - \sin^2\theta = 1 - 2\sin^2\theta$.

5. $\cot x + \tan x = \sec x \csc x$.

6. $\csc^2 x \tan^2 x = \tan^2 x + 1$.

7. $(\sin\theta + \cos\theta)^2 = 1 + 2\sin\theta\cos\theta$.

8. $(\cot x + 1)^2 = \csc^2 x + 2\cot x$.

9. $\tan\theta = \dfrac{\sec\theta}{\csc\theta}$.

10. $\sin\theta = \dfrac{\cos\theta}{\cot\theta}$.

11. $\dfrac{1-\sin^2 x}{\sin x} = \dfrac{\cos x}{\tan x}$.

12. $\dfrac{1-\cos^2\beta}{\cos\beta} = \sin\beta\tan\beta$.

13. $\dfrac{\cos^2\theta}{1-\sin\theta} = 1 + \sin\theta$.

14. $\dfrac{\tan^2\beta}{\sec^2\beta} + \dfrac{\cot^2\beta}{\csc^2\beta} = 1$.

15. $\dfrac{1-\tan^2 x}{1+\tan^2 x} = 1 - 2\sin^2 x$.

16. $\dfrac{\tan^2\theta + 1}{\cot^2\theta + 1} = \tan^2\theta$.

17. $\dfrac{1+\csc x}{\sec x} = \cos x + \cot x$.

18. $\dfrac{\tan\theta - 1}{\tan\theta + 1} = \dfrac{1-\cot\theta}{1+\cot\theta}$.

19. $\dfrac{\sin y - \cos y}{\sin y + \cos y} = \dfrac{\tan y - 1}{\tan y + 1}$.

20. $\dfrac{\sin x - \cos y}{\sin x + \cos y} = \dfrac{\sec y - \csc x}{\sec y + \csc x}$.

21. $\dfrac{\sec x}{\cot x + \tan x} = \sin x$.

22. $\sec x + \tan x = \dfrac{\sin^2 x + \sin x + \cos^2 x}{\cos x}$.

23. $\dfrac{\tan x - \cos x \cot x}{\csc x} = \dfrac{\sin x}{\cot x} - \dfrac{\cos x}{\sec x}$.

24. $\cot x - \tan x = 2\cos x\csc x - \sec x\csc x$.

25. $\dfrac{\tan x - \tan y}{1 + \tan x \tan y} = \dfrac{\cot y - \cot x}{\cot x \cot y + 1}$.

26. $\dfrac{\sec^2 x}{\sec^2 x - 1} = \csc^2 x$.

27. $\dfrac{\sin x - \cos x}{\tan x \csc x - \sec x \cot x} = \sin x \cos x$.

28. $\dfrac{\sec^2 x + 2\tan x}{1 + \tan x} = 1 + \tan x$.

29. $1 + \sin x = \dfrac{\cos x}{\sec x - \tan x}$.

30. $(\csc x + \sec x)^2 = \dfrac{\sec^2 x + 2 \tan x}{\sin^2 x}.$

31. $\dfrac{1}{\csc x - \cot x} - \dfrac{1}{\csc x + \cot x} = \dfrac{2}{\tan x}.$

32. $\cos^4 x - \sin^4 x = 1 - 2 \sin^2 x.$

33. $\sec^4 x - \tan^4 x = \dfrac{1 + \sin^2 x}{\cos^2 x}.$

34. $\dfrac{\cos x \cos y - \sin x \sin y}{\cos x \sin y + \sin x \cos y} = \dfrac{\cot x \cot y - 1}{\cot x + \cot y}.$

35. $\dfrac{\sin x \cos y + \cos x \sin y}{\cos x \cos y - \sin x \sin y} = \dfrac{\tan x + \tan y}{1 - \tan x \tan y}.$

36. $\dfrac{1 + \sin x}{\cos x} = \dfrac{\cos x}{1 - \sin x}.$

37. $\sqrt{\dfrac{1 - \sin x}{1 + \sin x}} = \sec x - \tan x.$

38. $\dfrac{1}{\sec x + \tan x} = \dfrac{1 - \sin x}{\cos x}.$

39. $\sqrt{\dfrac{\csc x - \cot x}{\csc x + \cot x}} = \dfrac{1 - \cos x}{\sin x}.$

40. $\sqrt{\dfrac{\sec x - 1}{\sec x + 1}} = \dfrac{\sin x}{1 + \cos x}.$

41. $\sqrt{\dfrac{\sec x - \tan x}{\sec x + \tan x}} = \dfrac{\cos x}{1 + \sin x}.$

79. Elementary trigonometric equations in one variable

The most simple type of trigonometric equation is one which is linear in the value of one trigonometric function of one number θ, and thus gives this function value immediately. Then, there are usually two corresponding solutions for θ on the interval $0 \leqq \theta < 2\pi$, as we observed geometrically (with θ interpreted as an angle) in Illustration 1 on page 42. On account of the periodicity of the trigonometric functions, usually a trigonometric equation possesses *infinitely many* solutions, with unbounded absolute values. In this book, unless otherwise stated, *to solve* a trigonometric equation in θ will mean to obtain only those solutions on the interval $0 \leqq \theta < 2\pi$ or, if θ is interpreted as an angle in degree measure, on the interval $0° \leqq \theta < 360°$.

EXAMPLE 1. Solve: $\quad 2 \cos \theta + 1 = 0.$

SOLUTION. 1. We find $2 \cos \theta = -1$ or $\cos \theta = -\frac{1}{2}$.

2. Let α be on the interval $0 \leqq \alpha \leqq \frac{1}{2}\pi$, with $\cos \alpha = \frac{1}{2}$. Then, $\alpha = \frac{1}{3}\pi$. Hence, α is the reference number for any solution θ, and θ is on an interval in quadrant II or quadrant III, where the cosine function is negative. Thus, $\theta = \pi - \frac{1}{3}\pi$ or $\theta = \pi + \frac{1}{3}\pi$, or the solutions are $\frac{2}{3}\pi$ and $\frac{4}{3}\pi$.

Comment. Since $\cos \theta$ is periodic with the period 2π, the set of all solutions of $2 \cos \theta + 1 = 0$ consists of all numbers θ of the following form, where n takes on all integral values, positive, negative, or zero:

$$\theta = \tfrac{2}{3}\pi + 2n\pi \quad \text{or} \quad \theta = \tfrac{4}{3}\pi + 2n\pi.$$

In Example 1, we employed the following method, which was met earlier in Illustration 4 on page 61.

Summary. *To find θ on the interval $0 \leqq \theta < 2\pi$ when the value of one trigonometric function, T, is known at the point θ; or, with $T(\theta) = b$, to solve for θ when b is known.*

1. *From a trigonometric table or from memory of the trigonometric functions of $0, \frac{1}{6}\pi, \frac{1}{4}\pi, \frac{1}{3}\pi$, and $\frac{1}{2}\pi$, find α on the interval $0 \leqq \alpha \leqq \frac{1}{2}\pi$ so that $T(\alpha) = |b|$.*

2. *From knowledge of the signs of the trigonometric functions for the various quadrant intervals, locate the numbers θ on the interval $0 \leqq \theta < 2\pi$ having α as the corresponding reference number.*

Example 2. Find all angles θ satisfying $0° \leqq \theta < 360°$ if $\sin \theta = -.9872$.

Solution. 1. Let α be the acute reference angle for θ. Then, $\sin \alpha = .9872$. From Table VII, $\alpha = 80° 50'$.

2. The sine function is negative in quadrants III and IV. Hence, the solutions for θ are $\theta = 180° + 80° 50'$ and $\theta = 360° - 80° 50'$, which can be verified from a figure. Thus, the solutions are $260° 50'$ and $279° 10'$.

80. Solution of trigonometric equations by factoring

A trigonometric equation * in one variable x, which is in the *quadratic form* in the value of one trigonometric function of x, can be solved by use of methods met with quadratic equations in algebra. In particular, solution by factoring may apply.

Example 1. Solve: $$2 \sin^2 x - \sin x - 1 = 0.$$

Solution. 1. We say that this equation is in the quadratic form in $\sin x$ because, if we should let $v = \sin x$ (which is unnecessary), the equation would become $2v^2 - v - 1 = 0$. To solve the given equation, we first factor:

$$(2 \sin x + 1)(\sin x - 1) = 0. \tag{1}$$

2. The equation is satisfied if:

$2 \sin x + 1 = 0$; *then* $\sin x = -\frac{1}{2}$, *and* $x = \frac{7}{6}\pi$ *or* $x = \frac{11}{6}\pi$.

$\sin x - 1 = 0$; *then* $\sin x = 1$, *and* $x = \frac{1}{2}\pi$.

Hence, the solutions are $\frac{1}{2}\pi$, $\frac{7}{6}\pi$, and $\frac{11}{6}\pi$.

To solve an equation by use of factoring, recall that the equation must first be written with *one member zero*.

Example 2. Solve: $$\sin x \cos x = \cos x. \tag{2}$$

Solution. 1. Subtract $\cos x$ from both sides; then factor:

$$\sin x \cos x - \cos x = 0; \qquad \cos x(\sin x - 1) = 0.$$

2. If $\cos x = 0$, then $x = \frac{1}{2}\pi$ or $\frac{3}{2}\pi$. If $\sin x - 1 = 0$, then $x = \frac{1}{2}\pi$. Thus, (2) has the solutions $\frac{1}{2}\pi$ and $\frac{3}{2}\pi$.

* We shall consider obtaining the solutions only of equations in a *single* variable.

INCORRECT SOLUTION. Divide both sides by $\cos x$: $\sin x = 1$; $x = \frac{1}{2}\pi$.

Comment. If both sides of an equation are divided by an expression **involving the unknowns, remember that solutions may be lost.** Thus, the division by $\cos x$ caused the loss of the solution $\frac{3}{2}\pi$, for which $\cos x = 0$.

EXAMPLE 3. Solve: $$2 \sin^2 x - 1 = 0.$$

SOLUTION. 1. $2 \sin^2 x = 1$; $\sin^2 x = \frac{1}{2}$. Hence,

$$\sin x = \pm \sqrt{\tfrac{1}{2}}; \quad \sin x = \tfrac{1}{2}\sqrt{2} \quad or \quad \sin x = -\tfrac{1}{2}\sqrt{2}.$$

2. From $\sin x = \frac{1}{2}\sqrt{2}$, the solutions are $x = \frac{1}{4}\pi$ and $x = \frac{3}{4}\pi$. The solutions of $\sin x = -\frac{1}{2}\sqrt{2}$ are $x = \frac{5}{4}\pi$ and $x = \frac{7}{4}\pi$. Thus, the given equation has the four solutions $\frac{1}{4}\pi$, $\frac{3}{4}\pi$, $\frac{5}{4}\pi$, and $\frac{7}{4}\pi$.

EXERCISE 41

Find all numbers x on the interval $0 \leqq x < 2\pi$ which satisfy the equation, or which correspond to the given statement about an infinite limit. In a few problems, also write expressions for all solutions of the equation.

1. $\tan x = 1$. **2.** $\cos x = \frac{1}{2}$. **3.** $\sec x = -1$. **4.** $\cos x = 0$.
5. $\sin x = \frac{1}{2}\sqrt{2}$. **6.** $\sec x = \frac{1}{3}$. **7.** $\sin x = 2$. **8.** $\cot x = -1$.
9. $\tan x$ is *infinite*. **10.** $\sec x$ is *infinite*. **11.** $\csc x$ is *infinite*.
12. $2 \sin x - 1 = 0$. **13.** $2 \cos x + \sqrt{2} = 0$. **14.** $\tan x - \sqrt{3} = 0$.
15. $3 \cot x + \sqrt{3} = 0$. **16.** $\cos x + 2 = 0$. **17.** $2 \sin x + \sqrt{3} = 0$.
18. $\sin^2 x = 1$. **19.** $\tan^2 x = 1$. **20.** $2 \cos^2 x - 1 = 0$.
21. $4 \sin^2 x - 3 = 0$. **22.** $\sec^2 x = 2$. **23.** $4 \cos^2 x - 3 = 0$.
24. $3 \tan^2 x - 1 = 0$. **25.** $(\sin x + 1)(2 \sin x - 1) = 0$.
26. $\cos x(2 \cos x - 1) = 0$. **27.** $(\tan x - \sqrt{3})(\tan x + 1) = 0$.
28. $2 \cos^2 x - \cos x - 1 = 0$. **29.** $\sin^2 x - 2 \sin x + 1 = 0$.
30. $\csc^2 x - 4 \csc x + 4 = 0$. **31.** $2 \cos^2 x + 3 \cos x + 1 = 0$.
32. $4 \cos^2 x - 1 = 0$. **33.** $\sin^2 x = \sin x$. **34.** $2 \cos^2 x = -\cos x$.
35. $\sec^2 x - 3 \sec x + 2 = 0$. **36.** $\csc^2 x - \csc x - 2 = 0$.
37. $2 \sin^2 x + \sqrt{2} \sin x = 0$. **38.** $3 \tan^2 x - \sqrt{3} \tan x = 0$.
39. $\sin x \sec^2 x - 2 \sin x = 0$. **40.** $\cos x \cot^2 x - 3 \cos x = 0$.

Find all angles in degree measure on the domain $0° \leqq \theta < 360°$ which satisfy the equation. Use Table VII.

41. $\cos \theta = .9224$. **42.** $\sin \theta = .4318$. **43.** $\tan \theta = 1.621$.
44. $\tan \theta = 4.449$. **45.** $\cot \theta = -7.770$. **46.** $\cos \theta = -.8225$.

★*Solve by factoring, for x on the interval $0 \leqq x < 2\pi$.*

47. $2 \sin^4 x - 3 \sin^2 x + 1 = 0$. **48.** $3 \tan^3 x - \tan x = 0$.
49. $3 \cot^4 x + 2 \cot^2 x - 1 = 0$. **50.** $\sin^2 x - 8 \sin x + 15 = 0$.

81. Extraneous solutions

In solving an equation, we sometimes employ one or both of the following operations.

I. *Square both sides, or raise both sides to some specified power.*

II. *Multiply both sides by an expression involving the variable.*

It is important to realize that (I) or (II) may lead to a new equation which is not equivalent to the given equation. That is, if x represents the variable, a value $x = a$ may be a solution of the *new* equation and yet fail to satisfy the given equation. A value $x = a$, as just described, then is called an **extraneous solution.** We illustrated the preceding remarks for the case of (II) on page 10.

ILLUSTRATION 1. Consider solving the equation $\sin x = 1$. On squaring both sides we obtain

$$\sin^2 x = 1, \quad \textit{which is satisfied if} \quad \sin x = 1 \quad \textit{or if} \quad \sin x = -1.$$

On the interval $0 \leqq x < 2\pi$, the solutions of $\sin^2 x = 1$ are $x = \frac{1}{2}\pi$ and $x = \frac{3}{2}\pi$, whereas the only solution of $\sin x = 1$ is $x = \frac{1}{2}\pi$. Hence, the extraneous solution $x = \frac{3}{2}\pi$ was introduced by the squaring operation.

On account of the danger of introducing extraneous solutions, whenever (I) or (II) is used in the process of solving an equation *it is essential to test* all values obtained for the variable, to reject extraneous solutions, if any.

Note 1. If $A = B$, then $A^2 = B^2$. Hence, if an equation $A = B$ in a variable x has a solution $x = c$, then *c likewise is a solution of* $A^2 = B^2$. In Illustration 1, we exhibited a special case where the *converse* of the preceding result is *not* true. That is, the equation $A^2 = B^2$ may have a solution $x = c$ which does *not* satisfy the equation $A = B$, because $A^2 = B^2$ has all the solutions possessed by the two equations $A = B$ and $A = -B$.

82. Trigonometric equations solved with the aid of identities

In solving a trigonometric equation, we aim to find one or more equations, each involving the value of just one trigonometric function of one unknown number, which are *equivalent* to the given equation. To accomplish this aim, it may be useful to modify given expressions by use of known identities. The following actions should be thought of as possibilities. If method (I) below does not apply, consider using (II).

I. *Express the value of each trigonometric function of the unknown, x, in terms of one function of x.*

II. *Express the value of each trigonometric function of x in terms of the sine and cosine.*

EXAMPLE 1. Solve: $$\cos x + 1 = \sin x. \tag{1}$$

SOLUTION. 1. From $\sin^2 x = 1 - \cos^2 x$,

$$\sin x = \pm \sqrt{1 - \cos^2 x}, \tag{2}$$

where the sign + or − depends on the value of x. From (2), (1) becomes

$$\cos x + 1 = \pm \sqrt{1 - \cos^2 x}. \tag{3}$$

2. Square both sides: $$(1 + \cos x)^2 = 1 - \cos^2 x;$$

$$1 + 2 \cos x + \cos^2 x = 1 - \cos^2 x; \qquad 2 \cos x + 2 \cos^2 x = 0;$$

$$2 \cos x(1 + \cos x) = 0. \tag{4}$$

From (4), $$\cos x = 0 \quad or \quad \cos x = -1.$$

Hence, (4) has the solutions $x = \frac{1}{2}\pi$, $x = \frac{3}{2}\pi$, and $x = \pi$. By Note 1 on page 140, **if (1) has any solutions,** they are among the numbers $\frac{1}{2}\pi$, $\frac{3}{2}\pi$, and π.

Test of values. Substitute $x = \frac{3}{2}\pi$ in (1):

Does $\cos \frac{3}{2}\pi + 1 = \sin \frac{3}{2}\pi$? *Or does* $0 + 1 = -1$? **NO.**

Hence, $x = \frac{3}{2}\pi$ is not a solution of (1). Similarly, we find that $x = \frac{1}{2}\pi$ and $x = \pi$ satisfy (1), and thus are the desired solutions.

EXAMPLE 2. Solve: $$\sec x - 2 \cos x - \tan x = 0. \tag{5}$$

SOLUTION. 1. Express each function value in terms of $\sin x$ and $\cos x$:

$$\frac{1}{\cos x} - 2 \cos x - \frac{\sin x}{\cos x} = 0. \tag{6}$$

2. Multiply both sides of (6) by $\cos x$ and use $\cos^2 x = 1 - \sin^2 x$:

$$1 - 2 \cos^2 x - \sin x = 0; \tag{7}$$

$$1 - 2(1 - \sin^2 x) - \sin x = 0, \quad or \quad 2 \sin^2 x - \sin x - 1 = 0; \quad or$$

$$(2 \sin x + 1)(\sin x - 1) = 0. \tag{8}$$

3. From (8), $\sin x = 1$ or $\sin x = -\frac{1}{2}$. Hence, (8) has the solutions $x = \frac{1}{2}\pi$, $x = \frac{7}{6}\pi$, and $x = \frac{11}{6}\pi$.

Test of values. In (5), x cannot have a value such that $\cos x = 0$, because then $\sec x$ and $\tan x$ are not defined; hence, $x = \frac{1}{2}\pi$ cannot be a solution of (5). On substituting $x = \frac{7}{6}\pi$ in (5), we find that it becomes

$$-\frac{2}{\sqrt{3}} + 2\left(\frac{\sqrt{3}}{2}\right) - \frac{1}{\sqrt{3}} = 0, \quad or \quad -\tfrac{2}{3}\sqrt{3} + \sqrt{3} - \tfrac{1}{3}\sqrt{3} = 0,$$

which is true. Hence $\frac{7}{6}\pi$ is a solution of (5). Similarly, $\frac{11}{6}\pi$ also is a solution. Thus, (5) has two solutions on the interval $0 \leq x < 2\pi$.

EXAMPLE 3. Solve for x on the interval $0 \leqq x < 2\pi$:

$$\cos x - \sin x = 0. \qquad (9)$$

SOLUTION. Divide by $\cos x$: $$1 = \frac{\sin x}{\cos x}, \quad or \quad \tan x = 1. \qquad (10)$$

We see that (10) has the solutions $x = \frac{1}{4}\pi$ and $x = \frac{5}{4}\pi$.

Test of values. If $x = \frac{1}{4}\pi$, then (9) becomes $\frac{1}{2}\sqrt{2} - \frac{1}{2}\sqrt{2} = 0$, which is true; hence $\frac{1}{4}\pi$ is a solution. Similarly, $\frac{5}{4}\pi$ also is a solution.

★*Comment.* If x has a value such that $\cos x \neq 0$, then (10) is true when (9) is true; also, (9) is true when (10) is true, because (9) can be obtained by multiplying both sides of (10) by $\cos x$. Hence, on the interval $0 \leqq x < 2\pi$, (9) and (10) are equivalent, if we rule out $x = \frac{1}{2}\pi$ and $x = \frac{3}{2}\pi$.

EXERCISE 42

Find all solutions of the equation on the interval $0 \leqq x < 2\pi$.

1. $2 \cos^2 x + \sin x - 1 = 0.$
2. $3 + 3 \cos x = 2 \sin^2 x.$
3. $\cos^2 x + \sin x + 1 = 0.$
4. $3 \sin^2 x - \cos^2 x - 1 = 0.$
5. $2 \sin^2 x - 2 \cos^2 x = 3.$
6. $\sqrt{3} \cot x + 1 = \csc^2 x.$
7. $\sec^2 x - 1 = \tan x.$
8. $2 \sec x + 3 = 2 \cos x.$
9. $3 \csc x + 2 = \sin x.$
10. $\csc^2 x - \cot x - 1 = 0.$
11. $\tan^2 x + \sec^2 x = 7.$
12. $\cot^2 x + \csc^2 x = 3.$
13. $\tan x = 3 \cot x.$
14. $\cos x = \sin x.$
15. $3 \sin x = \sqrt{3} \cos x.$
16. $3 \tan x - \cot x = 0.$
17. $\tan^2 x - \sec x = 1.$
18. $3 \cos x = -\sqrt{3} \sin x.$
19. $\cot^2 x + 3 \csc x + 3 = 0.$
20. $\csc x - 2 \sin x = \cot x.$
21. $\sec x = \cos x - \tan x.$
22. $3 \sec x + 3 \tan x = 2 \cos x.$
23. $\csc x + \cot x = 2 \sin x.$
24. $\csc x = \sin x - \cot x.$
25. $\sin x + 1 = \cos x.$
26. $\sin x = 1 + \cos x.$
27. $\cos x = 1 - \sin x.$
28. $\cot x + 1 = \csc x.$
29. $\tan x = \sec x + 1.$
30. $\sec x + \tan x = 1.$
31. $\sin^2 x \sec x + 2 \sec x - \cos x = 3 \tan x.$
32. $3 \cot x - \cos^2 x \csc x - 2 \csc x + \sin x = 0.$
33. $9 \csc^2 x = 4 \tan^2 x.$
34. $2 \cot^2 x = \sec^2 x.$
35. $\sec^2 x - 1 = \cot^2 x.$
36. $\sec^2 x + 3 \cot^2 x = 5.$
37. $3 \csc^2 x - \tan^2 x = 1.$

Find all angles θ in degree measure which satisfy the equation. Use Table VII *if necessary.*

38. $\tan^2 \theta + \sec^2 \theta = 9.$
39. $\cot^2 \theta + \csc^2 \theta = 19.$
40. $\sec \theta + 3 = \tan \theta.$
41. $\cot \theta = \csc \theta + 2.$

REVIEW EXERCISE 43

Prove that each equation is an identity by use of equations on page 33.

1. $\cot\theta = \dfrac{\csc\theta}{\sec\theta}$. **2.** $\cos\theta = \dfrac{\cot\theta}{\csc\theta}$. **3.** $\dfrac{\tan^2\phi}{\sec^2\phi} + \dfrac{\cot^2\phi}{\csc^2\phi} = 1$.

4. By use of identities, find the values of all functions of the angle θ if (a) θ is in quadrant II and $\cos\theta = -\frac{7}{25}$; ($b$) θ is in quadrant III and $\tan\theta = \frac{24}{7}$.

5. Express (a) $\sin\theta$ in terms of $\cot\theta$; (b) $\csc\theta$ in terms of $\tan\theta$.

Find all solutions if the variable x is on the interval $0 \leqq x < 2\pi$. Use Table XIII *if necessary, obtaining results to the nearest hundredth.*

6. $\sin x = -\frac{1}{2}$. **7.** $\sec x = 2$. **8.** $\tan x = -\frac{1}{3}\sqrt{3}$.

9. $\cos x = .90045$. **10.** $\cos x = -.54030$. **11.** $\tan x = -2.6503$.

12. $3\sin x = 7$. **13.** $5\sec x = -3$. **14.** $6\csc x = 5$.

15. $1 + \sin x - 2\sin^2 x = 0$. **16.** $2\cot x\sin x - \cot x = 0$.

17. $4\cos^2 x = 3$. **18.** $2\sin^2 x = 1$. **19.** $3\tan x = \cot x$.

20. $\csc x + \cot x = 1$. **21.** $\sec x + \tan x = 2\cos x$.

Find all solutions for the angle θ if $0° \leqq \theta < 360°$, by use of Table VII.

22. $5\sin\theta = -2$. **23.** $\tan\theta = .7173$. **24.** $\cos\theta = -.2812$.

Prove that the equation is an identity by use of the fundamental identities.

25. $\dfrac{\sin x}{\sin x + \cos x} = \dfrac{\sec x}{\sec x + \csc x}$. **26.** $\dfrac{\sin x}{\sin x - \tan x} = \dfrac{\cos x}{\cos x - 1}$.

27. $\dfrac{\sin x}{\sin x + \sec x} = \dfrac{\cos x}{\cos x + \csc x}$. **28.** $\dfrac{\cos x}{\cos x - \sin x} = \dfrac{1}{1 - \tan x}$.

29. $\dfrac{\sin x - \sec y}{\sin x + \sec y} = \dfrac{\cos y - \csc x}{\cos y + \csc x}$. **30.** $\dfrac{\tan\theta - \csc\theta}{\tan\theta + \csc\theta} = \dfrac{\sin^2\theta - \cos\theta}{\sin^2\theta + \cos\theta}$.

31. $\cos^2\alpha\tan\alpha = \dfrac{2\sin\alpha}{\sec\alpha + \cos\alpha + \sin^2\alpha\sec\alpha}$.

32. $\sec^4\alpha + \tan^4\alpha = 1 + 2\sec^2\alpha\tan^2\alpha$.

33. $\dfrac{\sin\alpha\cos\beta + \cos\alpha\sin\beta}{\cos\alpha\cos\beta - \sin\alpha\sin\beta} = \dfrac{\tan\alpha\cot\beta + 1}{\cot\beta - \tan\alpha}$.

★*Solve the equation, for $0 \leqq x < 2\pi$, or prove that the equation is an identity.*

34. $8\sin^4 x + 10\cos^2 x - 7 = 0$.

35. $(\sin x - \cos x)^2 = 1 - 2\cot x\sin^2 x$.

36. $(1 + \sec x)(1 - \cos x) = \tan x\sin x$.

37. $3 - \cos^2 x\csc x - 3\sin^2 x = 2\cos^2 x$.

38. $(\tan x + \cot x)^3 = \tan x\sec^2 x + \cot x\csc^2 x + 2\tan x + 2\cot x$.

39. $\sin x\tan x - 2\sin^2 x\cos x + \tan x - 2\tan x\cos^2 x = 0$.

8

APPLICATIONS OF THE ADDITION FORMULAS

83. Addition formulas for the analytic sine, cosine, and tangent

In this chapter, we shall number with Roman numerals those identities to which we shall refer frequently. The following addition formulas (I) and (III), and their special cases (II) and (IV), respectively, were proved on page 50 for the sine and cosine when the domain of these functions was thought of as all angles. We now interpret x and y in (I)–(IV) as variables whose domain is all *real numbers*, and the identities are available for the analytic trigonometric functions of numbers as introduced on page 124. However, whenever convenient, we may return to the interpretation of (I)–(IV) as identities for the geometric trigonometric functions of angles, with x and y as symbols for angles whose measures are x and y in terms of *any* angular unit.

$$\sin (x + y) = \sin x \cos y + \cos x \sin y. \tag{I}$$

$$\sin (x - y) = \sin x \cos y - \cos x \sin y. \tag{II}$$

$$\cos (x + y) = \cos x \cos y - \sin x \sin y. \tag{III}$$

$$\cos (x - y) = \cos x \cos y + \sin x \sin y. \tag{IV}$$

ILLUSTRATION 1. In (II), if $y = \frac{3}{2}\pi$, we obtain the following reduction formula, because $\sin \frac{3}{2}\pi = -1$ and $\cos \frac{3}{2}\pi = 0$.

$$\sin (x - \tfrac{3}{2}\pi) = -\cos x \sin \tfrac{3}{2}\pi = \cos x.$$

By use of (I) and (III), we shall prove the addition formula (V) for the tangent function, and then obtain the special case (VI), of (V), by applying (4) of page 122.

$$\tan (x + y) = \frac{\tan x + \tan y}{1 - \tan x \tan y}. \tag{V}$$

$$\tan (x - y) = \frac{\tan x - \tan y}{1 + \tan x \tan y}. \tag{VI}$$

Proof of (V). 1. From (I) and (III), when $\cos(x+y) \neq 0$,

$$\tan(x+y) = \frac{\sin(x+y)}{\cos(x+y)} = \frac{\sin x \cos y + \cos x \sin y}{\cos x \cos y - \sin x \sin y}. \tag{1}$$

2. In (1), divide numerator and denominator on the right by $\cos x \cos y$, with the assumption that $\cos x \neq 0$ and $\cos y \neq 0$, which is true whenever $\tan x$ and $\tan y$ exist in (1):

$$\tan(x+y) = \frac{\dfrac{\sin x \cos y}{\cos x \cos y} + \dfrac{\cos x \sin y}{\cos x \cos y}}{\dfrac{\cos x \cos y}{\cos x \cos y} - \dfrac{\sin x \sin y}{\cos x \cos y}} = \frac{\dfrac{\sin x}{\cos x} + \dfrac{\sin y}{\cos y}}{1 - \dfrac{\sin x}{\cos x}\cdot\dfrac{\sin y}{\cos y}},$$

which is identical with the fraction at the right in (V). Hence, (V) is true at all values of x and y for which the two sides of (V) have meaning.

Proof of (VI). In (V), replace y by $-y$, and recall from page 122 that $\tan(-\theta) = -\tan\theta$. Then, (V) becomes (VI).

EXAMPLE 1. Find $\tan 75°$ by use of $\tan 45°$ and $\tan 30°$.

SOLUTION. In (V), we interpret x and y as angles, and use x as 45° and y as 30°. Then,

$$\tan 75° = \tan(45° + 30°)$$
$$= \frac{\tan 45° + \tan 30°}{1 - \tan 45° \tan 30°};$$

$$\tan 75° = \frac{1 + \frac{1}{3}\sqrt{3}}{1 - \frac{1}{3}\sqrt{3}} = \frac{3+\sqrt{3}}{3-\sqrt{3}}, \tag{2}$$

where we multiplied both numerator and denominator by 3. In (2), on the right we multiply numerator and denominator by $(3+\sqrt{3})$ to rationalize the denominator, and obtain

$$\tan 75° = \frac{(3+\sqrt{3})^2}{9-3} = 2 + \sqrt{3}.$$

EXERCISE 44

By use of (I)–(VI), *find the function values for the specified number by expressing it as a sum or difference of the suggested numbers.*

1. Find $\cos \frac{3}{4}\pi$ and $\sin \frac{3}{4}\pi$ by using function values at $\frac{1}{2}\pi$ and $\frac{1}{4}\pi$.
2. Find $\sin \frac{5}{4}\pi$ and $\tan \frac{5}{4}\pi$ by using function values at π and $\frac{1}{4}\pi$.
3. Find $\tan \frac{7}{6}\pi$ and $\cos \frac{7}{6}\pi$ by using function values at π and $\frac{1}{6}\pi$.
4. Find $\cos \frac{11}{6}\pi$ by using function values at $\frac{3}{2}\pi$ and $\frac{1}{3}\pi$.
5. Find $\cos \frac{7}{4}\pi$ and $\tan \frac{7}{4}\pi$ by using function values at 2π and $\frac{1}{4}\pi$.
6. Find $\cos \frac{5}{6}\pi$ and $\cot \frac{5}{6}\pi$ by using function values at π and at $\frac{1}{6}\pi$.
7. Find $\sin \pi$ and $\cos \pi$ by using function values at $\frac{4}{3}\pi$ and $\frac{1}{3}\pi$.
8. Obtain $\cos 45°$ and $\tan 45°$ by use of 180° and 135°.

Find the tangent and cotangent of the angle without using tables; the result may be left in radical form. Solve by first expressing the angle as a sum or difference of convenient angles.

9. 15°. **10.** 105°. **11.** 165°. **12.** 195°. **13.** 285°. **14.** 255°.

Expand by use of (I)–(VI) *and insert known function values.*

15. $\cos(\frac{1}{4}\pi - x)$. **16.** $\tan(x + \frac{1}{4}\pi)$. **17.** $\tan(\frac{1}{4}\pi - x)$.

18. $\cos(x - \frac{1}{4}\pi)$. **19.** $\sin(x + \frac{1}{3}\pi)$. **20.** $\sin(x - \frac{1}{6}\pi)$.

21. $\tan(x - \frac{3}{4}\pi)$. **22.** $\sin(\frac{2}{3}\pi - x)$. **23.** $\cos(\frac{5}{3}\pi - x)$.

24. $\tan(x + \frac{5}{4}\pi)$. **25.** $\sin(\frac{7}{6}\pi + x)$. **26.** $\cos(\frac{7}{4}\pi + x)$.

27. By use of (I) and (III), prove the following addition formula for the cotangent function. Then, obtain $\cot(x - y)$ by use of $\cot(-y) = -\cot y$.

$$\cot(x + y) = \frac{\cot x \cot y - 1}{\cot x + \cot y}; \qquad \cot(x - y) = \frac{\cot x \cot y + 1}{\cot y - \cot x}.$$

28. Compute (*a*) $(\sin 30° + \sin 45°)$ and $\sin(30° + 45°)$; (*b*) $(\tan 60° - \tan 45°)$ and $\tan(60° - 45°)$.

Do not expand or substitute function values on the left-hand side; complete each equality with a right-hand member which is a number symbol or a single trigonometric function value.

29. $\sin 25° \cos 65° + \cos 25° \sin 65° = ?$

30. $\cos 125° \cos 55° - \sin 125° \sin 55° = ?$

31. $\dfrac{\tan 15° + \tan 30°}{1 - \tan 15° \tan 30°} = ?$ **32.** $\dfrac{\tan 240° - \tan 15°}{1 + \tan 240° \tan 15°} = ?$

33. $\sin A \cos 10° - \cos A \sin 10° = ?$

34. $\cos A \cos 40° + \sin A \sin 40° = ?$

35. $\cos 15° \cos 60° - \sin 15° \sin 60° = ?$

36. $\sin 2A \cos A + \cos 2A \sin A = ?$

37. $\dfrac{\tan 2x + \tan x}{1 - \tan 2x \tan x} = ?$ **38.** $\dfrac{\tan 3x - \tan x}{1 + \tan 3x \tan x} = ?$

Without tables, find the values of all trigonometric functions of $(\alpha + \beta)$ and $(\alpha - \beta)$, if α and β are acute angles.

39. $\sin\alpha = \frac{3}{5}$; $\cos\beta = \frac{12}{13}$. **40.** $\tan\alpha = \frac{4}{3}$; $\cot\beta = \frac{12}{5}$.

41. $\tan\alpha = \frac{8}{15}$; $\sin\beta = \frac{12}{13}$. **42.** $\sin\alpha = \frac{5}{13}$; $\cos\beta = \frac{24}{25}$.

43. Without tables, find the quadrant in which the angle $(\alpha - \beta)$ lies in case α and β are acute, $\sin\alpha = \frac{5}{13}$, and $\cos\beta = \frac{7}{25}$.

Prove the identity.

44. $\sin(\frac{1}{4}\pi + x) - \sin(\frac{1}{4}\pi - x) = \sqrt{2}\sin x$.

45. $\cos(\frac{1}{6}\pi + x)\cos(\frac{1}{6}\pi - x) - \sin(\frac{1}{6}\pi + x)\sin(\frac{1}{6}\pi - x) = \frac{1}{2}$.

46. $\cos(\pi + x)\cos(\pi - x) + \sin(\pi + x)\sin(\pi - x) = \cos 2x$.

47. $\cot\left(\frac{1}{4}\pi + x\right) = \dfrac{1 - \tan x}{\tan x + 1}.$ **48.** $\tan\left(\frac{1}{4}\pi - x\right) = \dfrac{\cot x - 1}{\cot x + 1}.$

49. $\dfrac{\tan x + \tan (y + z)}{1 - \tan x \tan (y + z)} = \dfrac{\tan y + \tan (x + z)}{1 - \tan y \tan (x + z)}.$

Express in terms of $\tan A$ *and* $\tan B$, *without using radicals:*

50. $\dfrac{3 \sin A \cos B - \cos A \sin B}{3 \sin A \sin B + \cos A \cos B}.$ **51.** $\dfrac{\cos A \sin B + 3 \cos A \cos B}{\sin A \sin B + 3 \cos A \sin B}.$

84. Double-angle formulas

On substituting $y = x$ in (I) and (III), we find

$$\sin (x + x) = \sin 2x = \sin x \cos x + \cos x \sin x = 2 \sin x \cos x;$$

$$\cos (x + x) = \cos 2x = \cos x \cos x - \sin x \sin x = \cos^2 x - \sin^2 x.$$

Thus, we obtain (VII) and (VIII_a) below. We substitute $\sin^2 x = 1 - \cos^2 x$ in (VIII_a) to prove (VIII_b). To obtain (VIII_c), substitute $\cos^2 x = 1 - \sin^2 x$ in (VIII_a). To derive (IX), let $y = x$ in (V).

$$\mathbf{\sin 2x = 2 \sin x \cos x.} \qquad \text{(VII)}$$

$$\mathbf{\cos 2x = \cos^2 x - \sin^2 x.} \qquad (\text{VIII}_a)$$

$$\mathbf{\cos 2x = 2 \cos^2 x - 1.} \qquad (\text{VIII}_b)$$

$$\mathbf{\cos 2x = 1 - 2 \sin^2 x.} \qquad (\text{VIII}_c)$$

$$\mathbf{\tan 2x = \frac{2 \tan x}{1 - \tan^2 x}.} \qquad \text{(IX)}$$

These results are called *double-angle formulas*. They express trigonometric functions of $2x$ in terms of trigonometric functions of x. From (VIII_b) and (VIII_c) we obtain

$$\mathbf{1 + \cos 2x = 2 \cos^2 x; \qquad 1 - \cos 2x = 2 \sin^2 x.} \qquad \text{(X)}$$

ILLUSTRATION 1. From (VIII_b) with $x = \frac{1}{3}\pi$,

$$\cos \tfrac{2}{3}\pi = \cos 2\left(\tfrac{1}{3}\pi\right) = 2 \cos^2 \tfrac{1}{3}\pi - 1 = 2\left(\frac{1}{2}\right)^2 - 1 = -\frac{1}{2}.$$

85. Half-angle formulas

To exhibit (X) in different notation, we replace x by $\frac{1}{2}x$ on both sides of each equation in (X), to obtain

$$\mathbf{2 \cos^2 \frac{x}{2} = 1 + \cos x; \qquad 2 \sin^2 \frac{x}{2} = 1 - \cos x.} \qquad \text{(XI)}$$

From (XI),

$$\cos^2 \frac{x}{2} = \frac{1 + \cos x}{2}; \qquad \sin^2 \frac{x}{2} = \frac{1 - \cos x}{2}; \qquad (1)$$

$$\tan^2 \frac{x}{2} = \frac{\sin^2 \frac{1}{2}x}{\cos^2 \frac{1}{2}x} = \frac{1 - \cos x}{1 + \cos x}; \qquad (2)$$

$$\sin \frac{x}{2} = \pm \sqrt{\frac{1 - \cos x}{2}}; \qquad \cos \frac{x}{2} = \pm \sqrt{\frac{1 + \cos x}{2}}; \qquad \text{(XII)}$$

$$\tan \frac{x}{2} = \pm \sqrt{\frac{1 - \cos x}{1 + \cos x}}. \qquad \text{(XIII)}$$

In (XII) and (XIII), the sign to use on the right depends on the quadrant interval where $\frac{1}{2}x$ lies. The student is advised to concentrate on memorizing (XI), instead of (XII) and (XIII), which can be derived from (XI). We call (XI)–(XIII) the *half-angle formulas* because they express trigonometric functions of $\frac{1}{2}x$ in terms of functions of x.

Illustration 1. By use of (XIII) with $x = \frac{2}{3}\pi$,

$$\tan \tfrac{1}{3}\pi = \sqrt{\frac{1 - \cos \frac{2}{3}\pi}{1 + \cos \frac{2}{3}\pi}} = \sqrt{\frac{1 - (-\frac{1}{2})}{1 - \frac{1}{2}}} = \sqrt{\frac{\frac{3}{2}}{\frac{1}{2}}} = \sqrt{3},$$

where the "+" sign was used on the right in (XIII) because $\frac{1}{3}\pi$ is on an interval in quadrant I, where the tangent function is positive valued.

Example 1. Prove that the following equation is true at all values of x where $\cot x$ exists, with $\cot x \neq -1$ and $\cos 2x \neq 0$:

$$\frac{\cot x - 1}{\cot x + 1} = \frac{1 - \sin 2x}{\cos 2x}. \qquad (3)$$

Solution.
$$\frac{1 - \sin 2x}{\cos 2x} = \frac{1 - 2 \sin x \cos x}{\cos^2 x - \sin^2 x} \qquad \text{(VII) and (VIII}_a\text{)}$$

$$= \frac{\sin^2 x + \cos^2 x - 2 \sin x \cos x}{\cos^2 x - \sin^2 x} \qquad (1 = \sin^2 x + \cos^2 x)$$

$$= \frac{(\cos x - \sin x)^2}{(\cos x - \sin x)(\cos x + \sin x)} = \frac{\cos x - \sin x}{\cos x + \sin x} \qquad (4)$$

$$= \frac{\frac{\cos x}{\sin x} - \frac{\sin x}{\sin x}}{\frac{\cos x}{\sin x} + \frac{\sin x}{\sin x}} = \frac{\cot x - 1}{\cot x + 1}, \qquad (5)$$

where we divided both numerator and denominator on the right in (4) by $\sin x$ to obtain (5), which proves (3) when $\sin x \neq 0$. (We know that $\sin x \neq 0$ when $\cot x$ exists, which we assumed.)

Example 2. Express $\sin 3x$ in terms of trigonometric functions (*a*) of $6x$; (*b*) of $\frac{3}{2}x$. Or, with $3x$ thought of as an angle, express $\sin 3x$ in terms of functions of *twice the angle*, and functions of *half of the angle* $3x$.

Solution. 1. Since $3x = \frac{1}{2}(6x)$, we use (XII) with x replaced by $6x$:

$$\sin 3x = \pm \sqrt{\frac{1 - \cos 6x}{2}}, \quad \textit{or} \quad 2 \sin^2 3x = 1 - \cos 6x.$$

2. From (VII) with x replaced by $\frac{3}{2}x$, $\qquad \sin 3x = 2 \sin \frac{3}{2}x \cos \frac{3}{2}x.$

EXERCISE 45

From (VII)–(XIII), *find the sine, cosine, and tangent of the first angle, in radian measure or degree measure, by use of the second angle.*

1. $60°$ by use of $30°$.
2. $60°$ by use of $120°$.
3. $\frac{2}{3}\pi$ by use of $\frac{4}{3}\pi$.
4. $\frac{2}{3}\pi$ by use of $\frac{1}{3}\pi$.
5. $\frac{1}{6}\pi$ by use of $\frac{1}{3}\pi$.
6. $\frac{5}{3}\pi$ by use of $\frac{5}{6}\pi$.
7.* $\frac{1}{2}\pi$ by use of $\frac{1}{4}\pi$.
8.* $\frac{1}{2}\pi$ by use of π.
9.* $-\frac{3}{4}\pi$ by use of $-\frac{3}{2}\pi$.
10.* $-\frac{3}{2}\pi$ by use of $-\frac{3}{4}\pi$.

By use of (VII)–(XIII), *give a right-hand member without radicals which involves the value of only one function of some angle.*

11. $2 \sin 65° \cos 65° = ?$
12. $\cos^2 40° - \sin^2 40° = ?$
13. $1 - 2 \sin^2 80° = ?$
14. $2 \cos^2 125° - 1 = ?$
15. $2 \cos^2 20° = ?$
16. $2 \sin^2 20° = ?$
17. $1 + \cos B = ?$
18. $1 - \cos B = ?$
19. $2 \cos^2 40° = ?$
20. $1 + \cos 2B = ?$
21. $1 - \cos 2B = ?$
22. $2 \sin^2 80° = ?$
23. $1 + \cos 50° = ?$
24. $1 - \cos 70° = ?$
25. $\dfrac{2 \tan 38°}{1 - \tan^2 38°} = ?$
26. $\dfrac{1 - \cos x}{1 + \cos x} = ?$
27. $\dfrac{1 + \cos 40°}{1 - \cos 40°} = ?$

Prove the identity.

28. $\tan x = \dfrac{\sin 2x}{1 + \cos 2x}$.
29. $\cot x = \dfrac{1 + \cos 2x}{\sin 2x}$.
30. $\sec 2x = \dfrac{1}{1 - 2 \sin^2 x}$.
31. $\sec^2 x = \dfrac{2}{1 + \cos 2x}$.
32. $\csc^2 x = \dfrac{2}{1 - \cos 2x}$.
33. $\cot 2\theta = \dfrac{\csc \theta - 2 \sin \theta}{2 \cos \theta}$.
34. $(\sin \alpha + \cos \alpha)^2 = 1 + \sin 2\alpha$.
35. $2 \cos \theta - \cos 2\theta \sec \theta = \sec \theta$.
36. $\sec^2 \theta \cos 2\theta = \sec^2 \theta - 2 \tan^2 \theta$.
37. $\dfrac{\sec^2 x}{4 \sin^2 x} = \dfrac{1}{\sin^2 2x}$.
38. $\sec 2\alpha = \dfrac{\sec^2 \alpha}{1 - \tan^2 \alpha}$.
39. $\sec 2\alpha = \dfrac{\csc^2 \alpha}{\cot^2 \alpha - 1}$.
40. $\dfrac{\tan 2\alpha}{2 \tan \alpha} = \dfrac{\cot^2 \alpha}{\cot^2 \alpha - 1}$.
41. $\dfrac{1 - \tan x}{1 + \tan x} = \dfrac{1 - \sin 2x}{\cos 2x}$.
42. $\tan 2x = \dfrac{2}{\cot x - \tan x}$.

Express the sine, cosine, and tangent of the first number in terms of trigonometric functions of the second number.

43. 4α, in terms of 2α.
44. $2A$, in terms of $4A$.
45. $4x$, in terms of $8x$.
46. $8x$, in terms of $4x$.

* Where possible.

47. $\frac{1}{4}x$, in terms of $\frac{1}{2}x$.

48. α, in terms of $\frac{1}{2}\alpha$.

49. 3θ, in terms of $\frac{3}{2}\theta$.

50. $\frac{3}{2}x$, in terms of $3x$.

Express the first function value in terms of the second.

51. $\sin 3x$, in terms of $\sin x$.

52. $\cos 3x$, in terms of $\cos x$.

53. $\sin 4x$, in terms of $\sin x$.

54. $\tan 3x$, in terms of $\tan x$.

86. Product formulas

We recall the following identities:

$$\sin(\alpha + \beta) = \sin\alpha\cos\beta + \cos\alpha\sin\beta; \tag{1}$$

$$\sin(\alpha - \beta) = \sin\alpha\cos\beta - \cos\alpha\sin\beta; \tag{2}$$

$$\cos(\alpha + \beta) = \cos\alpha\cos\beta - \sin\alpha\sin\beta; \tag{3}$$

$$\cos(\alpha - \beta) = \cos\alpha\cos\beta + \sin\alpha\sin\beta. \tag{4}$$

On adding corresponding sides in (1) and (2), we obtain the following formula (XIV). On adding in (3) and (4) we obtain (XV). On subtracting in the order (3) from (4) we obtain (XVI). On subtracting sides in the order (2) from (1) we obtain (XVII).

$$\mathbf{2\sin\alpha\cos\beta = \sin(\alpha + \beta) + \sin(\alpha - \beta).} \tag{XIV}$$

$$\mathbf{2\cos\alpha\cos\beta = \cos(\alpha + \beta) + \cos(\alpha - \beta).} \tag{XV}$$

$$\mathbf{2\sin\alpha\sin\beta = \cos(\alpha - \beta) - \cos(\alpha + \beta).} \tag{XVI}$$

$$\mathbf{2\cos\alpha\sin\beta = \sin(\alpha + \beta) - \sin(\alpha - \beta).} \tag{XVII}$$

Although (XIV)–(XVII) occasionally are useful in applications, their main importance in this text is that they give a means for proving formulas in the next section.

ILLUSTRATION 1. From (XIV),

$$2\sin 150^\circ \cos 30^\circ = \sin(150^\circ + 30^\circ) + \sin(150^\circ - 30^\circ)$$
$$= \sin 180^\circ + \sin 120^\circ = 0 + \tfrac{1}{2}\sqrt{3} = \tfrac{1}{2}\sqrt{3}.$$

Note 1. Since $\sin(\alpha - \beta) = \sin[-(\beta - \alpha)] = -\sin(\beta - \alpha)$, we observe that (XVII) is the same as (XIV) with a mere interchange of α and β.

ILLUSTRATION 2. From (XV), $\quad 2\cos 8\theta\cos 2\theta = \cos 10\theta + \cos 6\theta.$

87. Sums and differences of sines and cosines

In (XIV)–(XVII), let

$$\boldsymbol{x = \alpha + \beta; \qquad y = \alpha - \beta.} \tag{1}$$

Then, $\qquad x + y = 2\alpha; \qquad x - y = 2\beta.$

Hence, $$\boldsymbol{\alpha = \tfrac{1}{2}(x + y); \qquad \beta = \tfrac{1}{2}(x - y).} \tag{2}$$

We use (1) and (2) in (XIV), (XVII), (XV), and (XVI), respectively:

$$\sin x + \sin y = 2 \sin \frac{x+y}{2} \cos \frac{x-y}{2}; \qquad \text{(XVIII)}$$

$$\sin x - \sin y = 2 \cos \frac{x+y}{2} \sin \frac{x-y}{2}; \qquad \text{(XIX)}$$

$$\cos x + \cos y = 2 \cos \frac{x+y}{2} \cos \frac{x-y}{2}; \qquad \text{(XX)}$$

$$\cos x - \cos y = -2 \sin \frac{x+y}{2} \sin \frac{x-y}{2}. \qquad \text{(XXI)}$$

ILLUSTRATION 1. By use of (XVIII),

$$\sin 50° + \sin 10° = 2 \sin \tfrac{1}{2}(60°) \cos \tfrac{1}{2}(40°) = 2 \sin 30° \cos 20°;$$

$$\sin 20° + \sin 80° = 2 \sin \tfrac{1}{2}(100°) \cos \tfrac{1}{2}(-60°) = 2 \sin 50° \cos (-30°)$$

[Since $\cos(-\theta) = \cos\theta$] $\qquad = 2 \sin 50° \cos 30°.$

Comment. By use of the identities for $\sin(-\theta)$ and $\cos(-\theta)$, whenever the negative of a number appears as the argument of a sine or cosine, we may change to a form where the negative sign is removed, as in Illustration 1.

ILLUSTRATION 2. By use of (XX), with $x = 4A$ and $y = 2A$,

$$\cos 4A + \cos 2A = 2 \cos \tfrac{1}{2}(6A) \cos \tfrac{1}{2}(2A) = 2 \cos 3A \cos A.$$

EXAMPLE 1. Prove the identity: $\dfrac{\cos 5\alpha + \cos 3\alpha}{\sin 5\alpha - \sin 3\alpha} = \cot \alpha.$

SOLUTION. Apply (XX) in the numerator and (XIX) in the denominator:

$$\frac{\cos 5\alpha + \cos 3\alpha}{\sin 5\alpha - \sin 3\alpha} = \frac{2 \cos 4\alpha \cos \alpha}{2 \cos 4\alpha \sin \alpha} = \frac{\cos \alpha}{\sin \alpha} = \cot \alpha.$$

EXERCISE 46

Check (XIV)–(XVII) *for the given angles.*

1. $\alpha = 60°, \beta = 30°.$ **2.** $\alpha = 30°, \beta = 60°.$ **3.** $\alpha = 60°, \beta = 300°.$

Express as a sum or difference involving functions of multiples of θ.

4. $2 \sin 3\theta \cos 5\theta.$ **5.** $2 \sin 2\theta \cos 5\theta.$ **6.** $2 \sin 3\theta \cos \theta.$

7. $2 \sin 3\theta \sin 5\theta.$ **8.** $2 \cos 3\theta \cos 5\theta.$ **9.** $2 \sin \theta \sin 9\theta.$

Express each sum or difference as a product.

10. $\sin 60° - \sin 20°.$ **11.** $\cos 40° - \cos 80°.$

12. $\sin 4x - \sin 2x.$ **13.** $\cos 2x - \cos 4x.$ **14.** $\sin 7y + \sin 9y.$

15. $\cos 3x - \cos x.$ **16.** $\sin x - \sin 3x.$ **17.** $\cos 3y + \cos 8y.$

Prove each identity.

18. $\dfrac{\sin 5x + \sin 3x}{\sin 5x - \sin 3x} = \dfrac{\tan 4x}{\tan x}.$ **19.** $\dfrac{\cos x + \cos 9x}{\sin x + \sin 9x} = \cot 5x.$

20. $\dfrac{\sin 4x - \sin 2x}{\sin 4x + \sin 2x} = \dfrac{\tan x}{\tan 3x}.$

21. $\dfrac{\sin 3x + \sin 7x}{\cos 7x + \cos 3x} = \tan 5x.$

22. $\dfrac{\cos 3x + \cos x}{\cos 3x - \cos x} = -\dfrac{\cot 2x}{\tan x}.$

23. $\dfrac{\sin 3x - \sin 5x}{\cos 5x - \cos 3x} = \cot 4x.$

24. $\dfrac{\cos 4x - \cos 2x}{\cos 4x + \cos 2x} = -\dfrac{\tan 3x}{\cot x}.$

25. $\dfrac{\cos 2x - \cos 6x}{\sin 6x - \sin 2x} = \tan 4x.$

26. $\dfrac{\sin 5x + \sin 3x}{\cos 5x - \cos 3x} = -\cot x.$

27. $\dfrac{\sin 2x - \sin x}{\cos 2x + \cos x} = \tan \dfrac{x}{2}.$

28. $\dfrac{\cos 5x + \cos 2x}{\sin 5x + \sin 2x} = \cot \dfrac{7x}{2}.$

29. $\dfrac{\sin 4x - \sin 2x}{\cos 4x + \cos 2x} = \tan x.$

Express as a product involving only tangents or cotangents.

30. $\dfrac{\sin 75° + \sin 15°}{\sin 75° - \sin 15°}.$

31. $\dfrac{\sin 6A + \sin 7A}{\cos 6A + \cos 7A}.$

32. $\dfrac{\cos \alpha + \cos \beta}{\sin \alpha + \sin \beta}.$

33. $\dfrac{\cos 75° + \cos 15°}{\cos 75° - \cos 15°}.$

34. $\dfrac{\sin 5B - \sin 4B}{\sin 5B + \sin 4B}.$

35. $\dfrac{\sin \alpha + \sin \beta}{\cos \alpha - \cos \beta}.$

88. Miscellaneous trigonometric identities

We give renewed emphasis to the following suggestions for proving trigonometric identities or solving trigonometric equations.

I. *If possible, avoid introducing radicals.*

II. *Usually, it is best to express any cotangent, secant, or cosecant of a complicated number in terms of the tangent, cosine, or sine, because of the nature of the formulas we have derived.*

III. *It may be convenient to express all function values in terms of function values for a single number.*

EXAMPLE 1. Prove the identity: $\cos 3x = \cos x - 4 \sin^2 x \cos x.$

SOLUTION. By (III), $\cos 3x = \cos (x + 2x) = \cos x \cos 2x - \sin x \sin 2x$

$$= \cos x(1 - 2 \sin^2 x) - \sin x(2 \sin x \cos x)$$

$$= \cos x - 4 \sin^2 x \cos x.$$

EXAMPLE 2. Prove the identity: $\dfrac{\cos x}{\sec 3x} + \dfrac{\sin x}{\csc 3x} = \cos 2x.$

SOLUTION. Since $\sec 3x = \dfrac{1}{\cos 3x}$ *and* $\csc 3x = \dfrac{1}{\sin 3x},$

$$\frac{\cos x}{\sec 3x} + \frac{\sin x}{\csc 3x} = \cos x \cos 3x + \sin x \sin 3x = \cos (3x - x) = \cos 2x.$$

EXAMPLE 3. Prove the identity: $\sin 3\theta - \sin \theta = 2 \cos^2 \theta \sin \theta - 2 \sin^3 \theta.$

SOLUTION. By (XIX) and (VIII_a), $\sin 3\theta - \sin \theta = 2 \cos 2\theta \sin \theta$

$$= 2(\cos^2 \theta - \sin^2 \theta) \sin \theta = 2 \cos^2 \theta \sin \theta - 2 \sin^3 \theta.$$

EXAMPLE 4. Prove the identity: $\cot \frac{\theta}{2} = \frac{\sin \theta}{1 - \cos \theta}$.

SOLUTION. By use of (VII) with $x = \frac{1}{2}\theta$, and (XI),

$$\frac{\sin \theta}{1 - \cos \theta} = \frac{2 \sin \frac{\theta}{2} \cos \frac{\theta}{2}}{2 \sin^2 \frac{\theta}{2}} = \frac{\cos \frac{\theta}{2}}{\sin \frac{\theta}{2}} = \cot \frac{\theta}{2}.$$

Comment. A more complicated solution would result from use of (XIII). A trigonometric function of any number is more conveniently expressible in terms of functions of *half of the number* rather than *twice the number.*

EXERCISE 47

Prove the identity.

1. $\tan \alpha \sin 2\alpha = 2 \sin^2 \alpha$.
2. $2 \cos \alpha = \csc \alpha \sin 2\alpha$.
3. $\cot \alpha \sin 2\alpha = 1 + \cos 2\alpha$.
4. $(\sin x + \cos x)^2 = 1 + \sin 2x$.
5. $\cos 3x + \cos x = 4 \cos^3 x - 2 \cos x$.
6. $\sin 3x = 3 \cos^2 x \sin x - \sin^3 x$.
7. $\sin 4x = 4 \sin x \cos x \cos 2x$.
8. $\cos (x + \frac{1}{6}\pi) \cos (x - \frac{1}{6}\pi) + \sin (x + \frac{1}{6}\pi) \sin (x - \frac{1}{6}\pi) = \frac{1}{2}$.
9. $\frac{\sin x}{\sec 2x} + \frac{\cos x}{\csc 2x} = \sin 3x$.
10. $\csc 2\alpha = \frac{\tan \alpha}{2 \sin^2 \alpha}$.
11. $\frac{\cos 2x}{\sec x} - \frac{\sin x}{\csc 2x} = \cos 3x$.
12. $\frac{2 \tan \alpha}{\tan 2\alpha} = 1 - \tan^2 \alpha$.
13. $\cot 3\alpha = \frac{1 - 3 \tan^2 \alpha}{3 \tan \alpha - \tan^3 \alpha}$.
14. $\sec 2\alpha = \frac{\sec \alpha}{2 \cos \alpha - \sec \alpha}$.
15. $\sec 2\alpha = \frac{\sec \alpha}{\cos \alpha - \sin \alpha \tan \alpha}$.
16. $2 \tan \alpha = \frac{1 - \tan^2 \alpha}{\cot 2\alpha}$.
17. $\tan^2 \theta + \cos 2\theta = 1 - \cos 2\theta \tan^2 \theta$.
18. $\frac{\cos 3x}{\sec x} - \frac{\sin x}{\csc 3x} = \cos^2 2x - \sin^2 2x$.
19. $\cot 2\alpha = \frac{\cos \alpha - \sin \alpha \tan \alpha}{2 \sin \alpha}$.
20. $\frac{1 + \cot x}{\cot x - 1} = \frac{1 + \sin 2x}{\cos 2x}$.
21. $\frac{\csc x - \sec x}{\sec x + \csc x} = \frac{\cos 2x}{1 + \sin 2x}$.
22. $\frac{\sin x + \sin 3x}{\cos x + \cos 3x} = \frac{2 \cot x}{\cot^2 x - 1}$.
23. $\cos (\alpha + \beta) \cos (\alpha - \beta) = \cos^2 \beta - \sin^2 \alpha$.
24. $\sin 3x \cot x + \cos 3x = \sin 4x \csc x$.
25. $\cos \theta - \sin \theta \tan 2\theta = \cos 3\theta \sec 2\theta$.
26. $\frac{\tan 2x}{1 + \tan 2x} = \frac{2 \tan x}{1 + 2 \tan x - \tan^2 x}$.
27. $\sec (\alpha + \beta) = \frac{\sec \alpha \sec \beta}{1 - \tan \alpha \tan \beta}$.

28. $\sec 3x \sin 6x = 2 \tan 3x \cos 3x.$

29. $2 \cos 2\alpha = \csc 2\alpha \sin 4\alpha.$

30. $2 \cot 4x = \cot 2x - \tan 2x.$

31. $\sin 6\alpha \tan 3\alpha = 2 \sin^2 3\alpha.$

32. $\sec^2 2x - 1 = \dfrac{1 - \cos 4x}{1 + \cos 4x}.$

33. $\dfrac{1 + \cos 6x}{1 - \cos 6x} = \csc^2 3x - 1.$

34. $\dfrac{\cos x}{\cos \frac{1}{2}x + \sin \frac{1}{2}x} = \cos \frac{1}{2}x - \sin \frac{1}{2}x.$

35. $\dfrac{\sin x}{1 + \cos x} = \tan \dfrac{x}{2}.$

36. $\dfrac{\cos^3 x + \sin^3 x}{2 - \sin 2x} = \dfrac{\sin x + \cos x}{2}.$

37. $2 \cot x = \cot \dfrac{x}{2} - \tan \dfrac{x}{2}.$

38. $\dfrac{1 + \cos x}{1 - \cos x} = \csc^2 \dfrac{x}{2} - 1.$

39. $\cot^2 \dfrac{x}{2} - 1 = \csc^2 \dfrac{x}{2} \cos x.$

40. $\dfrac{1 + \sin x}{\cos x} = \dfrac{\tan \frac{1}{2}x + 1}{1 - \tan \frac{1}{2}x}.$

★*Prove the identity.*

41. $\dfrac{\cos x}{1 + \sin x} = \dfrac{\cot \frac{1}{2}x - 1}{\cot \frac{1}{2}x + 1}.$

42. $\sec 2x = \dfrac{1}{\cos^4 x - \sin^4 x}.$

43. $2 \sin 3\alpha \cos 2\alpha - \sin \alpha = \sin 5\alpha.$

44. $\cos 4\alpha = \cos 2\alpha - 2 \sin 3\alpha \sin \alpha.$

45. $1 + \cot \alpha \cot 3\alpha = \dfrac{2 \cos 2\alpha}{\cos 2\alpha - \cos 4\alpha}.$

46. $4 \cos 6x \sin 2x \cos 4x = \sin 4x - \sin 8x + \sin 12x.$

HINT. Alter the right-hand side by use of (XIX).

47. $4 \cos 3x \sin 2x \sin 5x - 1 = \cos 6x - \cos 4x - \cos 10x.$

48. $\sin 5x - \sin 3x + \sin 2x = 4 \sin x \cos \frac{5}{2}x \cos \frac{3}{2}x.$

49. $\cos 4\alpha = 8 \cos^4 \alpha + 8 \sin^2 \alpha - 7.$

50. $\sin 5\alpha = 16 \sin^5 \alpha - 15 \sin \alpha + 20 \sin \alpha \cos^2 \alpha.$

51. $\sin x - \sin (x + y) + \sin (x + 2y) = \sin (x + y) \cos \frac{3}{2}y \sec \frac{1}{2}y.$

52. $4 \sin^3 \theta = 3 \sin \theta - \sin 3\theta.$

53. $4 \cos^3 \theta = 3 \cos \theta + \cos 3\theta.$

89. Miscellaneous equations

An equation in x which states the value of one trigonometric function of some constant multiple of a variable x should be solved without alteration, by inspection or perhaps with the aid of a trigonometric table.

EXAMPLE 1. Find all solutions of $\sin 3x = \frac{1}{2}$ on the interval $0 \leqq x < 2\pi$.

SOLUTION. Recall that $\sin \frac{1}{6}\pi = \frac{1}{2} = \sin \frac{5}{6}\pi$. Hence, $\frac{1}{6}\pi$ or $\frac{5}{6}\pi$, or either of these plus any integral multiple of 2π is a value of $3x$ which satisfies the given equation. To obtain all solutions for x on the interval $0 \leqq x < 2\pi$, we first list the corresponding values of $3x$ on the interval $0 \leqq 3x < 6\pi$:

for $3x$: $\quad \frac{1}{6}\pi,\ \frac{5}{6}\pi,\ (2\pi + \frac{1}{6}\pi),\ (2\pi + \frac{5}{6}\pi),\ (4\pi + \frac{1}{6}\pi),\ (4\pi + \frac{5}{6}\pi).$

To find the values of x which are solutions, we divide each of the preceding numbers by 3, which gives

solutions for x: $\frac{1}{18}\pi, \frac{5}{18}\pi, \frac{13}{18}\pi, \frac{17}{18}\pi, \frac{25}{18}\pi, \frac{29}{18}\pi.$

To solve a trigonometric equation in a variable x, we aim to find one or more equations, each involving only *one* trigonometric function of *one* constant multiple of x, whose solutions include all solutions of the given equation. If the operations in our work are of types which produce equations equivalent to our given equation, no test of the final results is necessary. However, if we employ operations which might introduce extraneous roots, final results must be tested in the original equation.

EXAMPLE 2. Solve for the angle θ: $\sin \frac{\theta}{2} = \frac{\sqrt{3}}{2}$.

SOLUTION. 1. Recall that $\sin 60° = \frac{1}{2}\sqrt{3} = \sin 120°$.

2. Hence, $\frac{1}{2}\theta = 60°$ or $\frac{1}{2}\theta = 120°$. Therefore, $\theta = 120°$ or $\theta = 240°$.

EXAMPLE 3. Solve for the number x: $\cos 2x - \cos x = 0.$

SOLUTION. 1. Use (VIII_b) to eliminate functions of $2x$:

$$2 \cos^2 x - 1 - \cos x = 0, \quad \textit{or} \quad (2 \cos x + 1)(\cos x - 1) = 0.$$

2. We solve $2 \cos x + 1 = 0$ and $\cos x - 1 = 0$ and obtain

$$x = 0, \quad x = \tfrac{2}{3}\pi, \quad \textit{and} \quad x = \tfrac{4}{3}\pi.$$

EXAMPLE 4. Solve for the number x: $\sin 5x - \sin x = \cos 3x.$

SOLUTION. 1. Use (XIX): $2 \cos 3x \sin 2x = \cos 3x.$

$$2 \cos 3x \sin 2x - \cos 3x = 0; \qquad \cos 3x\,(2 \sin 2x - 1) = 0.$$

2. Hence, $\cos 3x = 0$ *or* $2 \sin 2x - 1 = 0.$

The student should complete the solution of these equations as in Example 1.

EXAMPLE 5. Solve for the number x: $\tan 3x - \cot x = 0.$ (1)

SOLUTION. 1.
$$\frac{\sin 3x}{\cos 3x} - \frac{\cos x}{\sin x} = 0; \tag{2}$$

$$\sin 3x \sin x - \cos x \cos 3x = 0, \quad \textit{or} \quad \cos x \cos 3x - \sin 3x \sin x = 0; \tag{3}$$

from (III),
$$\cos (3x + x) = 0. \tag{4}$$

2. From $\cos 4x = 0$, we find $x = \frac{1}{8}\pi, \frac{3}{8}\pi, \frac{5}{8}\pi, \frac{7}{8}\pi, \cdots, \frac{15}{8}\pi.$

Comment. The domain of x in (1) does not contain any number x where $\cos 3x = 0$ or $\sin x = 0$, because then $\tan 3x$ or $\cot x$ would be infinite. We multiplied both sides of (2) by $\sin x \cos 3x$, which is not zero, to obtain (3), and then (4). Hence, any solution of (1) also is a solution of (4).

Thus, all solutions of (1) are contained in the list in Step 2. At any value of x in Step 2, we observe that $\cos 3x \neq 0$ and $\sin x \neq 0$, and hence [on dividing by $\cos 3x \sin x$ in (3)] equation (2) has x as a solution. Thus, the solutions of (1) consist of all angles in Step 2.

EXERCISE 48

Solve for all values of x on the interval $0 \leqq x < 2\pi$. If no solutions exist on this interval, find just one positive solution if there is any. Use Table XIII *if necessary, with $\pi = 3.14$, to obtain results to two decimal places.*

1. $\sin 2x = 0.$ **2.** $\sin 2x = -\frac{1}{2}.$ **3.** $\cos 2x = -1.$

4. $\tan 4x = \sqrt{3}.$ **5.** $\cos 2x = \frac{1}{2}\sqrt{3}.$ **6.** $\sin 3x = -1.$

7. $\csc 2x = -1.$ **8.** $\sin 3x = \frac{1}{2}\sqrt{3}.$ **9.** $\cos 3x = -\frac{1}{2}\sqrt{2}.$

10. $\cot 4x = 1.$ **11.** $\tan 3x = -1.$ **12.** $\sec 2x$ is infinite.

13. $\sin \frac{1}{2}x = \frac{1}{2}.$ **14.** $\tan \frac{1}{2}x = -1.$ **15.** $\tan \frac{1}{3}x = -\sqrt{3}.$

16. $\cot \frac{1}{2}x = 1.$ **17.** $\cos \frac{1}{2}x = -\frac{1}{2}\sqrt{3}.$ **18.** $\sin \frac{1}{3}x = \frac{1}{2}\sqrt{2}.$

19. $\cos 2x = 1.$ **20.** $\sin 3x = \frac{1}{2}.$ **21.** $\tan 2x = \frac{1}{3}\sqrt{3}.$

22. $\sin 2x = 2 \sin x.$ **23.** $\cos x = \sin 2x.$ **24.** $\cos 2x = \sin x.$

25. $\cos 2x = -\cos x.$ **26.** $\sin 2x = -\sin x.$ **27.** $\tan 2x = -\tan x.$

28. $\cos 2x = \cos^2 x.$ **29.** $\cos 2x = -\sin^2 x.$ **30.** $\sin 2x = 2\cos^2 x.$

31. $\sin 2x = .89121.$ **32.** $\cos 3x = -.38942.$ **33.** $\tan 2x = 1.1156.$

34. $\sin x + \cos 2x - 1 = 0.$ **35.** $\cos 2x - \cos x + 1 = 0.$

36. $\cos 2x = 2\sin^2 x - 2.$ **37.** $\cos 2x - 3\cos x + 2 = 0.$

38. $4\cos^2 3x = 3.$ **39.** $2 - \sec^2 2x = 0.$ **40.** $3 - \tan^2 2x = 0.$

41. $\cos 4x = \cos 2x.$ **42.** $\cos 4x = \cos^2 2x.$ **43.** $\sin 4x = 3\cos 2x.$

44. $\tan 4x = \tan 2x.$ **45.** $\sin 4x = 5 \sin 2x.$ **46.** $\cot 4x + \cot 2x = 0.$

47. $\cos 2x \cos x + \sin 2x \sin x = 1.$ **48.** $\sin \frac{1}{2}x = \sin x.$

49. $\sin x = 2\cos \frac{1}{2}x.$ **50.** $\cos x = \sin \frac{1}{2}x.$

51. $\sin 3x + \sin x = 0.$ **52.** $\cos 3x - \cos x = 0.$

53. $\cos 2x - \cos 6x = 0.$ **54.** $\cos 2x + \cos 3x = 0.$

55. $\sin 2x + \sin 4x = \sin 3x.$ **56.** $\sin x + \sin 5x = -\sin 3x.$

57. $\cos x - \cos 5x + 2\sin 3x = 0.$ **58.** $\sin 3x = \sin 5x.$

59. $\csc \frac{1}{2}x + \cot \frac{1}{2}x = 2 \sin \frac{1}{2}x.$ **60.** $\cot^2 \frac{1}{2}x + 3\csc \frac{1}{2}x + 3 = 0.$

61. $6\sin^2 2x + 5\sin 2x = 6.$ **62.** $\cot 3x + \cot x = 0.$

63. $\tan 3x \cos x - \sin x = 0.$ **64.** $\tan 5x - \tan 3x = 0.$

65. $\sin 3x + \sin 5x + \cos 2x - \cos 6x = 0.$

66. $\tan 2x - 2\sin x = 0.$ **67.** $\tan 4x + 2\sin 2x = 0.$

68. $\sin 2x - \sin 6x = 0.$ **69.** $\cos 5x - \cos x = 2\sin 2x.$

70. $\cot 2x - \tan x = 1 + \cot 2x \tan x.$

REVIEW EXERCISE 49

Find the sine, cosine, and tangent of the given angle by the specified method, without using a table. Rationalize denominators.

1. $75°$, by use of functions of the sum of two angles.

2. $105°$, by use of functions of the difference of two angles.

3. $60°$; use double-angle formulas. **4.** $22\frac{1}{2}°$; use half-angle formulas.

5. If α and β are acute angles, with $\sin\alpha = \frac{3}{5}$ and $\cos\beta = \frac{8}{17}$, find the sine, cosine, tangent of (*a*) $\alpha + \beta$; (*b*) 2α; (*c*) $\frac{1}{2}\alpha$.

6. Express as a sum: $2\cos 6°\sin 4°$; $2\sin 10°\cos 8°$; $2\cos 2\theta\cos 4\theta$.

7. Express as a product:

$$\cos 4\alpha + \cos 5\alpha; \qquad \sin 35° + \sin 45°; \qquad \cos 3\alpha - \cos 5\alpha.$$

Prove the identity.

8. $\cos 2\alpha\sec\alpha = 2\cos\alpha - \sec\alpha$. **9.** $\cos^4 2x - \sin^4 2x = \cos 4x$.

10. $\sin 2\alpha + \cos 2\alpha\tan 3\alpha = \sin 5\alpha\sec 3\alpha$.

11. $\dfrac{\cos 2x + \sin 2x}{\cos 2x - \sin 2x} = \dfrac{\cot 2x + 1}{\cot 2x - 1}$. **12.** $\cot\dfrac{\theta}{2} = \dfrac{1+\cos\theta}{\sin\theta}$.

13. $\dfrac{\cos x - \cos 3x}{\cos 3x + \cos x} = \dfrac{\tan x}{\cot 2x}$. **14.** $\dfrac{\sin x - \cos 2x}{\sin x + 1} = 2\sin x - 1$.

15. $\left(\dfrac{1+\tan x}{1-\tan x}\right)^2 = \dfrac{1+\sin 2x}{1-\sin 2x}$. **16.** $\sec\alpha = \dfrac{\sec\frac{1}{2}\alpha}{2\cos\frac{1}{2}\alpha - \sec\frac{1}{2}\alpha}$.

17. $\dfrac{\sin x}{\sec 2x} + \dfrac{\cos x}{\csc 2x} = \dfrac{1}{\csc 3x}$. **18.** $\dfrac{\sin 2x}{\cot x} = \dfrac{1-\sin 2x - \cos 2x}{1-\cot x}$.

Find all solutions on the interval $0 \leqq x < 2\pi$. If no solutions exist on this interval, find just one positive solution if there is any.

19. $\sin 2x = \frac{1}{2}\sqrt{3}$. **20.** $\tan^2 3x = 1$. **21.** $\tan 2x$ is infinite.

22. $\sin\frac{1}{2}x = -\frac{1}{2}\sqrt{2}$. **23.** $\cos 2x = \cos^2 x$. **24.** $\sin 3x = 3\sin x$.

25. $\tan^2 2x + \sec^2 2x = 7$. **26.** $\cos 3x = 1 - \sin 3x$.

27. $\cos 4x + 2\cos^2 2x = 2$. **28.** $\cos x + 2\sin^2\frac{1}{2}x = 2$.

★*Express each function value in terms of the specified function values.*

29. $\sin(\alpha + \beta - \gamma)$; in terms of the sines and cosines of α, β, and γ.

30. $\tan(\alpha - \beta - \gamma)$; in terms of the tangents of α, β, and γ.

31. $\cos 4x$; in terms of $\cos x$. **32.** $\sin 3\beta$; in terms of $\sin\beta$.

If $\alpha + \beta + \gamma = \pi$, prove the identity.

33. $\sin\alpha + \sin\beta - \sin\gamma = 4\sin\frac{1}{2}\alpha\sin\frac{1}{2}\beta\cos\frac{1}{2}\gamma$.

HINT. Finally use $\frac{1}{2}\gamma = \frac{1}{2}\pi - \frac{1}{2}(\alpha + \beta)$.

34. $\sin\alpha + \sin\beta + \sin\gamma = 4\cos\frac{1}{2}\alpha\cos\frac{1}{2}\beta\cos\frac{1}{2}\gamma$.

35. $\cos\alpha + \cos\beta + \cos\gamma = 1 + 4\sin\frac{1}{2}\alpha\sin\frac{1}{2}\beta\sin\frac{1}{2}\gamma$.

36. $\tan\alpha + \tan\beta + \tan\gamma = \tan\alpha\tan\beta\tan\gamma$.

37. $\sin^2\alpha + \sin^2\beta + \sin^2\gamma = 2 + 2\cos\alpha\cos\beta\cos\gamma$.

9

OBLIQUE TRIANGLES

90. Terminology about triangles

An *oblique triangle* is one which has no angle equal to 90°. This chapter bears its indicated name because the objective is to develop formulas applicable to oblique triangles. However, the formulas will apply not only to oblique triangles but also to right triangles, although no essential new information about them is gained. Hence, we proceed to consider *any* triangle ABC, as in Figure 88, where α, β, and γ are the measures of the angles at A, B, and C, respectively, and a, b, and c are the lengths of the corresponding opposite sides. Also, we shall use α, β, γ, a, b, and c as symbols for the angles and sides of which these letters represent the measures.

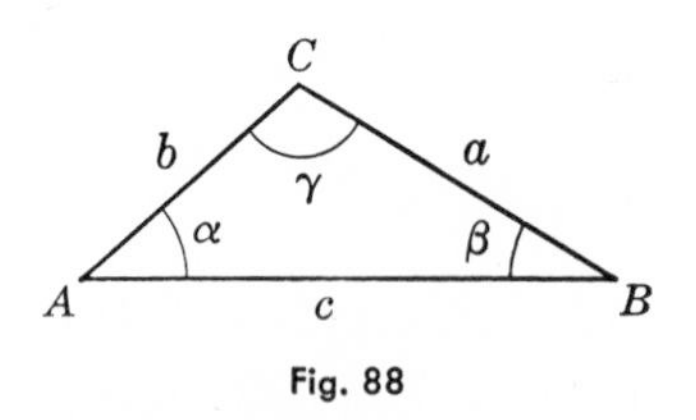

Fig. 88

Note 1. In this chapter, the trigonometric functions will be considered as functions of *angles*, as in Definition I on page 33, with any symbol such as θ in $\sin\theta$ representing an angle whose degree measure is θ.

The angles α, β, and γ, and the sides a, b, and c in $\triangle ABC$ will be called its *parts*. The student should recall from elementary geometry that we can construct $\triangle ABC$ if three of its parts, including at least one side, are given. Such data fall into four categories:

I. *Given two angles and a side.*

II. *Given two sides and an angle opposite one of them.*

III. *Given two sides and the included angle.*

IV. *Given three sides.*

In this chapter, we shall develop methods for computing the unknown parts of a triangle under each of Cases I to IV. The computation of the unknown parts is called the *solution* of the triangle.

91. Law of cosines

In any triangle, the square of any side is equal to the sum of the squares of the other sides minus twice their product times the cosine of their included angle. That is,

$$a^2 = b^2 + c^2 - 2bc \cos \alpha; \tag{1}$$

$$b^2 = a^2 + c^2 - 2ac \cos \beta; \tag{2}$$

$$c^2 = a^2 + b^2 - 2ab \cos \gamma. \tag{3}$$

On solving (1), (2), and (3) for the cosines, we obtain

$$\cos \alpha = \frac{b^2 + c^2 - a^2}{2bc}; \quad \cos \beta = \frac{a^2 + c^2 - b^2}{2ac}; \quad \cos \gamma = \frac{a^2 + b^2 - c^2}{2ab}. \tag{4}$$

Note 1. Suppose that triangle ABC is a *right* triangle with $\gamma = 90°$. Then, $\cos \gamma = 0$, $\cos \alpha = \frac{b}{c}$, and $\cos \beta = \frac{a}{c}$. Hence, from (1), (2), and (3),

$$a^2 = b^2 + c^2 - 2b^2, \quad \text{or} \quad a^2 = c^2 - b^2; \qquad b^2 = c^2 - a^2; \qquad c^2 = a^2 + b^2.$$

Thus, *for a right triangle, the law of cosines gives the Pythagorean theorem.*

Proof of the law of cosines. 1. Consider any $\triangle ABC$, and place it on an xy-system of coordinates with vertex A at the origin, B on the positive side of the x-axis, and C above the x-axis, as in Figure 89. The coordinates of B are $(c, 0)$. Let (k, h) be the coordinates of C. The radius vector of C is b. Notice that angle α is in its standard position on the coordinate system. Then, from Definition I on page 33, with $C:(k, h)$ as a point on the terminal side of α,

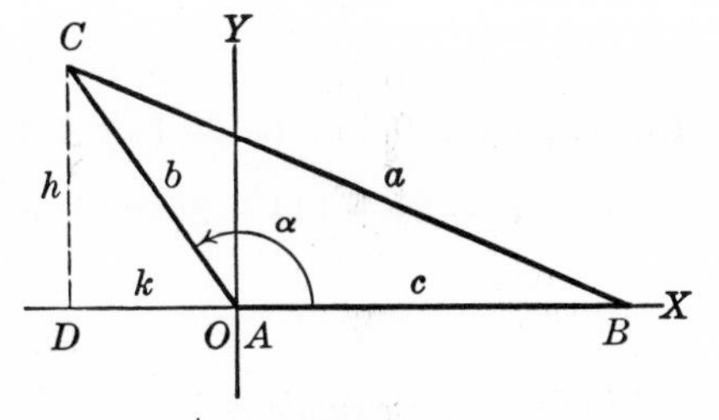

Fig. 89

$$\cos \alpha = \frac{k}{b} \quad \text{and} \quad \sin \alpha = \frac{h}{b}; \qquad k = b \cos \alpha \quad \text{and} \quad h = b \sin \alpha.$$

2. By use of the distance formula (1) of page 14 as applied to CB, with $C:(b \cos \alpha, b \sin \alpha)$ and $B:(c, 0)$, we obtain

$$\begin{aligned} a^2 = \overline{CB}^2 &= (b \cos \alpha - c)^2 + (b \sin \alpha - 0)^2 \\ &= b^2 \cos^2 \alpha - 2bc \cos \alpha + c^2 + b^2 \sin^2 \alpha \\ &= b^2(\sin^2 \alpha + \cos^2 \alpha) - 2bc \cos \alpha + c^2, \end{aligned}$$

which gives (1) because $\sin^2 \alpha + \cos^2 \alpha = 1$.

3. Since side a may be referred to as *any* side of the triangle, we obtain (2) and (3) by using (b, β) and (c, γ), respectively, in place of (a, α) as in (1).

92. Application of law of cosines to Case IV in solving triangles

The law of cosines is not well fitted for logarithmic computation. However, the formulas are used frequently without logarithms, particularly in physics. If a table of squares is available, or if convenient numbers are involved, problems of certain types can be solved efficiently by use of the law of cosines and natural values of the trigonometric functions.

OUTLINE. *Application of the law of cosines to solve* $\triangle ABC$ *under Case* IV, *that is, to find the angles when all sides are given.*

1. *Find each angle by use of its cosine, from* (4) *on page* 159.

2. *Check the solution by means of* $\alpha + \beta + \gamma = 180°$.

EXAMPLE 1. Solve $\triangle ABC$ if $a = 5$, $b = 7$, and $c = 11$.

SOLUTION. 1. From (4) on page 159,

$$\cos \alpha = \frac{145}{154} = .9416; \quad \cos \beta = \frac{97}{110} = .8818; \quad \cos \gamma = -\frac{47}{70} = -.6714.$$

2. By use of Table VII, we find $\alpha = 19° \, 41'$; $\beta = 28° \, 8'$.

3. Since $\cos \gamma$ is negative, $\gamma > 90°$. Let θ be the reference angle for γ, so that θ is acute and $\gamma = 180° - \theta$. Then, $\cos \theta = .6714$. From Table VII, $\theta = 47° \, 50'$. Hence, $\gamma = 180° - 47° \, 50' = 132° \, 10'$.

Check. $\qquad \alpha + \beta + \gamma = 19° \, 41' + 28° \, 8' + 132° \, 10' = 179° \, 59'$.

ILLUSTRATION 1. If $a = 5$, $b = 12$, and $\gamma = 60°$, then $\cos \gamma = \frac{1}{2}$ and, from (3) on page 159 and Table I or Table XII, we find

$$c^2 = 25 + 144 - 2(5)(12) \cos 60° = 109; \quad c = \sqrt{109} = 10.4.$$

EXERCISE 50

Find the obtuse angle α *by use of Table* VII.

1. $\sin \alpha = .2447$. **2.** $\cos \alpha = -.1363$. **3.** $\cos \alpha = -.7969$.

Solve without trigonometric tables if possible. Otherwise use Table VII.

4. $a = 3$, $b = 2$, $\gamma = 60°$; find c.

5. $b = 4$, $c = \sqrt{3}$, $\alpha = 30°$; find a.

6. $b = \sqrt{2}$, $a = 8$, $\gamma = 45°$; find c.

7. $b = 7$, $c = \sqrt{2}$, $\alpha = 135°$; find a.

8. $a = \sqrt{3}$, $c = 4$, $\beta = 150°$; find b.

9. $a = 2$, $c = 2$, $\beta = 120°$; find b.

10. $a = 3$, $b = 10$, $c = 8$; find γ.

11. $a = 7$, $b = 9$, $c = 4$; find α.

12. $a = 5$, $b = 6$, $c = 7$; find β.

13. $a = 9$, $b = 10$, $c = 7$; find γ.

14. $a = 13$, $b = 7$, $c = 8$; find α.

15. $a = 6$, $b = 12$, $c = 9$; find β.

By use of Table VII, *solve* $\triangle ABC$ *and check, if all sides are given. Otherwise, just find the requested side. Use logarithms where pertinent.*

16. $a = 5$, $b = 6$, $c = 4$.

17. $a = 8$, $b = 5$, $c = 7$.

18. $a = 6$, $b = 14$, $c = 10$.

19. $a = 13$, $b = 6$, $c = 9$.

20. $a = 5$, $b = 7$, $\gamma = 32°$; find c.

21. $a = 6$, $c = 10$, $\beta = 155°\ 30'$; find b.

22. $b = 5$, $c = 12$, $\alpha = 120°\ 40'$; find a.

23. $b = 4$, $c = 11$, $\alpha = 65°\ 38'$; find a.

24. Find the sides of a parallelogram if the lengths of its diagonals are 12 inches and 16 inches and one angle formed by the diagonals is 37°.

25. At 1 P.M., a train leaves a city T at 30 miles per hour in a direction due east, and a second train travels from T in the direction $N\ 20°\ W$ at 40 miles per hour. How far apart are the trains at the end of 2 hours?

26. In a storm cloud, an airplane meets an air current flowing vertically upward at a rate of 100 miles per hour. The pilot aims his plane 58° from the horizontal downward and his instruments show that his airspeed is 250 miles per hour. Find the resultant speed of the plane and the inclination of its path to the horizontal.

Find the magnitude of the resultant of the given forces acting simultaneously on the same object, by solving an oblique triangle.

27. 200 pounds and 300 pounds: angle between their directions is 78°.

28. 150 pounds and 250 pounds: angle between their directions is 67°.

29. 40 pounds and 70 pounds: angle between their directions is 123°.

93. Law of sines

In any triangle, the lengths of the sides are proportional to the sines of the opposite angles. That is,

$$\mathbf{a : b : c = \sin\alpha : \sin\beta : \sin\gamma}, \textit{ or} \tag{1}$$

$$\frac{\mathbf{a}}{\sin\alpha} = \frac{\mathbf{b}}{\sin\beta} = \frac{\mathbf{c}}{\sin\gamma}. \tag{2}$$

In (2), we are abbreviating three equations:

$$\frac{\mathbf{a}}{\sin\alpha} = \frac{\mathbf{b}}{\sin\beta}; \quad \frac{\mathbf{b}}{\sin\beta} = \frac{\mathbf{c}}{\sin\gamma}; \quad \frac{\mathbf{c}}{\sin\gamma} = \frac{\mathbf{a}}{\sin\alpha}. \tag{3}$$

Proof of (3). 1. Let α and β represent any two angles of $\triangle ABC$. At least one of α and β is acute; hence, without loss of generality in our proof, we may assume that the triangle is lettered so that β is acute. Then, let $\triangle ABC$ be placed on an xy-coordinate system, as in Figure 90 with A at the origin, B on the positive side of the x-axis, and C above the x-axis. Thus, α is in its standard position on the coordinate system. Let h be the ordinate of C, in Figure 90.

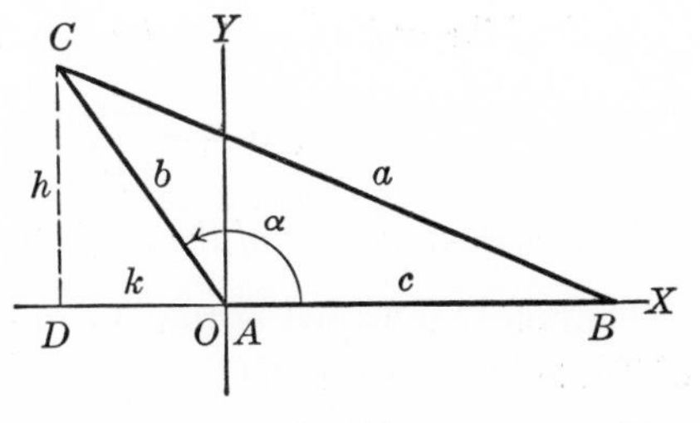

Fig. 90

2. From Definition I on page 33, with C as a point on the terminal side of α, we have $y = h$, $r = b$, and

$$\sin \alpha = \frac{h}{b}, \quad \text{or} \quad h = b \sin \alpha. \tag{4}$$

From right $\triangle DBC$, and the formulas of page 44 for acute angles,

$$\sin \beta = \frac{h}{a}, \quad \text{or} \quad h = a \sin \beta. \tag{5}$$

From (4) and (5),

$$a \sin \beta = b \sin \alpha, \quad \text{or} \quad \frac{a}{\sin \alpha} = \frac{b}{\sin \beta}, \tag{6}$$

where we divided both sides of $a \sin \beta = b \sin \alpha$ by $\sin \alpha \sin \beta$. Thus, we obtain the equation at the left in (3). Since α and β represented any two angles of $\triangle ABC$, we also claim that our proof justifies the other two equations in (3).

★*Note 1.* Let $k = AD$ be the abscissa of C in Figure 90. Then $\cos \alpha = k/b$, or $k = b \cos \alpha$, and D has the coordinates $(b \cos \alpha, 0)$. Also, B has the coordinates $(c, 0)$. From (4) on page 6 with $x_1 = b \cos \alpha$ and $x_2 = c$, we have

$$\overline{DB} = c - b \cos \alpha. \tag{7}$$

Also, from right $\triangle DBC$, $\cos \beta = \overline{DB}/a$, or $\overline{DB} = a \cos \beta$. Hence, by use of equation (7),

$$a \cos \beta = c - b \cos \alpha, \quad \text{or} \quad c = a \cos \beta + b \cos \alpha. \tag{8}$$

As a consequence of (8), for a and b on the left as well as c, we have the following results, called **projection formulas:**

$$\left.\begin{array}{ll} \mathbf{c = a \cos \beta + b \cos \alpha;} & \mathbf{a = b \cos \gamma + c \cos \beta;} \\ \multicolumn{2}{c}{\mathbf{b = a \cos \gamma + c \cos \alpha.}} \end{array}\right\} \tag{9}$$

These formulas are sometimes useful in checking the solution of a triangle.

94. Solution of Case I by the law of sines

To solve $\triangle ABC$ if two angles and a side are given, for instance α, β, and c.

1. *Find the third angle by use of $\alpha + \beta + \gamma = 180°$.*

2. *Find the unknown sides by use of the law of sines:*

$$\mathbf{a = \frac{c \sin \alpha}{\sin \gamma}; \qquad b = \frac{c \sin \beta}{\sin \gamma}.} \tag{1}$$

3. *To check, use one of the projection formulas* (9) *above.*

The solution as just outlined can be carried out without logarithms by use of Table IV or Table VII, or with logarithms by use of Tables V and VI.

Example 1. Solve $\triangle ABC$ if $b = 5$, $\alpha = 65°$, and $\beta = 30°$.

SOLUTION. 1. From (3) on page 161, $\dfrac{a}{\sin 65°} = \dfrac{5}{\sin 30°}$;

$$a = \frac{5}{\sin 30°}(\sin 65°) = 10(.9063) = 9.063. \qquad (\sin 30° = \tfrac{1}{2};\ \text{Table VII})$$

2. From $\alpha + \beta + \gamma = 180°$, $\gamma = 180° - 95° = 85°$.

From (1), $c/\sin\gamma = b/\sin\beta$, *or* $c = 10 \sin 85° = 9.962$.

The solution gives $\gamma = 85°$, $a = 9.063$, and $c = 9.962$.

EXAMPLE 2. Solve $\triangle ABC$ if $\beta = 37° 6'$, $\gamma = 42° 38'$, and $c = 21.37$.

SOLUTION. We employ the four-place Tables V and VI.

Formulas	*Computation*
	Data: $c = 21.37$, $\beta = 37° 6'$, $\gamma = 42° 38'$.
$\alpha = 180° - (\beta + \gamma)$.	$\alpha = 180° - (37° 6' + 42° 38') = 100° 16'$.
$\dfrac{b}{\sin\beta} = \dfrac{c}{\sin\gamma}$, *or* $b = \dfrac{c \sin\beta}{\sin\gamma}$.	$\log c = 1.3298$ (Table V) $\log \sin\beta = 9.7805 - 10\ (+)$ (Table VI) $\log c \sin\beta = 11.1103 - 10$ $\log \sin\gamma = 9.8308 - 10\ (-)$ $\log b = 1.2795$; $b = 19.03$.
$\dfrac{a}{\sin\alpha} = \dfrac{c}{\sin\gamma}$, *or* $a = \dfrac{c \sin\alpha}{\sin\gamma}$.	$\sin 100° 16' = \sin(180° - 100° 16') = \sin 79° 44'$. $\log c = 1.3298$ $\log \sin\alpha = 9.9930 - 10\ (+)$ $\log c \sin\alpha = 11.3228 - 10\ (-)$ $\log \sin\gamma = 9.8308 - 10\ (-)$ $\log a = 1.4920$; $a = 31.04$.
Summary.	$a = 31.04$, $b = 19.03$, $\alpha = 100° 16'$.

Check. $c = a \cos\beta + b \cos\alpha$.

$\cos\alpha = \cos 100° 16' = -\cos(180° - 100° 16') = -\cos 79° 44'$.

$a \cos\beta = 31.04(.7976) = 24.76$. (Table VII)

$b \cos\alpha = -19.03 \cos 79° 44' = -19.03(.1782) = -3.39$.

$a \cos\beta + b \cos\alpha = 24.76 - 3.39 = 21.37 \rightarrow \leftarrow c = 21.37$; *satisfactory.*

EXERCISE 51

Solve $\triangle ABC$ without logarithms by use of Table VII.

1. $b = 5$, $\alpha = 75°$, $\beta = 30°$.
2. $c = 3$, $\beta = 37°$, $\gamma = 30°$.
3. $a = 50$, $\alpha = 37° 30'$, $\beta = 71° 10'$.
4. $a = 200$, $\alpha = 32° 21'$, $\gamma = 21° 39'$.

Solve by use of four-place or five-place logarithms, and check.

5. $c = 15.67$; $\alpha = 42° 20'$; $\gamma = 53° 40'$.
6. $b = 231.6$; $\alpha = 19° 10'$; $\beta = 82° 40'$.
7. $a = 1.056$; $\beta = 23° 20'$; $\gamma = 53° 50'$.

8. $c = 6019$; $\alpha = 16° 30'$; $\beta = 59° 20'$.
9. $\alpha = 19° 41'$; $\beta = 28° 8'$; $a = 5.37$.
10. $\alpha = 64° 9'$; $\beta = 13° 0'$; $a = 12.3$.
11. $\alpha = 23° 54'$; $\gamma = 85° 16'$; $b = .4317$.
12. $\beta = 101° 36'$; $\gamma = 21° 44'$; $c = .04198$.
13. $\alpha = 23° 42'$; $\beta = 98° 18'$; $a = .03152$.
14. $\alpha = 31° 18'$; $\gamma = 42° 32'$; $b = .01571$.

★*Solve by use of five-place logarithms.*

15. $\alpha = 21° 36.4'$; $\beta = 82° 13.6'$; $a = 13.159$.
16. $\beta = 48° 23.7'$; $\gamma = 17° 16.3'$; $b = 27.001$.
17. $\beta = 23° 19.2'$; $\gamma = 33° 40.8'$; $a = 513.52$.
18. $\alpha = 83° 45.1'$; $\beta = 24° 18.9'$; $c = .75846$.
19. $\alpha = 19° 34.5'$; $\beta = 80° 14.5'$; $c = .011105$.
20. $\alpha = 58° 11.4'$; $\gamma = 63° 25.6'$; $b = .0031478$.
21. A polygon is inscribed in a circle whose radius is 6 inches. One of the sides subtends an angle of 27° at the center of the circle; find the length of this side by use of the law of sines.
22. One side of a parallelogram is 56 inches long. The diagonals of the parallelogram make the angles 35° and 47°, respectively, with this side. Find the lengths of the diagonals.
23. In triangle ABC, suppose that $\gamma = 90°$. Show that in this case the equations of the law of sines give merely the well-known expressions for the sines of the two acute angles of the right triangle ABC.
24. A battery commander B is ordered to shoot at a target T from a position G, from which T is visible. To check on the range GT as found by a range finder, B locates an observation point H from which T is visible. The bearing of T from G is $N\ 12°\ 48'\ E$, of T from H is $N\ 6°\ 23'\ W$, and of H from G is $S\ 82°\ 53'\ E$. From a map, it is found that $GH = 3250$ yards. Find the range of the target from G.
25. From Figure 90 on page 161, prove that the area, K, of $\triangle ABC$ is given by $K = \frac{1}{2}bc \sin \alpha$. Also, write two other similar formulas for K.
26. By use of Problem 25, prove that $K = (b^2 \sin \alpha \sin \gamma)/2 \sin \beta$. Then, write two other similar formulas for K.
27–30. Find the areas of the triangles in Problems 1–4, respectively, by use of two formulas, one from Problem 25 and one from Problem 26.

95. Solution of Case II, the ambiguous case

If two sides of a triangle ABC and an angle opposite one of these sides are given, we shall find that there may exist *two* solutions, or just *one* solution, or *no* solution for the triangle, depending on the given values. Since there may be two solutions, Case II is called the *ambiguous case.*

Note 1. Recall that, if k is a positive number less than 1, the equation $\sin \alpha = k$ has *two* positive solutions less than 180°, one *acute* and the other *obtuse*. This existence of *two* solutions is the fact which accounts for the possibility of two triangles as solutions in Case II.

If the given parts of a triangle ABC are a, b, and α, any triangle satisfying the data may be obtained geometrically as follows.

1. *Construct α with one side AD horizontal. On the other side, measure distance b from A to locate vertex C.*

2. *With C as center and radius equal to side a, strike an arc. The vertex B may then be located at any point where this arc cuts AD.*

In Figures 91 and 96, the arc does *not meet* AD, and hence there is *no* solution. In Figure 92, the arc is tangent to AD and there is just *one* position for B, with $\beta = 90°$. In Figure 93, the arc cuts AD twice, at B and B_1; hence there are *two* solutions, triangles AB_1C and ABC. In Figure 94 and in Figure 95, there is just *one* solution.

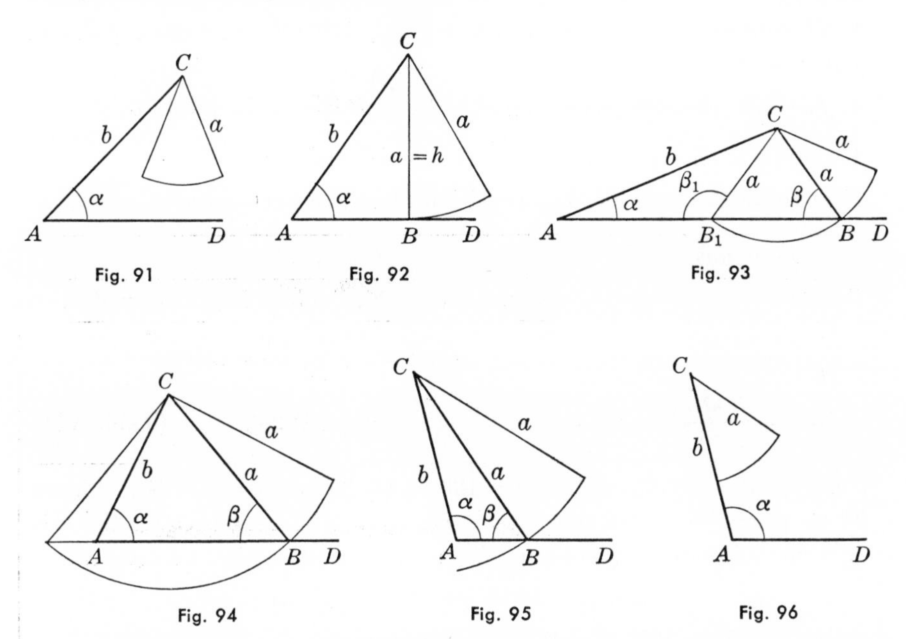

Fig. 91 Fig. 92 Fig. 93

Fig. 94 Fig. 95 Fig. 96

In a triangle ABC, let h be the perpendicular distance from C to side AB. Then, as in Figure 92, $\sin \alpha = h/b$ or $h = b \sin \alpha$. In Figures 91–93, where $a < b$ and $\alpha < 90°$, we observe that we have *no* solution, *just one* solution, or *two* solutions according as side a, the radius of the arc, is *less than, equal to,* or *greater than* h.

Note 2. The preceding remarks and Figures 91–96 justify the following summary of possibilities in case the given parts under Case II are a, b, and α:

$$\alpha < 90^\circ \begin{cases} \boldsymbol{a < b \sin \alpha}; & \textit{no solution} \text{ (Figure 91).} \\ \boldsymbol{a = b \sin \alpha}; & \textit{just one solution, with } \beta = 90^\circ \text{ (Figure 92).} \\ \boldsymbol{a > b \sin \alpha}, \textit{ but } \boldsymbol{a < b}; & \textit{two solutions} \text{ (Figure 93).} \\ \boldsymbol{a \geqq b}; & \textit{just one solution} \text{ (Figure 94).} \end{cases}$$

$$\alpha \geqq 90^\circ \begin{cases} \boldsymbol{a > b}; & \textit{just one solution} \text{ (Figure 95).} \\ \boldsymbol{a \leqq b}; & \textit{no solution} \text{ (Figure 96).} \end{cases}$$

Instead of memorizing the preceding summary, the student should *draw a figure roughly to scale for each problem* to learn the number of solutions.

OUTLINE. *To solve $\triangle ABC$ under Case II, with the given parts a, b, and α:*

1. *Construct the triangle approximately to scale.*
2. *Find β by use of* $\sin \beta = (b \sin \alpha)/a$. *If this gives*

   $\sin \beta > 1$, *or* $\log \sin \beta > 0$, *there is no solution;*

   $\sin \beta = 1$, *or* $\log \sin \beta = 0$, *then* $\beta = 90^\circ$, *just one solution;*

   $\sin \beta < 1$, *find one acute and one obtuse value for β.*
3. *Discard any value of β for which $\alpha + \beta \geqq 180^\circ$; for each value of β, compute $\gamma = 180^\circ - (\alpha + \beta)$.*
4. *For each pair of values of β and γ, compute $c = (a \sin \gamma)/\sin \alpha$.*

EXAMPLE 1. Solve $\triangle ABC$ if $a = 20$, $b = 10$, and $\alpha = 30^\circ$.

SOLUTION. A figure like Figure 94 indicates just one solution.

Formulas	*Computation*
	Data: $\boldsymbol{a = 20}$, $\boldsymbol{b = 10}$, $\boldsymbol{\alpha = 30^\circ}$.
$\dfrac{\sin \beta}{b} = \dfrac{\sin \alpha}{a}$, *or* $\boldsymbol{\sin \beta = \dfrac{b \sin \alpha}{a}}$.	$\sin \beta = \dfrac{10 \sin 30^\circ}{20} = .2500.$ $\beta = 14^\circ\, 29'$. (Table VII)
Comment. We also obtain $\beta = 180^\circ - 14^\circ\, 29'$, or $\beta = 165^\circ\, 31'$. Figure 94 on page 165 shows that this value cannot be used because there is only one solution, with β acute. To prove this otherwise, we compute $\alpha + \beta = 30^\circ + 165^\circ\, 31' = 195^\circ\, 31'$; since $195^\circ\, 31' > 180^\circ$, $\beta = 165^\circ\, 31'$ is impossible.	
$\boldsymbol{\gamma = 180^\circ - (\alpha + \beta)}$.	$\gamma = 180^\circ - (30^\circ + 14^\circ\, 29') = 135^\circ\, 31'$.
$\dfrac{c}{\sin \gamma} = \dfrac{a}{\sin \alpha}$, *or* $\boldsymbol{c = \dfrac{a \sin \gamma}{\sin \alpha}}$.	$\sin 135^\circ\, 31' = \sin (180^\circ - 135^\circ\, 31') = \sin 44^\circ\, 29'$. $c = \dfrac{20 \sin 44^\circ\, 29'}{\sin 30^\circ} = 28.03.$ (Table VII)
Summary. One solution:	$\boldsymbol{c = 28.03}$, $\boldsymbol{\beta = 14^\circ\, 29'}$, $\boldsymbol{\gamma = 135^\circ\, 31'}$.

EXAMPLE 2. Solve $\triangle ABC$ if $b = 4.157$, $c = 3.446$, and $\gamma = 51° 48'$.

SOLUTION. From Figure 97 below, two solutions are indicated.

Formulas	*Computation*
	Data: $\mathbf{b = 4.157,\quad c = 3.446,\quad \gamma = 51° 48'.}$
$\frac{\sin\beta}{b} = \frac{\sin\gamma}{c}$, *or* $\boldsymbol{\sin\beta = \frac{b\sin\gamma}{c}.}$	$\log b = 0.6188$ (Table V) $\log\sin\gamma = 9.8953 - 10$ (+) (Table VI) $\log b\sin\gamma = 10.5141 - 10$ $\log c = 0.5373$ (−) $\log\sin\beta = 9.9768 - 10;\ \beta = 71° 26'$. (Table VI) *Hence,* $\beta_1 = 180° - \beta = 108° 34'$.
	Solution for $\triangle ABC$, *Figure 97*
$\boldsymbol{\alpha = 180° - (\beta + \gamma).}$	$\alpha = 180° - (71° 26' + 51° 48') = 56° 46'$.
$\frac{a}{\sin\alpha} = \frac{c}{\sin\gamma}$, *or* $\boldsymbol{a = \frac{c\sin\alpha}{\sin\gamma}.}$	$\log c = 0.5373$ $\log\sin\alpha = 9.9224 - 10$ (+) $\log c\sin\alpha = 10.4597 - 10$ $\log\sin\gamma = 9.8953 - 10$ (−) $\log a = 0.5644;\quad a = 3.668$.
	Solution for $\triangle AB_1C$, *Figure 97*
$\boldsymbol{\alpha_1 = 180° - (\beta_1 + \gamma).}$	$\alpha_1 = 180° - (108° 34' + 51° 48') = 19° 38'$.
$\boldsymbol{a_1 = \frac{c\sin\alpha_1}{\sin\gamma}.}$	$\log c = 0.5373$ $\log\sin\alpha_1 = 9.5263 - 10$ (+) $\log c\sin\alpha_1 = 10.0636 - 10$ $\log\sin\gamma = 9.8953 - 10$ (−) $\log a_1 = 0.1683;\quad a_1 = 1.473$.
Summary. *First solution:*	$\mathbf{a = 3.668,\quad \alpha = 56° 46',\quad \beta = 71° 26'.}$
Second solution:	$\mathbf{a_1 = 1.473,\quad \alpha_1 = 19° 38',\quad \beta_1 = 108° 34'.}$

EXAMPLE 3. Solve $\triangle ABC$ if $a = 2$, $b = 6$, and $\alpha = 30°$.

SOLUTION *without logarithms.*

$$\sin\beta = \frac{b\sin\alpha}{a} = \frac{6(\frac{1}{2})}{2} = 1.5 > 1.$$

Hence, there is *no solution* because no value of the sine exceeds 1. A figure for this problem would look like Figure 91 on page 165.

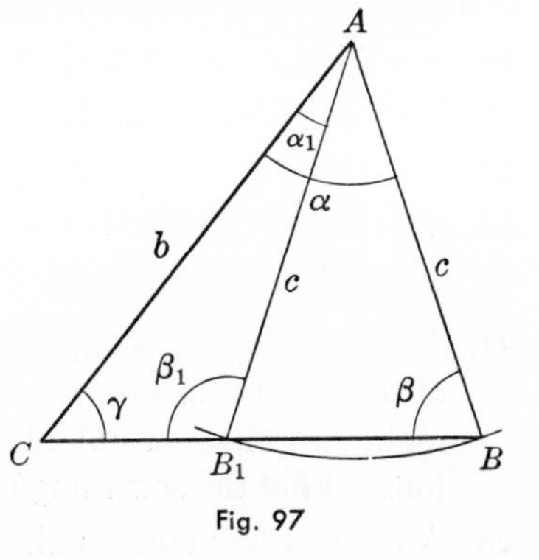

Fig. 97

SOLUTION *with logarithms.* If the logarithm of a number is *positive*, the number is *greater than* 1. Hence, on finding $\log\sin\beta = 0.1762$ on page 168, we see that

$\sin \beta > 1$, which is *impossible.* Therefore, there is *no solution.*

$$\sin \beta = b\frac{\sin a}{a}: \quad \begin{array}{r l} \log b = & 0.7782 \\ \log \sin \alpha = & 9.6990 - 10\ (+) \\ \hline \log b \sin \alpha = & 0.4772 \\ \log a = & 0.3010 \qquad (-) \\ \hline \log \sin \beta = & 0.1762, \textit{ which is positive; no solution.} \end{array}$$

Note 3. A solution under Case II may be checked as in Case I.

EXAMPLE 4. How many triangles exist with $a = 4$, $b = 8$, and $\alpha = 30°$?

SOLUTION. 1. A figure for this problem would look like Figure 92.

2. To find β: $$\sin \beta = \frac{b \sin \alpha}{a} = \frac{8 \sin 30°}{4} = \frac{8(\frac{1}{2})}{4}.$$

Hence, $\sin \beta = 1$ and $\beta = 90°$. There is just *one* solution, a right $\triangle$.

EXERCISE 52

Solve $\triangle ABC$ without logarithms by use of Table VII.

1. $\beta = 30°$, $a = 4$, $b = 5$.

2. $\gamma = 22° 20'$, $a = 50$, $c = 38$.

3. $\gamma = 65° 30'$, $b = 97.5$, $c = 91$.

4. $\alpha = 30°$, $b = 3$, $a = 5$.

5. $\gamma = 75°$, $c = 7$, $b = 7$.

6. $\alpha = 150°$, $a = 5$, $c = 8$.

7. $\alpha = 31° 20'$, $b = .25$, $a = .13$.

8. $\alpha = 157° 40'$, $a = 38$, $b = 25$.

9. $\gamma = 148° 40'$, $a = 20$, $c = 26$.

10. $\beta = 114° 30'$, $b = 13$, $c = 10$.

Solve by use of four-place or five-place logarithms.

11. $\beta = 42° 30'$, $b = 16.7$, $c = 12.3$.

12. $\alpha = 67° 40'$, $a = 2.39$, $c = 1.67$.

13. $\alpha = 76° 19'$, $a = .0572$, $b = .139$.

14. $\alpha = 71° 45'$, $a = .9632$, $b = .9632$.

15. $\beta = 36° 53'$, $c = .07531$, $b = .05126$.

16. $\gamma = 49° 46'$, $b = .9652$, $c = .4738$.

17. $\alpha = 113° 20'$, $a = 11.56$, $c = 7.282$.

18. $\gamma = 147° 5'$, $b = 19.36$, $c = 15.17$.

★*Solve by use of five-place logarithms.*

19. $\alpha = 24° 7.4'$, $a = 1.2695$, $b = 1.5873$.

20. $\gamma = 36° 48.9'$, $c = 7.4261$, $b = 5.1379$.

21. $\beta = 44° 13.3'$, $c = 6.6260$, $b = 4.6212$.

22. $\alpha = 35° 28'$, $a = 9.8470$, $b = 5.7135$.

23. $\gamma = 127° 19'$, $a = .74215$, $c = .97316$.

24. A telegraph pole is supported by two guy wires which run from the top of the pole to the ground on opposite sides. One wire is 53.6 feet long and makes an angle of 65° 20′ with the ground. The other wire is 57.5 feet long. Find the acute angle which the second wire makes with the ground.

25. A force of 85 pounds pulls due east on P. A second force pulls N 37° W on P. The resultant force is 73 pounds. Find the second force.

Without solving the triangle, construct all triangles which satisfy the data. Also, compute a perpendicular h, as referred to in Section 95, and apply a corresponding analytical test about the value of h to verify the geometrical conclusion.

26. $\alpha = 58°$, $a = 42$, $b = 50$.

27. $\gamma = 73°$, $a = 60$, $c = 58$.

28. $\beta = 115°$, $a = 35$, $b = 56$.

29. $\gamma = 41°$, $a = 200$, $c = 135$.

96. Solution of Case III by the laws of cosines and sines

Suppose that two sides and the included angle of a $\triangle ABC$ are known. Then, with any data which extend to, say, only three-figure accuracy, the following outline gives the solution of $\triangle ABC$ with reasonable convenience.

OUTLINE. *Solution of* Case III *for* $\triangle ABC$ *by the laws of cosines and sines, with the data consisting of the values of* b, c, *and* α.

1. *Find* a^2 *by use of* $a^2 = b^2 + c^2 - 2bc \cos \alpha$; *then compute side a either by use of a table of square roots or by use of logarithms.*

2. *Use* $\sin \beta = (b \sin \alpha)/a$ *to find* β. *Then use* $\gamma = 180° - \alpha - \beta$.

3. *If a check is desired, investigate* $(\sin \gamma)/c = (\sin \alpha)/a$.

EXAMPLE 1. Solve $\triangle ABC$ if $\alpha = 78° 50'$, $b = 73$, and $c = 94$, to obtain angles to the nearest $10'$ and side a to the nearest integer.

SOLUTION. We solve by use of Tables I, V, and VI.

Data: $\boldsymbol{\alpha = 78° 50'}$, $\boldsymbol{b = 73}$, $\boldsymbol{c = 94}$.	
Formula: $\boldsymbol{a^2 = b^2 + c^2 - 2bc \cos \alpha}$.	
(+) $\log 2 = 0.3010$ $\log b = 1.8633$ $\log c = 1.9731$ $\log \cos \alpha = 9.2870 - 10$ $\log 2bc \cos \alpha = 3.4244$;	*From Table* I, $b^2 = 5{,}329$ $c^2 = 8{,}836$ $b^2 + c^2 = 14{,}165$ $2bc \cos \alpha = 2{,}657$ (−) $\boldsymbol{a^2} = 11{,}508$.
From Table V,	$\log 11{,}510 = 4.0611$ $\frac{1}{2} \log 11{,}510 = 2.0306 = \log a$ $\boldsymbol{a = 107.3}$.
Formulas: $\boldsymbol{\sin \beta = \dfrac{b \sin \alpha}{a}}$.	$\log b = 1.8633$ (+) $\log \sin \alpha = 9.9917 - 10$ $\log b \sin \alpha = 1.8550$ (−) $\log a = 2.0306$ $\log \sin \beta = 9.8244 - 10$; $\beta = 41° 50'$ (*to nearest* $10'$).
$\boldsymbol{\gamma = 180° - (\alpha + \beta)}$	$\alpha + \beta = 120° 40'$; $\gamma = 180° - 120° 40' = 59° 20'$.
Summary.	$\boldsymbol{\beta = 41° 50'}$, $\boldsymbol{\gamma = 59° 20'}$, $\boldsymbol{a = 107}$.

Note 1. The method of the outline is convenient if slide-rule computation is permitted. In any case, we may state that all cases of solution of $\triangle ABC$ may be treated by use of *just the laws of cosines and sines.**

EXERCISE 53

Solve $\triangle ABC$ for the given data. Find any unknown sides to three significant digits, and unknown angles to the nearest 10′ *by use of Tables* I, V, VI, *and* VII, *as desired.*

1. $a = 12, b = 8, \gamma = 30°$.
2. $b = 30, c = 25, \alpha = 50°$.
3. $a = 50, c = 25, \beta = 110°$.
4. $a = 10, b = 15, \gamma = 150°$.
5. $b = 39, c = 14, \alpha = 68°$.
6. $a = 10, b = 44, \gamma = 43°$.
7. $a = .94, c = .35, \beta = 72°$.
8. $b = .66, c = .32, \alpha = 108°$.
9. $b = 13, c = 23, \alpha = 69° 40'$.
10. $a = 21, b = 9, \gamma = 70° 20'$.

11. The sides of a parallelogram are of lengths 185′ and 263′, and one angle is 39°. Find the length of the longer diagonal.

12. Two forces whose magnitudes are 341 pounds and 264 pounds act simultaneously on an object. If the angle between the directions of the forces is 64°, find the magnitude of the resultant force.

97. The law of tangents for a triangle

In a triangle, the difference of any two sides, divided by their sum, is equal to the tangent of one half of the difference of the opposite angles divided by the tangent of one half of their sum:

$$\frac{a-b}{a+b} = \frac{\tan \frac{1}{2}(\alpha - \beta)}{\tan \frac{1}{2}(\alpha + \beta)}; \qquad \frac{c-a}{c+a} = \frac{\tan \frac{1}{2}(\gamma - \alpha)}{\tan \frac{1}{2}(\gamma + \alpha)}; \tag{1}$$

$$\frac{b-c}{b+c} = \frac{\tan \frac{1}{2}(\beta - \gamma)}{\tan \frac{1}{2}(\beta + \gamma)}. \tag{2}$$

Proof. 1. Let b and c be any two sides and let us prove (2).

2. By the law of sines, $$\frac{b}{c} = \frac{\sin \beta}{\sin \gamma}. \tag{3}$$

3. Subtract 1 on both sides of (3); also, add 1 on both sides:

$$\frac{b}{c} - 1 = \frac{\sin \beta}{\sin \gamma} - 1; \text{ or } \qquad \frac{b-c}{c} = \frac{\sin \beta - \sin \gamma}{\sin \gamma}. \tag{4}$$

$$\frac{b}{c} + 1 = \frac{\sin \beta}{\sin \gamma} + 1; \text{ or } \qquad \frac{b+c}{c} = \frac{\sin \beta + \sin \gamma}{\sin \gamma}. \tag{5}$$

4. Divide each side of (4) by the corresponding side of (5); then use (XVIII) and (XIX) from page 151.

* It follows that, if minimum emphasis on computation is desired, the remaining sections of the chapter devoted to the law of tangents and half-angle formulas could be omitted.

$$\frac{b-c}{b+c} = \frac{\sin\beta - \sin\gamma}{\sin\beta + \sin\gamma} = \frac{2\sin\frac{1}{2}(\beta-\gamma)\cos\frac{1}{2}(\beta+\gamma)}{2\cos\frac{1}{2}(\beta-\gamma)\sin\frac{1}{2}(\beta+\gamma)}.$$

Hence, $$\frac{b-c}{b+c} = \tan\tfrac{1}{2}(\beta-\gamma)\cot\tfrac{1}{2}(\beta+\gamma) = \frac{\tan\frac{1}{2}(\beta-\gamma)}{\tan\frac{1}{2}(\beta+\gamma)}.$$

Note 1. Corresponding to (1) and (2), we obtain equivalent equations by changing the order of the letters. Thus, instead of (2), we find

$$\frac{c-b}{c+b} = \frac{\tan\frac{1}{2}(\gamma-\beta)}{\tan\frac{1}{2}(\gamma+\beta)}. \tag{6}$$

In any application, we use (6) if $c > b$ and (2) if $c < b$, in order to keep *the differences positive* for convenience in the formula employed.

We may solve a problem under Case III by use of the law of tangents. This method is convenient if logarithms are to be used.

EXAMPLE 1. Solve $\triangle ABC$ if $\alpha = 78° 48'$, $b = 726$, and $c = 938$.

SOLUTION. We solve by use of the four-place Tables V and VI.

Formulas	*Computation*
	Data: $\boldsymbol{\alpha = 78° 48'}$, $\boldsymbol{b = 726}$, $\boldsymbol{c = 938}$.
$\boldsymbol{\frac{1}{2}(\gamma+\beta) = \frac{1}{2}(180° - \alpha)}$.	$\frac{1}{2}(\gamma+\beta) = \frac{1}{2}(180° - 78° 48') = 50° 36'$.
$\frac{\tan\frac{1}{2}(\gamma-\beta)}{\tan\frac{1}{2}(\gamma+\beta)} = \frac{c-b}{c+b}$; *or* $\boldsymbol{\tan\frac{1}{2}(\gamma-\beta) = \frac{(c-b)\tan\frac{1}{2}(\gamma+\beta)}{c+b}}$.	$c - b = 212$; $c + b = 1664$. $\log(c-b) = 2.3263$ $\log\tan\frac{1}{2}(\gamma+\beta) = 0.0855$ (+) log numerator $= 12.4118 - 10$ $\log(c+b) = 3.2211$ (−) $\log\tan\frac{1}{2}(\gamma-\beta) = 9.1907 - 10$ $\frac{1}{2}(\gamma-\beta) = 8° 49'$. (Table VI)
$\boldsymbol{\beta = \frac{1}{2}(\gamma+\beta) - \frac{1}{2}(\gamma-\beta)}$. $\boldsymbol{\gamma = \frac{1}{2}(\gamma+\beta) + \frac{1}{2}(\gamma+\beta)}$.	$\frac{1}{2}(\gamma+\beta) = 50° 36'$ } *Add to get* γ. $\frac{1}{2}(\gamma-\beta) = 8° 49'$ } *Subtract to get* β. $\gamma = 59° 25'$; $\beta = 41° 47'$.
$\frac{a}{\sin\alpha} = \frac{c}{\sin\gamma}$, *or* $\boldsymbol{a = \frac{c\sin\alpha}{\sin\gamma}}$.	$\log c = 2.9722$ $\log\sin\alpha = 9.9916 - 10$ (+) $\log c\sin\alpha = 12.9638 - 10$ $\log\sin\gamma = 9.9350 - 10$ (−) $\log a = 3.0288$; $a = 1069$.
Summary.	$\boldsymbol{\beta = 41° 47'}$, $\boldsymbol{\gamma = 59° 25'}$, $\boldsymbol{a = 1069}$.
Check. $\boldsymbol{\frac{a}{\sin\alpha} = \frac{b}{\sin\beta}}$. $\log a = 13.0289 - 10$ $\log\sin\alpha = 9.9916 - 10$ (−) $\log(a/\sin\alpha) = 3.0373$ ⟶	$\log b = 12.8609 - 10$ $\log\sin\beta = 9.8237 - 10$ (−) ⟵ $\log(b/\sin\beta) = 3.0372$; *satisfactory*.

Note 2. Refined checks of solutions of triangles obtained under Cases I, II, and III are provided by formulas of the law of tangents.

ILLUSTRATION 1. In Example 1, we could have checked the solution by computing the logarithms of the two sides of either formula of the law of tangents not used in solving Example 1. For instance, we could have tested by use of the formula at the left in (1).

EXAMPLE 2. Check the first solution in Example 2, Section 95.

SOLUTION. The data were $b = 4.157$, $c = 3.446$, and $\gamma = 51°\,48'$. The solution was $a = 3.668$, $\alpha = 56°\,46'$, and $\beta = 71°\,26'$.

Check formula:

$$\frac{b-a}{b+a} = \frac{\tan\frac{1}{2}(\beta-\alpha)}{\tan\frac{1}{2}(\beta+\alpha)}.$$

$$b = 4.157 \qquad \beta = 71°\,26'$$
$$a = 3.668 \qquad \alpha = 56°\,46'$$
$$b + a = 7.825 \qquad \beta + \alpha = 128°\,12'$$
$$b - a = .489 \qquad \beta - \alpha = 14°\,40'$$
$$\tfrac{1}{2}(\beta+\alpha) = 64°\,6'; \quad \tfrac{1}{2}(\beta-\alpha) = 7°\,20'.$$

$$\begin{cases}\log(b-a) = 9.6893 - 10\\ \log(b+a) = 0.8935 \qquad (-)\end{cases} \qquad \begin{cases}\log\tan\frac{1}{2}(\beta-\alpha) = 9.1096 - 10\\ \log\tan\frac{1}{2}(\beta+\alpha) = 0.3137 \qquad (-)\end{cases}$$

$$\log\frac{b-a}{b+a} = 8.7958 - 10 \longrightarrow \quad \longleftarrow \log\frac{\tan\frac{1}{2}(\beta-\alpha)}{\tan\frac{1}{2}(\beta+\alpha)} = 8.7959 - 10.$$

OUTLINE. *Solution of $\triangle ABC$ with given parts a, b, and γ, by use of the law of tangents.*

1. *Compute* $\frac{1}{2}(\alpha+\beta) = \frac{1}{2}(180° - \gamma)$.
2. *Find* $\frac{1}{2}(\alpha-\beta)$ *by use of the formula of the law of tangents involving* a, b, α, β.
3. *Compute* $\alpha = \frac{1}{2}(\alpha+\beta) + \frac{1}{2}(\alpha-\beta)$; $\beta = \frac{1}{2}(\alpha+\beta) - \frac{1}{2}(\alpha-\beta)$.
4. *Find c from the law of sines.*
5. *Check by a formula of the law of sines not used in solving.*

★*Note 3.* It can be proved that, in any $\triangle ABC$,

$$\frac{a-b}{c} = \frac{\sin\frac{1}{2}(\alpha-\beta)}{\cos\frac{1}{2}\gamma}; \qquad \frac{b-c}{a} = \frac{\sin\frac{1}{2}(\beta-\gamma)}{\cos\frac{1}{2}\alpha}; \text{ etc.;} \tag{7}$$

$$\frac{a+b}{c} = \frac{\cos\frac{1}{2}(\alpha-\beta)}{\sin\frac{1}{2}\gamma}; \qquad \frac{b+c}{a} = \frac{\cos\frac{1}{2}(\beta-\gamma)}{\sin\frac{1}{2}\alpha}; \text{ etc.} \tag{8}$$

These results are called **Mollweide's equations,** in recognition of their use by a German astronomer KARL MOLLWEIDE (1774–1825), although the formulas were known before his time. Equations (7) and (8) give sensitive checks on the solution of a triangle because each formula involves all parts of the triangle. Proofs of (7) and (8) resemble the derivation of the law of tangents.

EXERCISE 54

1–4. Find the unknown angles in Problems 1–4, respectively, of Exercise 53 on page 170 by use of the law of tangents without logarithms.

Solve $\triangle ABC$ by use of four-place or five-place logarithms, and check as directed by the instructor.

5. $b = 387$, $c = 136$, $\alpha = 68°$. **6.** $a = 102$, $b = 437$, $\gamma = 43°$.

7. $a = .936$, $c = .348$, $\beta = 72°$. **8.** $b = .657$, $c = .319$, $\alpha = 108°$.

9. $a = 13.16$, $c = 22.78$, $\beta = 69° 40'$. **10.** $a = 21.45$, $b = 9.36$, $\gamma = 70° 25'$.

11. $a = 773.6$, $c = 993.4$, $\beta = 120° 30'$.

★*Solve and check by use of five-place logarithms.*

12. $a = 21.467$, $b = 13.218$, $\gamma = 19° 20.6'$.

13. $b = 316.25$, $c = 158.67$, $\alpha = 61° 19.8'$.

14. $a = .98315$, $c = 1.25670$, $\beta = 57° 35.7'$.

15. $b = .84107$, $c = 1.36450$, $\alpha = 98° 16.8'$.

16. $a = 31024$, $c = 65937$, $\beta = 58° 7' 25''$.

17. $b = 13056.0$, $c = 8947.2$, $\alpha = 105° 6' 29''$.

18. Two forces whose magnitudes are 340.6 pounds and 263.5 pounds act simultaneously on an object. If the angle between the directions of the forces is 63° 48′, find the magnitude of the resultant force.

19. A battery B is to fire at an invisible target T. An observation point H is located from which B and T are visible. With a range finder, it is determined that $\overline{HB} = 1250$ yards and $\overline{HT} = 5350$ yards. If the bearing of T from H is $N\,38°\,16'\,W$ and of B from H is $S\,20°\,5'\,W$, find the range $\overline{BT}$ and the direction of T from B.

98. Tangents of the half-angles

We recall that the bisectors of the angles of a triangle ABC, as in Figure 98, meet at the center O of the *inscribed circle*. Let r be its radius. Then, in Figure 98,

$$\overline{OD} = \overline{OE} = \overline{OF} = r.$$

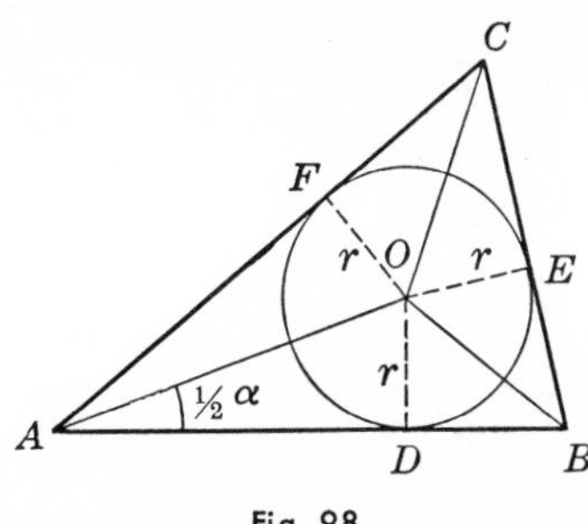

Fig. 98

Later, we shall obtain a formula for r in terms of sides a, b, and c. Let s be one half of the perimeter of triangle ABC:

$$s = \tfrac{1}{2}(a + b + c). \tag{1}$$

Then, we shall prove the following results:

$$\tan\frac{\alpha}{2} = \frac{r}{s - a}; \qquad \tan\frac{\beta}{2} = \frac{r}{s - b}; \qquad \tan\frac{\gamma}{2} = \frac{r}{s - c}. \tag{2}$$

Proof. 1. From right $\triangle ADO$ in Figure 98,

$$\tan\frac{\alpha}{2} = \frac{\overline{OD}}{\overline{AD}} = \frac{r}{\overline{AD}}. \tag{3}$$

2. The whole perimeter is

$$2s = (\overline{AD} + \overline{AF}) + (\overline{BE} + \overline{BD}) + (\overline{CE} + \overline{CF}.)$$

But, from Figure 98, $\overline{AF} = \overline{AD}$; $\overline{BD} = \overline{BE}$; $\overline{CF} = \overline{CE}$. Therefore,

$$2s = 2\overline{AD} + 2\overline{BE} + 2\overline{CE}; \text{ or}$$

$$s = \overline{AD} + (\overline{BE} + \overline{CE}).$$

Since $\overline{BE} + \overline{CE} = \overline{BC} = a$, then $s = \overline{AD} + a$, or

$$\overline{AD} = s - a.$$

3. Hence, from (3) we obtain (2) for $\alpha/2$. From symmetry, we obtain the two other formulas in (2).

Note 1. Observe that (2) will not be useful until a formula for r is obtained in the following section, which also gives a second proof for (2).

99. Sines, cosines, and tangents of the half-angles

Let α be any angle of triangle ABC. Then, without use of the preceding section, we shall show that

$$\sin\frac{\alpha}{2} = \sqrt{\frac{(s-b)(s-c)}{bc}}; \quad \cos\frac{\alpha}{2} = \sqrt{\frac{s(s-a)}{bc}}; \quad \tan\frac{\alpha}{2} = \frac{r}{s-a}. \tag{1}$$

Proof. 1. Since $2s = a + b + c$, then $2s - 2b = a + c - b$. This proves the second equation in (2) below. Each of (3) is proved similarly.

$$a + b + c = 2s; \qquad a + c - b = 2(s - b); \tag{2}$$

$$b + c - a = 2(s - a); \qquad a + b - c = 2(s - c). \tag{3}$$

2. By the law of cosines,
$$\cos\alpha = \frac{b^2 + c^2 - a^2}{2bc}. \tag{4}$$

From (XI) on page 147, $2\cos^2\frac{1}{2}\alpha = 1 + \cos\alpha$. Hence, from (4),

$$2\cos^2\frac{\alpha}{2} = 1 + \frac{b^2 + c^2 - a^2}{2bc} = \frac{(b^2 + 2bc + c^2) - a^2}{2bc};$$

$$\cos^2\frac{\alpha}{2} = \frac{(b+c)^2 - a^2}{4bc} = \frac{(b+c+a)(b+c-a)}{4bc}. \tag{5}$$

On using (2) and (3) in (5), we obtain

$$\cos^2\frac{\alpha}{2} = \frac{s(s-a)}{bc}, \quad \text{or} \quad \cos\frac{\alpha}{2} = \sqrt{\frac{s(s-a)}{bc}}. \tag{6}$$

3. Similarly, since $2\sin^2 \frac{1}{2}\alpha = 1 - \cos\alpha$, from (4) we derive

$$\sin\frac{\alpha}{2} = \sqrt{\frac{(a-b+c)(a+b-c)}{4bc}} = \sqrt{\frac{(s-b)(s-c)}{bc}}. \tag{7}$$

4. From (6) and (7), $\tan\frac{1}{2}\alpha = \dfrac{\sin\frac{1}{2}\alpha}{\cos\frac{1}{2}\alpha} = \sqrt{\dfrac{(s-b)(s-c)}{s(s-a)}}.$

Multiply numerator and denominator of the radicand by $(s-a)$:

$$\tan\frac{\alpha}{2} = \sqrt{\frac{(s-a)(s-b)(s-c)}{s(s-a)^2}} = \frac{1}{s-a}\sqrt{\frac{(s-a)(s-b)(s-c)}{s}}. \tag{8}$$

If we let

$$\boldsymbol{r} = \sqrt{\frac{(\boldsymbol{s}-\boldsymbol{a})(\boldsymbol{s}-\boldsymbol{b})(\boldsymbol{s}-\boldsymbol{c})}{\boldsymbol{s}}}, \tag{9}$$

then

$$\tan\frac{\alpha}{2} = \frac{r}{s-a}. \tag{10}$$

In arriving at (10), we made no use of Section 98, and r was introduced in (9) *merely as an abbreviation for a radical.* But, we may now compare equation (10) above with $\tan\frac{1}{2}\alpha$ in (2) in Section 98 on page 173; since the denominators are the *same* in the right-hand members, the numerators must represent the *same quantity*. Hence, we have proved that *the radius r of the inscribed circle of a triangle ABC is given by* (9).

Note 1. By altering the letters in formulas (1), we obtain similar formulas for functions of $\beta/2$ and $\gamma/2$. Thus,

$$\sin\frac{\beta}{2} = \sqrt{\frac{(s-a)(s-c)}{ac}}; \qquad \cos\frac{\gamma}{2} = \sqrt{\frac{s(s-c)}{ab}}.$$

100. Solution of Case IV by the half-angle formulas

Suppose that all sides of triangle ABC are given. *If just one* of its angles is desired, we may use the preceding formulas for the *sine* or *cosine* of half of the angle, because then it is *unnecessary to find* r or its logarithm. If *all* angles of the triangle are desired, it is best to use tangents of the half-angles.

SUMMARY. *To obtain the angles when the sides are known.*

1. *Compute* s, $(s-a)$, $(s-b)$, $(s-c)$, *and then* $\log r$, *by use of*

$$r = \sqrt{\frac{(s-a)(s-b)(s-c)}{s}}.$$

2. *Find* α, β, *and* γ *by use of the tangents of the half-angles.*

3. *Check by use of* $\alpha + \beta + \gamma = 180°$.

EXAMPLE 1. Solve $\triangle ABC$ if $a = 173$, $b = 267$, $c = 412$.

SOLUTION. We apply the summary, and four-place logarithms.

Formulas	*Computation*
$\mathbf{s = \frac{1}{2}(a + b + c)}$. *To check here, notice that* $(s-a)+(s-b)+(s-c)$ $= 3s - (a+b+c) = s$.	$\left.\begin{array}{r} a = 173 \\ b = 267 \\ c = 412 \end{array}\right\}(+)$ $2s = 852 \longrightarrow$; $\left.\begin{array}{r} s-a = 253 \\ s-b = 159 \\ s-c = 14 \end{array}\right\}(+)$ $\longleftarrow s = 426$
$r = \sqrt{\dfrac{(s-a)(s-b)(s-c)}{s}}$; $\mathbf{r^2 = \dfrac{(s-a)(s-b)(s-c)}{s}}$. $\mathbf{\log r = \frac{1}{2}\log r^2}$.	$\left.\begin{array}{r} \log (s-a) = 2.4031 \\ \log (s-b) = 2.2014 \\ \log (s-c) = 1.1461 \end{array}\right\}(+)$ log numerator = 5.7506; $\log s =$ 2.6294 (−); $\log r^2 =$ 3.1212; (÷ by 2); $\log r =$ 1.5606.
$\mathbf{\tan \dfrac{\alpha}{2} = \dfrac{r}{s-a}}$.	$\log r = 11.5606 - 10$; $\log (s-a) = 2.4031$ (−); $\log \tan \frac{1}{2}\alpha = 9.1575 - 10$; $\frac{1}{2}\alpha = 8° 11'$; $\alpha = 16° 22'$.
Similarly,	$\begin{cases} \frac{1}{2}\beta = 12° 53'; & \beta = 25° 46'; \\ \frac{1}{2}\gamma = 68° 56'; & \gamma = 137° 52'. \end{cases}$
Summary.	$\mathbf{\alpha = 16° 22', \quad \beta = 25° 46', \quad \gamma = 137° 52'}$.
Check. $\alpha + \beta + \gamma = 16° 22' + 25° 46' + 137° 52' = 180° 0'$; *satisfactory.*	

EXERCISE 55

Solve $\triangle ABC$ by use of four-place or five-place logarithms.

1. $a = 17, b = 26, c = 35$.
2. $a = 8, b = 7, c = 11$.
3. $a = 5.26, b = 4.38, c = 9.34$.
4. $a = .986, b = .726, c = .648$.
5. $a = 136, b = 472, c = 450$.
6. $a = 4.614, b = 6.213, c = 5.709$.
7. $a = 73.09, b = 91.27, c = 59.86$.
8. $a = .1931, b = .1137, c = .2625$.

Find the desired angle by use of the sine or cosine of half of the angle.

9. $a = 13, b = 17, c = 9$; find β.
10. $a = 27, b = 36, c = 42$; find γ.

11. Two forces with the magnitudes 19 pounds and 21 pounds act simultaneously on an object. The magnitude of the resultant force is 35 pounds. Find the smallest positive angle between the directions of the forces.

12. Two forces with the magnitudes 132.5 pounds and 217.3 pounds act simultaneously on an object. The magnitude of the resultant force is 265.3 pounds. Find the smallest positive angle between the directions of the given forces.

★*Solve $\triangle ABC$ by use of five-place logarithms.*

13. $a = 12.379, b = 26.423, c = 25.603$.

14. $a = 3812.6, b = 5372.4, c = 7635.8$.

15. $a = .91315$, $b = .80263$, $c = .74137$.

16. $a = 9.8314$, $b = 6.1041$, $c = 7.0308$.

17. $a = 111.78$, $b = 235.67$, $c = 204.38$.

★**18.** An airplane heads in a northerly direction at an airspeed of 300 miles per hour while a wind is blowing due east at 50 miles per hour. The resultant groundspeed is 330 miles per hour. Find the heading.

101. Heron's formula for the area of a triangle

The great Greek geometer HERON (or HERO) of Alexandria, who lived in the first century A.D., proved the following result for the area, K, of $\triangle ABC$:

$$[s = \tfrac{1}{2}(a+b+c)] \qquad \boldsymbol{K = \sqrt{s(s-a)(s-b)(s-c)}}. \tag{1}$$

Proof. 1. From Problem 25, page 164, $K = \frac{1}{2}bc \sin \alpha$. From (VII), page 147,

$$\sin \alpha = 2 \sin \tfrac{1}{2}\alpha \cos \tfrac{1}{2}\alpha, \quad \textit{and hence} \quad K = bc \sin \tfrac{1}{2}\alpha \cos \tfrac{1}{2}\alpha. \tag{2}$$

2. By use of (2) and formulas (1) on page 174,

$$K = bc\sqrt{\frac{(s-b)(s-c)}{bc}}\sqrt{\frac{s(s-a)}{bc}} = \sqrt{s(s-a)(s-b)(s-c)}.$$

EXERCISE 56

Compute the area by use of four-place or five-place logarithms.

1. $a = 4.908$, $b = 3.578$, $c = 7.404$.

2. $a = 128.3$, $b = 140.7$, $c = 188.4$.

3. $a = .3158$, $b = .2893$, $c = .1642$.

102. Summary for logarithmic solution of triangles

I. *Given two angles and a side.*	*Solve by law of sines and check by law of tangents.*
II. *Given two sides and an opposite angle.*	*Solve by law of sines, with particular attention to the number of solutions. Check by law of tangents.**
III. *Given two sides and the included angle.*	1. *Find the angles by law of tangents and the third side by law of sines. Check by law of sines or law of tangents.** 2. *If* **only** *the third side is desired, perhaps use law of cosines (not adapted to logarithms).*
IV. *Given three sides.*	1. *Solve by half-angle formulas and check by* $\alpha + \beta + \gamma = 180°$. 2. *Solve by law of cosines (not adapted to logarithms) and check by* $\alpha + \beta + \gamma = 180°$.

* Or Mollweide's equations; or formulas like $c = a \cos \beta + b \cos \alpha$.

CHAPTER REVIEW EXERCISE 57

Solve $\triangle ABC$ completely except where only one part is requested.

Solve by use of Tables I *and* VII *without logarithms.*

1. $b = 20$, $\beta = 30°$, $\gamma = 57°$; find only a.

2. $a = 3$, $b = 5$, $c = 7$; find only β.

3. $a = 4$, $b = 5$, $c = 8$; find only γ.

4. $a = 20$, $\alpha = 30°$, $\gamma = 42°\ 7'$.

5. $b = 81$, $c = 50$, $\beta = 164°\ 20'$.

6. $c = 910$, $\gamma = 65°\ 30'$, $\beta = 100°$.

7. $c = 40$, $\beta = 90°$, $\gamma = 26°\ 12'$.

8. $a = 50$, $b = 38$, $\beta = 22°\ 20'$.

9. $a = 76$, $c = 20$, $\alpha = 157°\ 40'$.

10. $b = 10$, $c = 5$, $\alpha = 74°\ 20'$; find only a (law of cosines).

11. $a = 12$, $c = 5$, $\beta = 114°\ 50'$; find only b (law of cosines).

Solve $\triangle ABC$ by use of four-place or five-place logarithms, where needed.

12. $a = .956$, $b = .734$, $c = .526$.

13. $a = 1.315$, $b = 2.673$, $\gamma = 80°\ 19'$.

14. $b = 1573$, $c = 6132$, $\beta = 82°\ 14'$.

15. $a = 2395$, $c = 4647$, $\alpha = 25°\ 17'$.

16. $a = 863$, $c = 457$, $\gamma = 121°\ 53'$.

17. $a = 395.6$, $b = 524.7$, $\beta = 73°\ 6'$.

18. $a = 13.17$, $\alpha = 26°\ 33'$, $\gamma = 82°\ 58'$.

Employ at least one oblique triangle in each of the following problems. Use logarithms where convenient.

19. The lengths of two sides and a diagonal of a parallelogram are, respectively, 30 feet, 40 feet, and 60 feet. Find the angles of the parallelogram without logarithms.

20. An aviator finds that, after traveling 300 miles in an easterly direction and then 250 miles in a southerly direction, he is 400 miles due east of his starting point. Without logarithms, find the direction in which he traveled on the first leg of his journey.

21. A telegraph pole, which leans 15° 10′ from the vertical toward the sun, casts a shadow 39.8 feet long when the angle of elevation of the sun is 63° 40′. Find the length of the pole.

22. At a point $3\frac{1}{2}$ miles from one end of a lake and $5\frac{3}{4}$ miles from the other end, the lake subtends an angle of 78° 53′. How long is the lake?

23. Along one bank of a river, as in Figure 99, a surveyor measures

$$AB = 183.5 \text{ feet}, \angle BAC = 67°\ 45',$$
$$\text{and } \angle ABC = 43°\ 26',$$

where C is a point on the opposite bank. Find the width of the river.

Outline. In $\triangle ABC$, find only $\log b$ from $b = (c \sin \beta)/\sin \gamma$. Then, from right $\triangle ADC$, $CD = b \sin \alpha$.

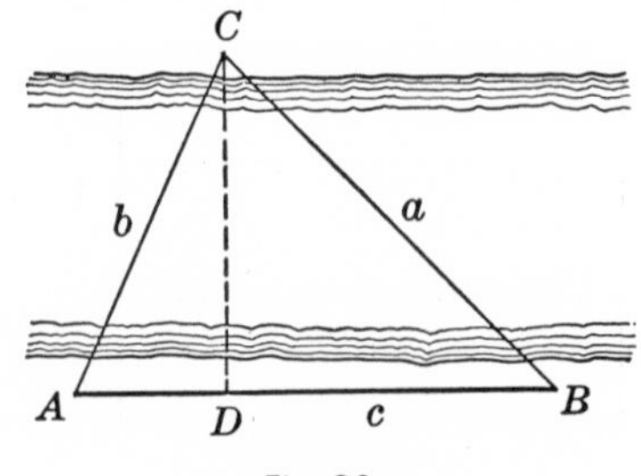

Fig. 99

24. A ship is sailing $N\ 23° 25' W$. From A on the ship's track, the navigator sights a point of land P with bearing $N\ 33° 40' E$. After sailing 2.85 miles farther to a point B, the bearing of P is $N\ 42° 30' E$. Find the distance to P when it is nearest to the ship. (This is said to be the distance at which P is passed **abeam.**)

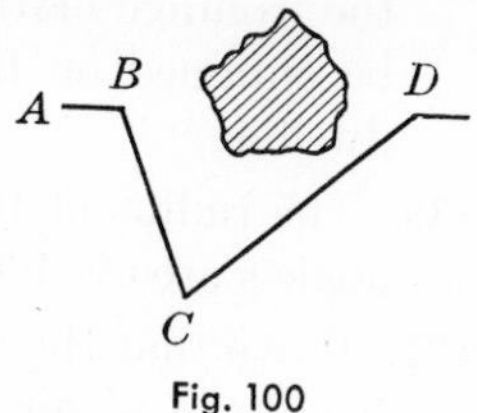

Fig. 100

25. A surveyor runs a line $AB = 1326$ feet in the direction $N\ 37° 28' E$, then $BC = 1184$ feet in a southerly direction, and then $CA = 1016$ feet, back to his starting point. As a check, he measures the direction of CA. Find this direction.

26. A surveyor desires to prolong an east-west line AB due east past an obstruction, as in Figure 100. He measures $BC = 785.4$ feet, $S\ 23° 17' E$, and then runs CD in the direction $N\ 47° 53' E$. Find the length of CD if D is to be due east of B.

27. In Figure 101, to find the distance between the inaccessible points C and D, on one side of the river, a surveyor on the other side measures

$AB = 157.8$ feet; $\delta = 32° 26'$;

$\theta = 27° 45'$; $\beta = 40° 29'$;

$\gamma = 35° 18'$.

Find CD.

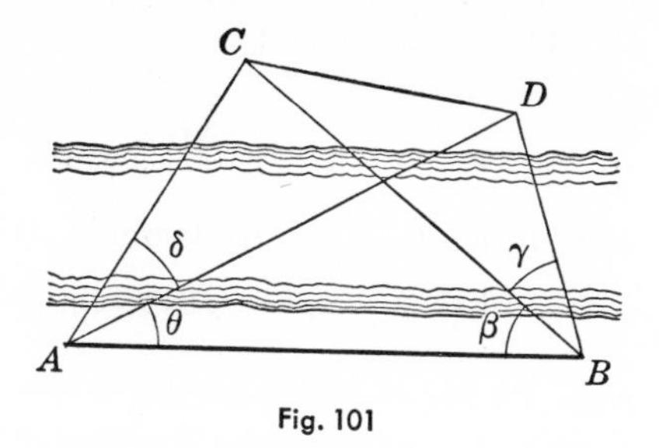

Fig. 101

Find the magnitude and direction of the resultant of the given forces which are acting together on an object.

28. 585 pounds directed $N\ 26° 25' E$; 243 pounds directed $N\ 78° 47' W$.

29. 41.7 pounds directed $S\ 17° 5' E$; 39.4 pounds directed $N\ 21° 14' E$.

30. One force of 8 pounds is directed due east. The magnitude of a second force is 12 pounds, and the magnitude of the resultant of these two forces is 15 pounds. Find the direction of the second force if it acts somewhat east of north, and find the direction of the resultant.

Find the course, groundspeed, and drift angle for an airplane, corresponding to the specified airspeed, heading, and wind. All speeds are "per hour." Each direction is an azimuth.

31. Airspeed = 200 miles; heading = 130°; wind = 40 miles, from 350°.

32. Airspeed = 300 miles; heading = 32°; wind = 50 miles, from 340°.

33. A ship heads with azimuth 141° 35′ at a speed of 36 knots * with respect to the water. A current is flowing with azimuth 73° 40′ at a speed of 4 knots. Find the ship's course and its groundspeed.

34. Under the conditions in Problem 33, in which direction should the ship head at 36 knots in order to follow a track with azimuth 314° 30′?

* A **knot** is a speed of one nautical mile, or 1.1508 statute miles, per hour.

★**35.** The building regulations in a city specify that a two-family dwelling may not be placed on a lot whose area is less than 15,000 square feet. The angle at the street corner of a triangular corner lot is 78° 36′ and the frontage of the lot on one street is 163 feet. What frontage must be obtained on the other street to permit the erection of a two-family dwelling?

★**36.** The radius of the inscribed circle in a triangle is 6.8 feet and the triangle's area is 496 square feet. Find the sides if one angle is 57° 26′.

★**37.** Prove that the area of any parallelogram is equal to the product of the lengths of a pair of adjacent sides times the sine of their included angle.

★**38.** Prove that the area of any convex quadrilateral is equal to one half of the product of the lengths of its diagonals times the sine of either angle formed by the diagonals.

★**39.** Let R represent the radius of the circumscribed circle for a triangle ABC. Prove that

$$2R = \frac{a}{\sin \alpha} = \frac{b}{\sin \beta} = \frac{c}{\sin \gamma}.$$

★**40.** Prove that, in any triangle ABC,

$$s = R(\sin \alpha + \sin \beta + \sin \gamma).$$

★**41.** By use of half-angle formulas, prove that

$$R = \frac{abc}{4\sqrt{s(s-a)(s-b)(s-c)}}, \quad \textit{or} \quad K = \frac{abc}{4R},$$

where K is the area of triangle ABC.

★**42.** In any triangle ABC, prove that

$$r = s \tan \tfrac{1}{2}\alpha \tan \tfrac{1}{2}\beta \tan \tfrac{1}{2}\gamma; \qquad r = c \sin \tfrac{1}{2}\alpha \sin \tfrac{1}{2}\beta \sec \tfrac{1}{2}\gamma.$$

★**43.** In any triangle ABC, prove that

$$K = \frac{abc}{s} \cos \frac{\alpha}{2} \cos \frac{\beta}{2} \cos \frac{\gamma}{2}.$$

★**44.** A flagpole of height h feet at the top of a wall inclines at an angle α from the vertical toward an observer. From a point A on a level with the base of the wall, the angles of elevation of the bottom and the top of the pole are observed to be β and γ, respectively. Derive a formula for the height of the wall in terms of h, α, β, and γ.

10

INVERSE TRIGONOMETRIC FUNCTIONS

103. Remarks about inverse functions*

From page 82, we recall consequences arising if a function f is a *steadily increasing* or a *steadily decreasing* function when the independent variable increases over its domain. Thus, in Figure 64 on page 82, f steadily increases. For each number y on the *range*, R, for f, there exists just one corresponding number x on the *domain*, D, for f such that the pair (x, y) satisfies the equation $y = f(x)$. This correspondence of values of x and y defines a function g such that the value $x = g(y)$ satisfies $y = f(x)$ at each value of y, or $y = f(g(y))$. On page 82, we agreed to call g the **inverse** *of the function f, and conversely.* That is, f and g are called *inverse functions.* If f has the *domain* D and *range* R, then the inverse function g has R as its *domain* and D as its *range.*

ILLUSTRATION 1. We shall use the preceding remarks as a basis for future discussion, with the roles of x and y interchanged. Thus, assume that f is a steadily increasing function, when the independent variable y increases on the domain D of f, and let R be the range of f. Then there exists an inverse function g, whose *domain* is R and *range* is D, and

$$x = f(y) \quad \textit{is equivalent to} \quad y = g(x), \quad \textit{or} \tag{1}$$

$$x = f(g(x)) \quad \textit{and} \quad y = g(f(y)). \tag{2}$$

104. The inverse sine function

The graph of the equation $x = \sin y$ is the sine curve along the y-axis in Figure 102 on page 182. For each eligible value of x, the equation $x = \sin y$ is satisfied by *infinitely many values of y.* Thus, if $x = \frac{1}{2}$, we obtain $\sin y = \frac{1}{2}$, which is satisfied by

$$y = \tfrac{1}{6}\pi + 2n\pi \quad \textit{and} \quad y = \tfrac{5}{6}\pi + 2n\pi, \tag{1}$$

for all integral values of n. It can be said that the equation $x = \sin y$ de-

* The student should review Section 47 on page 81.

fines y as an *infinitely many-valued function of* x. However, this complicated function has no essential merit for use in trigonometry or calculus. Hence, we proceed as follows to arrive at a *single-valued inverse* for the sine function.

In Figure 102 notice that arc AB has the characteristic appearance observed in Figure 64 on page 82. Accordingly, we consider the restricted relation

$$\left\{\begin{array}{ll} x \text{ on } D: & -1 \leqq x \leqq 1; \\ y \text{ on } R: & -\tfrac{1}{2}\pi \leqq y \leqq \tfrac{1}{2}\pi. \end{array}\right\} \quad \mathbf{x = \sin y}, \tag{2}$$

$x = \sin y$

Fig. 102

whose graph is arc AB in Figure 102, transferred also to Figure 103, with enlarged scale. For each number x in D, there exists *just one number* y *in* R. Hence, (2) *defines* y *as a function of* x, to be called the **Arcsine function,** with the value Arcsin x for any number x in D. That is,

$$\left\{\begin{array}{l} \textit{with } -1 \leqq x \leqq 1, \\ -\tfrac{1}{2}\pi \leqq y \leqq \tfrac{1}{2}\pi. \end{array}\right\} \qquad \left.\begin{array}{c} \mathbf{x = \sin y} \\ \textit{is equivalent to} \\ \mathbf{y = \text{Arcsin}\ x.} \end{array}\right\} \tag{3}$$

Thus, for the restricted range of y in (3), the Arcsine function is the *inverse of the sine function.* It is important to remember that

$$(\textit{for all } x) \qquad -\tfrac{1}{2}\pi \leqq \textbf{Arcsin}\ x \leqq \tfrac{1}{2}\pi. \tag{4}$$

The graph of $y = \text{Arcsin}\ x$ is the same as the graph of $x = \sin y$ with y restricted to lie on the interval $-\frac{1}{2}\pi \leqq y \leqq \frac{1}{2}\pi$, as in Figure 103. To find Arcsin x at any value of x, we use (3).

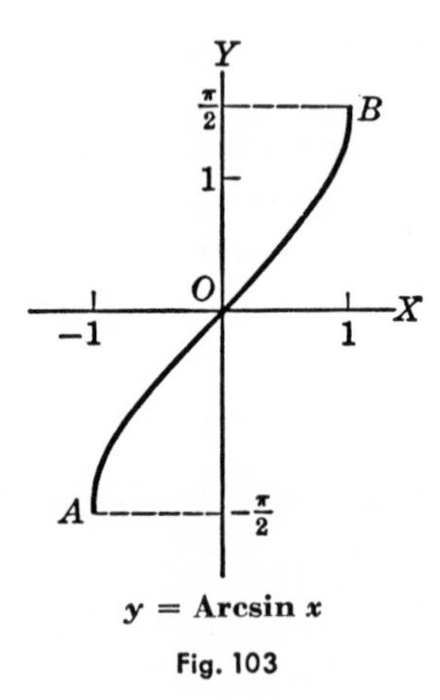

$y = \text{Arcsin}\ x$

Fig. 103

ILLUSTRATION 1. To find Arcsin $(-\frac{1}{2})$, we let $y = \text{Arcsin}\ (-\frac{1}{2})$; then we obtain $\sin y = -\frac{1}{2}$ and $-\frac{1}{2}\pi \leqq y \leqq \frac{1}{2}\pi$. Hence, $y = -\frac{1}{6}\pi$.

ILLUSTRATION 2. To construct a table of values for graphing the function $y = \text{Arcsin}\ x$, first use (3); thus $x = \sin y$. Then, to make up the following table, assign values to y on the domain in (3) and compute x. The student may check the table against the graph in Figure 103.

$x = \sin y$	-1	$-.87$	$-.5$	0	.5	.87	1
$y = \text{Arcsin}\ x$	$-\frac{1}{2}\pi$	$-\frac{1}{3}\pi$	$-\frac{1}{6}\pi$	0	$\frac{1}{6}\pi$	$\frac{1}{3}\pi$	$\frac{1}{2}\pi$
y, *dec. form*	-1.57	-1.05	$-.52$	0	.52	1.05	1.57

ILLUSTRATION 3. By the definition in (3),

$$x = \sin(\operatorname{Arcsin} x); \quad also \quad y = \operatorname{Arcsin}(\sin y). \tag{5}$$

For the moment, interpret Arcsin x as the measure of an *angle* in radians. Then, sometimes, "Arcsin x" is referred to as "*an angle whose sine is* x," which is equivalent to "$\sin(\operatorname{Arcsin} x) = x$," in (5).

EXAMPLE 1. Find $\sin[\operatorname{Arcsin}\frac{1}{2} + \operatorname{Arcsin}(-\frac{3}{5})]$.

SOLUTION. 1. Let $\alpha = \operatorname{Arcsin}\frac{1}{2}$; then $\sin\alpha = \frac{1}{2}$ and $0 < \alpha < \frac{1}{2}\pi$. Let $\beta = \operatorname{Arcsin}(-\frac{3}{5})$; $\sin\beta = -\frac{3}{5}$ and $-\frac{1}{2}\pi < \beta < 0$. We desire $\sin(\alpha + \beta)$.

2. We obtain $\cos\alpha = \sqrt{1 - \frac{1}{4}} = \frac{1}{2}\sqrt{3}$; $\cos^2\beta = 1 - \sin^2\beta = 1 - \frac{9}{25} = \frac{16}{25}$. Hence, $\cos\beta = \pm\frac{4}{5}$ but, since $-\frac{1}{2}\pi < \beta < 0$, we take $\cos\beta = \frac{4}{5}$. By the addition formula for the sine on page 144,

$$\sin(\alpha + \beta) = \tfrac{1}{2}(\tfrac{4}{5}) + \tfrac{1}{2}\sqrt{3}(-\tfrac{3}{5}) = \tfrac{1}{10}(4 - 3\sqrt{3}).$$

★*Note 1.* In some texts, we first find a definition of the so-called *complete* or *infinitely many-valued* function $y = \arcsin x$ (written with *small* "a" in *arcsin*), introduced as equivalent to the relation $x = \sin y$, with no limitation on the range for y. In such a case, our function Arcsin x (written in many texts with *capital* A as here) is called the **principal value** of the complete arcsine function. Thereafter, in calculus, *all applications refer to the principal value function.* In the present text, we have eliminated the complete arcsine function because it has negligible utility and also is a source for student errors. We use capital A in Arcsin so that the student will not be forced to a change in notation if he reads a text where our function Arcsin x is met after a different introduction.

★*Note 2.* In certain books, instead of "**Arcsin x**" we find "**$\sin^{-1} x$**," which then is read "*inverse sine x*." We prefer not to use $\sin^{-1}$ because of possible confusion with exponents applied to the sine function.

EXAMPLE 2. Find all trigonometric functions of $\operatorname{Arcsin}(-\frac{2}{3})$.

SOLUTION. 1. Let $y = \operatorname{Arcsin}(-\frac{2}{3})$. Then, $\sin y = -\frac{2}{3}$ and $-\frac{1}{2}\pi < y < 0$ because $\sin y$ is negative. If, for the moment, we interpret y as an angle of y radians, and let z be the reference angle for y, then we have $0 < z < \frac{1}{2}\pi$ and $\sin z = \frac{2}{3}$.

2. From the reference triangle for z in Figure 104, and knowledge of the signs of the trigonometric functions in quadrant IV,

$$\cos z = \frac{\sqrt{5}}{3}, \qquad \tan z = \frac{2}{\sqrt{5}}, \qquad \cot z = \frac{\sqrt{5}}{2}, \quad etc.;$$

hence, $\cos y = \frac{1}{3}\sqrt{5}$, $\tan y = -\frac{2}{5}\sqrt{5}$, $\cot y = -\frac{1}{2}\sqrt{5}$, *etc.*

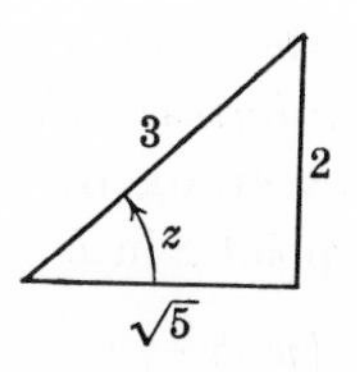

Fig. 104

ILLUSTRATION 4. To find Arcsin $(-.444)$, let $y = \text{Arcsin}\,(-.444)$. Then, $\sin y = -.444$ and, from (4), $-\frac{1}{2}\pi < y < 0$. Let z be such that $\sin z = .444$ and $0 < z < \frac{1}{2}\pi$; that is, z is the reference number for y. Then, from the "Rad." column of Table IV, z is between .454 and .471. We interpolate by the principle of proportional parts.

$$.017\left[\;d\left[\begin{array}{l}\sin .454 = .438\\ \sin z \quad\;\; = .444\end{array}\right]6\quad\;\; \sin .471 = .454\right]16 \qquad \frac{d}{.017} = \frac{6}{16}; \quad d = \tfrac{3}{8}(.017) = .006.$$

$$\boldsymbol{z = .454 + d = .454 + .006 = .460.}$$

Since $\sin y = -\sin z$, we have $y = -z$, or Arcsin $(-.444) = -.460$.

EXAMPLE 3. Prove that the following equation is an identity for all values of u on the interval $-1 \leqq u \leqq 1$:

$$\textbf{Arcsin}\,(-u) = -\,\textbf{Arcsin}\,u. \tag{6}$$

SOLUTION. 1. From Figure 103 on page 182, if y_1 and y_2 are two values of y on the range $-\frac{1}{2}\pi \leqq y \leqq \frac{1}{2}\pi$, and if $\sin y_1 = \sin y_2$, then $y_1 = y_2$.

2. To prove (6) for any value of u as specified, take the sines of the numbers on the two sides:

on the left, by (5),
$$\sin[\text{Arcsin}\,(-u)] = -u. \tag{7}$$

on the right, by use of (5) and the identity $\sin(-\theta) = -\sin\theta$,

$$\sin[-\text{Arcsin}\,u] = -\sin(\text{Arcsin}\,u) = -u. \tag{8}$$

From Step 1 of the proof, (7) and (8) show that (6) is true.

105. The inverse tangent function

The complete graph of the equation $x = \tan y$ consists of the branch in Figure 105 on page 185 and its repetitions above and below without end. To define a single-valued inverse for the tangent function, we consider the restricted relation

$$\left\{\begin{array}{ll} x \text{ on } D: & -\infty < x < \infty; \\ y \text{ on } R: & -\frac{1}{2}\pi < y < \frac{1}{2}\pi. \end{array}\right\} \qquad \boldsymbol{x = \tan y,} \tag{1}$$

whose graph is in Figure 105. We notice that *y increases steadily if the value of x increases steadily.* Hence, (1) defines y as a *function of x*, to be called the **Arctangent** function, with the value **Arctan x,** read "*arctangent x,*" at any point x in D. That is, by definition

$$\left\{\begin{array}{l} \textit{with} -\infty < x < \infty, \\ -\frac{1}{2}\pi < y < \frac{1}{2}\pi. \end{array}\right\} \quad \boldsymbol{x = \tan y} \quad \textit{is equivalent to} \quad \boldsymbol{y = \textbf{Arctan}\,x.} \tag{2}$$

From (2), the Arctangent function, with the domain D of (1), is the *inverse of the tangent function,* whose domain is R of (1). It is important to remember

$$-\tfrac{1}{2}\pi < \text{Arctan } x < \tfrac{1}{2}\pi. \tag{3}$$

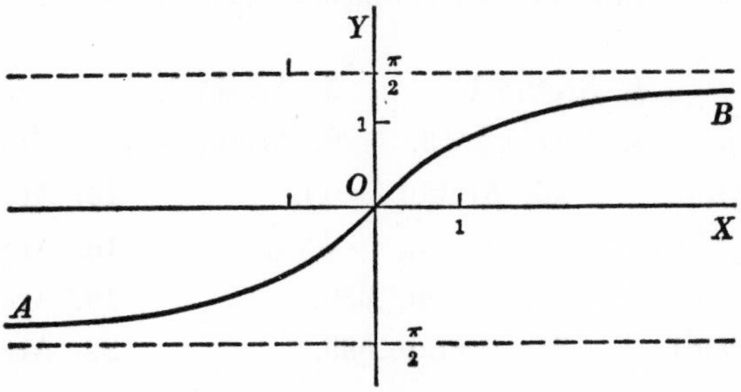

$y = \text{Arctan } x$

Fig. 105

From (2), the graph of $y = \text{Arctan } x$ is one branch of the graph of $x = \tan y$, with the range for y in (1). To find the value $y = \text{Arctan } x$ for any particular value of x, we use (2) and write $x = \tan y$; then we solve this equation for y with x known. From (2),

$$x = \tan(\text{Arctan } x); \qquad y = \text{Arctan}(\tan y). \tag{4}$$

ILLUSTRATION 1. To find Arctan $\sqrt{3}$, let $y = \text{Arctan } \sqrt{3}$. Then $\tan y = \sqrt{3}$ and $-\tfrac{1}{2}\pi < y < \tfrac{1}{2}\pi$. Hence, $y = \tfrac{1}{3}\pi$.

ILLUSTRATION 2. To obtain the graph of $y = \text{Arctan } x$ in Figure 105, we use (2) to obtain $x = \tan y$. Then, we form a table of values of x and y by selecting values of y on the range $-\tfrac{1}{2}\pi < y < \tfrac{1}{2}\pi$. Since $|\tan y| \to \infty$ when $y \to \tfrac{1}{2}\pi$, and also as $y \to -\tfrac{1}{2}\pi$, the graph in Figure 105 has the lines $y = \tfrac{1}{2}\pi$ and $y = -\tfrac{1}{2}\pi$ as **asymptotes.** Since $\tan y < 0$ if $-\tfrac{1}{2}\pi < y < 0$, it follows that $\tan y \to -\infty$ as y approaches $-\tfrac{1}{2}\pi$ on this domain. If y is on the interval $0 < y < \tfrac{1}{2}\pi$, then $\tan y > 0$; if $y \to \tfrac{1}{2}\pi$, then $\tan y \to +\infty$, or $x \to +\infty$ on the graph in Figure 105.

$x = \tan y$	$x \to -\infty$	-1.7	-1	0	1	1.7	$x \to \infty$
$y = \text{Arctan } x$	$y \to -\tfrac{1}{2}\pi$	$-\tfrac{1}{3}\pi$	$-\tfrac{1}{4}\pi$	0	$\tfrac{1}{4}\pi$	$\tfrac{1}{3}\pi$	$y \to \tfrac{1}{2}\pi$
y, *dec. value*	-1.57	-1.05	$-.79$	0	$.79$	1.05	1.57

EXAMPLE 1. Find $\tan(2 \text{ Arctan } x)$.

SOLUTION. Let $y = \text{Arctan } x$; then $\tan y = x$ and we desire $\tan 2y$. From (IX) on page 147,

$$\tan(2 \text{ Arctan } x) = \tan 2y = \frac{2 \tan y}{1 - \tan^2 y} = \frac{2x}{1 - x^2}.$$

EXERCISE 58

Graph the function, with the same unit for distance used on both axes.

1. $y = \text{Arcsin } x$. **2.** $y = \text{Arctan } x$.

Find each function value either from memory or by use of the "Rad." column in Table IV.

3. Arcsin $\frac{1}{2}$. **4.** Arctan 1. **5.** Arcsin 0. **6.** Arctan 0.
7. Arcsin $\frac{1}{2}\sqrt{3}$. **8.** Arcsin $\frac{1}{2}\sqrt{2}$. **9.** Arctan $\sqrt{3}$. **10.** Arctan $\frac{1}{3}\sqrt{3}$.
11. Arcsin $(-\frac{1}{2})$. **12.** Arctan (-1). **13.** Arctan $(-\sqrt{3})$.
14. Arcsin $(-\frac{1}{2}\sqrt{3})$. **15.** Arctan $(-\frac{1}{3}\sqrt{3})$. **16.** Arcsin $(-\frac{1}{2}\sqrt{2})$.
17. Arcsin .407. **18.** Arctan .839. **19.** Arcsin .423.
20. Arcsin $(-.946)$. **21.** Arctan .683. **22.** Arctan (-1.160).

Find the value of the expression without using a table.

23. sin Arcsin $\frac{1}{3}$. **24.** tan Arctan (-2). **25.** sin Arcsin $(-\frac{2}{5})$.
26. tan Arctan $2z$. **27.** sin Arcsin $(-3x)$. **28.** sin Arcsin u^2.
29. cos Arcsin $(-\frac{1}{2})$. **30.** tan Arcsin $(-\frac{1}{2})$. **31.** sin Arctan $\sqrt{3}$.
32. cos Arctan (-1). **33.** cot Arcsin $(-\frac{1}{2}\sqrt{2})$. **34.** sin Arctan (-1).

Find $\sin(y+z)$, $\cos(y+z)$, $\sin 2y$, $\cos 2y$, *and* $\tan 2y$ *for the data.*

35. $y = \text{Arcsin } \frac{1}{2}$; $z = \text{Arcsin } \frac{1}{2}\sqrt{3}$.
36. $y = \text{Arcsin } (-1)$; $z = \text{Arcsin } (-\frac{1}{2})$.
37. $y = \text{Arcsin } \frac{3}{5}$; $z = \text{Arctan } (-\sqrt{3})$.
38. $y = \text{Arcsin } \frac{5}{13}$; $z = \text{Arcsin } (-\frac{7}{25})$.
39. $y = \text{Arctan } 2$; $z = \text{Arcsin } \frac{1}{2}\sqrt{2}$. **40.** $y = \text{Arctan } (-\frac{3}{5})$; $z = \text{Arctan } \frac{4}{3}$.
41. $y = \text{Arctan } (-2)$; $z = \text{Arcsin } \frac{1}{4}$.
42. Find all trigonometric functions of Arcsin $(-\frac{12}{13})$.
43. Find all trigonometric functions of Arctan $(-\frac{3}{4})$.
44. Prove the identity Arctan $(-x) = -$ Arctan x.
45. Solve for the unknown number x: Arcsin $4x$ = Arcsin $(2x - 1)$.

106. Other inverse trigonometric functions

The modern tendency in calculus is to emphasize use of the Arcsine and Arctangent functions. However, occasionally it proves convenient to employ the Arccosine and Arccotangent functions, which we proceed to describe.

With the following restriction on the domain for y, the equation $x = \cos y$ defines y as a function of x, called the **Arccosine** function, the *inverse of the cosine function* on the indicated domain. Thus, by definition

$$\left\{\begin{matrix} \text{with } -1 \leqq x \leqq 1; \\ 0 \leqq y \leqq \pi. \end{matrix}\right\} \quad \boldsymbol{x = \cos y} \quad \textit{is equivalent to} \quad \boldsymbol{y = \text{Arccos } x;} \tag{1}$$

that is, for all x,

$$\boldsymbol{0 \leqq \text{Arccos } x \leqq \pi.} \tag{2}$$

Similarly, Arccot x is defined as follows:

$$\left\{\begin{array}{c} \textit{with } -\infty < x < \infty; \\ 0 < y < \pi \end{array}\right\} \quad \mathbf{x = \cot y} \quad \textit{is equivalent to} \quad \mathbf{y = \text{Arccot } x}; \qquad (3)$$

that is, for all x,

$$\mathbf{0 < \text{Arccot } x < \pi.} \qquad (4)$$

A graph of $y = \text{Arccos } x$ is the graph of $x = \cos y$ with $0 \leqq y \leqq \pi$, as seen in Figure 106. A graph of $y = \text{Arccot } x$ is the graph of $x = \cot y$ with $0 < y < \pi$, as seen in Figure 107.

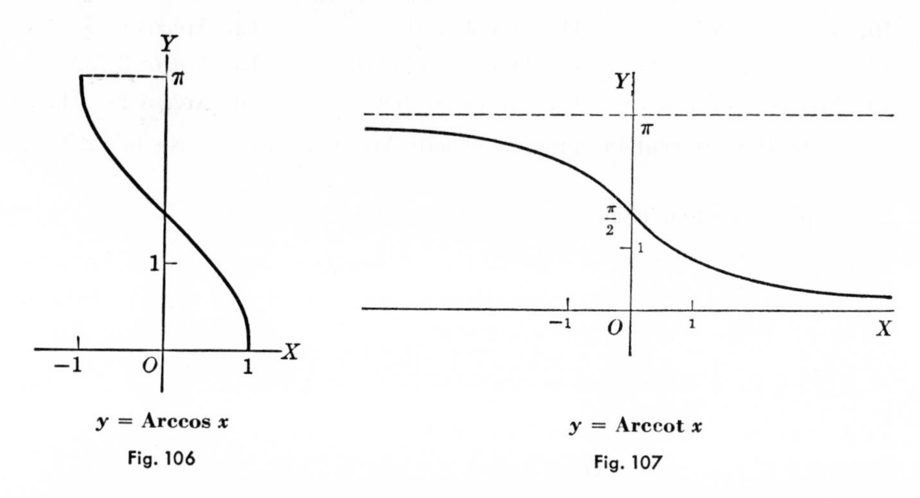

y = **Arccos** x

Fig. 106

y = **Arccot** x

Fig. 107

Note 1. For contrast with the *inverse* trigonometric functions Arcsine, Arccosine, etc., sometimes the functions sin x, cos x, tan x, cot x, sec x, and csc x are called the *direct* trigonometric functions.

Note 2. The Arcsecant and Arccosecant functions are used so seldom that, in this text, treatment of them is restricted to problems in the next exercise. The definitions of these functions will be given at that time.

SUMMARY. *The domain for the independent variable, x, and the range for each of the functions are listed below for each of the important inverse trigonometric functions.*

Domain: $-1 \leqq x \leqq 1.$ *Range:* $-\frac{1}{2}\pi \leqq \mathbf{\text{Arcsin } x} \leqq \frac{1}{2}\pi.$ (5)

Domain: $-\infty < x < \infty.$ *Range:* $-\frac{1}{2}\pi < \mathbf{\text{Arctan } x} < \frac{1}{2}\pi.$ (6)

Domain: $-1 \leqq x \leqq 1.$ *Range:* $0 \leqq \mathbf{\text{Arccos } x} \leqq \pi.$ (7)

Domain: $-\infty < x < \infty.$ *Range:* $0 < \mathbf{\text{Arccot } x} < \pi.$ (8)

Note 3. Observe that, for any one of the inverse functions in (5)–(8) with $x > 0$, the value, y, of the function at the point x in its domain lies on the interval $0 \leqq y \leqq \frac{1}{2}\pi$.

EXERCISE 59

1. Graph the function $y = \text{Arccot } x$ on an xy-plane where the same unit for distance is used on both axes.
2. Repeat Problem 1 for $y = \text{Arccos } x$.

Find each function value either from memory or by use of the "Rad." column in Table IV.

3. Arccot $\sqrt{3}$.
4. Arccos 1.
5. Arccos $\frac{1}{2}$.
6. Arccot 1.
7. Arccos (-1).
8. Arccot $(-\frac{1}{3}\sqrt{3})$.
9. Arccos $(-\frac{1}{2}\sqrt{2})$.
10. Arccot $(-\sqrt{3})$.
11. Arccot (-1).
12. Arccos $(-\frac{1}{2})$.
13. Arccos $(\frac{1}{2}\sqrt{3})$.
14. Arccos $(-\frac{1}{2}\sqrt{3})$.
15. Arccot 3.732.
16. Arccos (.485).
17. Arccos $(-.880)$.
18. Arccot $(-.842)$.
19. State the interval of numbers where Arccos x lies in case (*a*) $x \geqq 0$; (*b*) $x \leqq 0$.
20. Repeat Problem 19 for the case of Arccot x.

Note 1. The following definitions for the functions Arcsec x and Arccsc x harmonize with their rare applications in some texts on integral calculus. Thus, we define Arcsec x by stating that

$$x = \sec y \quad \textit{is equivalent to} \quad y = \text{Arcsec } x, \tag{1}$$

subject to the following restrictions: if $1 \leqq x$ then $0 \leqq y < \frac{1}{2}\pi$; if $x \leqq -1$ then $-\pi \leqq y < -\frac{1}{2}\pi$. Or,

$$\left\{\begin{matrix} \textit{if } x \geqq 1: \\ \textit{if } x \leqq -1: \end{matrix}\right\} \qquad \left.\begin{matrix} 0 \leqq \text{Arcsec } x < \frac{1}{2}\pi; \\ -\pi \leqq \text{Arcsec } x < -\frac{1}{2}\pi. \end{matrix}\right\} \tag{2}$$

Similarly, Arccsc x is defined by the statement that

$$x = \csc y \quad \textit{is equivalent to} \quad y = \text{Arccsc } x, \tag{3}$$

subject to the following restrictions: if $1 \leqq x$ then $0 < y \leqq \frac{1}{2}\pi$; if $x \leqq -1$ then $-\pi < y \leqq -\frac{1}{2}\pi$. Or,

$$\left\{\begin{matrix} \textit{if } x \geqq 1: \\ \textit{if } x \leqq -1: \end{matrix}\right\} \qquad \left.\begin{matrix} 0 < \text{Arccsc } x \leqq \frac{1}{2}\pi; \\ -\pi < \text{Arccsc } x \leqq -\frac{1}{2}\pi. \end{matrix}\right\} \tag{4}$$

★21. Draw a graph of $x = \sec y$ and verify that, with the restrictions on y following (1), the equation defines y as a function of x. Thus, obtain a graph of $y = \text{Arcsec } x$.

★22. Draw a graph of $x = \csc y$ subject to the restrictions on y following (3), and repeat Problem 21 for the function $y = \text{Arccsc } x$.

★ *Graph the equation.*

23. $y = \text{Arcsin } 2x$.
24. $y = \text{Arctan } 3x$.
25. $y = \text{Arccos } \frac{1}{2}x$.

EXERCISE 60

REVIEW OF CHAPTERS 1–8 AND 10

Except where otherwise specified, employ four-place or five-place logarithms in any problem where it appears that they would be useful.

1. Sketch an angle of 125° in its standard position on a coordinate system. Give the values of one negative and one positive coterminal angle.

2. Construct the acute angle α and find the values of all of its trigonometric functions from a triangle if (*a*) $\tan \alpha = \frac{5}{12}$; (*b*) $\sec \alpha = \frac{17}{8}$.

3. Prove that, if the angle θ is in quadrant III, then $\tan \theta$ and $\cot \theta$ are positive.

Find the values of all trigonometric functions of the angle θ if the terminal side of θ, in its standard position, goes through the given point.

4. $(-3, 4)$. **5.** $(15, -8)$. **6.** $(0, 3)$. **7.** $(-2, 0)$. **8.** $(2, 5)$.

9. Find the trigonometric functions of 45° by use of a right triangle.

10. Find the trigonometric functions of 30° and 60° from a right triangle.

Find each function value by use of Table VII.

11. tan 62° 37′. **12.** sin 79° 33′. **13.** sin 130°. **14.** tan 160°.
15. tan 243°. **16.** sin (− 15°). **17.** cos (− 115°). **18.** sec 623°.

19. Describe what is meant by writing "tan 270° *is infinite.*"

20. Find the acute angle α to the nearest minute by interpolation in some table: (*a*) $\tan \alpha = 1.706$; (*b*) $\cos \alpha = .4138$; (*c*) $\sin \alpha = .9705$.

Find all trigonometric functions of the angle without using a table.

21. 210°. **22.** 150°. **23.** − 135°. **24.** 315°. **25.** − 120°. **26.** − 225°.

27. Place the angle in standard position, and find its trigonometric functions by use of their definitions: (*a*) 120°; (*b*) 225°.

Solve right $\triangle ABC$ without logarithms; use Table VII.

28. $c = 17.5$; $a = 10.5$. **29.** $\alpha = 42° 36'$; $b = .45$. **30.** $c = 63$; $\alpha = 6° 35'$.

31. Solve right $\triangle ABC$ without logarithms by interpolation in Table XI if $\beta = 69° 16.7'$ and $a = 250$.

32–35. Solve Problems 28 to 31, inclusive, by use of four-place or five-place logarithms and check the solutions.

36. For a right $\triangle ABC$, write a formula for a in terms of β and b; for finding α by use of a and c.

Solve for the angle x, in degree measure, on the domain $0° \leqq x < 360°$.

37. $\sin x = \frac{1}{2}$. **38.** $\tan x = 1$. **39.** $\cot^2 x = 1$. **40.** $\cos x = -\frac{1}{2}$.
41. $\sin^2 x = 1$. **42.** $\sec x = -2$. **43.** $\csc x = \sqrt{2}$. **44.** $\cot x = \sqrt{3}$.
45. $\cos x = -\frac{1}{2}\sqrt{2}$. **46.** $\sin x = -\frac{1}{2}\sqrt{3}$. **47.** $\sin x = .4899$.
48. $\cos x = -.8192$. **49.** $\tan x = -.4734$. **50.** $\cot x = 1.492$.

Solve for the number x, on the interval $0 \leqq x < 2\pi$.

51. $2\cos^2 x = 5\cos x$. **52.** $\sin 3x = 1$. **53.** $\cot x + \sin x \cot x = 0$.

54. $2\sin^2 x + \sin x = 1$. **55.** $\tan \frac{1}{2}x = -1$. **56.** $1 + \csc^2 x = 7\cot^2 x$.

Prove the identity by use of Definition I *on page* 33, *without using other identities.*

57. $\dfrac{\cos^2\theta}{\cot^2\theta} + \dfrac{\sin^2\theta}{\tan^2\theta} = 1$. **58.** $\tan\theta = \dfrac{\sec\theta}{\csc\theta}$. **59.** $\sec\theta = \dfrac{\tan\theta}{\sin\theta}$.

60. By use of fundamental identities, find all trigonometric functions of the angle θ if θ is in quadrant III and $\tan\theta = \frac{15}{8}$.

Obtain the number N whose logarithm is given.

61. $\log_3 N = 4$. **62.** $\log_5 N = 2$. **63.** $\log_2 N = -4$. **64.** $\log_{16} N = \frac{3}{4}$.

Compute by use of four-place or five-place logarithms.

65. $(2.68)^3$. **66.** $\sqrt[4]{.00314}$. **67.** $1/.689$.

68. $\dfrac{21.9567}{86.7353}$. **69.** $\dfrac{9.32(.0418)}{65(-.152613)}$. **70.** $\dfrac{.739(10^{.215})}{432\sqrt[3]{.0185}}$.

71. Find N by use of Table V if $\log N = -3.0567$.

72. Find the length of arc intercepted on a circle of radius 10 inches by a central angle of 3.7 radians.

73. Find the measure in radians of a central angle in a circle with radius 15 inches, if the angle intercepts an arc 45 inches long.

74. Graph each direct trigonometric function of x from $x = -\pi$ to $x = \pi$ by use of only a few points, and then describe the variation of the function as x increases from $x = -\pi$ to $x = \pi$.

Prove the identity.

75. $\dfrac{\sec x - \cos x}{\csc x} = \sin^2 x \tan x$. **76.** $\dfrac{\csc y - \sec y}{\csc y + \sec y} = \dfrac{\cos y - \sin y}{\cos y + \sin y}$.

77. $\dfrac{\cot^2 x + 1}{\tan^2 x + 1} = \cot^2 x$. **78.** $1 + \cos x = \dfrac{\sin x}{\csc x - \cot x}$.

79. $\dfrac{\sin^2 x}{1 - \cos x} = 1 + \cos x$. **80.** $\dfrac{\cot x - \sin x \tan x}{\sec x} = \dfrac{\cos x}{\tan x} - \dfrac{\sin x}{\csc x}$.

81. Change to radian measure: (*a*) 325°; (*b*) 160° 35′.

82. Change to degree measure: (*a*) 1.5 radians; (*b*) $\frac{11}{6}\pi$ radians.

83. What is meant by saying that the sine function is periodic, and what is its smallest period? Also, tell another period of the sine. Repeat the problem for the tangent function.

84. The bearing of a point P as seen from A is $N\,26°\,37'\,E$. How far north and how far east is P from A if $PA = 36{,}723$ feet?

85. If P is 650 yards south and 316 yards west of A, find the bearing of A as seen from P.

Without tables, find the indicated function values in radical form by using the specified angle or angles, and identities.

86. cos 165°; use 45°, 120°.
87. sin 285°; use 330°, 45°.
88. sin 75°; use 150°.
89. cos 120°; use 60°.
90. tan 240°; use 120°.
91. tan 75°; use 120°, 45°.

92. Without tables, find the trigonometric functions of $(\alpha + \beta)$ and of $(\alpha - \beta)$ if α is an angle in quadrant II, β is an angle in quadrant III, $\sin \alpha = \frac{8}{17}$, and $\cos \beta = -\frac{5}{13}$.

Prove the identity.

93. $\dfrac{2 \cot \theta}{\tan 2\theta} = \cot^2 \theta - 1.$

94. $\sec 2x = \dfrac{\sec^2 x \cot^2 x}{\cot^2 x - 1}.$

95. $\sec 2\theta = \dfrac{1}{\cos^2 \theta - \sin^2 \theta}.$

96. $\dfrac{\sin 5x - \sin 3x}{\cos 5x + \cos 3x} = \tan x.$

97. $\csc 2x = \dfrac{\csc^2 x}{2 \cot x}.$

98. $\tan (x - \frac{1}{4}\pi) = \dfrac{1 - \cot x}{1 + \cot x}.$

99. $\sin (x - 30°) - \cos (120° - x) = 0.$

100. $\cos 3x = 4 \cos^3 x - 3 \cos x.$

Solve for x on the interval $0 \leqq x < 2\pi$.

101. $\cos 2x + \cos x = 0.$
102. $\sin 2x - 2 \cos x = 0.$
103. $\sin 5x - \sin 3x = 0.$
104. $\cos 4x + \cos 2x = \cos x.$

Express in terms of a function value for an acute angle less than 45°.

105. sin 73°.
106. tan 142°.
107. sec 310°.
108. csc 253°.
109. sin (– 153°).
110. cot (– 220°).
111. sin 645°.
112. csc (– 895°).

Express the function value in terms of a value of a trigonometric function of x.

113. $\sin (\frac{3}{2}\pi + x).$
114. $\cot (\frac{1}{2}\pi + x).$
115. $\sec (2\pi - x).$
116. $\cos (\pi + x).$
117. $\tan (\frac{3}{2}\pi + x).$
118. $\csc (-x).$

119. Angles α and β are in their standard positions on a coordinate system, where a circle of radius 1 is drawn with center at the origin. The terminal sides of α and β intersect the circle at points A and B, respectively. Compute the length of line segment AB in terms of trigonometric functions of α and of β.

120. Graph the function f on the domain $-2 \leqq x \leqq 3$, if

$$f(x) = 3 - x \quad \textit{if} \quad -2 \leqq x \leqq 0, \quad \textit{and} \quad f(x) = 2 + 3x \quad \textit{if} \quad 0 < x \leqq 3.$$

Find the value of the expression.

121. Arcsin $\frac{1}{2}$.
122. Arcsin (– 1).
123. sin Arcsin $(-\frac{2}{3})$.
124. Arctan (– 1).
125. cos Arccos $\frac{1}{5}$.
126. sec Arctan (– 1).

Prove the identity. If a radical occurs, assume that $0 \leqq x \leqq \frac{1}{2}\pi$.

127. $\dfrac{\cos x}{\sec 4x} + \dfrac{\sin x}{\csc 4x} = \cos 3x.$

128. $\dfrac{1}{\cos x - 1} = \dfrac{2 \cos x + 1}{\cos 2x - \cos x}.$

129. $\tan \frac{x}{2} = \frac{\sec x - 1}{\sin x \sec x}.$

130. $\frac{\cos 6x - 1}{\cos 6x + 1} = 1 - \sec^2 3x.$

131. $\sqrt{\frac{\csc x - 1}{\csc x + 1}} = \frac{1 - \sin x}{\cos x}.$

132. $\frac{1}{\cot x + \csc x} = \frac{1 - \cos x}{\sin x}.$

133. $\sin 5x + \sin 3x - \sin 2x = 4 \cos x \cos \frac{5x}{2} \sin \frac{3x}{2}.$

Solve the equation, with x on the interval $0 \leqq x < 2\pi$. Use $\pi = 3.14$ and Table XIII *if desirable.*

134. $\csc x - \cot x = 1.$

135. $4 \cos 2x = 5.$

136. $\tan 3x - \tan x = \sec 3x.$

137. $5 \tan 3x - 2 = 0.$

138. $\cos x - \sqrt{3} \sin x = 0.$

139. $\cos x + 1 = \sin x.$

Compute the expression; assume that $x > 0$ and $y > 0$.

140. $\sin [\frac{1}{2}\pi + \text{Arccos}(-\frac{7}{25})].$

141. $\tan (\pi + \text{Arcsin} \frac{5}{13}).$

142. $\sin (\text{Arccos}\, x - \text{Arcsin}\, y).$

143. $\cot \text{Arcsin}\, x.$

144. Graph $y = 3 \sin \frac{1}{2}x$ from $x = 0$ to $x = 4\pi$.

145. Graph $y = \sin 2x - \cos x$ from $x = 0$ to $x = 2\pi$.

146. Find the unknown base: (1) $\log_a 343 = 3$; (2) $\log_a 125 = \frac{3}{2}$.

147. Find the specified logarithm: (1) $\log_6 216$; (2) $\log_{100} .0001$.

148. Solve for x: $5(1.03)^{2x} = 15.731.$

149. Find $\log_e 3784$ and $\log_e .02393$ from Table XIV.

150. Find formulas for the values of the inverse functions f, with x as the independent variable, and g, with y as the independent variable, which are defined by the equation $2x + 5y = 7$. Draw a graph of f in an xy-plane.

151. Graph the functions 3^x and $\log_3 x$ on the same xy-plane. What physical act with the paper, on which this plane is located, would cause the two graphs to coincide?

152. Prove the reduction formulas for the following function values by use of the addition formulas: $\sin (\frac{3}{2}\pi - x)$; $\cos (\frac{5}{2}\pi + x)$.

153. Graph the equation $y = 3 \cos 2x - 4 \sin 2x$ by first expressing the right-hand member in the form $H \sin (2x + \alpha)$, where $H > 0$.

★ 11

COMPLEX NUMBERS

107. Foundation for complex numbers

In order to produce square roots for negative numbers, in Note 1 of the Appendix on page 208 we introduce the *imaginary unit* i with the property that $i^2 = -1$. We shall start at this point again in expanding the number system.

Let us join i to the system of real numbers. If b is any real number, the product of b and i is defined as a *new number*, written bi or $+bi$, with the agreement that $0 \cdot i = 0$ and $1 \cdot i = i$. If a and b are real, the sum of a and bi is defined as a *new number*, to be written $(a + bi)$, and called a **complex number.** We agree to use $(0 + bi)$ and $(a + 0i)$ as optional symbols for bi and a, respectively. In $(a + bi)$, we call a the *real part*, bi the *imaginary part*, and b its *coefficient*. Then, we introduce the following terminology.

1. *$(a + bi)$ is called an* **imaginary number** *if $b \neq 0$.*
2. *If $a = 0$ and $b \neq 0$, $(a + bi)$ is called a* **pure imaginary number.**
3. *If $b = 0$, then $(a + bi)$ is called a* **real number.**

The number system now consists of *all complex numbers*, including real numbers as special cases. We call $(a + bi)$ the *standard form* for a complex number. Unless otherwise stated, any literal number symbol except i will represent a real number.

ILLUSTRATION 1. $(5 + 7i)$ is an imaginary number. $4i$, or $(0 + 4i)$, is a pure imaginary number. The real number 6 can be written $(6 + 0i)$.

We agree to use the same system of notation for sums and products of complex numbers as in the case of real numbers. Then, we *define* addition and multiplication by specifying that *any sum or product of complex numbers shall have that value which is obtained on the following basis.*

FUNDAMENTAL AGREEMENT. *In addition and multiplication, i acts as if it were a real number with its positive integral powers subject to the condition $i^2 = -1$.*

Illustration 2. By the preceding agreement,

$$(-i)^2 = [(-1)i]^2 = 1 \cdot i^2 = -1.$$

Hence, $-i$ as well as i is a square root of -1.

If $P > 0$, $\quad (i\sqrt{P})^2 = i^2P = -P; \quad (-i\sqrt{P})^2 = i^2P = -P. \qquad (1)$

Thus, **$-P$ has the two square roots $\pm\sqrt{-P} = \pm i\sqrt{P}$.**

By the Fundamental Agreement, we obtain (2) and (3) below for the *sum* and the *product* of two complex numbers.

$$\mathbf{(a + bi) + (c + di) = a + c + (b + d)i.} \tag{2}$$

$$(a + bi)(c + di) = ac + (bc + ad)i + bdi^2, \quad or$$

$$\mathbf{(a + bi)(c + di) = (ac - bd) + (bc + ad)i.} \tag{3}$$

Illustration 3. From $i^2 = -1$, we have $i^4 = 1$. $i^9 = i^8i = (i^4)^2i = i$.

For complex numbers, we accept the usual definition of subtraction holding for real numbers. Thus, to subtract a complex number N, we add its negative, $-N$. Division for complex numbers will be met later.

Definition I. *To say that two complex numbers $(a + bi)$ and $(c + di)$ are equal means that $a = c$ and $b = d$.*

From Definition I, since $0 = 0 + 0i$,

$$\mathbf{a + bi = 0} \quad \textit{means that} \quad \mathbf{a = 0 \ \textit{and} \ b = 0.} \tag{4}$$

Example 1. Find the real numbers x and y such that

$$2ix - 3iy + x + 2y - i - 4 = 0. \tag{5}$$

Solution. 1. Write the left-hand side in the standard form $A + Bi$:

$$(x + 2y - 4) + i(2x - 3y - 1) = 0. \tag{6}$$

2. From (4) and (6),

$$x + 2y - 4 = 0 \quad and \quad 2x - 3y - 1 = 0. \tag{7}$$

On solving system (7), we obtain $(x = 2, y = 1)$.

The **conjugate complex number** for any complex number $(a + bi)$ is defined as $(a - bi)$. Thus, the conjugate of $(a - bi)$ is $[a - (-bi)]$ or $(a + bi)$. Hence, we call $(a + bi)$ and $(a - bi)$ *conjugate complex numbers;* each is *the conjugate of the other.*

Illustration 4. The conjugate of $(3 + 2i)$ is $(3 - 2i)$. The conjugate of $(4 - 5i)$ is $(4 + 5i)$.

Illustration 5. If $c + di \neq 0$, then c and d are not both zero, and

$$(c + di)(c - di) = c^2 - d^2i^2 = c^2 + d^2 \neq 0.$$

ILLUSTRATION 6. We verify that the *difference* of two conjugate numbers is a *pure imaginary number;* the *sum* and *product* of the conjugate numbers are *real numbers:*

$$(a + bi) - (a - bi) = 2bi; \qquad (a + bi) + (a - bi) = 2a;$$
$$(a + bi)(a - bi) = a^2 - b^2i^2 = a^2 + b^2.$$

108. Division for complex numbers

We define division for complex numbers by specifying that, if $c + di \neq 0$, the quotient $(a + bi)/(c + di)$ is the complex number obtained by the following method:

$$\left\{\begin{array}{c}\textit{Multiply both numerator and denominator}\\ \textit{by the conjugate of the denominator.}\end{array}\right\} \tag{1}$$

That is, by definition,

$$\frac{a + bi}{c + di} = \frac{(a + bi)(c - di)}{(c + di)(c - di)} = \frac{(a + bi)(c - di)}{c^2 + d^2}, \tag{2}$$

where $c^2 + d^2 \neq 0$ since $c + di \neq 0$. By use of (2), we may express any quotient $(a + bi)/(c + di)$ in the standard form $A + Bi$. We agree that $(a + bi)^{-n}$, where n is a positive integer, means $1/(a + bi)^n$.

ILLUSTRATION 1. $$\frac{5 + 2i}{3 - 4i} = \frac{5 + 2i}{3 - 4i} \cdot \frac{3 + 4i}{3 + 4i} = \frac{15 + 26i + 8i^2}{9 - 16i^2}$$
$$= \frac{15 + 26i - 8}{9 + 16} = \frac{7}{25} + \frac{26}{25}i.$$

If we think of $3 - 4i = 3 - 4\sqrt{-1}$, then the preceding operation, where the numerator and denominator were multiplied by $3 + 4\sqrt{-1}$, is analogous to the procedure used in rationalizing denominators on page 213.

EXERCISE 61

Express in terms of i and simplify. Assume that $a > 0$ and $b > 0$.

1. $\sqrt{-121}$. **2.** $\sqrt{-75}$. **3.** $\sqrt{-81a^2}$. **4.** $\sqrt{-48b^3}$. **5.** $\sqrt{-\frac{25}{9}}$.

6. State the two square roots of -64; -45; $-25a^2$; $-\frac{3}{49}b^2$.

7. Specify the conjugate of $(5 - 7i)$; $-5i$; $6i$; 8; $(2 - 3\sqrt{-5})$.

Perform the indicated operation and simplify to the form $a + bi$.

8. i^9. **9.** i^{10}. **10.** i^5. **11.** i^{39}. **12.** $3i(8i^4)$.

13. $(2 + 3i) - (5 - 7i)$. **14.** $(8 + \sqrt{-4}) - (3 - \sqrt{-25})$.

15. $2i^4(3i^3)$. **16.** $(2i)^5$. **17.** $(3i^3)^2$. **18.** $(5i)^4$.

19. $\sqrt{-5}\sqrt{-20}$. **20.** $\sqrt{-2}\sqrt{-18}$. **21.** $\sqrt{-3}\sqrt{-15}$.

22. $(3 + 4i)(2 - 7i)$. **23.** $(4 - i)(3 + 5i)$. **24.** $(2 - 7i)(2 + 7i)$.

25. $(\sqrt{-5}+2)(\sqrt{-5}-2)$. **26.** $(3-4\sqrt{-2})(3+4\sqrt{-2})$.

27. $\dfrac{2+3i}{5+4i}$. **28.** $\dfrac{5+i}{2-i}$. **29.** $\dfrac{3+2i}{4-3i}$. **30.** $\dfrac{5}{3+2i}$.

31. $\dfrac{3+\sqrt{-25}}{1+\sqrt{-4}}$. **32.** $\dfrac{7}{4-\sqrt{-9}}$. **33.** $\dfrac{36+5i}{3i}$. **34.** $\dfrac{6-5i}{4i}$.

35. $\dfrac{6}{5i}$. **36.** $\dfrac{-3}{2i}$. **37.** $\dfrac{-5}{4i}$. **38.** $\dfrac{1}{i}$. **39.** $\dfrac{3}{i^3}$. **40.** $\dfrac{-4}{3i^5}$.

41. $(2\sqrt{-5})^3$. **42.** $(3i-5)^2$. **43.** $2i^{-5}$. **44.** $3i^{-7}$.

45. $(2+i)^3$. **46.** $(3-2i)^3$. **47.** $(2+\sqrt{-3})^3$. **48.** $(3+2i)^{-1}$.

49. Find the reciprocal of $(-4+\sqrt{-50})$ in the form $(a+bi)$.

Find the real numbers x and y to satisfy the equation.

50. $x-3+iy=6i$. **51.** $3x-y+ix+2iy=4-i$.

52. If $c^2+d^2=1$, find $(c+di)^{-1}$ in the standard form.

★**53.** Suppose that $c+di \neq 0$. Let $(a+bi)/(c+di)$ be defined (as in division for real numbers) as *the number* $(x+yi)$, *if it exists, such that*

$$a+bi=(c+di)(x+yi). \tag{1}$$

Prove that the number on the right in (2) on page 195 satisfies (1). Also, multiply both sides of (1) by $(c-di)/(c^2+d^2)$, to prove that only one number $(x+yi)$ satisfies (1). Thus, the present definition is equivalent to (2) on page 195.

109. The complex plane

Let $(x+yi)$ be any complex number. Then, we shall represent it geometrically in a coordinate plane by the *point P* whose abscissa is x and ordinate is y. Or, we may think of $(x+yi)$ as represented by the **vector** OP from the origin to the point $P:(x, y)$. This form of representation is illustrated in Figure 108.

ILLUSTRATION 1. In Figure 108, $(3+4i)$ is represented by $D:(3, 4)$ or by the vector OD, as we choose. The real number 3, or $(3+0i)$, is represented by A. The pure imaginary number $-4i$, or $(0-4i)$, is represented by B. Point C represents the number $(-4+2i)$.

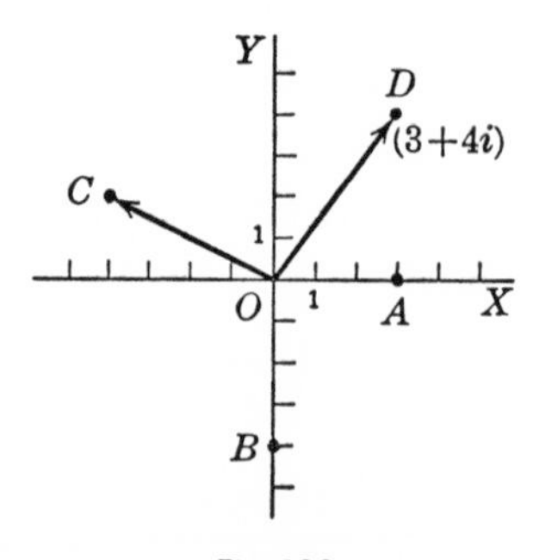

Fig. 108

In Figure 108, all real numbers are represented by the points on the horizontal axis OX, and all pure imaginary numbers by the points on OY. When we use a coordinate plane in this way, we call the horizontal axis *the axis of real numbers*, the vertical axis *the axis of pure imaginary numbers*, and the whole plane *the complex plane*.

The vector representation of a complex number is important as well as interesting because of the following result, which states that, as vectors, complex numbers obey the parallelogram law for vector addition.

THEOREM I. *If z_1 and z_2 are complex numbers, and $z = z_1 + z_2$, the vector OP representing z is obtained by drawing the vectors for z_1 and z_2 from the origin, completing the parallelogram with these vectors as sides, and drawing the diagonal OP of this parallelogram.*

Proof. 1. Let $z_1 = a + bi$; $z_2 = c + di$. Then $z = (a + c) + (b + d)i$. Vectors OM and ON represent z_1 and z_2, respectively, in Figure 109.

2. In Figure 109, P has the coordinates $x = OR$ and $y = RP$. By considering congruent triangles, it can be verified that, for all positions of M and N,

$$OR = OS + SR = OS + OK = a + c; \tag{1}$$

$$RP = RH + HP = SM + KN = b + d. \tag{2}$$

Hence, from (1) and (2), OP represents z.

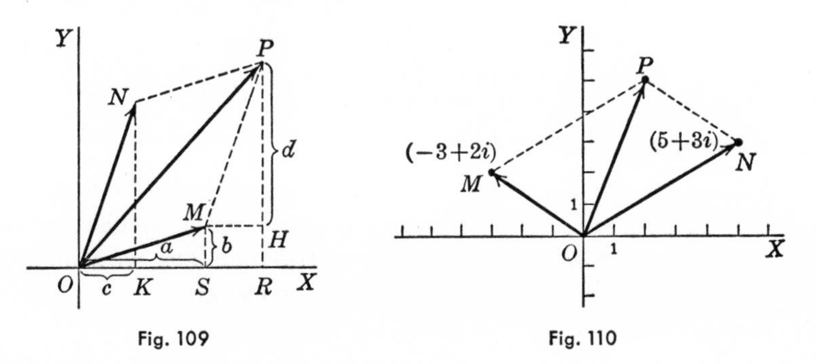

Fig. 109

Fig. 110

ILLUSTRATION 2. In Figure 110, we find

$$z = (5 + 3i) + (-3 + 2i) = 2 + 5i$$

by adding the vectors for $(5 + 3i)$ and $(-3 + 2i)$.

Note 1. To *subtract* $(c + di)$ from $(a + bi)$ geometrically, we geometrically *add* $(-c - di)$ to $(a + bi)$.

ILLUSTRATION 3. In Figure 110, we obtain

$$z = (5 + 3i) - (3 - 2i) = (5 + 3i) + (-3 + 2i).$$

Note 2. Imaginary numbers were introduced in the 16th century by CARDANO but were not thoroughly appreciated until 100 years later. The words *real* and *imaginary*, as now employed in references to numbers, were introduced by DESCARTES (1637), and the symbol i for $\sqrt{-1}$ by EULER (1748). A Norwegian surveyor, WESSEL (1797), was the first to employ the geometrical representation of complex numbers on a plane.

EXERCISE 62

Represent the complex number as a point, and also as a vector.

1. $3 + 4i$. **2.** $6i - 3$. **3.** $-4 - 5i$. **4.** $8i$. **5.** $-3i$.
6. $2 - i\sqrt{2}$. **7.** $3 - \sqrt{-9}$. **8.** $\sqrt{-24}$. **9.** $\sqrt{-25}$. **10.** -7.

On one plane, plot the number, its conjugate, and its negative.

11. $4 - 5i$. **12.** $-3 - 2i$. **13.** 6. **14.** $-5i$. **15.** $2 - \sqrt{-49}$.

Separately plot each number in parentheses, or its negative, and find the sum or difference geometrically. Read the sum from the figure.

16. $(2 + 2i) + (4 + i)$.
17. $(2 + i) + (-3 + 5i)$.
18. $(-2 + i) + (-6 - 3i)$.
19. $(-3 - 4i) + (7 - 2i)$.
20. $(5 + 0i) + (0 + 4i)$.
21. $(-3 + 0i) + (0 + 6i)$.
22. $(1 + 3i) + (5 - 4i)$.
23. $(-2 + 3i) - (4 + 2i)$.
24. $(-2i) + (4)$.
25. $(3i) + (-5)$.
26. $(2i) + (-4i)$.
27. $(-2 - i) - (3 + 6i)$.
28. $(5 + 2i) - (3 - 4i)$.
29. $(5 - 2i) + (3 + 2i) + (-4 + 3i)$.

30. Let z be a complex number. State and demonstrate a construction for locating the point representing $-z$; the conjugate of z.

110. Trigonometric form

In our future discussion in this chapter, in any representation of complex numbers in an xy-plane, we shall assume that the units for distance on the two axes are equal. Also, in use of trigonometric functions, we shall consider them as functions of *angles*, with the attitude of Definition I on page 33. As a rule, on account of our principal objectives, we shall use degree measure for angles.

In Figure 111, let OP represent $x + yi$, let r be the length of OP, and let $\theta = \angle XOP$. Then, θ is in its standard position on the coordinate system, and thus the following equations are a consequence of Definition I on page 33.

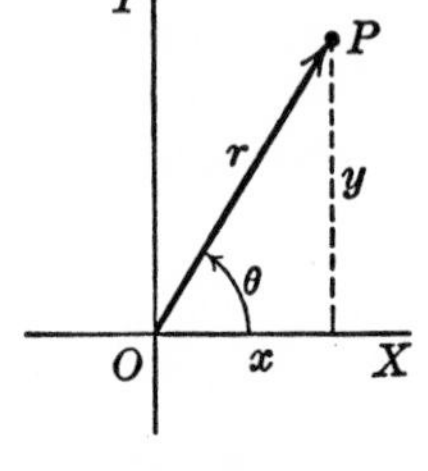

Fig. 111

$$r = \sqrt{x^2 + y^2}; \qquad \tan \theta = \frac{y}{x}; \tag{1}$$

$$x = r \cos \theta; \qquad y = r \sin \theta; \tag{2}$$

$$x + yi = r(\cos \theta + i \sin \theta). \tag{3}$$

We call $r(\cos \theta + i \sin \theta)$ the **trigonometric** (or **polar**) form, θ the **amplitude** (or **argument**), and the positive length r the **absolute value** (or **modulus**) of $x + yi$. The amplitude may be taken as any angle with initial side OX and terminal side OP, because the values of the trigonometric functions are the same for all such coterminal angles. Hence, if θ is one amplitude, the other permissible amplitudes are $(\theta + k \cdot 360°)$, where k is any integer. Usually, we select the amplitude as an angle which is positive or 0° and less than 360°. Two complex numbers are *equal* if and only if *their absolute values are equal* and *their amplitudes differ at most by an integral multiple of* 360°.

To plot $r(\cos\theta + i\sin\theta)$, *as in Figure* 111, *construct* $\angle XOP = \theta$, *with* $OP = r$; *then* P *represents the given complex number.*

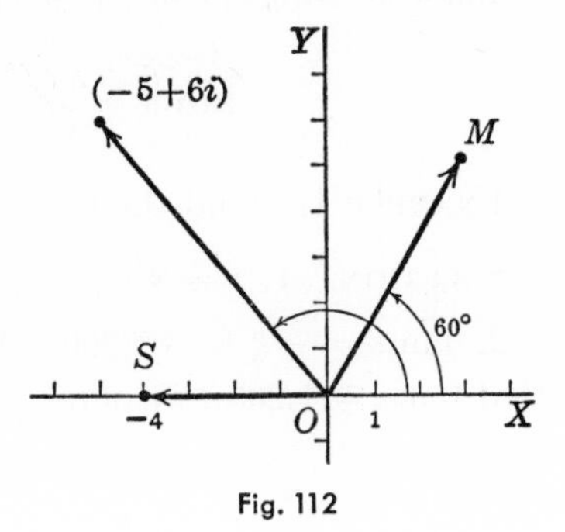

Fig. 112

ILLUSTRATION 1. In Figure 112, the vector OM represents

$$6(\cos 60° + i \sin 60°).$$

Instead of 60°, we could use 420°, or − 300°, etc., as the amplitude.

ILLUSTRATION 2. We may write

$$0 = 0 \cdot (\cos\theta + i\sin\theta),$$

where θ has any value. That is, the absolute value of zero is 0, and the amplitude is *any* angle whatever.

To change a complex number *from the trigonometric form to the form* $(x + yi)$, obtain $\cos\theta$ and $\sin\theta$ from a trigonometric table, or from memory if θ is 0°, 30°, 45°, 60°, 90°, or some corresponding angle greater than 90°.

ILLUSTRATION 3. $$3(\cos 45° + i \sin 45°) = \tfrac{3}{2}\sqrt{2} + \tfrac{3}{2}i\sqrt{2}.$$

$$6(\cos 35° + i \sin 35°) = 6(.819 + .574i) = 4.914 + 3.444i. \qquad \text{(Table IV)}$$

The absolute value of a real number a, or $(a + 0i)$, as defined for a *complex number*, is $\sqrt{a^2 + 0^2}$ or $\sqrt{a^2}$, which is $+a$ if $a \geqq 0$ and is $-a$ if $a < 0$; this is identical with $|a|$ as defined on page 4. Hence, *the two uses of the absolute value terminology are consistent.* Thus, it is consistent to use the symbol $|x + yi|$ to represent *the absolute value of* $(x + yi)$, that is, to represent r in the trigonometric form of $(x + yi)$:

$$|x + yi| = \sqrt{x^2 + y^2}. \qquad (4)$$

ILLUSTRATION 4. $|-4 + 0i| = |-4| = 4.$ $|3 + 4i| = \sqrt{25} = 5.$

ILLUSTRATION 5. To express the real number − 4 in polar form, we plot $(-4 + 0i)$, as vector OS in Figure 112. The amplitude is $\theta = 180°$. The absolute value is $r = \overline{OS} = 4$. Hence,

$$-4 = -4 + 0i = 4(\cos 180° + i \sin 180°).$$

SUMMARY. *To change from the form $(x + yi)$ to $r(\cos\theta + i\sin\theta)$.*

1. *Plot $(x + yi)$ as a vector OP, and indicate θ by an arrow.*

2. *If $(x + yi)$ is real or pure imaginary, read $r = \overline{OP}$ from the figure, observe the value of θ, and write the polar form.*

3. *If θ is not quadrantal, obtain $r = \sqrt{x^2 + y^2}$; find θ by noticing its quadrant, and also using one of the following functions of θ:*

$$\tan\theta = \frac{y}{x}; \qquad \sin\theta = \frac{y}{r}; \qquad \cos\theta = \frac{x}{r}. \tag{5}$$

EXAMPLE 1. Find the trigonometric form of $(-5 + 6i)$.

SOLUTION. 1. $r = \sqrt{61}$ and θ is in quadrant II (Figure 112 on page 199).

2. $\tan\theta = -\frac{6}{5} = -1.200$. In Table IV, we seek an acute angle α such that $\tan\alpha = 1.200$; we obtain $\alpha = 50.2°$. Hence, $\theta = 180° - 50.2° = 129.8°$;

$$-5 + 6i = \sqrt{61}(\cos 129.8° + i\sin 129.8°).$$

EXERCISE 63

Plot the number. Then, express it in the form $x + yi$.

1. $3(\cos 30° + i\sin 30°)$.
2. $4(\cos 210° + i\sin 210°)$.
3. $2(\cos 360° + i\sin 360°)$.
4. $5(\cos 90° + i\sin 90°)$.
5. $3(\cos 300° + i\sin 300°)$.
6. $7(\cos 135° + i\sin 135°)$.
7. $4(\cos 225° + i\sin 225°)$.
8. $3(\cos 60° + i\sin 60°)$.
9. $5(\cos 270° + i\sin 270°)$.
10. $6(\cos 180° + i\sin 180°)$.
11. $4(\cos 123° + i\sin 123°)$.
12. $10(\cos 328° + i\sin 328°)$.
13. $\cos(-135°) + i\sin(-135°)$.
14. $2[\cos(-45°) + i\sin(-45°)]$.

Change the given number to its polar form.

15. $3i$.
16. $-2i$.
17. -8.
18. 6.
19. $2 + 2i$.
20. $3 - 3i$.
21. $-8 + 8i$.
22. $\sqrt{3} + i$.
23. $i - \sqrt{3}$.
24. $-2 - 2i\sqrt{3}$.
25. $-4 + 4i\sqrt{3}$.
26. $3\sqrt{3} - 3i$.
27. $-5 - 5i$.
28. $3 + 4i$.
29. $-12 + 5i$.
30. $5 - 12i$.
31. $4 + 3i$.
32. $\cos 60° - i\sin 60°$.
33. $5(\cos 120° - i\sin 120°)$.
34. Change the number and its conjugate to polar form: $(1 + i)$.
35. Find the conjugate of $r(\cos\theta + i\sin\theta)$ in polar form.
36. Find the reciprocal of $r(\cos\theta + i\sin\theta)$ in polar form.
37. Compute $|5 - 12i|$; $|7 + 24i|$; $|h - ki|$.

111. Products and quotients in polar form

THEOREM II. *An amplitude for a product of complex numbers is the sum of their amplitudes, and the absolute value of the product is the product of the absolute values of the factors.*

Proof. Consider a product of just two complex numbers:

$$r_1(\cos\theta_1 + i\sin\theta_1)\cdot r_2(\cos\theta_2 + i\sin\theta_2)$$
$$= r_1r_2(\cos\theta_1\cos\theta_2 + i\sin\theta_1\cos\theta_2 + i\cos\theta_1\sin\theta_2 + i^2\sin\theta_1\sin\theta_2)$$
$$= r_1r_2[(\cos\theta_1\cos\theta_2 - \sin\theta_1\sin\theta_2) + i(\sin\theta_1\cos\theta_2 + \cos\theta_1\sin\theta_2)].$$

Hence, from the addition formulas of page 144,

$$\mathbf{r_1(\cos\theta_1 + i\sin\theta_1)\cdot r_2(\cos\theta_2 + i\sin\theta_2) = r_1r_2[\cos(\theta_1+\theta_2) + i\sin(\theta_1+\theta_2)].} \quad (1)$$

Note 1. We extend (1) to a product of any number of factors by successive applications of (1). Thus, we use (1) twice below:

$$r_1(\cos\theta_1 + i\sin\theta_1)\cdot r_2(\cos\theta_2 + i\sin\theta_2)\cdot r_3(\cos\theta_3 + i\sin\theta_3)$$
$$= r_1r_2[\cos(\theta_1+\theta_2) + i\sin(\theta_1+\theta_2)]\cdot r_3(\cos\theta_3 + i\sin\theta_3)$$
$$= r_1r_2r_3[\cos(\theta_1+\theta_2+\theta_3) + i\sin(\theta_1+\theta_2+\theta_3)]. \quad (2)$$

ILLUSTRATION 1. $3(\cos 40° + i\sin 40°)\cdot 5(\cos 170° + i\sin 170°)$
$= 15(\cos 210° + i\sin 210°).$

COROLLARY 1. *A product of complex numbers is equal to zero if and only if at least one factor is zero.*

Proof. The product is zero if and only if its absolute value is zero. This absolute value is the product of the absolute values of all factors. The product of these real numbers is zero if and only if *at least one factor is zero*, which means that at least one of the original complex numbers is *zero.*

A complex number is zero if and only if its absolute value is zero. Thus, in considering a fraction with the denominator $s(\cos\beta + i\sin\beta)$, an assumption that it is *not zero* is equivalent to the condition $s \neq 0$. We accept this fact in the following result.

THEOREM III. *The absolute value of the quotient of two complex numbers, where the divisor is not 0, is the quotient of their absolute values, and an amplitude for the quotient of the complex numbers is the amplitude of the dividend minus the amplitude of the divisor.*

Proof. 1. Consider $[r(\cos\alpha + i\sin\alpha)]/[s(\cos\beta + i\sin\beta)]$, multiply both numerator and denominator by $(\cos\beta - i\sin\beta)$, and recall the identities $\cos(-\beta) = \cos\beta$ and $\sin(-\beta) = -\sin\beta$:

$$\frac{r(\cos\alpha + i\sin\alpha)}{s(\cos\beta + i\sin\beta)} = \frac{r}{s}\cdot\frac{(\cos\alpha + i\sin\alpha)(\cos\beta - i\sin\beta)}{(\cos\beta + i\sin\beta)(\cos\beta - i\sin\beta)}$$
$$= \frac{r}{s}\cdot\frac{(\cos\alpha + i\sin\alpha)[\cos(-\beta) + i\sin(-\beta)]}{\cos^2\beta + \sin^2\beta}, \quad (3)$$

2. In (3), apply Theorem II and recall that $\sin^2 \beta + \cos^2 \beta = 1$:

$$\frac{r(\cos \alpha + i \sin \alpha)}{s(\cos \beta + i \sin \beta)} = \frac{r}{s} \cdot [\cos (\alpha - \beta) + i \sin (\alpha - \beta)]. \qquad (4)$$

ILLUSTRATION 2. $\dfrac{15(\cos 350° + i \sin 350°)}{5(\cos 240° + i \sin 240°)} = 3(\cos 110° + i \sin 110°)$.

THEOREM IV. **(De Moivre's Theorem)** *If n is any positive integer, then*

$$[r(\cos \theta + i \sin \theta)]^n = r^n(\cos n\theta + i \sin n\theta). \qquad (5)$$

ILLUSTRATION 3. From (2) with θ_1, θ_2, and θ_3 replaced by θ, and r_1, r_2, and r_3 replaced by r,

$$\begin{aligned} &[r(\cos \theta + i \sin \theta)]^3 \\ &\quad = r(\cos \theta + i \sin \theta) \cdot r(\cos \theta + i \sin \theta) \cdot r(\cos \theta + i \sin \theta) \\ &\quad = r \cdot r \cdot r \cdot [\cos (\theta + \theta + \theta) + i \sin (\theta + \theta + \theta)] \\ &\quad = r^3(\cos 3\theta + i \sin 3\theta). \end{aligned}$$

Proof of (5). The left-hand side in (5) indicates the product of n factors $r(\cos \theta + i \sin \theta)$. Hence, the absolute value of the nth power is the product of n factors r, or r^n, and an amplitude is the sum of n amplitudes θ, or $n\theta$. Hence, (5) is true.

EXAMPLE 1. Find $(1 - i)^4$ by use of De Moivre's Theorem.

SOLUTION. 1. Express $(1 - i)$ in polar form:

$r = \sqrt{2}$; $\quad \tan \theta = -1$, *with θ in quadrant* IV, *so that* $\theta = 315°$.

2. Hence, we obtain

$$(1 - i)^4 = [\sqrt{2}(\cos 315° + i \sin 315°)]^4$$
$$= (\sqrt{2})^4(\cos 1260° + i \sin 1260°) = 4(\cos 180° + i \sin 180°) = -4.$$

In the preceding details, we noticed that $1260° = 3 \cdot 360° + 180°$ and used the periodicity of the sine and cosine functions.

EXERCISE 64

Give the result in polar form, except when the final sine and cosine are known without using tables; in that case, express the result in the form $(x + yi)$. Compute any power by use of De Moivre's Theorem.

1. $3(\cos 18° + i \sin 18°) \cdot 4(\cos 42° + i \sin 42°)$.
2. $6(\cos 25° + i \sin 25°) \cdot 3(\cos 125° + i \sin 125°)$.
3. $2(\cos 85° + i \sin 85°) \cdot 6(\cos 310° + i \sin 310°)$.
4. $4(\cos 140° + i \sin 140°) \cdot 5(\cos 275° + i \sin 275°)$.
5. $[2(\cos 15° + i \sin 15°)]^3$.
6. $[3(\cos 60° + i \sin 60°)]^4$.
7. $[2(\cos 45° + i \sin 45°)]^6$.
8. $[5(\cos 250° + i \sin 250°)]^3$.

9. $(2 + 2i)^4$. **10.** $(-3 - 3i)^5$. **11.** $(-1 + i\sqrt{3})^5$. **12.** $(i + \sqrt{3})^6$.
13. $(-\sqrt{3} - i)^4$. **14.** $(1 - i\sqrt{3})^3$. **15.** $(-4 + 4i)^3$. **16.** $(3 + 4i)^3$.

17. $\dfrac{6(\cos 140° + i \sin 140°)}{2(\cos 30° + i \sin 30°)}$. **18.** $\dfrac{5(\cos 250° + i \sin 250°)}{20(\cos 310° + i \sin 310°)}$.

19. $\dfrac{15(\cos 150° + i \sin 150°)}{1 + i}$. **20.** $\dfrac{25(\cos 250° + i \sin 250°)}{5\sqrt{2} - 5i\sqrt{2}}$.

21. $\dfrac{2 - 2i\sqrt{3}}{3(\cos 150° + i \sin 150°)}$. **22.** $\dfrac{15(\cos 150° + i \sin 150°)}{5(\cos 30° - i \sin 30°)}$.

★**23.** If $z = r(\cos \theta + i \sin \theta)$, where $r \neq 0$, and if n is a positive integer, prove that $z^{-n} = r^{-n}[\cos(-n\theta) + i \sin(-n\theta)]$, so that *De Moivre's Theorem holds if the exponent is a negative integer.*

★**24.** In the complex plane with the origin at O, let U be the unit point on the real axis and let P and Q represent $r(\cos \alpha + i \sin \alpha)$ and $s(\cos \beta + i \sin \beta)$, respectively. Construct ΔUOP and $\angle QOM = \alpha$; complete ΔQOM similar to ΔUOP. (Give the figure for α and β acute, for convenience.) Prove that *M represents the product of the given complex numbers.*

112. The *n*th roots of a complex number

In this section, n always represents a *positive integer*. Then, to say that R is an nth root of a complex number z means that $z = R^n$.

Example 1. Find the cube roots of $8(\cos 150° + i \sin 150°)$.

Solution. 1. Let $r(\cos \alpha + i \sin \alpha)$ be any cube root. Then,

$$8(\cos 150° + i \sin 150°) = [r(\cos \alpha + i \sin \alpha)]^3.$$

Or, by De Moivre's Theorem,

$$8(\cos 150° + i \sin 150°) = r^3(\cos 3\alpha + i \sin 3\alpha). \tag{1}$$

2. If two complex numbers are equal, their absolute values are *equal* and their amplitudes *differ at most by some integral multiple of* 360°. Hence, from (1), the values of r and α which give cube roots satisfy

$$r^3 = 8, \quad \text{or} \quad r = 2;$$

$$3\alpha = 150° + k \cdot 360°, \text{ or}$$

$$\alpha = 50° + k \cdot 120°, \tag{2}$$

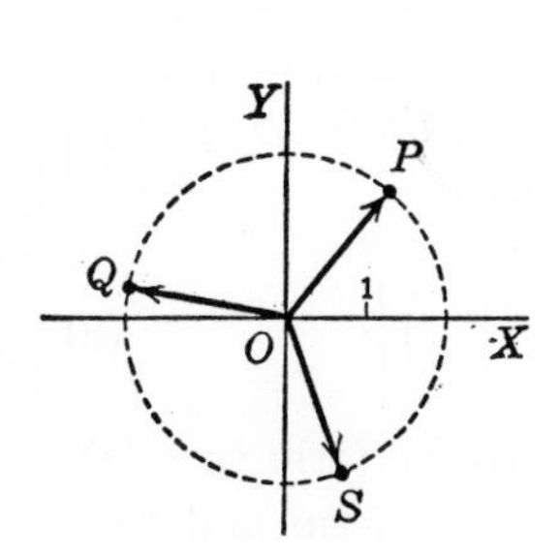

Fig. 113

where k is any integer. On placing $k = 0$, 1, and 2 in (2), we obtain 50°, 170°, and 290° as the values of α. These give the following cube roots:

$$2(\cos 50° + i \sin 50°); \quad 2(\cos 170° + i \sin 170°);$$
$$2(\cos 290° + i \sin 290°).$$

Comment. If $k = 3$ in (2), then $\alpha = 50° + 360°$, equivalent to the amplitude 50°. If $k = -1$, then $\alpha = 50° - 120° = -70° = 290° - 360°$, equivalent to 290°. Similarly, if k has any integral value in (2), the value found for α is equivalent to one of (50°, 170°, 290°). Hence, the roots obtained in Step 2 are the *only* cube roots. The cube roots are represented by P, Q, and S in Figure 113. These points lie on a circle whose radius is 2, because 2 is the modulus of each of the roots. Moreover, P, Q, and S divide the circumference into *three equal parts* because the amplitudes of the roots are 50°, 170°, and 290°, where adjacent angles differ by 120°.

THEOREM V. *If n is any positive integer, and $R > 0$, any complex number $R(\cos\theta + i\sin\theta)$ has just n distinct nth roots.*

Proof. 1. Suppose that $0 \leqq \theta < 360°$. Let $r(\cos\alpha + i\sin\alpha)$ be any nth root. Then, by De Moivre's Theorem,

$$R(\cos\theta + i\sin\theta) = [r(\cos\alpha + i\sin\alpha)]^n = r^n(\cos n\alpha + i\sin n\alpha). \quad (3)$$

2. From (3), $r^n = R$, or $\boldsymbol{r = \sqrt[n]{R}}$; and $n\alpha = \theta + k\cdot 360°$, or

$$\boldsymbol{\alpha = \frac{\theta}{n} + k\cdot\frac{360°}{n}}, \quad (4)$$

where k is any integer. On placing $k = 0, 1, 2, \cdots, (n-1)$ in (4), we obtain the following n distinct values for α, all less than 360°:

$$\frac{\theta}{n};\ \left(\frac{\theta}{n} + \frac{360°}{n}\right);\ \left(\frac{\theta}{n} + 2\,\frac{360°}{n}\right);\ \cdots;\ \left[\frac{\theta}{n} + (n-1)\,\frac{360°}{n}\right]. \quad (5)$$

Corresponding to (5), we obtain the following n distinct nth roots:

$$\sqrt[n]{R}\left(\cos\frac{\theta}{n} + i\sin\frac{\theta}{n}\right);\ \sqrt[n]{R}\left[\cos\left(\frac{\theta}{n} + \frac{360°}{n}\right) + i\sin\left(\frac{\theta}{n} + \frac{360°}{n}\right)\right];\ etc.$$

3. If k has any integral value other than $0, 1, 2, \cdots, (n-1)$ in (4), we obtain a value for α differing from some amplitude in (5) by an integral multiple of 360°. Hence, in (5) we have the only distinct amplitudes which give nth roots. Thus, $R(\cos\theta + i\sin\theta)$ has *exactly* n distinct nth roots, as obtained in Step 2.

SUMMARY. *The nth roots of $R(\cos\theta + i\sin\theta)$ are obtained by placing $k = 0, 1, 2, \cdots, (n-1)$ in the formula*

$$\boldsymbol{\sqrt[n]{R}\left[\cos\left(\frac{\theta}{n} + k\cdot\frac{360°}{n}\right) + i\sin\left(\frac{\theta}{n} + k\cdot\frac{360°}{n}\right)\right]}. \quad (6)$$

To obtain the nth roots of a complex number given in the form $(a + bi)$, that is, to solve $z^n = a + bi$ for z, express $(a + bi)$ in polar form and then use (6).

ILLUSTRATION 1. The 4th roots of $16(\cos 80° + i \sin 80°)$ are

$$2(\cos 20° + i \sin 20°),$$
$$2(\cos 110° + i \sin 110°),$$
$$2(\cos 200° + i \sin 200°),$$
$$2(\cos 290° + i \sin 290°).$$

ILLUSTRATION 2. To find the 5th roots of -32, or to solve $z^5 = -32$, first write -32 in polar form:

$$-32 = 32(\cos 180° + i \sin 180°).$$

Hence, the five values of z which satisfy $z^5 = -32$ are

$$2(\cos 36° + i \sin 36°),$$
$$2(\cos 108° + i \sin 108°),$$
$$2(\cos 180° + i \sin 180°),$$
$$2(\cos 252° + i \sin 252°),$$
$$2(\cos 324° + i \sin 324°).$$

We notice that the root with amplitude 180° is -2.

Note 1. ABRAHAM DE MOIVRE (1667–1754) was a French mathematician who was compelled to leave France for religious reasons. He settled in London, where he earned a precarious living by miscellaneous mathematical work, partly by solving problems associated with games of chance. He is particularly noted for his work entitled *The Doctrine of Chances*, which was published in 1718 and dedicated to SIR ISAAC NEWTON.

★*Note 2.* Let m and n be integers, with $n > 0$ and m/n in lowest terms. We define $a^{m/n}$ on page 211 as the principal nth root of a^m in case a is real and a^m has a *real* nth root. Also, we defined $\sqrt{-P}$ or $(-P)^{\frac{1}{2}}$ as $i\sqrt{P}$ if $P > 0$. Otherwise, *no meaning has been given to* $a^{m/n}$. Now, if $z = R(\cos \theta + i \sin \theta)$, define $z^{m/n}$ as an *n-valued symbol* to represent *any one of the* n*th roots of* z^m. Then $z^m = R^m(\cos m\theta + i \sin m\theta)$. Hence, all values of $z^{m/n}$ are given by (6) with θ replaced by $m\theta$. In particular, with $k = 0$ in (6), we obtain

$$z^{m/n} = R^{m/n}\left(\cos \frac{m\theta}{n} + i \sin \frac{m\theta}{n}\right), \tag{7}$$

which is the same as obtained from (5) on page 202 in De Moivre's Theorem with n replaced by m/n. That is, this theorem holds for *rational exponents* in the sense that the theorem gives *one of the values of* $z^{m/n}$, as in (7). In (6), with $k = 0$, we have one value of $z^{1/n}$.

EXERCISE 65

Leave any result in polar form, unless its amplitude is an angle for which the values of the trigonometric functions are known without tables; in the latter case, give the result in the form $(a + bi)$. *In each problem, find all of the specified roots, and plot them as vectors in a plane.*

1. 4th roots of $81(\cos 160° + i \sin 160°)$.

2. Cube roots of $125(\cos 60° + i \sin 60°)$.

3. Cube roots of $27(\cos 228° + i \sin 228°)$.

4. 5th roots of $32(\cos 210° + i \sin 210°)$.

5. Square roots of $9i$.

6. Square roots of $-25i$.

7. Cube roots of 27.

8. Cube roots of -1.

9. 5th roots of $32i$.

10. Cube roots of i.

11. 4th roots of 81.

12. 4th roots of -16.

13. 4th roots of $(8\sqrt{2} - 8i\sqrt{2})$.

14. Square roots of $(-2 + 2i\sqrt{3})$.

15. 4th roots of $(8 - 8i\sqrt{3})$.

16. Cube roots of $(-4\sqrt{2} - 4i\sqrt{2})$.

17. 4th roots of $(-8\sqrt{3} + 8i)$.

18. Square roots of $(7 - 24i)$.

For the given equation, find all roots in polar forms, or otherwise.

19. $z^4 = 16$.

20. $z^5 = 243$.

21. $z^6 - 64 = 0$.

22. $z^4 + 81i = 0$.

23. Prove the facts (1), (2), (3), and (4) about the nth roots of real numbers listed in Section 4 of Note 1 of the Appendix on page 209.

APPENDIX

NOTE 1

Review of Exponents and Radicals

1. Positive integral exponents

By definition, if m is a positive integer, then $a^m = a \cdot a \cdot a \cdots a$, to m factors. We call a^m the mth **power** of the **base** a and m the **exponent** of the power. By definition $a^1 = a$. Hence, when the exponent is 1, we shall usually omit it. We call a^2 the *square* of a and a^3 the *cube* of a. The following properties I–V of exponents are called **index laws,** and are proved in algebra.

Note 1. Until later, any number occurring in an exponent will be a positive integer.

I. *Law of exponents for multiplication:* $a^m a^n = a^{m+n}$.

II. *Law for finding a power of a power:* $(a^m)^n = a^{mn}$.

III. *Laws of exponents for division:* if $a \neq 0$,

$$\frac{a^m}{a^m} = 1; \qquad \frac{a^m}{a^n} = a^{m-n} \ (\textit{if } m > n); \qquad \frac{a^m}{a^n} = \frac{1}{a^{n-m}} \ (\textit{if } n > m).$$

IV. *Law for finding a power of a product:* $(ab)^n = a^n b^n$.

V. *Law for finding a power of a quotient:* $\left(\frac{a}{b}\right)^n = \frac{a^n}{b^n}$.

ILLUSTRATION 1. $(-3)^3 = (-3)\cdot(-3)\cdot(-3) = -27.$

ILLUSTRATION 2. $\left(\frac{3}{2}\right)^4 = \frac{3^4}{2^4} = \frac{81}{16}. \quad \left(\frac{4cd^2}{3x}\right)^2 = \frac{(4cd^2)^2}{(3x)^2} = \frac{16c^2d^4}{9x^2}.$

ILLUSTRATION 3. $\frac{-15a^3x^5}{10ax^9} = -\frac{3}{2}\cdot\frac{a^3}{a}\cdot\frac{x^5}{x^9} = -\frac{3a^{3-1}}{2x^{9-5}} = -\frac{3a^2}{2x^4}.$

2. Square roots

If $R^2 = A$, we call R a *square root* of A. If $A > 0$, then A has *two* square roots, one positive and one negative, with equal absolute values. The positive square root is denoted by $+\sqrt{A}$, or simply $\sqrt{A}$; the negative square root is

$-\sqrt{A}$. By "*the square root of* A" we mean its *positive* square root. Zero has just one square root, $\pm\sqrt{0} = 0$.

ILLUSTRATION 1. 16 has the square roots $\pm\sqrt{16}$, or ± 4. If $A > 0$, by definition we have $(\sqrt{A})^2 = A$. If $x > 0$ then $\sqrt{x^2} = x$. If $x < 0$, then $\sqrt{x^2} = -x = |x|$ because $\sqrt{x^2}$ represents the *positive* square root of x^2.

If H and K are positive,
$$\sqrt{HK} = \sqrt{H}\sqrt{K}. \tag{1}$$

If $D \neq 0$, then
$$\sqrt{\frac{N}{D}} = \frac{\sqrt{N}}{\sqrt{D}}. \tag{2}$$

An integer is said to be a **perfect square** if it is the square of an integer. At present, in any monomial, we shall suppose that the numerical coefficient is a rational number. Then, a monomial, or a quotient of monomials, is said to be a *perfect square* if it is the *square of an expression of similar type.* The square root of such a perfect square can be obtained by use of (1) and (2).

ILLUSTRATION 2. $\sqrt{\frac{4}{25}} = \frac{\sqrt{4}}{\sqrt{25}} = \frac{2}{5}.\quad \sqrt{225} = \sqrt{9}\sqrt{25} = 15.$

$$\sqrt{\frac{100a^6}{9x^4y^8}} = \frac{\sqrt{100a^6}}{\sqrt{9x^4y^8}} = \frac{10a^3}{3x^2y^4},\ \textit{if } a \geqq 0.$$
$$= -\frac{10a^3}{3x^2y^4},\ \textit{if } a < 0.$$

3. Foundation for imaginary numbers

If $P > 0$, then $-P$ has no positive or negative square root, R, because $R^2 > 0$ if $R \neq 0$. Hence, $-P$ can have *no real number R as a square root.* Therefore, in order for negative numbers to have square roots, numbers of a new variety, called **imaginary numbers,** are introduced in algebra. We let $\sqrt{-1}$, read *the square root of* -1, be a symbol for a new number, called an *imaginary number*, with the property that

$$\sqrt{-1}\sqrt{-1} = -1. \tag{1}$$

We let $i = \sqrt{-1}$. Thus, by definition, $\mathbf{i^2 = -1}$. We expand the number system by joining i to the system of real numbers. In the new system, we agree that the operations of addition, subtraction, and multiplication will be applied to combinations of i and real numbers *as if i were a real number*, with $i^2 = -1$. Then,

$$(-i)^2 = i^2 = -1, \tag{2}$$

so that $-i$, as well as $+i$, is a square root of -1. Any positive integral power of i can be computed by use of $i^2 = -1$. In particular,

$$i^4 = (i^2)(i^2) = (-1)(-1) = 1. \tag{3}$$

ILLUSTRATION 1. $i^{13} = i^{12}i = (i^4)^3 i = (1^3)(i) = i.$

If P is any positive number, we verify that, since $i^2 = -1$,

$$(i\sqrt{P})^2 = i^2P = -P; \qquad (-i\sqrt{P})^2 = i^2P = -P.$$

Hence, $-P$ has the square roots $\pm i\sqrt{P}$. Hereafter, $\sqrt{-P}$ will represent the particular root $i\sqrt{P}$. Then, $-P$ has the two square roots $\pm\sqrt{-P} = \pm i\sqrt{P}$. Thus, we proceed as follows with the square root of a negative number:

$$\sqrt{-P} = \sqrt{(-1)\cdot P} = \sqrt{-1}\sqrt{P} = i\sqrt{P}.$$

ILLUSTRATION 2. The square roots of -5 are $\pm i\sqrt{5}$.

ILLUSTRATION 3. $\sqrt{-4}\sqrt{-9} = (i\sqrt{4})(i\sqrt{9}) = 6i^2 = -6.$

Notice that $\sqrt{-4}\sqrt{-9} \neq \sqrt{(-4)(-9)} = \sqrt{36} = 6$. This result shows that (1) on page 208 is *not true* if H and K are negative.

If a and b are real numbers, we call $(a + bi)$ a **complex number,** whose *real part* is a and *imaginary part* is bi. If $b \neq 0$, we call $(a + bi)$ an *imaginary number.* A *pure imaginary number* is one whose real part is zero; that is, $(a + bi)$ is a pure imaginary if $a = 0$ and $b \neq 0$. Any real number a is thought of as a complex number in which the coefficient of the imaginary part is zero; that is, $a = a + 0i$. In particular, 0 means $(0 + 0i)$.

ILLUSTRATION 4. $(2 - 3i)$ is an imaginary number.

Note 1. In this text, unless otherwise stated, all literal numerals represent real numbers, except that hereafter i always will represent $\sqrt{-1}$, and any variables in a radical $\sqrt{A}$ will be supposed to represent positive numbers, if this is possible.

4. Roots of any order and radicals

We call R a *square root* of A if $R^2 = A$, a *cube root* of A if $R^3 = A$, and a fourth root if $R^4 = A$. If n is any positive integer, by definition,

$$\textbf{R is an nth root of A if } R^n = A. \qquad (1)$$

ILLUSTRATION 1. The only nth root of 0 is 0. 2 is a 5th root of 32 because $2^5 = 32$. -3 is a cube root of -27.

The following facts can be proved by use of Section 112, page 203. The proofs are requested in Problem 23 on page 206.

1. *Every real number A, not zero, has just n distinct* nth *roots, some or all of which may be imaginary numbers.*

2. *If n is even, every positive number A has just two real* nth *roots, one positive and one negative, with equal absolute values.*

3. *If n is odd, every real number A has just one real* nth *root, which is positive when A is positive and negative when A is negative.*

4. *If n is even and A is negative, all* nth *roots of A are imaginary numbers.*

If A is *positive*, its *positive* nth *root* is called the **principal** nth **root** of A. If A is *negative* and n is odd, the *negative* nth *root* of A is called its *principal* nth *root*. If A is zero, its only nth root, 0, is called the *principal* nth *root* of 0.

Illustration 2. The real 4th roots of 81 are ± 3, and $+ 3$ is the principal 4th root. The principal cube root of $+ 125$ is $+ 5$, and of $- 125$ is $- 5$. All 4th roots of $- 16$ are imaginary numbers (see Problem 12, page 206).

Illustration 3. The real cube root of 27 is 3. In Problem 7 on page 206 it is shown that 27 also has the imaginary cube roots $\frac{3}{2}(-1 \pm \sqrt{-3})$, or $\frac{3}{2}(-1 \pm i\sqrt{3})$.

The **radical** $\sqrt[n]{A}$, which we read "**the** nth *root of* A," is used to denote the *principal* nth root of A if it has a real nth root, and to denote any convenient nth root of A if all nth roots are imaginary. In $\sqrt[n]{A}$, the positive integer n is called the **index** or **order** of the radical, and A is called its **radicand.** When $n = 2$, we omit writing the index and use $\sqrt{A}$ instead of $\sqrt[2]{A}$ for the square root of A.

I. $\sqrt[n]{A}$ *is positive if A is positive.*

II. $\sqrt[n]{A}$ *is negative if A is negative and n is odd.*

III. $\sqrt[n]{A}$ *is imaginary if A is negative and n is even.*

Illustration 4. $\sqrt[4]{81} = 3$; $\sqrt[3]{-8} = -2$; $\sqrt[4]{-8}$ is imaginary. The two real 4th roots of 16 are $\pm \sqrt[4]{16}$ or ± 2.

By the definition of an nth root,

$$(\sqrt[n]{A})^n = A. \tag{2}$$

Illustration 5. $(\sqrt{3})^2 = 0.$ $(\sqrt[7]{169})^7 = 169.$ $(\sqrt[5]{2cd^3})^5 = 2cd^3.$

In this book, unless otherwise stated, if the index of a radical is an *even* integer, all literal number symbols in the radicand not used in exponents represent *positive* numbers. With this agreement, for every positive integer n we have *

$$\sqrt[n]{a^n} = a. \tag{3}$$

If $\sqrt[n]{A}$ is a rational number, from (2) we find that A must be the nth power of a rational number, and hence also is rational. Moreover, if A is *not* the nth power of a rational number, it follows that $\sqrt[n]{A}$ is *irrational.*

* If $a < 0$ and n is even, then $a^n > 0$ and the positive nth root of a^n is $-a$, or $\sqrt[n]{a^n} = -a$. This case is ruled out by the agreement above. For any a, $\sqrt[n]{a^n} = |a|$ if n is even.

ILLUSTRATION 6. $\sqrt{3}$ is irrational. $\sqrt[6]{64}$ is not irrational, because $\sqrt[6]{64} = \sqrt[6]{2^6} = 2$.

We may verify the following properties (4), (5), and (6) of radicals by taking the nth power of each side in each equation.

$$\sqrt[n]{ab} = \sqrt[n]{a}\sqrt[n]{b}. \tag{4}$$

$$\sqrt[n]{\frac{a}{b}} = \frac{\sqrt[n]{a}}{\sqrt[n]{b}}. \quad (b \neq 0) \tag{5}$$

If m, n, and m/n are positive integers, $$\sqrt[n]{a^m} = a^{\frac{m}{n}}. \tag{6}$$

ILLUSTRATION 7. $\sqrt[3]{ab} = \sqrt[3]{a}\sqrt[3]{b}$; $\sqrt[3]{a^{12}} = a^{\frac{12}{3}} = a^4$, because $(a^4)^3 = a^{12}$.

ILLUSTRATION 8. $\sqrt[4]{\frac{81}{16}} = \frac{\sqrt[4]{3^4}}{\sqrt[4]{2^4}} = \frac{3}{2}$. $\sqrt[3]{\frac{125y^9}{8x^6}} = \frac{\sqrt[3]{5^3}\sqrt[3]{y^9}}{\sqrt[3]{2^3}\sqrt[3]{x^6}} = \frac{5y^3}{2x^2}$.

An algebraic expression is said to be **rational** in certain variables if it can be expressed as a fraction whose numerator and denominator are polynomials in the variables. If the expression is not rational in the variables, it is said to be **irrational** in them.

ILLUSTRATION 9. Since $x^3 - 2x = \frac{x^3 - 2x}{1}$, hence $(x^3 - 2x)$ is rational in x. $\frac{x^3 - 3a^2}{x + a}$ is rational in a and x. $\sqrt{3x + y}$ is irrational in x and y.

In this note of the Appendix, unless otherwise stated, in any polynomial which is met, we shall assume that the numerical coefficients are rational numbers. Then, a rational expression will be called a *perfect* nth *power* if the expression is the nth power of some rational expression.

ILLUSTRATION 10. Since $32y^{15} = (2y^3)^5$, then $32y^{15}$ is a perfect 5th power: $\sqrt[5]{32y^{15}} = \sqrt[5]{(2y^3)^5} = 2y^3$. *By* (3) *and* (4), $\sqrt[3]{8x^3y^9} = \sqrt[3]{8}\sqrt[3]{x^3}\sqrt[3]{y^9} = 2xy^3$.

5. Fractions, zero, and negative numbers as exponents

If m and n are any positive integers, we define $a^{\frac{m}{n}}$ to be the *principal* nth root of a^m, or

$$a^{\frac{m}{n}} = \sqrt[n]{a^m}; \tag{1}$$

[*when* $m = 1$ *in* (1)] $$a^{\frac{1}{n}} = \sqrt[n]{a}. \tag{2}$$

When m/n is an integer, (1) is consistent with (6) above.

ILLUSTRATION 1. $8^{\frac{1}{3}} = \sqrt[3]{8} = 2$. $(-8)^{\frac{1}{3}} = \sqrt[3]{-8} = -2$. $x^{\frac{8}{3}} = \sqrt[3]{x^8}$.

$8^{\frac{2}{3}} = \sqrt[3]{8^2} = \sqrt[3]{64} = 4$. $\quad (-8)^{\frac{2}{3}} = \sqrt[3]{(-8)^2} = \sqrt[3]{64} = 4$.

In texts on algebra, it is proved that, as a consequence of (1) and the definition of a principal root,

$$a^{\frac{m}{n}} = (\sqrt[n]{a})^m, \tag{3}$$

which sometimes is more convenient than (1) for computing a fractional power.

ILLUSTRATION 2. By use of (3), $\quad 64^{\frac{5}{6}} = (\sqrt[6]{64})^5 = 2^5 = 32.$

We define a^0 and a^{-p}, where p is any positive rational number, as follows:

$$a^0 = 1; \qquad a^{-p} = \frac{1}{a^p}. \tag{4}$$

It can be proved that Laws I–V for integral exponents on page 207 apply when the exponents are allowed to be any rational numbers, positive, negative, or zero. Hereafter we shall make use of this result.

ILLUSTRATION 3. $\quad (x^6)^{\frac{2}{3}} = x^4. \qquad x^{\frac{1}{4}}x^{\frac{2}{3}} = x^{\frac{1}{4}+\frac{2}{3}} = x^{\frac{11}{12}}. \qquad 4^{-3} = \frac{1}{4^3} = \frac{1}{64}.$

$$(-\tfrac{1}{125})^{-\frac{2}{3}} = [(-\tfrac{1}{5})^3]^{-\frac{2}{3}} = (-\tfrac{1}{5})^{-2} = \frac{1}{(-\frac{1}{5})^2} = \frac{1}{\frac{1}{25}} = 25.$$

6. Multiplication and division involving radicals

In operations involving radicals, we use their properties in (2), (3), (4), (5), and (6) in Section 4 of this note of the Appendix.

ILLUSTRATION 1. $\quad \sqrt{147} = \sqrt{49 \cdot 3} = \sqrt{49}\sqrt{3} = 7\sqrt{3}.$

$$2\sqrt{3}(5\sqrt{6}) = 10\sqrt{3}\sqrt{3 \cdot 2} = 10(3)\sqrt{2} = 30\sqrt{2}.$$

$$\sqrt{\frac{3}{5}} = \frac{\sqrt{3}}{\sqrt{5}}. \qquad \sqrt[3]{\frac{ab}{b^5}} = \frac{\sqrt[3]{a}}{\sqrt[3]{b^4}} = \frac{\sqrt[3]{a}}{\sqrt[3]{b^3}\sqrt[3]{b}} = \frac{1}{b}\sqrt[3]{\frac{a}{b}}.$$

To rationalize a denominator in a radical of order n, after the radicand has been expressed as a simple fraction, multiply both numerator and denominator of the radicand by the simplest expression which will make the denominator a *perfect* nth *power*. If the radical is a square root, we make the denominator a perfect square; if a cube root, we make the denominator a perfect cube.

ILLUSTRATION 2. $\quad \sqrt{\frac{3}{7}} = \sqrt{\frac{3 \cdot 7}{7^2}} = \frac{\sqrt{21}}{7} = \frac{4.583}{7} = .655. \qquad$ (Table I)

ILLUSTRATION 3. $\quad \sqrt[3]{\frac{3}{4}} = \sqrt[3]{\frac{3 \cdot 2}{4 \cdot 2}} = \frac{\sqrt[3]{6}}{\sqrt[3]{8}} = \frac{\sqrt[3]{6}}{2}.$

ILLUSTRATION 4. $\quad \frac{\sqrt{3}}{\sqrt{5}} = \frac{\sqrt{3}}{\sqrt{5}} \cdot \frac{\sqrt{5}}{\sqrt{5}} = \frac{\sqrt{15}}{5}.$

If a denominator has the form $a\sqrt{b} - c\sqrt{d}$, we can rationalize it by multiplying by $a\sqrt{b} + c\sqrt{d}$.

ILLUSTRATION 5. $\dfrac{3\sqrt{2} - \sqrt{3}}{2\sqrt{2} - \sqrt{3}} = \dfrac{3\sqrt{2} - \sqrt{3}}{2\sqrt{2} - \sqrt{3}} \cdot \dfrac{2\sqrt{2} + \sqrt{3}}{2\sqrt{2} + \sqrt{3}}$

$$= \frac{6(\sqrt{2})^2 + (3 - 2)\sqrt{6} - (\sqrt{3})^2}{(2\sqrt{2})^2 - (\sqrt{3})^2} = \frac{9 + \sqrt{6}}{8 - 3} = \frac{9 + 2.449}{5} = 2.290.$$

NOTE 2

Introduction to Trigonometric Functions of Numbers without Use of Angles by the Winding Process

We propose to define outright the trigonometric functions of numbers, without any mention of angles. Then, later, we shall show how the geometric trigonometric functions of angles can be introduced as a second-stage event.

In Figure 114, a circle H of radius 1 with center at the origin is drawn in an xy-plane where a single unit is used for measuring all distances, and where this unit is the unit for length on the scales for both axes. We assume that the notion of *length of arc* is well defined for arcs on the circle. Let s be any real number. To each value of s, we make correspond a point T_s on the circle, in Figure 114, as follows:

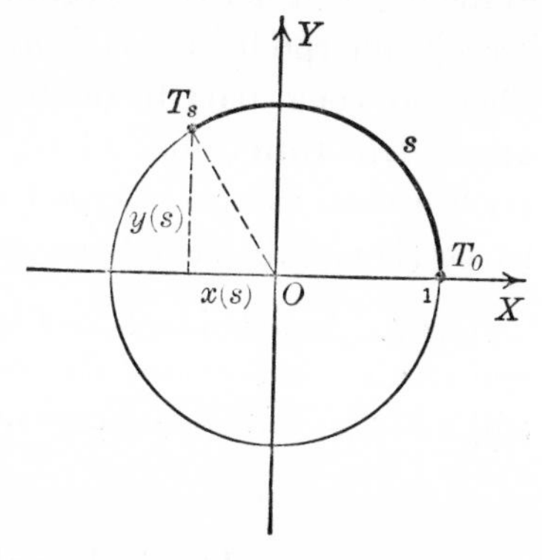

Fig. 114

If $s = 0$, T_0 *is the point with coordinates* $(1, 0)$.

If $s > 0$, T_s *is on* H *and such that arc* T_0T_s, *measured* **counterclockwise,** *has length* s.

If $s < 0$, T_s *is on* H *and such that arc* T_0T_s, *measured* **clockwise,** *has length* $|s|$.

ILLUSTRATION 1. The circumference of H has length 2π, since the radius is 1. Hence, if $s = \frac{1}{2}\pi$, then T_s is the point $(0, 1)$. If $s = -\frac{3}{4}\pi$, then T_s is in quadrant III, so that the line OT_s bisects the 90° angle between the axes in quadrant III; hence T_s has the coordinates $(-\frac{1}{2}\sqrt{2}, -\frac{1}{2}\sqrt{2})$.

We shall call T_s the **trigonometric point** corresponding to the number s. Let the coordinates of T_s for any value of s be denoted by $(x(s), y(s))$; thus, we introduce two *functions* x and y of the variable s, whose domain (the *domain* of the functions) is *all real numbers*. Then, we define the six functions sine, cosine, tangent, cotangent, secant, and cosecant by specifying that their values for any number s in their domain are as follows (except where zero denominators cause some functions to be undefined):

$$\left.\begin{array}{lll}\sin s = y(s); & \cos s = x(s); & \tan s = \dfrac{y(s)}{x(s)}; \\ \csc s = \dfrac{1}{y(s)}; & \sec s = \dfrac{1}{x(s)}; & \cot s = \dfrac{x(s)}{y(s)}\end{array}\right\} \quad (1)$$

The functions defined by (1) are called the **standard trigonometric functions of numbers.** We note that *no mention of angles* has occurred in reaching (1). On this basis, we could proceed to develop all of analytic trigonometry, again with no necessity for mentioning angles. In this background for (1), the role of the circle in Figure 114 gives *one* form of justification for calling the trigonometric functions **circular functions.**

In Figure 114, construct the broken-line segment OT_s. Since the radius of the circle is 1, we verify that s is the radian measure of the directed angle with initial side OT_0 and rotation counterclockwise or clockwise from OT_0 to the terminal side OT_s according as $s > 0$ or $s < 0$. Now, let the real number s be interpreted in (1) as a symbol for the angle with measure s radians. Then, we could refer to the functions defined by (1) as **geometrical trigonometric functions,** whose domain consists of all angles s. It can be verified that, as now interpreted, there is only a nonessential difference between (1) and the definitions on page 33.

Note 1. In defining T_s in Figure 114 on page 213, essentially we *wound a real number scale around the circle.* Hence, in (1), we might choose to call $x(s)$ and $y(s)$ *winding functions.*

NOTE 3

Line Values of the Trigonometric Functions

Let θ be any angle, in its standard position on a coordinate system, as in Figures 115 and 116. Construct a circle with radius 1 and center at the origin, intersecting the positive halves of the x-axis and y-axis at U and V, respectively. Construct tangents to the circle at U and V. Let P, T, and

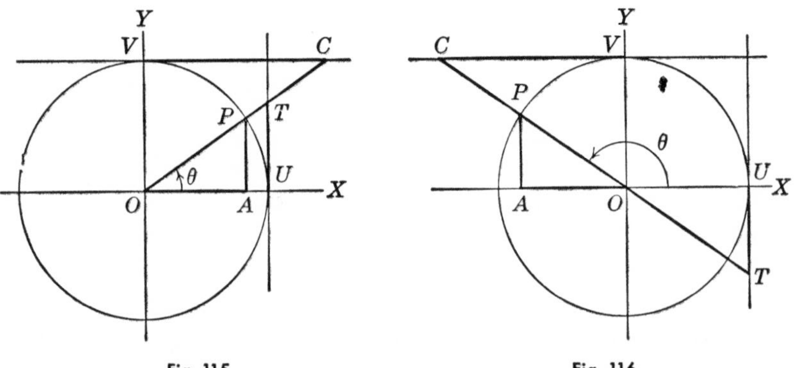

Fig. 115 Fig. 116

C be the points where the terminal side of θ, or this side extended through O, intersects the circle and its tangents at U and V, respectively. In the reference $\triangle OAP$ for θ, OA and AP represent the coordinates of P.

In the resulting diagram we agree that all line segments will be considered as *directed segments*, and that the unit of length will be that which is used for the coordinates. A segment parallel to a coordinate axis will be considered positive or negative as usual. On OP, we define the positive direction as that from O to P. In the following equations, the results for $\sin\theta$ and $\cos\theta$ were obtained on page 49. The other results * can be proved as in the following Illustration 1.

$$\left.\begin{array}{lll} \sin\theta = AP; & \tan\theta = UT; & \sec\theta = OT; \\ \cos\theta = OA; & \cot\theta = VC; & \csc\theta = OC. \end{array}\right\} \qquad (1)$$

ILLUSTRATION 1. In Figure 116, OT is negative and hence $OT = -\overline{OT}$, where $\overline{OT}$ is the positive number of units of length in OT. Let α be the acute angle XOT. Then,

$$\sec\alpha = \frac{\overline{OT}}{\overline{OU}} = \overline{OT},$$

because $OU = 1$. But, $\sec\theta = -\sec\alpha = -\overline{OT} = OT$. Hence, if θ is in quadrant II, we have proved that $\sec\theta = OT$.

The terminal side of θ may fall in any one of the four quadrants, or on either half of either axis. In each of these possible cases, it would be necessary to give a separate proof, like that of Illustration 1, for each of equations (1) for $\tan\theta$, $\cot\theta$, $\sec\theta$, and $\csc\theta$.

NOTE 4

Mil Measure for Angles

In the artillery and certain other branches of the Army of the United States, as well as in the military services of various other nations, angles are measured frequently in terms of a unit called the **mil,** which is defined by the equation

$$\mathbf{1600\ mils = 90^\circ.} \qquad (1)$$

$$1\text{ mil} = \frac{90^\circ}{1600} = 3.3750'; \qquad 1^\circ = \frac{1600}{90}\text{ mils} = 17.7778\text{ mils}. \qquad (2)$$

$$1\text{ radian} = \frac{180^\circ}{\pi} = \frac{180}{\pi}\cdot\frac{1600}{90}\text{ mils} = 1018.6\text{ mils}. \qquad (3)$$

Thus, with only a small error, of about 2%,

$$(\textit{approximate}) \qquad 1\text{ radian} = 1000\text{ mils}. \qquad (4)$$

* Special understandings are necessary if θ is a quadrantal angle.

Equation (4) is the basis for certain approximations employing mils. Thus, assume that (4) is *exactly* true. Then, let θ be the radian measure of $\angle CAB$ in Figure 117, and let α be its value in mils. Let $AC = b$ and $CB = a$.

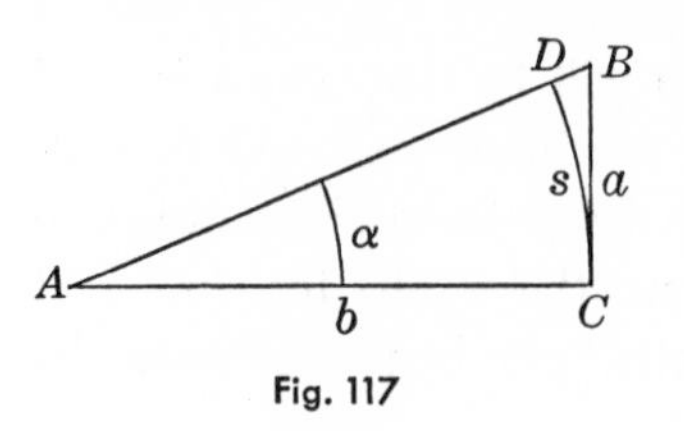

Fig. 117

On the circle with center A and radius b, let s represent the length of arc CD. Then, $s = b\theta$. Since θ radians is equal to 1000θ mils, we have $\alpha = 1000\theta$ and hence

$$s = \frac{b\alpha}{1000}. \tag{5}$$

If α is small, s is *approximately equal* to a. Then, on placing $s = a$ in (5) we obtain, approximately,

$$a = \frac{b\alpha}{1000}; \qquad \frac{a}{b} = \frac{\alpha}{1000}; \qquad \alpha = \frac{1000a}{b}. \tag{6}$$

From $\triangle ABC$, $\tan \alpha = a/b$. Hence, from (6),

$$\left\{\begin{matrix}\textit{approximate,} \\ \alpha \textit{ in mils}\end{matrix}\right\} \qquad \tan \alpha = \frac{\alpha}{1000}. \tag{7}$$

ILLUSTRATION 1. If $a = 1$ and $b = 1000$ in (6), then $\alpha = 1$. Hence, 1 *foot at a distance of* 1000 *feet subtends an angle of approximately* 1 *mil.*

ILLUSTRATION 2. If a line segment 30 yards long is perpendicular to our line of sight at a distance of 8000 yards, the segment subtends an angle α whose value in mils is approximately, from (6), $\alpha = 1000(30)/8000$, or $\alpha = 3.75$ mils.

NOTE 5

Logarithms of Functions of Angles near 0° and 90°

The tabular differences increase rapidly in Table IX as we approach 0° in the columns headed log sin, log tan, and log cot. Hence, if a logarithm is determined by interpolation in these columns, the error is extremely large on page 36 of Table IX and remains undesirably large (> .00001) until we reach page 40. Table X is provided for avoiding these large errors of interpolation. In Table X, we let

$$\frac{\sin \alpha}{M} = s \quad \textit{and} \quad \frac{\tan \alpha}{M} = t,$$

where M is the number of minutes in α. Then,

$$\sin \alpha = sM \quad \textit{and} \quad \tan \alpha = tM;$$

$$\log \sin \alpha = \log s + \log M; \qquad \log \tan \alpha = \log t + \log M.$$

If we let $S = \log s$ and $T = \log t$, then

$$\textbf{log sin } \alpha = S + \log M; \qquad \textbf{log tan } \alpha = T + \log M. \tag{1}$$

S and T are computed by the methods of advanced mathematics; the values of S and T are tabulated in Table X*a* for α between 0° and 3°.

I. *To find* **log sin α, log tan α,** *or* **log cot α** *for an acute angle α near* 0°:

1. *Express α in minutes and decimal parts of a minute, to find M.*
2. *Find* log M *from Table* VIII *and S and T from Table* X*a*.
3. *Use* (1) *to find* log sin α *and* log tan α; *to find* log cot α, *recall*

$$\cot \alpha = \frac{1}{\tan \alpha}, \quad \textit{or} \quad \log \cot \alpha = -\log \tan \alpha.$$

II. *To find* **log cos β, log tan β,** *or* **log cot β** *for an acute angle β near* 90°, *let* $\alpha = 90° - \beta$. *Recall* $\cos \beta = \sin \alpha$, $\tan \beta = \cot \alpha$, $\cot \beta = \tan \alpha$; *then use* (I).

III. *To find an acute angle α near* 0° *if* **log sin α** (*or* **log tan α**) *is given:*

1. *Find α* **to the nearest minute** *by inspection of Table* IX.
2. *Find S* (*or T*) *from Table* X*a*; *substitute for S and* log sin α *in* (1), *and find* log M; *then obtain M from Table* VIII.

IV. *To find an acute angle β near* 90° *if* **log cos β, log tan β,** *or* **log cot β** *is given, write* $\beta = 90° - \alpha$, *and first find α by use of* (III).

EXAMPLE 1. Find log sin 1° 26′ 12″.

SOLUTION. 1. $\frac{12}{60} = .20$; $M = 86.20'$. From Table X*a*, $S = 6.46368 - 10$.

2. From Table VIII, log 86.20 = 1.93551. Hence, from (1),

$$\log \sin 1° 26' 12'' = 1.93551 + 6.46368 - 10 = 8.39919 - 10.$$

Note 1. If log cot α is given for α near 0°, first find log tan α from log tan $\alpha = -$ log cot α, and then use (III).

ILLUSTRATION 1. If $\log \cot \beta = 8.65246 - 10$, then β is near 90°; if $\alpha = 90° - \beta$, then $\log \tan \alpha = 8.65246 - 10$. By use of (III) we could find α and then obtain $\beta = 90° - \alpha$.

EXAMPLE 2. Find α if $\log \sin \alpha = 8.66345 - 10$.

SOLUTION. 1. By inspection of page 38 of Table IX, we find that α is nearer 2° 38′ than 2° 39′. Hence, approximately, $M = 158'$; from Table X*a*, $S = 6.46357 - 10$.

2. In (1), substitute for log sin α and S:

$$8.66345 - 10 = 6.46357 - 10 + \log M;$$

$$\log M = 8.66345 - 6.46357 = 2.19988.$$

From Table VIII, $M = 158.44'$, or $\alpha = 2° \, 38.44' = 2° \, 38' \, 26''$.

Note 2. A second method for solving problems like Examples 1 and 2 is provided by Table X*b*, for angles *very* near 0°.

Note 3. A *slowly* changing function of an unknown angle α offers a poor means for determining α. Hence, when possible, we avoid using cos α in determining α if α is near 0°, or sin α if α is near 90°.

NOTE 6

Introduction to the Algebra of Sets

1. The operations of complement, union, and intersection for sets

Suppose that all sets to which we shall refer are included in a certain set T, which we shall call the **basic space.**

DEFINITION I. *If T is the basic space, the* **complement,** *H', of any set H is the set of elements of T which are not in H.*

Although the elements of T are thought of at present as abstract objects r, let us visualize them as points in a plane. Also, let T be thought of as all points of the plane inside or on some simple closed curve, such as C in Figure 118. Then, let H be the set of points inside or on the boundary of some curve, as in Figure 118 where H is not shaded. With this representation, the complement of H is the set H' which *is shaded* in T. This interpretation of a set as points in a plane is extremely useful; a corresponding figure like Figure 118 sometimes is called a **Venn diagram.**

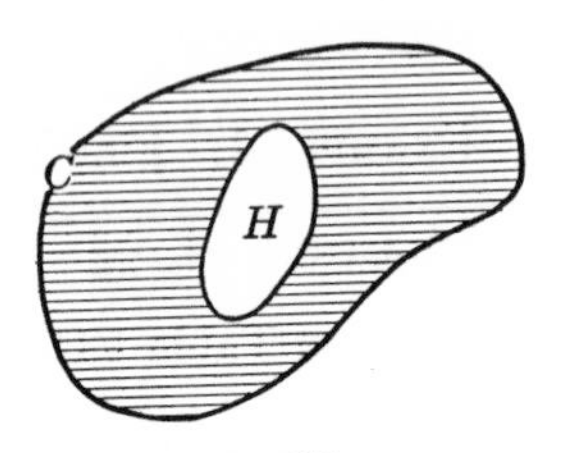

Fig. 118

ILLUSTRATION 1. If T is the interval of numbers x such that $2 \leqq x \leqq 7$, and H is the subset of T where $3 \leqq x \leqq 5$, then H' consists of the interval $2 \leqq x < 3$ and the interval $5 < x \leqq 7$.

ILLUSTRATION 2. If S is the set of points covered by horizontal rulings in Figure 119, and T is the whole plane, then S' is indicated by the radial lines.

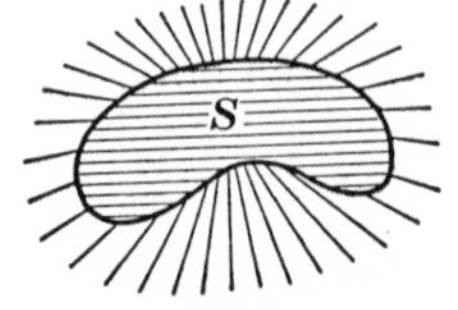

Fig. 119

DEFINITION II. *The* **union** *of any number of sets is the set consisting of all elements which are in one or more of the sets.*

If A and B are sets, "*the union of A and B*" is represented by "$A \cup B$." The order in which the sets are described is of no importance in Definition II. Thus, $A \cup B = B \cup A$. The "*union of three sets, A, B, and C*" is represented by "$A \cup B \cup C$," or any similar expression with the letters in any desired order. The symbol "$\cup$" may be read "*union*" wherever met.

ILLUSTRATION 3. Let T be the set of all points in the plane in Figure 120, and let A and B represent the sets of points indicated by the vertical and horizontal rulings, respectively. Then $A \cup B$ consists of all ruled points; this set includes some points which are in *both sets*, and thus have double rulings. In general, $A \cup B$ consists of all elements in A alone, or in B alone, or in both A and B.

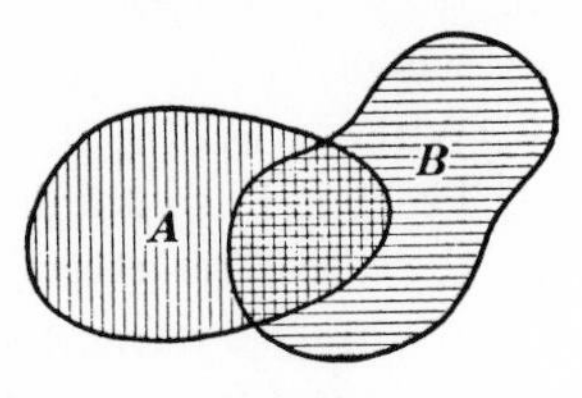

Fig. 120

DEFINITION III. *The* **intersection** *of any number of given sets is the set of elements belonging to all of the given sets.*

If A and B are sets, "*the intersection of A and B*" is denoted by "$A \cap B$"; it consists of all elements in *both A and B*. In Figure 120, $A \cap B$ consists of all points in the doubly ruled region. To denote "*the intersection of A, B, and C*," we write "$A \cap B \cap C$," where the order of the letters is immaterial. The symbol "$\cap$" may be read "*intersection*" wherever met.

DEFINITION IV. *To say that two sets A and B are* **mutually exclusive,** *or* **disjoint,** *means that they have no element in common, or* $A \cap B = \emptyset$. *To say that certain sets A, B, C, · · · are mutually exclusive, means that the intersection of any two of the sets is the empty set.*

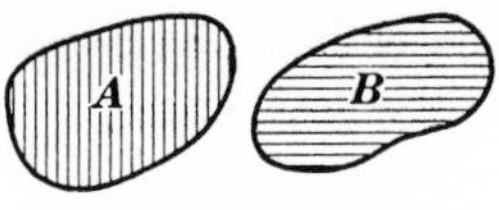

Fig. 121

ILLUSTRATION 4. In Figure 121, A and B are mutually exclusive sets of points in the plane.

EXERCISE 66

1. If the basic space T consists of all students in a class, and H is the set of all girls in the class, what is the complement of H?

Let the basic space T be the numbers x where $-5 \leqq x \leqq 10$. *Find the specified set corresponding to the given data.*

2. If H is all x such that $2 \leqq x \leqq 4$, describe the complement H'.
3. With H from Problem 2, and K as all x such that $-1 \leqq x \leqq 3$, describe $H \cup K$; $H \cap K$.

Let the basic space T be the points (x, y) in an xy-plane for which $-2 \leqq x \leqq 6$ *and* $-2 \leqq y \leqq 8$. *Describe the specified sets in the problems.*

4. If H is the square where $(|x| \leqq 2, |y| \leqq 2)$, show H' in a figure.

5. For H as in Problem 4, and K as the rectangle where $0 \leqq x \leqq 3$ and $0 \leqq y \leqq 4$, draw a figure and indicate the sets $H \cup K$ and $H \cap K$.
6. With H and K from Problems 4 and 5, let W be the set of points where $(0 \leqq x \leqq 5, 0 \leqq y \leqq 1)$. Describe $H \cup K \cup W$ and $H \cap K \cap W$.
7. If T is the set of all points on an x-axis, what statement can you make concerning the sets of points H: $(2 < x < 5)$ and K: $(8 < x < 10)$?
8. If the basic space T is the set of letters (a, b, c, d, e), write down all subsets of T.
9. Without writing down the sets, compute the number of subsets of T, in Problem 8, containing (*i*) 3 letters; (*ii*) any number of letters (including the case of no letters). Note that a subset is a *combination* * of the letters. We use ${}_nC_r$ to represent *the number of subsets of r elements each which can be formed from a set of n elements.*
10. If the basic space T is the set of figures (1, 2, 3, 4, 5, 6), write out all subsets consisting of three of the figures.
11. If the basic space T has 6 elements, how many subsets of T exist? How many exist if T has n elements?

2. Elementary algebra of sets

Sometimes, the *union* of sets A and B is referred to as their *sum*, and the *intersection* of A and B is called their *product*. Also, we have a definition of *equality* for two sets, as on page 8. Thus, we have a basis for development of what may be called an *algebra of sets* where the operations of union, $\cup$, and intersection, $\cap$, play roles similar to those indicated by "+" and "×," respectively, in ordinary algebra. We verify the following results, where T is the basic space.

(*Commutative laws*): $A \cup B = B \cup A; \qquad A \cap B = B \cap A.$ (1)

(*Associative law for* $\cup$):

$$A \cup B \cup C = (A \cup B) \cup C = A \cup (B \cup C). \tag{2}$$

(*Associative law for* $\cap$):

$$A \cap B \cap C = (A \cap B) \cap C = A \cap (B \cap C). \tag{3}$$

($\cap$ *is distributive with respect to* $\cup$):

$$A \cap (B \cup C) = (A \cap B) \cup (A \cap C). \tag{4}$$

($\cup$ *is distributive with respect to* $\cap$):

$$A \cup (B \cap C) = (A \cup B) \cap (A \cup C). \tag{5}$$

(*Properties of null set*): $A \cup \emptyset = A; \qquad A \cap \emptyset = \emptyset.$ (6)

* We use the term *combination* with the meaning introduced in college algebra, or in the typical course in fourth semester algebra at the high school level.

(*Transitive property of* $\subset$):

$$\text{"}A \subset B \text{ and } B \subset C\text{" implies } A \subset C. \tag{7}$$

(*T acts like a unit in intersections*):

$$T \cap A = A \cap T = A. \tag{8}$$

Results (1), (2), and (3) are true because, in Definitions II and III, the *order* in which the sets are mentioned is of no importance. We accept (6) because the empty set $\emptyset$ has *no member*. The student will have the opportunity to prove (5), (7), and (8) in problems of the next exercise.

Proof of (4). 1. If α is an element in $A \cap B$, then α is in A and in B, and hence is in $(B \cup C)$; therefore α is in $A \cap (B \cup C)$. Similarly, if α is in $A \cap C$, then α is in C and hence is in $B \cup C$; therefore, α is in $A \cap (B \cup C)$. Thus, any element in the right-hand set in (4) is in the set on the left.

2. Suppose that α is in $A \cap (B \cup C)$. Then, α is in A. Also, α is in $B \cup C$ and hence is in B alone or in C alone or in both B and C. Hence, α is in *both A and B*, or in *both A and C*. That is, α is in $(A \cap B) \cup (A \cap C)$, or each element α in the set on the left in (4) is in the set on the right. Hence, (4) is a true set equality.

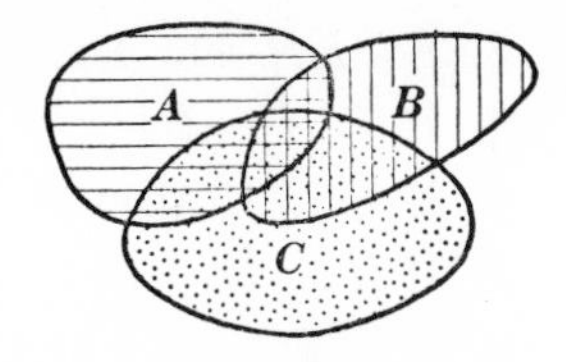

Fig. 122

ILLUSTRATION 1. In Figure 122, for sets A, B, and C in the plane, $A \cap (B \cap C)$, or $(A \cap C) \cap B$, or $(B \cap C) \cap A$, etc., is represented by the region which is dotted and also is crossed by both vertical and horizontal lines.

DEFINITION V. *The* **difference** *of two sets A and B, represented by** $A \setminus B$, *read "A minus B," is the set of all points of A which are not in B.*

We may refer to "$\setminus$" as a sign for *set subtraction*. It is important to notice that this operation is not so simple as subtraction in ordinary algebra.

ILLUSTRATION 2. For any set H in the basic space T, we have $H' = T \setminus H$. In Figure 123, where A is the set inside the outer curve and B is the set inside the inner curve, the difference $A \setminus B$ is the set of points covered just by vertical rulings. If $W = A \setminus B$, we verify that $A = W \cup B$, because $W \cup B$ merely replaces those points of A which were removed by subtracting B. Also, $B \setminus A = \emptyset$, because all points of B are in A; in this case, we do *not* have $B = \emptyset \cup A$ because $\emptyset \cup A = A$ and $B \neq A$.

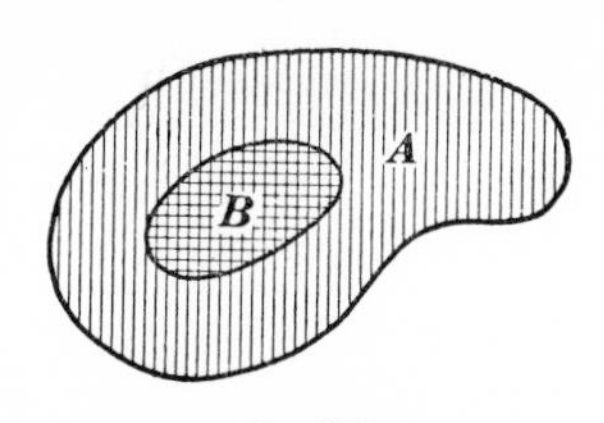

Fig. 123

ILLUSTRATION 3. In Figure 120 on page 219, $A \setminus B$ is the set covered just by vertical rulings. Again, if $W = A \setminus B$, we do *not* have $A = W \cup B$, because this set contains all of the points of B which are not in A.

* Frequently in mathematical literature, we find "$-$" used in place of "$\setminus$," which has been introduced in some recent research.

Various peculiarities are exhibited by results of set algebra, as compared to ordinary algebra [with $(+, \times, \leqq)$ thought of in place of $(\cup, \cap, \subset)$]. For instance, if A and B represent any sets in the basic space,

$$A \cup A = A; \qquad A \cap A = A; \qquad (A \cap B) \subset A;$$

$$\textit{if } A \subset B \quad \textit{then} \quad A \cup B = B.$$

EXERCISE 67

Let T be the basic space. All other letters represent subsets of T. First try to prove the relation by stating facts about an appropriate Venn diagram. After that, if directed by the teacher, prove the result by statements in words. Any result is available, if useful, to prove later results.

1. The complement of the complement of H is H. Or, $(H')' = H$.

2. For any sets A and B, $(A \cup B)' = A' \cap B'$. (Consider two cases, $A \cap B = \emptyset$ and $A \cap B \neq \emptyset$.)

3. For any sets A and B, $(A \cap B)' = A' \cup B'$.

4. $H \cap H' = \emptyset$.

5. $T' = \emptyset$.

6. If $H \subset K$, then $H \cap K' = \emptyset$.

7. If $H \cap K' = \emptyset$, then $H \subset K$.

8. For any sets A and B, we have $A = (A \cap B) \cup (A \cap B')$.

9. Set subtraction is expressible in terms of *union and taking of complement*, or of *intersection and taking of complement*. That is,

$$A \setminus B = (A' \cup B)' = A \cap B'.$$

10. Prove (5), (7), and (8) of pages 220–221 verbally. Check where possible by use of Venn diagrams. Show that the analog of (5) is not true in ordinary algebra.

ANSWERS TO EXERCISES

Note. Answers to most of the odd-numbered problems are given here. Answers to even-numbered problems are furnished in a separate pamphlet, when ordered by the instructor.

Exercise 1. Page 7

1. 3. **3.** 2. **5.** 8. **7.** $|AB| + |BC| = 6;\ |AC| = 6.$
9. $|AB| + |BC| = 10;\ |AC| = 2.$ **11.** $|AB| + |BC| = 17;\ |AC| = 7.$

Exercise 2. Page 11.

1. $\{1, 2, 3\}, \{2, 3, 5\}, \{5, 4, 1\}$, etc. (20 subsets).
3. 15; 55. **5.** $\{4, 16, 36, 81\}$. **7.** 3. **9.** $\pm 3i$.
11. $\frac{3}{2}$; 2. **13.** $\frac{1}{2}(-1 \pm \sqrt{2})$. **15.** $\frac{1}{4}(2 \pm 3i\sqrt{2})$. **17.** 0; $\frac{3}{5}$.
21. Substitute a value for x and make a verbal argument.

Exercise 3. Page 15

1. $(-5, -1)$. **3.** $y = -3$. **7.** $M{:}(2, 0)$, $N{:}(0, 4)$.
9. $M{:}(8, 0)$; $N{:}(0, -7)$. **11.** -6; 6. **13.** 7; 7.
15. $(y_2 - y_1)$; $|y_2 - y_1|$. **17.** 13. **19.** 13. **21.** $\sqrt{65}$. **23.** 6. **33.** 12.

Exercise 5. Page 23

1. $R = \{16, 9, 4, 1, 0\}$. F consists of $(-4, 16)$, $(-3, 9)$, etc.
9. $y = 4 - \frac{4}{3}x$; $x = 3 - \frac{3}{4}y$. **11.** $y = \frac{1}{2}x - \frac{7}{6}$; $x = 2y + \frac{7}{3}$.
13. x defined as a function of y; $x = 2y^2 - 8y + \frac{5}{3}$.
15. x is not defined as a function of y.

Exercise 6. Page 27

29. 5.099. **41.** -4; 18; -44; 32; $3x^2 + 9x + 2$.

Exercise 7. Page 32

1. $-675°$, etc. **3.** $-240°$, etc.

Exercise 8. Page 36

Note. Functions are in the order sine, cosine, tangent, cosecant, secant, cotangent.

1. $\frac{3}{5}, \frac{4}{5}, \frac{3}{4}, \frac{5}{3}, \frac{5}{4}, \frac{4}{3}$. **3.** $\frac{24}{25}, \frac{7}{25}, \frac{24}{7}, \frac{25}{24}, \frac{25}{7}, \frac{7}{24}$.
5. $-\frac{2}{13}\sqrt{13}, -\frac{3}{13}\sqrt{13}, \frac{2}{3}, -\frac{1}{2}\sqrt{13}, -\frac{1}{3}\sqrt{13}, \frac{3}{2}$.
7. $\frac{8}{17}, -\frac{15}{17}, -\frac{8}{15}, \frac{17}{8}, -\frac{17}{15}, -\frac{15}{8}$. **9.** $-\frac{4}{5}, \frac{3}{5}, -\frac{4}{3}, -\frac{5}{4}, \frac{5}{3}, -\frac{3}{4}$.
11. $-\frac{1}{2}\sqrt{3}, \frac{1}{2}, -\sqrt{3}, -\frac{2}{3}\sqrt{3}, 2, -\frac{1}{3}\sqrt{3}$. **13.** 1, 0, none, 1, none, 0.
15. -1, 0, none, -1, none, 0. **17.** $-\frac{1}{2}\sqrt{2}, -\frac{1}{2}\sqrt{2}, 1, -\sqrt{2}, -\sqrt{2}, 1$.
19. $\frac{5}{34}\sqrt{34}, -\frac{3}{34}\sqrt{34}, -\frac{5}{3}, \frac{1}{5}\sqrt{34}, -\frac{1}{3}\sqrt{34}, -\frac{3}{5}$.
23. $\sec\alpha = \frac{9}{4}$. **25.** $\cos\gamma = \frac{3}{7}$. **27.** II or IV. **29.** I or III.
31. II. **33.** III. **35.** II. **37.** III.

Exercise 9. Page 39

Note. Functions are in the order sine, cosine, tangent, cosecant, secant, cotangent.

1. 0, 1, 0, none, 1, none.
3. .5, .866, .577, 2, 1.155, 1.732.
5. .707, − .707, − 1, 1.414, − 1.414, − 1.
7. .5, − .866, − .577, 2, − 1.155, − 1.732.
9. 0, 1, 0, none, 1, none.
11. Prob. 3, with signs for quad. IV.
13. − 1, 0, none, − 1, none, 0.
15. Prob. 5, with signs for quad. IV.
17. Prob. 5, with signs for quad. III.
19. Same as Prob. 3.
21. Prob. 5, with signs for quad. III.
23. 0, − 1, 0, none, − 1, none.
25. Prob. 5, with signs for quad. III.

Exercise 10. Page 42

Note. Only sine, cosine, tangent are given, in that order. Cosecant, secant, cotangent are equal to the corresponding reciprocals.

1. $\frac{5}{13}, \frac{12}{13}, \frac{5}{12}$.
3. $\frac{4}{5}, -\frac{3}{5}, -\frac{4}{3}$.
5. $\frac{3}{5}, \frac{4}{5}, \frac{3}{4}$.
7. $-\frac{5}{13}, -\frac{12}{13}, \frac{5}{12}$.
9. $\frac{8}{17}, -\frac{15}{17}, -\frac{8}{15}$.
11. $-\frac{1}{2}\sqrt{2}, -\frac{1}{2}\sqrt{2}, 1$.
13. $-\frac{1}{4}\sqrt{7}, \frac{3}{4}, -\frac{1}{3}\sqrt{7}$.
15. $\frac{3}{5}, \frac{4}{5}, \frac{3}{4}$.
17. $\frac{15}{17}, -\frac{8}{17}, -\frac{15}{8}$.
19. θ in (I): $\frac{2}{13}\sqrt{13}, \frac{3}{13}\sqrt{13}, \frac{2}{3}$. θ in (III): $-\frac{2}{13}\sqrt{13}, -\frac{3}{13}\sqrt{13}, \frac{2}{3}$.
21. θ in (II): $\frac{1}{3}\sqrt{5}, -\frac{2}{3}, -\frac{1}{2}\sqrt{5}$. θ in (III): $-\frac{1}{3}\sqrt{5}, -\frac{2}{3}, \frac{1}{2}\sqrt{5}$.
35. − 18.
37. $\frac{1}{6}(3\sqrt{5} + 5)$.
39. $\sin x, \pm\sqrt{1 - \sin^2 x}, \pm \sin x/\sqrt{1 - \sin^2 x}$.
41. $\pm\sqrt{\sec^2 x - 1}/\sec x, 1/\sec x, \pm\sqrt{\sec^2 x - 1}$.

Exercise 11. Page 46

Note. See Note for answers to Exercise 10.

1. $\frac{3}{5}, \frac{4}{5}, \frac{3}{4}$.
3. $\frac{24}{25}, \frac{7}{25}, \frac{24}{7}$.
5. $\frac{8}{17}, \frac{15}{17}, \frac{8}{15}$.
7. $\frac{2}{3}, \frac{1}{3}\sqrt{5}, \frac{2}{5}\sqrt{5}$.
9. See page 38.
11. sin 75°.
13. tan 52°.
15. sec 78°.
17. cot 51°.
19. cos 23°.
21. cos 8°.

Exercise 12. Page 49

1. 59°.
3. 87°.
5. 70°.
7. − 1.280.
9. $-\frac{1}{2}\sqrt{2}$.
11. − 2.924.
13. − 1.483.
15. − 1.963.
17. $\frac{1}{2}\sqrt{3}$.
19. − 1.280.
21. 5.759.
23. − 2.
25. 1.305.
27. 1.743.
29. − .052.
31. 1.600.
33. $-\frac{1}{2}\sqrt{2}$.
35. − .675.
37. − .993.
41. $\sin\theta = \frac{3\sqrt{34}}{34}$; $\cos\theta = -\frac{5\sqrt{34}}{34}$; etc.
43. $\sin\theta = \frac{\sqrt{33}}{7}$; $\tan\theta = -\frac{\sqrt{33}}{4}$; etc.

Exercise 13. Page 53

1. $-\frac{1}{2}\sqrt{2}$; $-\frac{1}{2}\sqrt{2}$.
3. $-\frac{1}{2}\sqrt{2}$; $\frac{1}{2}\sqrt{2}$.
5. 0; − 1.
7. $\frac{1}{4}(\sqrt{2} + \sqrt{6})$; $\frac{1}{4}(\sqrt{6} - \sqrt{2})$.
9. $\frac{1}{4}(\sqrt{6} - \sqrt{2})$; $-\frac{1}{4}(\sqrt{2} + \sqrt{6})$.
11. $-\frac{1}{4}(\sqrt{2} + \sqrt{6})$; $\frac{1}{4}(\sqrt{6} - \sqrt{2})$.

13. $\sin(\alpha+\beta) = -\frac{33}{65}$; $\cos(\alpha+\beta) = -\frac{56}{65}$.
$\sin(\alpha-\beta) = -\frac{63}{65}$; $\cos(\alpha-\beta) = -\frac{16}{65}$.
15. $\sin(\alpha+\beta) = -\frac{36}{325}$; $\cos(\alpha+\beta) = \frac{323}{325}$.
$\sin(\alpha-\beta) = -\frac{204}{325}$; $\cos(\alpha-\beta) = \frac{253}{325}$.
17. $\frac{1}{2}(\cos\theta + \sqrt{3}\sin\theta)$. **19.** $\frac{1}{2}(\sqrt{3}\cos\theta + \sin\theta)$.
21. $-\sin\theta$. **23.** $-\cos\theta$. **25.** $-\sin\theta$. **27.** $-\cos\theta$.

Exercise 14. Page 57

1. $-\cos\theta$. **3.** $-\cos\theta$. **5.** $-\sin\theta$. **7.** $-\sin\theta$. **9.** $-\cos\theta$.
11. $\sin(270° - \theta) = -\cos\theta$; $\cos(270° - \theta) = -\sin\theta$; $\tan(270° - \theta) = \cot\theta$; etc.
13. $\sin(\theta + 90°) = \cos\theta$; $\cos(\theta + 90°) = -\sin\theta$; $\tan(\theta + 90°) = -\cot\theta$; etc.
15. $\sin(450° - \theta) = \cos\theta$; $\cos(450° - \theta) = \sin\theta$; $\tan(450° - \theta) = \cot\theta$; etc.
17. $\sin(630° - \theta) = -\cos\theta$; $\cos(630° - \theta) = -\sin\theta$; $\tan(630° - \theta) = \cot\theta$; etc.
19. $-\cos\theta$. **21.** $\cot\theta$. **23.** $\tan\theta$. **25.** $\csc\theta$.
27. $\sec\theta$. **29.** $\cos\theta$. **31.** $\cot\theta$. **33.** $\csc\theta$. **35.** $-\csc\theta$.
37. $\sin 63° = \cos 27°$; $\cos 63° = \sin 27°$; $\tan 63° = \cot 27°$.
39. $\sin 147° = \sin 33°$; $\cos 147° = -\cos 33°$; $\tan 147° = -\tan 33°$.
41. $\sin 176° = \sin 4°$; $\cos 176° = -\cos 4°$; $\tan 176° = -\tan 4°$.
43. $\sin 284° = -\cos 14°$; $\cos 284° = \sin 14°$; $\tan 284° = -\cot 14°$.
45. $\sin 352° = -\sin 8°$; $\cos 352° = \cos 8°$; $\tan 352° = -\tan 8°$.
47. $\sin(-56°) = -\cos 34°$; $\cos(-56°) = \sin 34°$; $\tan(-56°) = -\cot 34°$.
49. $\sin(-256°) = \cos 14°$; $\cos(-256°) = -\sin 14°$; $\tan(-256°) = -\cot 14°$.
51. $\sin 305° = -\cos 35°$; $\cos 305° = \sin 35°$; $\tan 305° = -\cot 35°$.
53. $\sin(-247°) = \cos 23°$; $\cos(-247°) = -\sin 23°$; $\tan(-247°) = -\cot 23°$.
55. $\sin(-283°) = \cos 13°$; $\cos(-283°) = \sin 13°$; $\tan(-283°) = \cot 13°$.

Exercise 15. Page 61

7. $90°$; $-270°$. **9.** $\pm 270°$; $\pm 90°$.
11. $0°$; $\pm 180°$; $\pm 360°$. **13.** $\pm 120°$; $\pm 240°$.
15. $\pm 45°$; $\pm 315°$. **17.** $-300°$; $-240°$; $60°$; $120°$.
19. $-135°$; $-45°$; $225°$; $315°$. **21.** $\pm 150°$; $\pm 210°$.
23. $g(800) = \frac{1}{2}\sqrt{2}$; $f(800) = .985$; $f(320) = -.643$; $g(320) = .309$.

Exercise 16. Page 66

7. $0°$; $\pm 180°$; $\pm 360°$. **9.** $\pm 90°$; $\pm 270°$.
11. $-225°$; $-45°$; $135°$; $315°$. **13.** $-270°$; $90°$.
15. $\pm 180°$. **17.** $-210°$; $-30°$; $150°$; $330°$.
19. $-300°$; $-120°$; $60°$; $240°$. **21.** $-300°$; $-240°$; $60°$; $120°$.
23. $0°$; $\pm 180°$; $\pm 360°$. **25.** $0°$; $\pm 180°$; $\pm 360°$.

Exercise 17. Page 67

3. For 330°, the reference angle is 30°, etc.
17. $-\frac{2}{5}\sqrt{5}$, $-\frac{1}{5}\sqrt{5}$, 2; $-\frac{1}{3}$, $\frac{2}{3}\sqrt{2}$, $-\frac{1}{4}\sqrt{2}$.
19. $\sin\theta$. **21.** $-\csc\theta$. **23.** $-\sin\theta$.
29. $-150°$; $150°$; $210°$. **31.** $-180°$; $0°$; $180°$.
33. $-90°$; $90°$; $270°$. **35.** $-60°$; $120°$; $300°$.

Exercise 18. Page 71

1. 10^7. **3.** 10^{-4}. **5.** 10^0. **7.** .21236; .212. **9.** .0021539; .00215. **11.** .049358; .0494. **13.** 612,920; 613,000. **15.** 15,980,000. **17.** .000008195. **19.** $8.9315(10^7)$. **21.** $3.64(10^{-6})$. **23.** 238.25″ and 238.35″. **25.** 42.155″ and 42.165″. **27.** 21.68; .701. **29.** 3.1; .89. **31.** $8.4260(10^6)$; $8.43(10^6)$. **33.** $4.2700(10^7)$; $4.27(10^7)$.

Exercise 19. Page 74

1. .2079. **3.** .6249. **5.** 1.046. **7.** .2334. **9.** .0816. **11.** 1.052. **13.** 22° 10′. **15.** 31° 0′. **17.** 22° 10′. **19.** 75° 30′. **21.** 72° 20′. **23.** .0925. **25.** .7404. **27.** .8363. **29.** 1.562. **31.** .6396. **33.** 1.196. **35.** .4708. **37.** 1.670. **39.** .8803. **41.** .1119. **43.** 29° 42′. **45.** 27° 35′. **47.** 32° 42′. **49.** 45° 52′. **51.** 52° 49′. **53.** 52° 54′. **55.** 2° 55′. **57.** 12° 50′. **59.** 12° 10′. **61.** 42° 40′. **63.** 39° 50′. **65.** 77° 30′.

Exercise 20. Page 75

1. .99548. **3.** .69277. **5.** 17° 0′. **7.** 47° 4′. **9.** .14821. **11.** .68827. **13.** .37014. **15.** 8° 10.6′.

Exercise 21. Page 77

Note. Legitimately different methods of solution of a triangle may lead to slightly different results. The answers in this chapter are given as obtained by use of secants and cosecants, when applicable, in avoiding division.

1. $b = 115.0$, $c = 125.4$, 66° 30′.
3. $a = 121.6$, $b = 28.82$, 76° 40′.
5. $\alpha = 41° 53'$, $\beta = 48° 7'$, 599.2.
7. $\alpha = 52° 40'$, $\beta = 37° 20'$, 107.2.
9. $\alpha = 26° 32'$, $\beta = 63° 28'$, 1.038.
11. $\alpha = 61° 28'$, $\beta = 28° 32'$, 2.617.
13. $\alpha = 54° 24'$, $\beta = 35° 36'$, .5936.
15. $a = .01676$, $c = .02120$, 37° 49′.
17. $a = 1.577$, $b = .2723$, 9° 48′.
19. $\alpha = 58° 27'$, $\beta = 31° 33'$, 7329.
21. $\alpha = 61° 29'$, $\beta = 28° 31'$, 2.618.
23. See Prob. 13.
25. $a = .01675$, $c = .02120$, 37° 49′.
27. See Prob. 17.
29. See Prob. 19.
31. $b = 89.873$, $c = 96.446$, 21° 16.7′.
33. $a = 13.089$, $b = 3.6943$, 15° 45.7′.
35. $\alpha = 26° 31.3'$, $\beta = 63° 28.7'$, 1.0379.

Exercise 22. Page 78

1. 1.54 ft. **3.** 44° 25′. **5.** 1926 ft. **7.** 1250 ft. **9.** 272 ft. **11.** 3988 ft. **13.** 1° 43.1′; 269.9 ft. **15.** 925 ft. **17.** 283 yd.

Exercise 24. Page 86

1. $\log_2 N = 6$. **3.** $\log_5 x = -2$. **5.** $\log_4 H = \frac{1}{3}$.
7. $\log_{10} N = .35$. **9.** $\log_5 625 = 4$. **11.** $\log_3 \frac{1}{27} = -3$.
13. 36. **15.** 10,000. **17.** 125.
19. 15. **21.** $\frac{1}{5}$. **23.** b.
25. 3. **27.** $\frac{1}{6}$. **29.** 9.
31. 2. **33.** 4. **35.** 2.
37. 5. **39.** $\frac{1}{2}$. **41.** -1.
43. -3. **45.** -3. **47.** $a = 2\sqrt{2}$.
49. $a = 10$. **51.** $a = 25$. **53.** $N = 216$.
55. $N = 343$. **57.** $N = \frac{1}{81}$. **59.** $x = \frac{1}{2}$. **61.** $x = \frac{1}{10}\sqrt{10}$.

Exercise 25. Page 89

1. 1.1461. **3.** 1.4771. **5.** 1.3222. **7.** .5441.
9. $-$ .3680. **11.** .0843. **13.** 2.3010. **15.** $-$ 1.0212.
17. .6778. **19.** 1.5050. **21.** .2386. **23.** .1840.

Exercise 26. Page 93

1. Ch. = 3; man. = .5217. **3.** Ch. = $-$ 3; man. = .550.
5. Ch. = $-$ 4; man. = .8418. **7.** Ch. = $-$ 5; man. = .2891.
9. 8.1356 $-$ 10. **11.** 6.5268 $-$ 10. **13.** 4. **15.** $-$ 5.
17. $-$ 6. **19.** 2.0934. **21.** 9.4166 $-$ 10. **23.** 8.7497 $-$ 10.
25. 4.3201. **27.** 9.9586 $-$ 10. **29.** 4.1818. **31.** 5.3404 $-$ 10.
33. 136. **35.** .523. **37.** 55.7. **39.** .0376.
41. 3.31. **43.** .00293. **45.** 32,900,000. **47.** .000429.
49. (*a*) .000250; (*b*) .00400. **51.** 2.29820. **53.** 0.14270.
55. 8.04844 $-$ 10. **57.** 9.40875 $-$ 10. **59.** 4.77525.
61. 17.83. **63.** .2674. **65.** 297.2. **67.** .03866.

Exercise 27. Page 96

1. 3.2840. **3.** 3.7646. **5.** 0.9748. **7.** 9.8509 $-$ 10.
9. 7.7106 $-$ 10. **11.** 6.3025 $-$ 10. **13.** 4.9036. **15.** 0.4950.
17. 4.4113. **19.** 7.7934 $-$ 10. **21.** 45.22. **23.** .1053.
25. 3.557. **27.** .04397. **29.** 108.6. **31.** .0001050.
33. .00008644. **35.** $1.088(10^7)$. **37.** 2298. **39.** .9008.
41. 9.708. **43.** 36.71. **45.** 4.26865. **47.** 0.67374.
49. 1.78956. **51.** 9.47898 $-$ 10. **53.** 9.87715 $-$ 10. **55.** 0.72605.
57. 8.86666 $-$ 10. **59.** 5.95274. **61.** 6.89570 $-$ 10. **63.** 8.78763 $-$ 20.
65. 6.11414. **67.** 8.69902. **69.** .45007. **71.** $1.0782(10^6)$.
73. .013267. **75.** $2.8641(10^5)$. **77.** .0087124. **79.** 9.3400.
81. .60003. **83.** 1.9400.

Exercise 28. Page 99

Note. Results obtained by use of **four-place** logarithms will be given in heavy black type in all problems in the exercises where *both four-place and five-place logarithms are possibilities.*

1. 24.91; 24.909. **3. .07942;** .079410.
5. .2009; .20086. **7. − .007667;** − .0076660.
9. 51.10; 51.098. **11. .8142;** .81422.
13. .1406; .14061. **15. .003069;** .0030681.
17. 5542; 5544.4. **19. 1.047(10^4);** 10,464.
21. 27.61; 27.609. **23. − 2.627(10^{-8});** − 2.6266(10^{-8}).
25. 1.580(10^{-5}); 1.5802(10^{-5}). **27. 38.96;** 38.955.
29. (*a*) **4.792(10^5);** 4.7922(10^5): (*b*) **8.065;** 8.0662.

Exercise 29. Page 101

1. 5358; 5359.5. **3. 3.125(10^{-5});** 3.1256(10^{-5}).
5. 56.19; 56.206. **7. 23.05;** 23.048.
9. 5.418; 5.4169. **11. .9500;** .94986.
13. .4199; .41984. **15. .1176;** .11759.
17. .1266; .12658. **19. 5.176(10^{-5});** 5.1759(10^{-5}).
21. 1.169; 1.1688. **23. .8630;** .86258.

Exercise 30. Page 102

1. 95.80; 95.848. **3. 16.72;** 16.700.
5. 93.74; 93.722. **7. .007638;** .0076403.
9. .08468; .084666. **11. 11.67;** 11.673.
13. 45.02; 45.023. **15. .1952;** .19522.
17. .2739; .27392. **19. 2.702;** 2.7031.
21. − 940.2; − 939.88. **23.** 19.231; 19.219. **25.** $14,897.
27. .9824; .98225 (sec.). **29. .6137;** .61374 (sq. in.).

Exercise 31. Page 104

1. 1.3820. **3.** − 11.972. **5.** .68123.
7. 4.913. **9.** − 6.9873. **11.** 25.18.
13. 1.5208(10^7). **15. 1.853;** 1.8532. **17. 4.317;** 4.3176.
19. − 1.449; − 1.4496. **21.** (*a*) .7407; (*b*) t = .9357.

Exercise 32. Page 107

1. (*a*) .2136; (*b*) 9.3296 − 10. **3.** 9.9912 − 10. **5.** 9.9046 − 10.
7. 9.6538 − 10. **9.** 9.8117 − 10. **11.** 0.3545. **13.** 9.2778 − 10.
15. 64° 7′. **17.** 20° 38′. **19.** 14° 44′. **21.** 78° 53′.
23. − .2866. **25.** − .8698. **27.** − .2489. **29.** 9.47557 − 10.
31. 0.01534. **33.** 9.79314 − 10. **35.** 0.38160. **37.** 9.91082 − 10.
39. 70° 19.7′. **41.** 21° 35.5′. **43.** 9° 1.0′.

Exercise 33. Page 109

1. b = **21.34**, 21.347; c = **26.50**, 26.498; 53° 40′.
3. α = **28° 30′**, 28° 30.2′; β = **61° 30′**, 61° 29.8′; **.7523**, .75228.
5. a = **.3396**, .33956; b = **.5950**, .59451; 60° 17′.
7. α = **42° 18′**, 42° 18.1′; β = **47° 42′**, 47° 41.9′; **.8518**, .85153.
9. b = **2.672**, 2.6715; c = **3.131**, 3.1304; 58° 35.3′.
11. a = **818.0**, 818.02; α = **63° 18′**, 63° 18.2′; β = **26° 42′**, 26° 41.8′.
13. b = **40.45**, 40.445; c = **58.99**, 58.982; 46° 42′ 26″.
15. k = **512.2**, 512.18; α = 55° 50′.
17. a = **402.5**, 402.58; c = **539.3**, 539.34; β = 29° 40′.
19. a = **43.50**, 43.507; β = **19° 54′**, 19° 53.6′; γ = **131° 50′**, 131° 50.8′.

Exercise 34. Page 111

1. 160 ft.
3. Vert., 40.9 ft.; hor., 131.3 ft.
5. 52° 58′.
7. 321°.
9. 252° 13′.
11. 264 mi. W; 280 mi. N.
13. 320 mi.; N 64° 28′ E; 64° 28′.
15. Pitch .385; 37° 40′.
17. Side 28.2 ft.; radius 34.0 ft.
19. 94.5 ft.
21. 215 mi ; azimuth 319° 43′.

Exercise 35. Page 117

1. Hor., 84.7 lb.; vert., 128.4 lb.
3. 22.07 lb. W; 36.49 lb. S.
5. 282 mi. S; 103 mi. E.
7. 171 lb.; N 18° 20′ E.
9. Groundspeed 202 mi. per hr.; course is azimuth 8° 32′; drift angle 8° 32′.
11. 18.25 mi. per hr.; course has bearing S 80° 32′ E, or azimuth 99° 28′.
13. 6816 lb.
15. 208 lb.
17. 218 lb.
19. 173 lb.; N 33° 38′ W.

Exercise 36. Page 120

1. $\frac{1}{6}\pi$.
3. $\frac{1}{3}\pi$.
5. $\frac{2}{3}\pi$.
7. $\frac{5}{6}\pi$.
9. $-\frac{1}{2}\pi$.
11. $\frac{4}{3}\pi$.
13. $\frac{5}{3}\pi$.
15. $\frac{5}{2}\pi$.
17. 60°.
19. 20°.
21. 210°.
23. 240°.
25. 84°.
27. 114° 35′.
29. 143° 14′.
35. $\frac{2}{15}\pi$.
37. $\frac{5}{6}\pi$.
39. 2.160.
41. 3.199.
43. 2565 ft.
45. 7.44 in.
47. 297 ft.
49. .631 rad.
51. 19.2 in.
53. 5027 ft. per minute.
55. 5.50 in.

Exercise 37. Page 123

5. 1.711.
7. 5.742.
13. .48012.
15. .76020.
17. $-\cos x$.
19. $-\sin x$.
21. $\sin x$.
23. $-\sin x$.
25. $-\tan x$.
27. $\cot x$.
29. $\sin x$.
31. $\sec x$.
33. $-\cot x$.
35. $-\sin x$.
37. $\sin x$.
39. $-\cot x$.
41. $-\csc x$.
43. $\sin x$.
45. $\cos x$.
47. $\cos x$.

Exercise 38. Page 129

7. $x = -\frac{1}{2}\pi$; $x = \frac{1}{2}\pi$; $x = \frac{3}{2}\pi$; $x = \frac{5}{2}\pi$.
9. Same as Prob. 7.
11. $\pm 2\pi$; $\pm \pi$; 0.

13. Same as Prob. 11.
15. No sol.
17. $-\frac{1}{2}\pi$; $\frac{3}{2}\pi$.
19. $-\frac{7}{4}\pi$; $-\frac{3}{4}\pi$; $\frac{1}{4}\pi$; $\frac{5}{4}\pi$.
21. $\pm 2\pi$; 0.
23. $-\frac{5}{6}\pi$; $-\frac{1}{6}\pi$; $\frac{7}{6}\pi$; $\frac{11}{6}\pi$.
25. $-\frac{4}{3}\pi$; $-\frac{1}{3}\pi$; $\frac{2}{3}\pi$; $\frac{5}{3}\pi$.
27. $\pm\frac{4}{3}\pi$; $\pm\frac{2}{3}\pi$.
29. $-\frac{7}{4}\pi$; $-\frac{5}{4}\pi$; $\frac{1}{4}\pi$; $\frac{3}{4}\pi$.
31. $-\frac{11}{6}\pi$; $-\frac{5}{6}\pi$; $\frac{1}{6}\pi$; $\frac{7}{6}\pi$.

Exercise 39. Page 132

21. $f(x) = 4 \sin (x + \frac{1}{3}\pi)$; period 2π.
23. $f(x) = 6 \sin (\frac{1}{2}x - \frac{1}{3}\pi)$; period 4π.

Exercise 41. Page 139

1. $\frac{1}{4}\pi$; $\frac{5}{4}\pi$.
3. π.
5. $\frac{1}{4}\pi$; $\frac{3}{4}\pi$.
7. No sol.
9. $\frac{1}{2}\pi$; $\frac{3}{2}\pi$.
11. 0; π.
13. $\frac{3}{4}\pi$; $\frac{5}{4}\pi$.
15. $\frac{2}{3}\pi$; $\frac{5}{3}\pi$.
17. $\frac{4}{3}\pi$; $\frac{5}{3}\pi$.
19. $\frac{1}{4}\pi$; $\frac{3}{4}\pi$; $\frac{5}{4}\pi$; $\frac{7}{4}\pi$.
21. $\frac{1}{3}\pi$; $\frac{2}{3}\pi$; $\frac{4}{3}\pi$; $\frac{5}{3}\pi$.
23. $\frac{1}{6}\pi$; $\frac{5}{6}\pi$; $\frac{7}{6}\pi$; $\frac{11}{6}\pi$.
25. $\frac{3}{2}\pi$; $\frac{1}{6}\pi$; $\frac{5}{6}\pi$.
27. $\frac{1}{3}\pi$; $\frac{4}{3}\pi$; $\frac{3}{4}\pi$; $\frac{7}{4}\pi$.
29. $\frac{1}{2}\pi$.
31. $\frac{2}{3}\pi$; π; $\frac{4}{3}\pi$.
33. 0; $\frac{1}{2}\pi$; π.
35. 0; $\frac{1}{3}\pi$; $\frac{5}{3}\pi$.
37. 0; π; $\frac{5}{4}\pi$; $\frac{7}{4}\pi$.
39. 0; $\frac{1}{4}\pi$; $\frac{3}{4}\pi$; π; $\frac{5}{4}\pi$; $\frac{7}{4}\pi$.
41. 22° 43′; 337° 17′.
43. 58° 20′; 238° 20′.
45. 172° 40′; 352° 40′.
47. $\frac{1}{4}\pi$; $\frac{1}{2}\pi$; $\frac{3}{4}\pi$; $\frac{5}{4}\pi$; $\frac{3}{2}\pi$; $\frac{7}{4}\pi$.
49. $\frac{1}{3}\pi$; $\frac{2}{3}\pi$; $\frac{4}{3}\pi$; $\frac{5}{3}\pi$.

Exercise 42. Page 142

1. $\frac{1}{2}\pi$; $\frac{7}{6}\pi$; $\frac{11}{6}\pi$.
3. $\frac{3}{2}\pi$.
5. No sol.
7. 0; $\frac{1}{4}\pi$; π; $\frac{5}{4}\pi$.
9. $\frac{3}{2}\pi$.
11. $\frac{1}{3}\pi$; $\frac{2}{3}\pi$; $\frac{4}{3}\pi$; $\frac{5}{3}\pi$.
13. $\frac{1}{3}\pi$; $\frac{2}{3}\pi$; $\frac{4}{3}\pi$; $\frac{5}{3}\pi$.
15. $\frac{1}{6}\pi$; $\frac{7}{6}\pi$.
17. $\frac{1}{3}\pi$; π; $\frac{5}{3}\pi$.
19. $\frac{7}{6}\pi$; $\frac{3}{2}\pi$; $\frac{11}{6}\pi$.
21. 0; π.
23. $\frac{1}{3}\pi$; $\frac{5}{3}\pi$.
25. 0; $\frac{3}{2}\pi$.
27. 0; $\frac{1}{2}\pi$.
29. π.
31. $\frac{1}{6}\pi$; $\frac{5}{6}\pi$.
33. $\frac{1}{3}\pi$; $\frac{2}{3}\pi$; $\frac{4}{3}\pi$; $\frac{5}{3}\pi$.
35. $\frac{1}{4}\pi$; $\frac{3}{4}\pi$; $\frac{5}{4}\pi$; $\frac{7}{4}\pi$.
37. $\frac{1}{3}\pi$; $\frac{2}{3}\pi$; $\frac{4}{3}\pi$; $\frac{5}{3}\pi$.
39. From Table VII, 18° 26′; 161° 34′; 198° 26′; 341° 34′.
41. 233° 7′.

Exercise 43. Page 143

5. $\pm 1/\sqrt{1 + \cot^2 \theta}$; $\csc \theta = \pm \sqrt{1 + \tan^2 \theta}/\tan \theta$.
7. $\frac{1}{3}\pi, \frac{5}{3}\pi$.
9. .45, 5.83.
11. 1.93, 5.07.
13. No sol.
15. $\frac{1}{2}\pi, \frac{7}{6}\pi, \frac{11}{6}\pi$.
17. $\frac{1}{6}\pi, \frac{5}{6}\pi, \frac{7}{6}\pi, \frac{11}{6}\pi$.
19. $\frac{1}{6}\pi, \frac{5}{6}\pi, \frac{7}{6}\pi, \frac{11}{6}\pi$.
21. $\frac{1}{6}\pi, \frac{5}{6}\pi$.
23. 35° 39′, 215° 39′.
37. $\frac{1}{2}\pi, \frac{3}{2}\pi$.
39. $0, \frac{1}{4}\pi, \frac{3}{4}\pi, \frac{1}{2}\pi, \frac{5}{4}\pi, \frac{7}{4}\pi$.

Exercise 44. Page 145

9. $(2 + \sqrt{3})$; $(2 - \sqrt{3})$.
11. $(\sqrt{3} - 2)$; $-(2 + \sqrt{3})$.
13. $-(2 + \sqrt{3})$; $(\sqrt{3} - 2)$.
15. $\frac{1}{2}\sqrt{2}(\cos x + \sin x)$.
17. $\dfrac{1 - \tan x}{1 + \tan x}$.
19. $\frac{1}{2}(\sin x + \sqrt{3} \cos x)$.
21. $\dfrac{1 + \tan x}{1 - \tan x}$.
23. $\frac{1}{2}(\cos x - \sqrt{3} \sin x)$.
25. $-\frac{1}{2}(\cos x + \sqrt{3} \sin x)$.

29. 1. **31.** 1. **33.** $\sin(A - 10°)$. **35.** $\cos 75°$. **37.** $\tan 3x$.

39. $(\alpha + \beta)$, $(\frac{56}{65}, \frac{33}{65}, \frac{56}{33})$; $(\alpha - \beta)$, $(\frac{16}{65}, \frac{63}{65}, \frac{16}{63})$.

41. $(\alpha + \beta)$, $(\frac{220}{221}, -\frac{21}{221}, -\frac{220}{21})$; $(\alpha - \beta)$, $(-\frac{140}{221}, \frac{171}{221}, -\frac{140}{171})$.

43. IV. **51.** $\dfrac{\tan B + 3}{\tan A \tan B + 3 \tan B}$.

Exercise 45. Page 149

11. $\sin 130°$. **13.** $\cos 160°$. **15.** $1 + \cos 40°$.

17. $2 \cos^2 \frac{1}{2}B$. **19.** $1 + \cos 80°$. **21.** $2 \sin^2 B$.

23. $2 \cos^2 25°$. **25.** $\tan 76°$. **27.** $\cot^2 20°$.

43. $2 \sin 2\alpha \cos 2\alpha$, $(\cos^2 2\alpha - \sin^2 2\alpha)$, $2 \tan 2\alpha/(1 - \tan^2 2\alpha)$.

45. $\pm\sqrt{\dfrac{1 - \cos 8x}{2}}$, $\pm\sqrt{\dfrac{1 + \cos 8x}{2}}$, $\pm\sqrt{\dfrac{1 - \cos 8x}{1 + \cos 8x}}$.

47. $\pm\sqrt{\dfrac{1 - \cos \frac{1}{2}x}{2}}$, $\pm\sqrt{\dfrac{1 + \cos \frac{1}{2}x}{2}}$, $\pm\sqrt{\dfrac{1 - \cos \frac{1}{2}x}{1 + \cos \frac{1}{2}x}}$.

49. $2 \sin \frac{3}{2}\theta \cos \frac{3}{2}\theta$, $(\cos^2 \frac{3}{2}\theta - \sin^2 \frac{3}{2}\theta)$, $2 \tan \frac{3}{2}\theta/(1 - \tan^2 \frac{3}{2}\theta)$.

51. $3 \sin x - 4 \sin^3 x$.

53. $\pm 4 \sin x\,(1 - 2 \sin^2 x)\sqrt{1 - \sin^2 x}$.

Exercise 46. Page 151

5. $\sin 7\theta - \sin 3\theta$. **7.** $\cos 2\theta - \cos 8\theta$. **9.** $\cos 3\theta - \cos 10\theta$.

11. $2 \sin 60° \sin 20°$. **13.** $2 \sin x \sin 3x$.

15. $-2 \sin x \sin 2x$. **17.** $2 \cos \frac{5}{2}y \cos \frac{11}{2}y$.

31. $\tan \frac{13}{2}A$. **33.** $-\cot 30° \cot 45°$. **35.** $\cot \frac{1}{2}(\beta - \alpha)$.

Exercise 48. Page 156

1. $0, \frac{1}{2}\pi, \pi, \frac{3}{2}\pi$. **3.** $\frac{1}{2}\pi, \frac{3}{2}\pi$. **5.** $\frac{1}{12}\pi, \frac{11}{12}\pi, \frac{13}{12}\pi, \frac{23}{12}\pi$. **7.** $\frac{3}{4}\pi, \frac{7}{4}\pi$.

9. $\frac{1}{4}\pi, \frac{5}{12}\pi, \frac{11}{12}\pi, \frac{13}{12}\pi, \frac{19}{12}\pi, \frac{7}{4}\pi$. **11.** $\frac{1}{4}\pi, \frac{7}{12}\pi, \frac{11}{12}\pi, \frac{5}{4}\pi, \frac{19}{12}\pi, \frac{23}{12}\pi$.

13. $\frac{1}{3}\pi, \frac{5}{3}\pi$. **15.** 2π. **17.** $\frac{5}{3}\pi$. **19.** $0, \pi$. **21.** $\frac{1}{12}\pi, \frac{7}{12}\pi, \frac{13}{12}\pi, \frac{19}{12}\pi$.

23. $\frac{1}{6}\pi, \frac{1}{2}\pi, \frac{5}{6}\pi, \frac{3}{2}\pi$. **25.** $\frac{1}{3}\pi, \pi, \frac{5}{3}\pi$. **27.** $0, \frac{1}{3}\pi, \frac{2}{3}\pi, \pi, \frac{4}{3}\pi, \frac{5}{3}\pi$.

29. $\frac{1}{2}\pi, \frac{3}{2}\pi$. **31.** .55, 1.02, 3.69, 4.16. **33.** .42, 1.99, 3.56, 5.13.

35. $\frac{1}{3}\pi, \frac{1}{2}\pi, \frac{3}{2}\pi, \frac{5}{3}\pi$. **37.** $0, \frac{1}{3}\pi, \frac{5}{3}\pi$. **39.** $\frac{1}{8}\pi, \frac{3}{8}\pi, \frac{5}{8}\pi, \frac{7}{8}\pi, \frac{9}{8}\pi, \frac{11}{8}\pi, \frac{13}{8}\pi, \frac{15}{8}\pi$.

41. $0, \frac{1}{3}\pi, \frac{2}{3}\pi, \pi, \frac{4}{3}\pi, \frac{5}{3}\pi$. **43.** $\frac{1}{4}\pi, \frac{3}{4}\pi, \frac{5}{4}\pi, \frac{7}{4}\pi$. **45.** $0, \frac{1}{2}\pi, \pi, \frac{3}{2}\pi$.

47. 0. **49.** π. **51.** $0, \frac{1}{2}\pi, \pi, \frac{3}{2}\pi$. **53.** $0, \frac{1}{4}\pi, \frac{1}{2}\pi, \frac{3}{4}\pi, \pi, \frac{5}{4}\pi, \frac{3}{2}\pi, \frac{7}{4}\pi$.

55. $0, \frac{1}{3}\pi, \frac{2}{3}\pi, \pi, \frac{4}{3}\pi, \frac{5}{3}\pi$. **57.** $0, \frac{1}{3}\pi, \frac{2}{3}\pi, \frac{3}{4}\pi, \pi, \frac{4}{3}\pi, \frac{5}{3}\pi, \frac{7}{4}\pi$. **59.** $\frac{2}{3}\pi$.

61. .36, 1.21, 3.50, 4.35. **63.** $0, \pi$. **65.** $0, \frac{1}{4}\pi, \frac{1}{2}\pi, \frac{3}{4}\pi, \pi, \frac{7}{6}\pi, \frac{5}{4}\pi, \frac{3}{2}\pi, \frac{7}{4}\pi, \frac{11}{6}\pi$.

67. $0, \frac{1}{6}\pi, \frac{1}{2}\pi, \frac{5}{6}\pi, \pi, \frac{7}{6}\pi, \frac{3}{2}\pi, \frac{11}{6}\pi$. **69.** $0, \frac{1}{2}\pi, \pi, \frac{7}{6}\pi, \frac{3}{2}\pi, \frac{11}{6}\pi$.

Exercise 49. Page 157

Note. Functions are given in the order sine, cosine, tangent.

1. $\frac{1}{4}(\sqrt{2} + \sqrt{6})$, $\frac{1}{4}(\sqrt{6} - \sqrt{2})$, $(2 + \sqrt{3})$.

5. (*a*) $\frac{84}{85}, -\frac{13}{85}, -\frac{84}{13}$; (*b*) $\frac{24}{25}, \frac{7}{25}, \frac{24}{7}$; (*c*) $\frac{1}{10}\sqrt{10}, \frac{3}{10}\sqrt{10}, \frac{1}{3}$.

7. $2 \cos \frac{9}{2}\alpha \cos \frac{1}{2}\alpha$; $2 \sin 40° \cos 5°$; $2 \sin \alpha \sin 4\alpha$.

19. $\frac{1}{6}\pi, \frac{1}{3}\pi, \frac{7}{6}\pi, \frac{4}{3}\pi$. **21.** $\frac{1}{4}\pi, \frac{3}{4}\pi, \frac{5}{4}\pi, \frac{7}{4}\pi$. **23.** $0, \pi$.

25. $\frac{1}{6}\pi, \frac{1}{3}\pi, \frac{2}{3}\pi, \frac{5}{6}\pi, \frac{7}{6}\pi, \frac{4}{3}\pi, \frac{5}{3}\pi, \frac{11}{6}\pi$. **27.** $\frac{1}{12}\pi, \frac{5}{12}\pi, \frac{7}{12}\pi, \frac{11}{12}\pi, \frac{13}{12}\pi, \frac{17}{12}\pi, \frac{19}{12}\pi, \frac{23}{12}\pi$.
29. $\sin\alpha\cos\beta\cos\gamma + \cos\alpha\sin\beta\cos\gamma - \cos\alpha\cos\beta\sin\gamma + \sin\alpha\sin\beta\sin\gamma$.
31. $8\cos^4 x - 8\cos^2 x + 1$.

Exercise 50. Page 160

1. 165° 50′. **3.** 142° 50′. **5.** 2.646. **7.** 8.062.
9. 3.464. **11.** 48° 11′. **13.** 42° 50′. **15.** 104° 29′.
17. $\alpha = 81° 47'$, $\beta = 38° 13'$, $\gamma = 60° 0'$.
19. $\alpha = 118° 47'$, $\beta = 23° 52'$, $\gamma = 37° 21'$. **21.** 15.7. **23.** 9.89.
25. 115 mi. **27.** 394 lb. **29.** 58.7 lb.

Exercise 51. Page 163

1. $a = c = 9.659$, 75° 0′. **3.** $b = 77.75$, $c = 77.83$, 71° 20′.
5. $a =$ **13.10**, 13.100; $b =$ **19.35**, 19.345; 84° 0′.
7. $b =$ **.4290**, .42897; $c =$ **.8744**, .87436; 102° 50′.
9. $b =$ **7.518**, 7.5175; $c =$ **11.81**, 11.814; 132° 11′.
11. $a =$ **.1852**, .18517; $c =$ **.4556**, .45548; 70° 50′.
13. $b =$ **.07758**, .077598; $c =$ **.06650**, .066503; 58° 0′.
15. $b = 35.408$, $c = 34.700$, 76° 10′. **17.** $b = 242.39$, $c = 339.55$, 123° 0′.
19. $a = .0037760$, $b = .011107$, 80° 11′. **21.** 2.80 in.
27. 23 33. **29.** 1841.

Exercise 52. Page 168

1. $\alpha = 23° 35'$, $\gamma = 126° 25'$, 8.048.
3. $\alpha = 37° 20'$, $\beta = 77° 10'$, 606.5; or,
$\alpha = 11° 40'$, $\beta = 102° 50'$, 202.2.
5. $\alpha = 30° 0'$, $\beta = 75° 0'$, 3.622.
7. $\beta = 90° 0'$, $\gamma = 58° 40'$, .2136.
9. $\alpha = 23° 35'$, $\beta = 7° 45'$, 6.740.
11. $\alpha =$ **107° 40′**, 107° 39.5′; **23.55**, 23.555; $\gamma =$ **29° 50′**, 29° 50.5′.
13. No solution.
15. $\alpha =$ **81° 15′**, 18° 15.6′; $\gamma =$ **61° 52′**, 61° 51.4′; **.08442**, .084415.
Or, $\alpha =$ **24° 59′**, 24° 58.4′; $\gamma =$ **118° 8′**, 118° 8.6′; **.03607**, .036058.
17. $\beta =$ **31° 21′**, 31° 19.7′; $\gamma =$ **35° 19′**, 35° 20.3′; **6.551**, 6.5460.
19. $\beta = 30° 43.9'$, $\gamma = 125° 8.7'$, 2.5399; or,
$\beta = 149° 16.1'$, $\gamma = 6° 36.5'$, .35745.
21. $\alpha = 45° 46.7'$, $\gamma = 90° 0'$, 4.7484.
23. $\alpha = 37° 20.2'$, $\beta = 15° 20.8'$, .32385.
25. 78 lb., *N* 31° *E*; or, 24 lb., *N* 75° *E*.
27. Two sol. **29.** Two sol.

Exercise 53. Page 170

1. $\alpha = 111° 40'$, $\beta = 38° 20'$, 6.46. **3.** $\alpha = 48° 10'$, $\gamma = 21° 50'$, 63.1.
5. $\beta = 89° 0'$, $\gamma = 21° 0'$, 36.2. **7.** $\alpha = 86° 10'$, $\gamma = 21° 50'$, .896.
9. $\gamma = 77° 0'$, $\beta = 33° 20'$, 22.1. **11.** 423.

Exercise 54. Page 173

1. $\alpha = 111° 44'$, $\beta = 38° 16'$.
3. $\alpha = 48° 8'$, $\gamma = 21° 52'$.
5. $\beta = $ **91° 26′**, 91° 25.9′; $\gamma = $ **20° 34′**, 20° 34.1′; **358.9**, 358.94.
7. $\alpha = $ **86° 13′**, 86° 13.4′; $\gamma = $ **21° 47′**, 21° 46.6′; **.8922**, .89216.
9. $\alpha = $ **34° 8′**, 34° 7.7′; $\gamma = $ **76° 12′**, 76° 12.3′; **22.00**, 21.995.
11. $\alpha = $ **25° 41′**, 25° 41.0′; $\gamma = $ **33° 49′**, 33° 49.0′; **1538**, 1538.0.
13. $\beta = 88° 34.0'$, $\gamma = 30° 6.2'$, 277.57.
15. $\beta = 29° 15.6'$, $\gamma = 52° 27.6'$, 1.7029.
17. $\beta = 45° 35.1'$, $\gamma = 29° 18.5'$, 17,646.
19. $\overline{BT} = 6099$ yd.; azimuth of BT is 331° 47′.

Exercise 55. Page 176

1. $\alpha = $ **27° 40′**, 27° 39.6′; $\beta = $ **45° 14′**, 45° 14.2′; $\gamma = $ **107° 6′**, 107° 6.2′.
3. $\alpha = $ **15° 44′**, 15° 44.0′; $\beta = $ **13° 4′**, 13° 3.0′; $\gamma = $ **151° 12′**, 151° 12 8′.
5. $\alpha = $ **16° 44′**, 16° 44.6′; $\beta = $ **90° 50′**, 90° 50.2′; $\gamma = $ **72° 26′**, 72° 25.0′.
7. $\alpha = $ **53° 2′**, 53° 1.8′; $\beta = $ **86° 6′**, 86° 6.0′; $\gamma = $ **40° 52′**, 40° 52.2′.
9. **99° 36′**, 99° 35.6′.
11. **122° 2′**, 122° 0.6′.
13. $\alpha = 27° 28.2'$, $\beta = 79° 57.2'$, $\gamma = 72° 34.4'$.
15. $\alpha = 72° 23.4'$, $\beta = 56° 54.4'$, $\gamma = 50° 42.0'$.
17. $\alpha = 28° 18.2'$, $\beta = 91° 36.0'$, $\gamma = 60° 6.0'$.

Exercise 56. Page 177

1. **7.552**, 7.5502.
3. **.02359**, .023594.

Exercise 57. Page 178

1. 39.94.
3. 125° 6′.
5. $\alpha = 6° 4'$, $\gamma = 9° 36'$, 31.71.
7. $a = 81.28$, $b = 90.60$, 63° 48′.
9. $\beta = 16° 36'$, $\gamma = 5° 44'$, 57.14.
11. 14.80.
13. $\alpha = $ **27° 52′**, 27° 51.9′; $\beta = $ **71° 48′**, 71° 49.1′; **2.774**, 2.7734.
15. $\beta = $ **30° 41′**, 30° 40.8′; $\gamma = $ **124° 2′**, 124° 2.2′; **2861**, 2861.3.
Or, $\beta = $ **98° 45′**, 98° 45.2′; $\gamma = $ **55° 58′**, 55° 57.8′; **5542**, 5542.6.
17. $\alpha = $ **46° 10′**, 46° 10.2′; $\gamma = $ **60° 44′**, 60° 43.8′; **478.4**, 478.37.
19. 62° 43′, 117° 17′.
21. 184 ft.
23. 125.2 ft.
25. N 83° 33′ W.
27. 89.08 ft.
29. 27.6 lb.; S 83° 16′ E.
31. Az. of track, 136° 22′; groundspeed, 232.1 mi. per hr.; drift angle, 6° 22′.
33. 37.7 knots, S 44° 4′ E.
35. 187.8 ft.

Exercise 58. Page 186

3. $\frac{1}{6}\pi$.
5. 0.
7. $\frac{1}{3}\pi$.
9. $\frac{1}{3}\pi$.
11. $-\frac{1}{6}\pi$.
13. $-\frac{1}{3}\pi$.
15. $-\frac{1}{6}\pi$.
17. .419.
19. .436.
21. .599.
23. $\frac{1}{3}$.
25. $-\frac{2}{5}$.
27. $-3x$.
29. $\frac{1}{2}\sqrt{3}$.
31. $\frac{1}{2}\sqrt{3}$.
33. -1.

Note. In Problems 35–41, results are given in the order sin $(y+z)$, cos $(y+z)$, sin $2y$, cos $2y$, and tan $2y$.

35. $1, 0, \frac{1}{2}\sqrt{3}, \frac{1}{2}, \sqrt{3}$. **37.** $(.3 - .4\sqrt{3}), (.4 + .3\sqrt{3}), \frac{24}{25}, \frac{7}{25}, \frac{24}{7}$.
39. $.3\sqrt{10}, -.1\sqrt{10}, \frac{4}{5}, -\frac{3}{5}, -\frac{4}{3}$.
41. $(-.5\sqrt{3} + .05\sqrt{5}), (.25\sqrt{3} + .1\sqrt{5}), -\frac{4}{5}, -\frac{3}{5}, \frac{4}{3}$.
43. Sine, $-\frac{3}{5}$; cosine, $\frac{4}{5}$; etc. **45.** $x = -\frac{1}{2}$.

Exercise 59. Page 188

3. $\frac{1}{6}\pi$. **5.** $\frac{1}{3}\pi$. **7.** π.
9. $\frac{3}{4}\pi$. **11.** $\frac{3}{4}\pi$. **13.** $\frac{1}{6}\pi$.
15. .262. **17.** 2.646.
19. $0 \leqq \text{Arccos}\, x \leqq \frac{1}{2}\pi$; $\frac{1}{2}\pi \leqq \text{Arccos}\, x \leqq \pi$.

Exercise 60. Page 189

Note. Where all trigonometric functions are requested, they are given in the order sine, cosine, tangent, cosecant, secant, cotangent.

5. $-\frac{8}{17}, \frac{15}{17}, -\frac{8}{15}, -\frac{17}{8}, \frac{17}{15}, -\frac{15}{8}$.
7. $0, -1, 0, \infty, -1, \infty$. **11.** 1.931. **13.** .7660.
15. 1.963. **17.** $-.4226$. **21.** $-\frac{1}{2}, -\frac{1}{2}\sqrt{3}, \frac{1}{3}\sqrt{3}, -2, -\frac{2}{3}\sqrt{3}, \sqrt{3}$.
23. $-\frac{1}{2}\sqrt{2}, -\frac{1}{2}\sqrt{2}, 1, -\sqrt{2}, -\sqrt{2}, 1$.
25. $-\frac{1}{2}\sqrt{3}, -\frac{1}{2}, \sqrt{3}, -\frac{2}{3}\sqrt{3}, -2, \frac{1}{3}\sqrt{3}$.
27. (*a*) See Prob. 25 with signs for quad. II. (*b*) See Prob. 23, with signs for quad. III.
29. $a = .4138$, $c = .6111$, 47° 24′. **31.** $b = 66.085$, $c = 70.655$, 20° 43.3′.
33. $a =$ **.4138**, .41379; $c =$ **.6114**, .61132; 47° 24′.
35. $b =$ **661.0**, 660.86; $c =$ **706.7**, 706.57; **20° 43′**, 20° 43.3′.
37. 30°, 150°. **39.** 45°, 135°, 225°, 315°. **41.** 90°, 270°.
43. 45°, 135°. **45.** 135°, 225°. **47.** 29° 20′, 150° 40′.
49. 154° 40′, 334° 40′. **51.** $\frac{1}{2}\pi, \frac{3}{2}\pi$. **53.** $\frac{1}{2}\pi, \frac{3}{2}\pi$.
55. $\frac{3}{2}\pi$. **61.** 81. **63.** $\frac{1}{16}$.
65. **19.24**, 19.248. **67.** **1.451**, 1.4514. **69.** $-$ **.03928**, $-$ .039275.
71. .0008776. **73.** 3. **81.** (*a*) $\frac{65}{36}\pi$; (*b*) 2.803.
85. *N* 25° 56′ *E*. **87.** $-\frac{1}{4}(\sqrt{2} + \sqrt{6})$. **89.** $-\frac{1}{2}$.
91. $2 + \sqrt{3}$. **101.** $\frac{1}{3}\pi, \frac{1}{2}\pi, \frac{5}{3}\pi$.
103. $0, \frac{1}{8}\pi, \frac{3}{8}\pi, \frac{5}{8}\pi, \frac{7}{8}\pi, \pi, \frac{9}{8}\pi, \frac{11}{8}\pi, \frac{13}{8}\pi, \frac{15}{8}\pi$.
105. cos 17°. **107.** csc 40°. **109.** $-$ sin 27°.
111. $-$ cos 15°. **113.** $-\cos x$. **115.** $\sec x$.
117. $-\cot x$. **119.** $\sqrt{2}\sqrt{1 - \cos(\alpha - \beta)}$. **121.** $\frac{1}{6}\pi$.
123. $-\frac{2}{3}$. **125.** $\frac{1}{5}$. **135.** No sol.
137. (Using $\pi = 3.14$ and Table XIII) .13, 1.17, 2.22, 3.26, 4.31, 5.35.
139. $\frac{1}{2}\pi, \pi$. **141.** $\frac{5}{12}$. **143.** $\sqrt{1 - x^2}/x$. **147.** 3; -2.
149. By interpolation: $\log_e 3784 = 8.23855$; $\log_e .02393 = -3.73264$.

Exercise 61. Page 195

1. $11i$. **3.** $9ai$. **5.** $\frac{5}{3}i$.
7. $5 + 7i$; $5i$; $-6i$; 8; $2 + 3i\sqrt{5}$. **9.** -1. **11.** $-i$.

13. $-3+10i$. 15. $-6i$. 17. -9. 19. -10.
21. $-3\sqrt{5}$. 23. $17+17i$. 25. -9. 27. $\frac{22}{41}+\frac{7}{41}i$.
29. $\frac{6}{25}+\frac{17}{25}i$. 31. $\frac{13}{5}-\frac{1}{5}i$. 33. $\frac{5}{3}-12i$. 35. $-\frac{6}{5}i$.
37. $\frac{5}{4}i$. 39. $3i$. 41. $-40i\sqrt{5}$. 43. $-2i$.
45. $2+11i$. 47. $-10+9i\sqrt{3}$.
49. $-\frac{2}{33}-\frac{5}{66}i\sqrt{2}$. 51. $x=1, y=-1$.

Exercise 63. Page 200

1. $\frac{3}{2}\sqrt{3}+\frac{3}{2}i$. 3. $2+0i$. 5. $\frac{3}{2}-\frac{3}{2}i\sqrt{3}$. 7. $-2\sqrt{2}-2i\sqrt{2}$.
9. $0-5i$. 11. $-2.180+3.356i$. 13. $-\frac{1}{2}\sqrt{2}-\frac{1}{2}i\sqrt{2}$.
15. $3(\cos 90° + i \sin 90°)$. 17. $8(\cos 180° + i \sin 180°)$.
19. $2\sqrt{2}(\cos 45° + i \sin 45°)$. 21. $8\sqrt{2}(\cos 135° + i \sin 135°)$.
23. $2(\cos 150° + i \sin 150°)$. 25. $8(\cos 120° + i \sin 120°)$.
27. $5\sqrt{2}(\cos 225° + i \sin 225°)$. 29. $13(\cos 157.4° + i \sin 157.4°)$.
31. $5(\cos 36.9° + i \sin 36.9°)$. 33. $5(\cos 240° + i \sin 240°)$.
35. $r[\cos(-\theta) + i \sin(-\theta)]$. 37. 13; 25; $\sqrt{h^2+k^2}$.

Exercise 64. Page 202

1. $6+6i\sqrt{3}$. 3. $12(\cos 35° + i \sin 35°)$. 5. $4\sqrt{2}+4i\sqrt{2}$.
7. $-64i$. 9. -64. 11. $-16-16i\sqrt{3}$. 13. $-8+8i\sqrt{3}$.
15. $128+128i$. 17. $3(\cos 110° + i \sin 110°)$.
19. $\frac{15}{2}\sqrt{2}(\cos 105° + i \sin 105°)$. 21. $-\frac{2}{3}\sqrt{3}+\frac{2}{3}i$.

Exercise 65. Page 206

1. $3(\cos 40° + i \sin 40°)$; other amplitudes are 130°, 220°, 310°.
3. $3(\cos 76° + i \sin 76°)$; other amplitudes are 196°, 316°.
5. $\frac{3}{2}\sqrt{2}+\frac{3}{2}i\sqrt{2}$; $-\frac{3}{2}\sqrt{2}-\frac{3}{2}i\sqrt{2}$. 7. 3; $\frac{3}{2}(-1+i\sqrt{3})$; $\frac{3}{2}(-1-i\sqrt{3})$.
9. $2(\cos 18° + i \sin 18°)$; $2i$; $2(\cos 162° + i \sin 162°)$; other amplitudes are 234° and 306°.
11. ± 3; $\pm 3i$.
13. $2(\cos 78.75° + i \sin 78.75°)$; other amplitudes are 168.75°, 258.75°, 348.75°
15. $2(\cos 75° + i \sin 75°)$; other amplitudes are 165°, 255°, 345°.
17. $2(\cos 37.5° + i \sin 37.5°)$; other amplitudes are 127.5°, 217.5°, 307.5°.
19. ± 2; $\pm 2i$. 21. ± 2; $(1 \pm i\sqrt{3})$; $(-1 \pm i\sqrt{3})$.

Exercise 66. Page 219

3. $H \cup K$ is all x such that $-1 \leqq x \leqq 4$.
$H \cap K$ is all x such that $2 \leqq x \leqq 3$.
7. $H \cap K = \emptyset$. 9. 10; 32. 11. 64; 2^n.

INDEX

TABLES

CONTENTS

I. SQUARES AND SQUARE ROOTS:* 1—200

N	N^2	$\sqrt{N}$	N	N^2	$\sqrt{N}$	N	N^2	$\sqrt{N}$	N	N^2	$\sqrt{N}$
1	1	1.000	**51**	2,601	7.141	**101**	10,201	10.050	**151**	22,801	12.288
2	4	1.414	**52**	2,704	7.211	**102**	10,404	10.100	**152**	23,104	12.329
3	9	1.732	**53**	2,809	7.280	**103**	10,609	10.149	**153**	23,409	12.369
4	16	2.000	**54**	2,916	7.348	**104**	10,816	10.198	**154**	23,716	12.410
5	25	2.236	**55**	3,025	7.416	**105**	11,025	10.247	**155**	24,025	12.450
6	36	2.449	**56**	3,136	7.483	**106**	11,236	10.296	**156**	24,336	12.490
7	49	2.646	**57**	3,249	7.550	**107**	11,449	10.344	**157**	24,649	12.530
8	64	2.828	**58**	3,364	7.616	**108**	11,664	10.392	**158**	24,964	12.570
9	81	3.000	**59**	3,481	7.681	**109**	11,881	10.440	**159**	25,281	12.610
10	100	3.162	**60**	3,600	7.746	**110**	12,100	10.488	**160**	25,600	12.649
11	121	3.317	**61**	3,721	7.810	**111**	12,321	10.536	**161**	25,921	12.689
12	144	3.464	**62**	3,844	7.874	**112**	12,544	10.583	**162**	26,244	12.728
13	169	3.606	**63**	3,969	7.937	**113**	12,769	10.630	**163**	26,569	12.767
14	196	3.742	**64**	4,096	8.000	**114**	12,996	10.677	**164**	26,896	12.806
15	225	3.873	**65**	4,225	8.062	**115**	13,225	10.724	**165**	27,225	12.845
16	256	4.000	**66**	4,356	8.124	**116**	13,456	10.770	**166**	27,556	12.884
17	289	4.123	**67**	4,489	8.185	**117**	13,689	10.817	**167**	27,889	12.923
18	324	4.243	**68**	4,624	8.246	**118**	13,924	10.863	**168**	28,224	12.962
19	361	4.359	**69**	4,761	8.307	**119**	14,161	10.909	**169**	28,561	13.000
20	400	4.472	**70**	4,900	8.367	**120**	14,400	10.954	**170**	28,900	13.038
21	441	4.583	**71**	5,041	8.426	**121**	14,641	11.000	**171**	29,241	13.077
22	484	4.690	**72**	5,184	8.485	**122**	14,884	11.045	**172**	29,584	13.115
23	529	4.796	**73**	5,329	8.544	**123**	15,129	11.091	**173**	29,929	13.153
24	576	4.899	**74**	5,476	8.602	**124**	15,376	11.136	**174**	30,276	13.191
25	625	5.000	**75**	5,625	8.660	**125**	15,625	11.180	**175**	30,625	13.229
26	676	5.099	**76**	5,776	8.718	**126**	15,876	11.225	**176**	30,976	13.266
27	729	5.196	**77**	5,929	8.775	**127**	16,129	11.269	**177**	31,329	13.304
28	784	5.292	**78**	6,084	8.832	**128**	16,384	11.314	**178**	31,684	13.342
29	841	5.385	**79**	6,241	8.888	**129**	16,641	11.358	**179**	32,041	13.379
30	900	5.477	**80**	6,400	8.944	**130**	16,900	11.402	**180**	32,400	13.416
31	961	5.568	**81**	6,561	9.000	**131**	17,161	11.446	**181**	32,761	13.454
32	1,024	5.657	**82**	6,724	9.055	**132**	17,424	11.489	**182**	33,124	13.491
33	1,089	5.745	**83**	6,889	9.110	**133**	17,689	11.533	**183**	33,489	13.528
34	1,156	5.831	**84**	7,056	9.165	**134**	17,956	11.576	**184**	33,856	13.565
35	1,225	5.916	**85**	7,225	9.220	**135**	18,225	11.619	**185**	34,225	13.601
36	1,296	6.000	**86**	7,396	9.274	**136**	18,496	11.662	**186**	34,596	13.638
37	1,369	6.083	**87**	7,569	9.327	**137**	18,769	11.705	**187**	34,969	13.675
38	1,444	6.164	**88**	7,744	9.381	**138**	19,044	11.747	**188**	35,344	13.711
39	1,521	6.245	**89**	7,921	9.434	**139**	19,321	11.790	**189**	35,721	13.748
40	1,600	6.325	**90**	8,100	9.487	**140**	19,600	11.832	**190**	36,100	13.784
41	1,681	6.403	**91**	8,281	9.539	**141**	19,881	11.874	**191**	36,481	13.820
42	1,764	6.481	**92**	8,464	9.592	**142**	20,164	11.916	**192**	36.864	13.856
43	1,849	6.557	**93**	8,649	9.644	**143**	20,449	11.958	**193**	37,249	13.892
44	1,936	6.633	**94**	8,836	9.695	**144**	20,736	12.000	**194**	37,636	13.928
45	2,025	6.708	**95**	9,025	9.747	**145**	21,025	12.042	**195**	38,025	13.964
46	2,116	6.782	**96**	9,216	9.798	**146**	21,316	12.083	**196**	38,416	14.000
47	2,209	6.856	**97**	9,409	9.849	**147**	21,609	12.124	**197**	38,809	14.036
48	2,304	6.928	**98**	9,604	9.899	**148**	21,904	12.166	**198**	39,204	14.071
49	2,401	7.000	**99**	9,801	9.950	**149**	22,201	12.207	**199**	39,601	14.107
50	2,500	7.071	**100**	10,000	10.000	**150**	22,500	12.247	**200**	40,000	14.142
N	N^2	$\sqrt{N}$	N	N^2	$\sqrt{N}$	N	N^2	$\sqrt{N}$	N	N^2	$\sqrt{N}$

* A more extensive table is found commencing on page 115.

II. THREE-PLACE LOGARITHMS OF NUMBERS

N	Log N	N	Log N
1.0	.000	**5.5**	.740
1.1	.041	5.6	.748
1.2	.079	5.7	.756
1.3	.114	5.8	.763
1.4	.146	5.9	.771
1.5	.176	**6.0**	.778
1.6	.204	6.1	.785
1.7	.230	6.2	.792
1.8	.255	6.3	.799
1.9	.279	6.4	.806
2.0	.301	**6.5**	.813
2.1	.322	6.6	.820
2.2	.342	6.7	.826
2.3	.362	6.8	.833
2.4	.380	6.9	.839
2.5	.398	**7.0**	.845
2.6	.415	7.1	.851
2.7	.431	7.2	.857
2.8	.447	7.3	.863
2.9	.462	7.4	.869
3.0	.477	**7.5**	.875
3.1	.491	7.6	.881
3.2	.505	7.7	.886
3.3	.519	7.8	.892
3.4	.531	7.9	.898
3.5	.544	**8.0**	.903
3.6	.556	8.1	.908
3.7	.568	8.2	.914
3.8	.580	8.3	.919
3.9	.591	8.4	.924
4.0	.602	**8.5**	.929
4.1	.613	8.6	.935
4.2	.623	8.7	.940
4.3	.633	8.8	.944
4.4	.643	8.9	.949
4.5	.653	**9.0**	.954
4.6	.663	9.1	.959
4.7	.672	9.2	.964
4.8	.681	9.3	.968
4.9	.690	9.4	.973
5.0	.699	**9.5**	.978
5.1	.708	9.6	.982
5.2	.716	9.7	.987
5.3	.724	9.8	.991
5.4	.732	9.9	.996
5.5	.740	**1.00**	1.000
N	**Log N**	**N**	**Log N**

III. THREE-PLACE LOGARITHMS OF FUNCTIONS

→	L Sin *	L Tan *	L Cot	L Cos *	
0°	——	——	——	10.000	**90°**
1°	8.242	8.242	1.758	10.000	89°
2°	.543	.543	.457	10.000	88°
3°	.719	.719	.281	9.999	87°
4°	.844	.845	.155	.999	86°
5°	8.940	8.942	1.058	9.998	**85°**
6°	9.019	9.022	0.978	9.998	84°
7°	.086	.089	.911	.997	83°
8°	.144	.148	.852	.996	82°
9°	.194	.200	.800	.995	81°
10°	9.240	9.246	0.754	9.993	**80°**
11°	9.281	9.289	0.711	9.992	79°
12°	.318	.327	.673	.990	78°
13°	.352	.363	.637	.989	77°
14°	.384	.397	.603	.987	76°
15°	9.413	9.428	0.572	9.985	**75°**
16°	9.440	9.458	0.543	9.983	74°
17°	.466	.485	.515	.981	73°
18°	.490	.512	.488	.978	72°
19°	.513	.537	.463	.976	71°
20°	9.534	9.561	0.439	9.973	**70°**
21°	9.554	9.584	0.416	9.970	69°
22°	.574	.606	.394	.967	68°
23°	.592	.628	.372	.964	67°
24°	.609	.649	.351	.961	66°
25°	9.626	9.669	0.331	9.957	**65°**
26°	9.642	9.688	0.312	9.954	64°
27°	.657	.707	.293	.950	63°
28°	.672	.726	.274	.946	62°
29°	.686	.744	.256	.942	61°
30°	9.699	9.761	0.239	9.938	**60°**
31°	9.712	9.779	0.221	9.933	59°
32°	.724	.796	.204	.928	58°
33°	.736	.813	.187	.924	57°
34°	.748	.829	.171	.919	56°
35°	9.759	9.845	0.155	9.913	**55°**
36°	9.769	9.861	0.139	9.908	54°
37°	.779	.877	.123	.902	53°
38°	.789	.893	.107	.897	52°
39°	.799	.908	.092	.891	51°
40°	9.808	9.924	0.076	9.884	**50°**
41°	9.817	9.939	0.061	9.878	49°
42°	.826	.954	.046	.871	48°
43°	.834	.970	.030	.864	47°
44°	.842	.985	.015	.857	46°
45°	9.849	10.000	0.000	9.849	**45°**
	L Cos *	**L Cot ***	**L Tan**	**L Sin ***	←

* Subtract 10 from each entry in this column.

IV. THREE-PLACE VALUES OF TRIGONOMETRIC FUNCTIONS AND DEGREES IN RADIAN MEASURE

Rad.	Deg.	Sin	Tan	Sec	Csc	Cot	Cos	Deg.	Rad.
.000	**0°**	.000	.000	1.000	——	——	1.000	**90°**	1.571
.017	**1°**	.017	.017	1.000	57.30	57.29	1.000	**89°**	1.553
.035	**2°**	.035	.035	1.001	28.65	28.64	0.999	**88°**	1.536
.052	**3°**	.052	.052	1.001	19.11	19.08	.999	**87°**	1.518
.070	**4°**	.070	.070	1.002	14.34	14.30	.998	**86°**	1.501
.087	**5°**	.087	.087	1.004	11.47	11.43	.996	**85°**	1.484
.105	**6°**	.105	.105	1.006	9.567	9.514	.995	**84°**	1.466
.122	**7°**	.122	.123	1.008	8.206	8.144	.993	**83°**	1.449
.140	**8°**	.139	.141	1.010	7.185	7.115	.990	**82°**	1.431
.157	**9°**	.156	.158	1.012	6.392	6.314	.988	**81°**	1.414
.175	**10°**	.174	.176	1.015	5.759	5.671	.985	**80°**	1.396
.192	**11°**	.191	.194	1.019	5.241	5.145	.982	**79°**	1.379
.209	**12°**	.208	.213	1.022	4.810	4.705	.978	**78°**	1.361
.227	**13°**	.225	.231	1.026	4.445	4.331	.974	**77°**	1.344
.244	**14°**	.242	.249	1.031	4.134	4.011	.970	**76°**	1.326
.262	**15°**	.259	.268	1.035	3.864	3.732	.966	**75°**	1.309
.279	**16°**	.276	.287	1.040	3.628	3.487	.961	**74°**	1.292
.297	**17°**	.292	.306	1.046	3.420	3.271	.956	**73°**	1.274
.314	**18°**	.309	.325	1.051	3.236	3.078	.951	**72°**	1.257
.332	**19°**	.326	.344	1.058	3.072	2.904	.946	**71°**	1.239
.349	**20°**	.342	.364	1.064	2.924	2.747	.940	**70°**	1.222
.367	**21°**	.358	.384	1.071	2.790	2.605	.934	**69°**	1.204
.384	**22°**	.375	.404	1.079	2.669	2.475	.927	**68°**	1.187
.401	**23°**	.391	.424	1.086	2.559	2.356	.921	**67°**	1.169
.419	**24°**	.407	.445	1.095	2.459	2.246	.914	**66°**	1.152
.436	**25°**	.423	.466	1.103	2.366	2.145	.906	**65°**	1.134
.454	**26°**	.438	.488	1.113	2.281	2.050	.899	**64°**	1.117
.471	**27°**	.454	.510	1.122	2.203	1.963	.891	**63°**	1.100
.489	**28°**	.469	.532	1.133	2.130	1.881	.883	**62°**	1.082
.506	**29°**	.485	.554	1.143	2.063	1.804	.875	**61°**	1.065
.524	**30°**	.500	.577	1.155	2.000	1.732	.866	**60°**	1.047
.541	**31°**	.515	.601	1.167	1.942	1.664	.857	**59°**	1.030
.559	**32°**	.530	.625	1.179	1.887	1.600	.848	**58°**	1.012
.576	**33°**	.545	.649	1.192	1.836	1.540	.839	**57°**	0.995
.593	**34°**	.559	.675	1.206	1.788	1.483	.829	**56°**	0.977
.611	**35°**	.574	.700	1.221	1.743	1.428	.819	**55°**	0.960
.628	**36°**	.588	.727	1.236	1.701	1.376	.809	**54°**	0.942
.646	**37°**	.602	.754	1.252	1.662	1.327	.799	**53°**	0.925
.663	**38°**	.616	.781	1.269	1.624	1.280	.788	**52°**	0.908
.681	**39°**	.629	.810	1.287	1.589	1.235	.777	**51°**	0.890
.698	**40°**	.643	.839	1.305	1.556	1.192	.766	**50°**	0.873
.716	**41°**	.656	.869	1.325	1.524	1.150	.755	**49°**	0.855
.733	**42°**	.669	.900	1.346	1.494	1.111	.743	**48°**	0.838
.750	**43°**	.682	.933	1.367	1.466	1.072	.731	**47°**	0.820
.768	**44°**	.695	0.966	1.390	1.440	1.036	.719	**46°**	0.803
.785	**45°**	.707	1.000	1.414	1.414	1.000	.707	**45°**	0.785
Rad.	**Deg.**	**Cos**	**Cot**	**Csc**	**Sec**	**Tan**	**Sin**	**Deg.**	**Rad.**

V. FOUR-PLACE LOGARITHMS OF NUMBERS

N	0	1	2	3	4	5	6	7	8	9
10	.0000	0043	0086	0128	0170	0212	0253	0294	0334	0374
11	.0414	0453	0492	0531	0569	0607	0645	0682	0719	0755
12	.0792	0828	0864	0899	0934	0969	1004	1038	1072	1106
13	.1139	1173	1206	1239	1271	1303	1335	1367	1399	1430
14	.1461	1492	1523	1553	1584	1614	1644	1673	1703	1732
15	.1761	1790	1818	1847	1875	1903	1931	1959	1987	2014
16	.2041	2068	2095	2122	2148	2175	2201	2227	2253	2279
17	.2304	2330	2355	2380	2405	2430	2455	2480	2504	2529
18	.2553	2577	2601	2625	2648	2672	2695	2718	2742	2765
19	.2788	2810	2833	2856	2878	2900	2923	2945	2967	2989
20	.3010	3032	3054	3075	3096	3118	3139	3160	3181	3201
21	.3222	3243	3263	3284	3304	3324	3345	3365	3385	3404
22	.3424	3444	3464	3483	3502	3522	3541	3560	3579	3598
23	.3617	3636	3655	3674	3692	3711	3729	3747	3766	3784
24	.3802	3820	3838	3856	3874	3892	3909	3927	3945	3962
25	.3979	3997	4014	4031	4048	4065	4082	4099	4116	4133
26	.4150	4166	4183	4200	4216	4232	4249	4265	4281	4298
27	.4314	4330	4346	4362	4378	4393	4409	4425	4440	4456
28	.4472	4487	4502	4518	4533	4548	4564	4579	4594	4609
29	.4624	4639	4654	4669	4683	4698	4713	4728	4742	4757
30	.4771	4786	4800	4814	4829	4843	4857	4871	4886	4900
31	.4914	4928	4942	4955	4969	4983	4997	5011	5024	5038
32	.5051	5065	5079	5092	5105	5119	5132	5145	5159	5172
33	.5185	5198	5211	5224	5237	5250	5263	5276	5289	5302
34	.5315	5328	5340	5353	5366	5378	5391	5403	5416	5428
35	.5441	5453	5465	5478	5490	5502	5514	5527	5539	5551
36	.5563	5575	5587	5599	5611	5623	5635	5647	5658	5670
37	.5682	5694	5705	5717	5729	5740	5752	5763	5775	5786
38	.5798	5809	5821	5832	5843	5855	5866	5877	5888	5899
39	.5911	5922	5933	5944	5955	5966	5977	5988	5999	6010
40	.6021	6031	6042	6053	6064	6075	6085	6096	6107	6117
41	.6128	6138	6149	6160	6170	6180	6191	6201	6212	6222
42	.6232	6243	6253	6263	6274	6284	6294	6304	6314	6325
43	.6335	6345	6355	6365	6375	6385	6395	6405	6415	6425
44	.6435	6444	6454	6464	6474	6484	6493	6503	6513	6522
45	.6532	6542	6551	6561	6571	6580	6590	6599	6609	6618
46	.6628	6637	6646	6656	6665	6675	6684	6693	6702	6712
47	.6721	6730	6739	6749	6758	6767	6776	6785	6794	6803
48	.6812	6821	6830	6839	6848	6857	6866	6875	6884	6893
49	.6902	6911	6920	6928	6937	6946	6955	6964	6972	6981
50	.6990	6998	7007	7016	7024	7033	7042	7050	7059	7067
N	**0**	**1**	**2**	**3**	**4**	**5**	**6**	**7**	**8**	**9**

Prop. Parts

	28	27	26
1	2.8	2.7	2.6
2	5.6	5.4	5.2
3	8.4	8.1	7.8
4	11.2	10.8	10.4
5	14.0	13.5	13.0
6	16.8	16.2	15.6
7	19.6	18.9	18.2
8	22.4	21.6	20.8
9	25.2	24.3	23.4

	22	21	20
1	2.2	2.1	2.0
2	4.4	4.2	4.0
3	6.6	6.3	6.0
4	8.8	8.4	8.0
5	11.0	10.5	10.0
6	13.2	12.6	12.0
7	15.4	14.7	14.0
8	17.6	16.8	16.0
9	19.8	18.9	18.0

	16	15	14
1	1.6	1.5	1.4
2	3.2	3.0	2.8
3	4.8	4.5	4.2
4	6.4	6.0	5.6
5	8.0	7.5	7.0
6	9.6	9.0	8.4
7	11.2	10.5	9.8
8	12.8	12.0	11.2
9	14.4	13.5	12.6

	13	12	11
1	1.3	1.2	1.1
2	2.6	2.4	2.2
3	3.9	3.6	3.3
4	5.2	4.8	4.4
5	6.5	6.0	5.5
6	7.8	7.2	6.6
7	9.1	8.4	7.7
8	10.4	9.6	8.8
9	11.7	10.8	9.9

	43	42	41	40	39		38	37	36	35	34		33	32	31	30	29	
1	4.3	4.2	4.1	4.0	3.9	1	3.8	3.7	3.6	3.5	3.4	1	3.3	3.2	3.1	3.0	2.9	1
2	8.6	8.4	8.2	8.0	7.8	2	7.6	7.4	7.2	7.0	6.8	2	6.6	6.4	6.2	6.0	5.8	2
3	12.9	12.6	12.3	12.0	11.7	3	11.4	11.1	10.8	10.5	10.2	3	9.9	9.6	9.3	9.0	8.7	3
4	17.2	16.8	16.4	16.0	15.6	4	15.2	14.8	14.4	14.0	13.6	4	13.2	12.8	12.4	12.0	11.6	4
5	21.5	21.0	20.5	20.0	19.5	5	19.0	18.5	18.0	17.5	17.0	5	16.5	16.0	15.5	15.0	14.5	5
6	25.8	25.2	24.6	24.0	23.4	6	22.8	22.2	21.6	21.0	20.4	6	19.8	19.2	18.6	18.0	17.4	6
7	30.1	29.4	28.7	28.0	27.3	7	26.6	25.9	25.2	24.5	23.8	7	23.1	22.4	21.7	21.0	20.3	7
8	34.4	33.6	32.8	32.0	31.2	8	30.4	29.6	28.8	28.0	27.2	8	26.4	25.6	24.8	24.0	23.2	8
9	38.7	37.8	36.9	36.0	35.1	9	34.2	33.3	32.4	31.5	30.6	9	29.7	28.8	27.9	27.0	26.1	9

V. FOUR-PLACE LOGARITHMS OF NUMBERS

Prop. Parts

	25	24	23
1	2.5	2.4	2.3
2	5.0	4.8	4.6
3	7.5	7.2	6.9
4	10.0	9.6	9.2
5	12.5	12.0	11.5
6	15.0	14.4	13.8
7	17.5	16.8	16.1
8	20.0	19.2	18.4
9	22.5	21.6	20.7

	19	18	17
1	1.9	1.8	1.7
2	3.8	3.6	3.4
3	5.7	5.4	5.1
4	7.6	7.2	6.8
5	9.5	9.0	8.5
6	11.4	10.8	10.2
7	13.3	12.6	11.9
8	15.2	14.4	13.6
9	17.1	16.2	15.3

	10	9
1	1.0	0.9
2	2.0	1.8
3	3.0	2.7
4	4.0	3.6
5	5.0	4.5
6	6.0	5.4
7	7.0	6.3
8	8.0	7.2
9	9.0	8.1

	8	7
1	0.8	0.7
2	1.6	1.4
3	2.4	2.1
4	3.2	2.8
5	4.0	3.5
6	4.8	4.2
7	5.6	4.9
8	6.4	5.6
9	7.2	6.3

	6	5	4
1	0.6	0.5	0.4
2	1.2	1.0	0.8
3	1.8	1.5	1.2
4	2.4	2.0	1.6
5	3.0	2.5	2.0
6	3.6	3.0	2 4
7	4.2	3.5	2.8
8	4.8	4.0	3.2
9	5.4	4.5	3.6

N	0	1	2	3	4	5	6	7	8	9
50	.6990	6998	7007	7016	7024	7033	7042	7050	7059	7067
51	.7076	7084	7093	7101	7110	7118	7126	7135	7143	7152
52	.7160	7168	7177	7185	7193	7202	7210	7218	7226	7235
53	.7243	7251	7259	7267	7275	7284	7292	7300	7308	7316
54	.7324	7332	7340	7348	7356	7364	7372	7380	7388	7396
55	.7404	7412	7419	7427	7435	7443	7451	7459	7466	7474
56	.7482	7490	7497	7505	7513	7520	7528	7536	7543	7551
57	.7559	7566	7574	7582	7589	7597	7604	7612	7619	7627
58	.7634	7642	7649	7657	7664	7672	7679	7686	7694	7701
59	.7709	7716	7723	7731	7738	7745	7752	7760	7767	7774
60	.7782	7789	7796	7803	7810	7818	7825	7832	7839	7846
61	.7853	7860	7868	7875	7882	7889	7896	7903	7910	7917
62	.7924	7931	7938	7945	7952	7959	7966	7973	7980	7987
63	.7993	8000	8007	8014	8021	8028	8035	8041	8048	8055
64	.8062	8069	8075	8082	8089	8096	8102	8109	8116	8122
65	.8129	8136	8142	8149	8156	8162	8169	8176	8182	8189
66	.8195	8202	8209	8215	8222	8228	8235	8241	8248	8254
67	.8261	8267	8274	8280	8287	8293	8299	8306	8312	8319
68	.8325	8331	8338	8344	8351	8357	8363	8370	8376	8382
69	.8388	8395	8401	8407	8414	8420	8426	8432	8439	8445
70	.8451	8457	8463	8470	8476	8482	8488	8494	8500	8506
71	.8513	8519	8525	8531	8537	8543	8549	8555	8561	8567
72	.8573	8579	8585	8591	8597	8603	8609	8615	8621	8627
73	.8633	8639	8645	8651	8657	8663	8669	8675	8681	8686
74	.8692	8698	8704	8710	8716	8722	8727	8733	8739	8745
75	.8751	8756	8762	8768	8774	8779	8785	8791	8797	8802
76	.8808	8814	8820	8825	8831	8837	8842	8848	8854	8859
77	.8865	8871	8876	8882	8887	8893	8899	8904	8910	8915
78	.8921	8927	8932	8938	8943	8949	8954	8960	8965	8971
79	.8976	8982	8987	8993	8998	9004	9009	9015	9020	9025
80	.9031	9036	9042	9047	9053	9058	9063	9069	9074	9079
81	.9085	9090	9096	9101	9106	9112	9117	9122	9128	9133
82	.9138	9143	9149	9154	9159	9165	9170	9175	9180	9186
83	.9191	9196	9201	9206	9212	9217	9222	9227	9232	9238
84	.9243	9248	9253	9258	9263	9269	9274	9279	9284	9289
85	.9294	9299	9304	9309	9315	9320	9325	9330	9335	9340
86	.9345	9350	9355	9360	9365	9370	9375	9380	9385	9390
87	.9395	9400	9405	9410	9415	9420	9425	9430	9435	9440
88	.9445	9450	9455	9460	9465	9469	9474	9479	9484	9489
89	.9494	9499	9504	9509	9513	9518	9523	9528	9533	9538
90	.9542	9547	9552	9557	9562	9566	9571	9576	9581	9586
91	.9590	9595	9600	9605	9609	9614	9619	9624	9628	9633
92	.9638	9643	9647	9652	9657	9661	9666	9671	9675	9680
93	.9685	9689	9694	9699	9703	9708	9713	9717	9722	9727
94	.9731	9736	9741	9745	9750	9754	9759	9763	9768	9773
95	.9777	9782	9786	9791	9795	9800	9805	9809	9814	9818
96	.9823	9827	9832	9836	9841	9845	9850	9854	9859	9863
97	.9868	9872	9877	9881	9886	9890	9894	9899	9903	9908
98	.9912	9917	9921	9926	9930	9934	9939	9943	9948	9952
99	.9956	9961	9965	9969	9974	9978	9983	9987	9991	9996
N	**0**	**1**	**2**	**3**	**4**	**5**	**6**	**7**	**8**	**9**

VI. FOUR-PLACE LOGARITHMS OF FUNCTIONS: 0° — 6°; 84° — 90°

→	L Sin*	d	L Tan*	c d	L Cot	L Cos*	
0° 00′						10.0000	90° 00′
10′	7.4637		7.4637		2.5363	.0000	89° 50′
20′	.7648		.7648		.2352	.0000	40′
30′	7.9408		7.9409		2.0591	.0000	30′
40′	8.0658		8.0658		1.9342	.0000	20′
0° 50′	.1627		.1627		.8373	10.0000	10′
1° 00′	8.2419		8.2419		1.7581	9.9999	89° 00′
10′	.3088		.3089		.6911	.9999	88° 50′
20′	.3668		.3669		.6331	.9999	40′
30′	.4179		.4181		.5819	.9999	30′
40′	.4637		.4638		.5362	.9998	20′
1° 50′	.5050		.5053		.4947	.9998	10′
2° 00′	8.5428		8.5431		1.4569	9.9997	88° 00′
10′	.5776		.5779		.4221	.9997	87° 50′
20′	.6097		.6101		.3899	.9996	40′
30′	.6397		.6401		.3599	.9996	30′
40′	.6677		.6682		.3318	.9995	20′
2° 50′	.6940		.6945		.3055	.9995	10′
3° 00′	8.7188		8.7194		1.2806	9.9994	87° 00′
10′	.7423		.7429		.2571	.9993	86° 50′
20′	.7645	222	.7652	223	.2348	.9993	40′
30′	.7857	212	.7865	213	.2135	.9992	30′
40′	.8059	202	.8067	202	.1933	.9991	20′
3° 50′	.8251	192	.8261	194	.1739	.9990	10′
4° 00′	8.8436	185	8.8446	185	1.1554	9.9989	86° 00′
10′	.8613	177	.8624	178	.1376	.9989	85° 50′
20′	.8783	170	.8795	171	.1205	.9988	40′
30′	.8946	163	.8960	165	.1040	.9987	30′
40′	.9104	158	.9118	158	.0882	.9986	20′
4° 50′	.9256	152	.9272	154	.0728	.9985	10′
5° 00′	8.9403	147	8.9420	148	1.0580	9.9983	85° 00′
10′	.9545	142	.9563	143	.0437	.9982	84° 50′
20′	.9682	137	.9701	138	.0299	.9981	40′
30′	.9816	134	.9836	135	.0164	.9980	30′
40′	8.9945	129	8.9966	130	1.0034	.9979	20′
5° 50′	9.0070	125	9.0093	127	0.9907	.9977	10′
6° 00′	9.0192	122	9.0216	123	0.9784	9.9976	84° 00′
	L Cos*	d	L Cot*	c d	L Tan	L Sin*	←

Prop. Parts

To avoid interpolating, for angles between 0° and 3°, or between 87° and 90°, use Table IX.

	2	223	222	213
1	0.2	22	22	21
2	0.4	45	44	43
3	0.6	67	67	64
4	0.8	89	89	85
5	1.0	112	111	106
6	1.2	134	133	128
7	1.4	156	155	149
8	1.6	178	178	170
9	1.8	201	200	192

	3	212	202	194
1	0.3	21	20	19
2	0.6	42	40	39
3	0.9	64	61	58
4	1.2	85	81	78
5	1.5	106	101	97
6	1.8	127	121	116
7	2.1	148	141	136
8	2.4	170	162	155
9	2.7	191	182	175

	192	185	178
1	19	18	18
2	38	37	36
3	58	56	53
4	77	74	71
5	96	92	89
6	115	111	107
7	134	130	125
8	154	148	142
9	173	166	160

	177	171	170	165	163
1	18	17	17	16	16
2	35	34	34	33	33
3	53	51	51	50	49
4	71	68	68	66	65
5	88	86	85	82	82
6	106	103	102	99	98
7	124	120	119	116	114
8	142	137	136	132	130
9	159	154	153	148	147

	158	154	152	148	147
1	16	15	15	15	15
2	32	31	30	30	29
3	47	46	46	44	44
4	63	62	61	59	59
5	79	77	76	74	74
6	95	92	91	89	88
7	111	108	106	104	103
8	126	123	122	118	118
9	142	139	137	133	132

	143	142	138	137	135
1	14	14	14	14	14
2	29	28	28	27	27
3	43	43	41	41	40
4	57	57	55	55	54
5	72	71	69	68	68
6	86	85	83	82	81
7	100	99	97	96	94
8	114	114	110	110	108
9	129	128	124	123	122

	134	130	129	127	125
1	13	13	13	13	12
2	27	26	26	25	25
3	40	39	39	38	38
4	54	52	52	51	50
5	67	65	64	64	62
6	80	78	77	76	75
7	94	91	90	89	88
8	107	104	103	102	100
9	121	117	116	114	112

	123	122	120	119	117
1	12	12	12	12	12
2	25	24	24	24	23
3	37	37	36	36	35
4	49	49	48	48	47
5	62	61	60	60	58
6	74	73	72	71	70
7	86	85	84	83	82
8	98	98	96	95	94
9	111	110	108	107	105

	115	114	113	111	109
1	12	11	11	11	11
2	23	23	23	22	22
3	34	34	34	33	33
4	46	46	45	44	44
5	58	57	56	56	54
6	69	68	68	67	65
7	80	80	79	78	76
8	92	91	90	89	87
9	104	103	102	100	98

→	L Sin*	d	L Tan*	c d	L Cot	L Cos*	
6° 00′	9.0192	119	9.0216	120	0.9784	9.9976	84° 00′
10′	.0311	115	.0336	117	.9664	.9975	83° 50′
20′	.0426	113	.0453	114	.9547	.9973	40′
30′	.0539	109	.0567	111	.9433	.9972	30′
40′	.0648	107	.0678	108	.9322	.9971	20′
6° 50′	.0755	104	.0786	105	.9214	.9969	10′
7° 00′	9.0859	102	9.0891	104	0.9109	9.9968	83° 00′
10′	.0961	99	.0995	101	.9005	.9966	82° 50′
20′	.1060	97	.1096	98	.8904	.9964	40′
30′	.1157	95	.1194	97	.8806	.9963	30′
40′	.1252	93	.1291	94	.8709	.9961	20′
7° 50′	.1345	91	.1385	93	.8615	.9959	10′
8° 00′	9.1436	89	9.1478	91	0.8522	9.9958	82° 00′
10′	.1525	87	.1569	89	.8431	.9956	81° 50′
20′	.1612	85	.1658	87	.8342	.9954	40′
30′	.1697	84	.1745	86	.8255	.9952	30′
40′	.1781	82	.1831	84	.8169	.9950	20′
8° 50′	.1863	80	.1915	82	.8085	.9948	10′
9° 00′	9.1943	79	9.1997	81	0.8003	9.9946	81° 00′
10′	.2022	78	.2078	80	.7922	.9944	80° 50′
20′	.2100	76	.2158	78	.7842	.9942	40′
30′	.2176	75	.2236	77	.7764	.9940	30′
40′	.2251	73	.2313	76	.7687	.9938	20′
9° 50′	.2324	73	.2389	74	.7611	.9936	10′
10° 00′	9.2397	71	9.2463	73	0.7537	9.9934	80° 00′
10′	.2468	70	.2536	73	.7464	.9931	79° 50′
20′	.2538	68	.2609	71	.7391	.9929	40′
30′	.2606	68	.2680	70	.7320	.9927	30′
40′	.2674	66	.2750	69	.7250	.9924	20′
10° 50′	.2740	66	.2819	68	.7181	.9922	10′
11° 00′	9.2806	64	9.2887	66	0.7113	9.9919	79° 00′
10′	.2870	64	.2953	67	.7047	.9917	78° 50′
20′	.2934	63	.3020	65	.6980	.9914	40′
30′	.2997	61	.3085	64	.6915	.9912	30′
40′	.3058	61	.3149	63	.6851	.9909	20′
11° 50′	.3119	60	.3212	63	.6788	.9907	10′
12° 00′	9.3179		9.3275		0.6725	9.9904	78° 00′
	L Cos*	d	L Cot*	c d	L Tan	L Sin*	←

Prop. Parts

Subtract 10 *from each entry in the columns marked with "*" throughout the table.*

	108	107	105
1	10.8	10.7	10.5
2	21.6	21.4	21.0
3	32.4	32.1	31.5
4	43.2	42.8	42.0
5	54.0	53.5	52.5
6	64.8	64.2	63.0
7	75.6	74.9	73.5
8	86.4	85.6	84.0
9	97.2	96.3	94.5

	104	102	101
1	10.4	10.2	10.1
2	20.8	20.4	20.2
3	31.2	30.6	30.3
4	41.6	40.8	40.4
5	52.0	51.0	50.5
6	62.4	61.2	60.6
7	72.8	71.4	70.7
8	83.2	81.6	80.8
9	93.6	91.8	90.9

	99	98	97	95
1	9.9	9.8	9.7	9.5
2	19.8	19.6	19.4	19.0
3	29.7	29.4	29.1	28.5
4	39.6	39.2	38.8	38.0
5	49.5	49.0	48.5	47.5
6	59.4	58.8	58.2	57.0
7	69.3	68.6	67.9	66.5
8	79.2	78.4	77.6	76.0
9	89.1	88.2	87.3	85.5

	94	93	91	89		87	86	85	84	82		81	80	79	78	77	
1	9.4	9.3	9.1	8.9	1	8.7	8.6	8.5	8.4	8.2	1	8.1	8	7.9	7.8	7.7	1
2	18.8	18.6	18.2	17.8	2	17.4	17.2	17.0	16.8	16.4	2	16.2	16	15.8	15.6	15.4	2
3	28.2	27.9	27.3	26.7	3	26.1	25.8	25.5	25.2	24.6	3	24.3	24	23.7	23.4	23.1	3
4	37.6	37.2	36.4	35.6	4	34.8	34.4	34.0	33.6	32.8	4	32.4	32	31.6	31.2	30.8	4
5	47.0	46.5	45.5	44.5	5	43.5	43.0	42.5	42.0	41.0	5	40.5	40	39.5	39.0	38.5	5
6	56.4	55.8	54.6	53.4	6	52.2	51.6	51.0	50.4	49.2	6	48.6	48	47.4	46.8	46.2	6
7	65.8	65.1	63.7	62.3	7	60.9	60.2	59.5	58.8	57.4	7	56.7	56	55.3	54.6	53.9	7
8	75.2	74.4	72.8	71.2	8	69.6	68.8	68.0	67.2	65.6	8	64.8	64	63.2	62.4	61.6	8
9	84.6	83.7	81.9	80.1	9	78.3	77.4	76.5	75.6	73.8	9	72.9	72	71.1	70.2	69.3	9

	76	75	74	73	71		70	69	68	67	66		65	64	63	61	60	
1	7.6	7.5	7.4	7.3	7.1	1	7	6.9	6.8	6.7	6.6	1	6.5	6.4	6.3	6.1	6	1
2	15.2	15.0	14.8	14.6	14.2	2	14	13.8	13.6	13.4	13.2	2	13.0	12.8	12.6	12.2	12	2
3	22.8	22.5	22.2	21.9	21.3	3	21	20.7	20.4	20.1	19.8	3	19.5	19.2	18.9	18.3	18	3
4	30.4	30.0	29.6	29.2	28.4	4	28	27.6	27.2	26.8	26.4	4	26.0	25.6	25.2	24.4	24	4
5	38.0	37.5	37.0	36.5	35.5	5	35	34.5	34.0	33.5	33.0	5	32.5	32.0	31.5	30.5	30	5
6	45.6	45.0	44.4	43.8	42.6	6	42	41.4	40.8	40.2	39.6	6	39.0	38.4	37.8	36.6	36	6
7	53.2	52.5	51.8	51.1	49.7	7	49	48.3	47.6	46.9	46.2	7	45.5	44.8	44.1	42.7	42	7
8	60.8	60.0	59.2	58.4	56.8	8	56	55.2	54.4	53.6	52.8	8	52.0	51.2	50.4	48.8	48	8
9	68.4	67.5	66.6	65.7	63.9	9	63	62.1	61.2	60.3	59.4	9	58.5	57.6	56.7	54.9	54	9

→	L Sin *	d	L Tan *	c d	L Cot	L Cos *	
12° 00′	9.3179	59	9.3275	61	0.6725	9.9904	**78° 00′**
10′	.3238	58	.3336	61	.6664	.9901	77° 50′
20′	.3296	57	.3397	61	.6603	.9899	40′
30′	.3353	57	.3458	59	.6542	.9896	30′
40′	.3410	56	.3517	59	.6483	.9893	20′
12° 50′	.3466	55	.3576	58	.6424	.9890	10′
13° 00′	9.3521	54	9.3634	57	0.6366	9.9887	**77° 00′**
10′	.3575	54	.3691	57	.6309	.9884	76° 50′
20′	.3629	53	.3748	56	.6252	.9881	40′
30′	.3682	52	.3804	55	.6196	.9878	30′
40′	.3734	52	.3859	55	.6141	.9875	20′
13° 50′	.3786	51	.3914	54	.6086	.9872	10′
14° 00′	9.3837	50	9.3968	53	0.6032	9.9869	**76° 00′**
10′	.3887	50	.4021	53	.5979	.9866	75° 50′
20′	.3937	49	.4074	53	.5926	.9863	40′
30′	.3986	49	.4127	51	.5873	.9859	30′
40′	.4035	48	.4178	52	.5822	.9856	20′
14° 50′	.4083	47	.4230	51	.5770	.9853	10′
15° 00′	9.4130	47	9.4281	50	0.5719	9.9849	**75° 00′**
10′	.4177	46	.4331	50	.5669	.9846	74° 50′
20′	.4223	46	.4381	49	.5619	.9843	40′
30′	.4269	45	.4430	49	.5570	.9839	30′
40′	.4314	45	.4479	48	.5521	.9836	20′
15° 50′	.4359	44	.4527	48	.5473	.9832	10′
16° 00′	9.4403	44	9.4575	47	0.5425	9.9828	**74° 00′**
10′	.4447	44	.4622	47	.5378	.9825	73° 50′
20′	.4491	42	.4669	47	.5331	.9821	40′
30′	.4533	43	.4716	46	.5284	.9817	30′
40′	.4576	42	.4762	46	.5238	.9814	20′
16° 50′	.4618	41	.4808	45	.5192	.9810	10′
17° 00′	9.4659	41	9.4853	45	0.5147	9.9806	**73° 00′**
10′	.4700	41	.4898	45	.5102	.9802	72° 50′
20′	.4741	40	.4943	44	.5057	.9798	40′
30′	.4781	40	.4987	44	.5013	.9794	30′
40′	.4821	40	.5031	44	.4969	.9790	20′
17° 50′	.4861	39	.5075	43	.4925	.9786	10′
18° 00′	9.4900	39	9.5118	43	0.4882	9.9782	**72° 00′**
10′	.4939	38	.5161	42	.4839	.9778	71° 50′
20′	.4977	38	.5203	42	.4797	.9774	40′
30′	.5015	37	.5245	42	.4755	.9770	30′
40′	.5052	38	.5287	42	.4713	.9765	20′
18° 50′	.5090	36	.5329	41	.4671	.9761	10′
19° 00′	9.5126		9.5370		0.4630	9.9757	**71° 00′**
	L Cos *	d	L Cot *	c d	L Tan	L Sin *	←

Prop. Parts

	61	59	58
1	6.1	5.9	5.8
2	12.2	11.8	11.6
3	18.3	17.7	17.4
4	24.4	23.6	23.2
5	30.5	29.5	29.0
6	36.6	35.4	34.8
7	42 7	41.3	40.6
8	48.8	47.2	46.4
9	54.9	53.1	52.2

	57	56	55
1	5.7	5.6	5.5
2	11.4	11.2	11.0
3	17.1	16.8	16.5
4	22.8	22.4	22.0
5	28.5	28.0	27.5
6	34.2	33.6	33.0
7	39.9	39.2	38.5
8	45.6	44.8	44.0
9	51.3	50.4	49.5

	54	53	52
1	5.4	5.3	5.2
2	10.8	10.6	10.4
3	16.2	15.9	15.6
4	21.6	21.2	20.8
5	27.0	26.5	26.0
6	32.4	31.8	31.2
7	37.8	37.1	36.4
8	43.2	42.4	41.6
9	48.6	47.7	46.8

	51	50	49
1	5.1	5	4.9
2	10.2	10	9.8
3	15.3	15	14.7
4	20.4	20	19.6
5	25.5	25	24.5
6	30.6	30	29.4
7	35.7	35	34.3
8	40.8	40	39.2
9	45.9	45	44.1

	48	47	46		45	44	43	42		41	40	39	
1	4.8	4.7	4.6	1	4.5	4.4	4.3	4.2	1	4.1	4	3.9	1
2	9.6	9.4	9.2	2	9.0	8.8	8.6	8.4	2	8.2	8	7.8	2
3	14.4	14.1	13.8	3	13.5	13.2	12.9	12.6	3	12.3	12	11.7	3
4	19.2	18.8	18.4	4	18.0	17.6	17.2	16.8	4	16.4	16	15.6	4
5	24.0	23.5	23.0	5	22.5	22.0	21.5	21.0	5	20.5	20	19.5	5
6	28.8	28.2	27.6	6	27.0	26.4	25.8	25.2	6	24.6	24	23.4	6
7	33.6	32.9	32.2	7	31.5	30.8	30.1	29.4	7	28.7	28	27.3	7
8	38.4	37.6	36.8	8	36.0	35.2	34.4	33.6	8	32.8	32	31.2	8
9	43.2	42.3	41.4	9	40.5	39.6	38.7	37.8	9	36.9	36	35.1	9

* Subtract 10 from each entry in this column.

→	L Sin *	d	L Tan *	c d	L Cot	L Cos *	
19° 00′	9.5126	37	9.5370	41	0.4630	9.9757	**71° 00′**
10′	.5163	36	.5411	40	.4589	.9752	70° 50′
20′	.5199	36	.5451	40	.4549	.9748	40′
30′	.5235	35	.5491	40	.4509	.9743	30′
40′	.5270	36	.5531	40	.4469	.9739	20′
19° 50′	.5306	35	.5571	40	.4429	.9734	10′
20° 00′	9.5341	34	9.5611	39	0.4389	9.9730	**70° 00′**
10′	.5375	34	.5650	39	.4350	.9725	69° 50′
20′	.5409	34	.5689	38	.4311	.9721	40′
30′	.5443	34	.5727	39	.4273	.9716	30′
40′	.5477	33	.5766	38	.4234	.9711	20′
20° 50′	.5510	33	.5804	38	.4196	.9706	10′
21° 00′	9.5543	33	9.5842	37	0.4158	9.9702	**69° 00′**
10′	.5576	33	.5879	38	.4121	.9697	68° 50′
20′	.5609	32	.5917	37	.4083	.9692	40′
30′	.5641	32	.5954	37	4046	.9687	30′
40′	.5673	31	.5991	37	.4009	.9682	20′
21° 50′	.5704	32	.6028	36	.3972	.9677	10′
22° 00′	9.5736	31	9.6064	36	0.3936	9.9672	**68° 00′**
10′	.5767	31	.6100	36	.3900	.9667	67° 50′
20′	.5798	30	.6136	36	.3864	.9661	40′
30′	.5828	31	.6172	36	.3828	.9656	30′
40′	.5859	30	.6208	35	.3792	.9651	20′
22° 50′	.5889	30	.6243	36	.3757	.9646	10′
23° 00′	9.5919	29	9.6279	35	0.3721	9.9640	**67° 00′**
10′	.5948	30	.6314	34	.3686	.9635	66° 50′
20′	.5978	29	.6348	35	.3652	.9629	40′
30′	.6007	29	.6383	34	.3617	.9624	30′
40′	.6036	29	.6417	35	.3583	.9618	20′
23° 50′	.6065	28	.6452	34	.3548	.9613	10′
24° 00′	9.6093	28	9.6486	34	0.3514	9.9607	**66° 00′**
10′	.6121	28	.6520	33	.3480	.9602	65° 50′
20′	.6149	28	.6553	34	.3447	.9596	40′
30′	.6177	28	.6587	33	.3413	.9590	30′
40′	.6205	27	.6620	34	.3380	.9584	20′
24° 50′	.6232	27	.6654	33	.3346	.9579	10′
25° 00′	9.6259	27	9.6687	33	0.3313	9.9573	**65° 00′**
10′	.6286	27	.6720	32	.3280	.9567	64° 50′
20′	.6313	27	.6752	33	.3248	.9561	40′
30′	.6340	26	.6785	32	.3215	.9555	30′
40′	.6366	26	.6817	33	.3183	.9549	20′
25° 50′	.6392	26	.6850	32	.3150	.9543	10′
26° 00′	9.6418	26	9.6882	32	0.3118	9.9537	**64° 00′**
10′	.6444	26	.6914	32	.3086	.9530	63° 50′
20′	.6470	25	.6946	31	.3054	.9524	40′
30′	.6495	26	.6977	32	.3023	.9518	30′
40′	.6521	25	.7009	31	.2991	.9512	20′
26° 50′	.6546	24	.7040	32	.2960	.9505	10′
27° 00′	9.6570		9.7072		0.2928	9.9499	**63° 00′**
	L Cos *	d	L Cot *	c d	L Tan	L Sin *	←

Prop. Parts

	2	3	4
1	0.2	0.3	0.4
2	0.4	0.6	0.8
3	0.6	0.9	1.2
4	0.8	1.2	1.6
5	1.0	1.5	2.0
6	1.2	1.8	2.4
7	1.4	2.1	2.8
8	1.6	2.4	3.2
9	1.8	2.7	3.6

	5	6	7
1	0.5	0.6	0.7
2	1.0	1.2	1.4
3	1.5	1.8	2.1
4	2.0	2.4	2.8
5	2.5	3.0	3.5
6	3.0	3.6	4.2
7	3.5	4.2	4.9
8	4.0	4.8	5.6
9	4.5	5.4	6.3

	38	37	36
1	3.8	3.7	3.6
2	7.6	7.4	7.2
3	11.4	11.1	10.8
4	15.2	14.8	14.4
5	19.0	18.5	18.0
6	22.8	22.2	21.6
7	26.6	25.9	25.2
8	30.4	29.6	28.8
9	34.2	33.3	32.4

	35	34	33
1	3.5	3.4	3.3
2	7.0	6.8	6.6
3	10.5	10.2	9.9
4	14.0	13.6	13.2
5	17.5	17.0	16.5
6	21.0	20.4	19.8
7	24.5	23.8	23.1
8	28.0	27.2	26.4
9	31.5	30.6	29.7

	32	31	30	29		28	27	26	25	24	
1	3.2	3.1	3	2.9	1	2.8	2.7	2.6	2.5	2.4	1
2	6.4	6.2	6	5.8	2	5.6	5.4	5.2	5.0	4.8	2
3	9.6	9.3	9	8.7	3	8.4	8.1	7.8	7.5	7.2	3
4	12.8	12.4	12	11.6	4	11.2	10.8	10.4	10.0	9.6	4
5	16.0	15.5	15	14.5	5	14.0	13.5	13.0	12.5	12.0	5
6	19.2	18.6	18	17.4	6	16.8	16.2	15.6	15.0	14.4	6
7	22.4	21.7	21	20.3	7	19.6	18.9	18.2	17.5	16.8	7
8	25.6	24.8	24	23.2	8	22.4	21.6	20.8	20.0	19.2	8
9	28.8	27.9	27	26.1	9	25.2	24.3	23.4	22.5	21.6	9

VI. FOUR-PLACE LOGARITHMS OF FUNCTIONS: 27° — 36°; 54° — 63°

⟶	L Sin *	d	L Tan *	c d	L Cot	L Cos *	
27° 00′	9.6570		9.7072		0.2928	9.9499	**63° 00′**
		25		31			
10′	.6595		.7103		.2897	.9492	62° 50′
		25		31			
20′	.6620		.7134		.2866	.9486	40′
		24		31			
30′	.6644		.7165		.2835	.9479	30′
		24		31			
40′	.6668		.7196		.2804	.9473	20′
		24		30			
27° 50′	.6692		.7226		.2774	.9466	10′
		24		31			
28° 00′	9.6716		9.7257		0.2743	9.9459	**62° 00′**
		24		30			
10′	.6740		.7287		.2713	.9453	61° 50′
		23		30			
20′	.6763		.7317		.2683	.9446	40′
		24		31			
30′	.6787		.7348		.2652	.9439	30′
		23		30			
40′	.6810		.7378		.2622	.9432	20′
		23		30			
28° 50′	.6833		.7408		.2592	.9425	10′
		23		30			
29° 00′	9.6856		9.7438		0.2562	9.9418	**61° 00′**
		22		29			
10′	.6878		.7467		.2533	.9411	60° 50′
		23		30			
20′	.6901		.7497		.2503	.9404	40′
		22		29			
30′	.6923		.7526		.2474	.9397	30′
		23		30			
40′	.6946		.7556		.2444	.9390	20′
		22		29			
29° 50′	.6968		.7585		.2415	.9383	10′
		22		29			
30° 00′	9.6990		9.7614		0.2386	9.9375	**60° 00′**
		22		30			
10′	.7012		.7644		.2356	.9368	59° 50′
		21		29			
20′	.7033		.7673		.2327	.9361	40′
		22		28			
30′	.7055		.7701		.2299	.9353	30′
		21		29			
40′	.7076		.7730		.2270	.9346	20′
		21		29			
30° 50′	.7097		.7759		.2241	.9338	10′
		21		29			
31° 00′	9.7118		9.7788		0.2212	9.9331	**59° 00′**
		21		28			
10′	.7139		.7816		.2184	.9323	58° 50′
		21		29			
20′	.7160		.7845		.2155	.9315	40′
		21		28			
30′	.7181		.7873		.2127	.9308	30′
		20		29			
40′	.7201		.7902		.2098	.9300	20′
		21		28			
31° 50′	.7222		.7930		.2070	.9292	10′
		20		28			
32° 00′	9.7242		9.7958		0.2042	9.9284	**58° 00′**
		20		28			
10′	.7262		.7986		.2014	.9276	57° 50′
		20		28			
20′	.7282		.8014		.1986	.9268	40′
		20		28			
30′	.7302		.8042		.1958	.9260	30′
		20		28			
40′	.7322		.8070		.1930	.9252	20′
		20		27			
32° 50′	.7342		.8097		.1903	.9244	10′
		19		28			
33° 00′	9.7361		9.8125		0.1875	9.9236	**57° 00′**
		19		28			
10′	.7380		.8153		.1847	.9228	56° 50′
		20		27			
20′	.7400		.8180		.1820	.9219	40′
		19		28			
30′	.7419		.8208		.1792	.9211	30′
		19		27			
40′	.7438		.8235		.1765	.9203	20′
		19		28			
33° 50′	.7457		.8263		.1737	.9194	10′
		19		27			
34° 00′	9.7476		9.8290		0.1710	9.9186	**56° 00′**
		18		27			
10′	.7494		.8317		.1683	.9177	55° 50′
		19		27			
20′	.7513		.8344		.1656	.9169	40′
		18		27			
30′	.7531		.8371		.1629	.9160	30′
		19		27			
40′	.7550		.8398		.1602	.9151	20′
		18		27			
34° 50′	.7568		.8425		.1575	.9142	10′
		18		27			
35° 00′	9.7586		9.8452		0.1548	9.9134	**55° 00′**
		18		27			
10′	.7604		.8479		.1521	.9125	54° 50′
		18		27			
20′	.7622		.8506		.1494	.9116	40′
		18		27			
30′	.7640		.8533		.1467	.9107	30′
		17		26			
40′	.7657		.8559		.1441	.9098	20′
		18		27			
35° 50′	.7675		.8586		.1414	.9089	10′
		17		27			
36° 00′	9.7692		9.8613		0.1387	9.9080	**54° 00′**
	L Cos *	d	L Cot *	c d	L Tan	L Sin *	⟵

Prop. Parts

	31	30	29
1	3.1	3	2.9
2	6.2	6	5.8
3	9.3	9	8.7
4	12.4	12	11.6
5	15.5	15	14.5
6	18.6	18	17.4
7	21.7	21	20.3
8	24.8	24	23.2
9	27.9	27	26.1

	28	27	26
1	2.8	2.7	2.6
2	5.6	5.4	5.2
3	8.4	8.1	7.8
4	11.2	10.8	10.4
5	14.0	13.5	13.0
6	16.8	16.2	15.6
7	19.6	18.9	18.2
8	22.4	21.6	20.8
9	25.2	24.3	23.4

	25	24
1	2.5	2.4
2	5.0	4.8
3	7.5	7.2
4	10.0	9.6
5	12.5	12.0
6	15.0	14.4
7	17.5	16.8
8	20.0	19.2
9	22.5	21.6

	23	22
1	2.3	2.2
2	4.6	4.4
3	6.9	6.6
4	9.2	8.8
5	11.5	11.0
6	13.8	13.2
7	16.1	15.4
8	18.4	17.6
9	20.7	19.8

	21	20
1	2.1	2
2	4.2	4
3	6.3	6
4	8.4	8
5	10.5	10
6	12.6	12
7	14.7	14
8	16.8	16
9	18.9	18

* Subtract 10 from each entry in this column.

VI. FOUR–PLACE LOGARITHMS OF FUNCTIONS: 36° — 45°; 45° — 54°

Prop. Parts

	19	18
1	1.9	1.8
2	3.8	3.6
3	5.7	5.4
4	7.6	7.2
5	9.5	9.0
6	11.4	10.8
7	13.3	12.6
8	15.2	14.4
9	17.1	16.2

	17	16	15
1	1.7	1.6	1.5
2	3.4	3.2	3.0
3	5.1	4.8	4.5
4	6.8	6.4	6.0
5	8.5	8.0	7.5
6	10.2	9.6	9.0
7	11.9	11.2	10.5
8	13.6	12.8	12.0
9	15.3	14.4	13.5

	14	13	12
1	1.4	1.3	1.2
2	2.8	2.6	2.4
3	4.2	3.9	3.6
4	5.6	5.2	4.8
5	7.0	6.5	6.0
6	8.4	7.8	7.2
7	9.8	9.1	8.4
8	11.2	10.4	9.6
9	12.6	11.7	10.8

	11	10	9
1	1.1	1.0	0.9
2	2.2	2.0	1.8
3	3.3	3.0	2.7
4	4.4	4.0	3.6
5	5.5	5.0	4.5
6	6.6	6.0	5.4
7	7.7	7.0	6.3
8	8.8	8.0	7.2
9	9.9	9.0	8.1

	8	7	6
1	0.8	0.7	0.6
2	1.6	1.4	1.2
3	2.4	2.1	1.8
4	3.2	2.8	2.4
5	4.0	3.5	3.0
6	4.8	4.2	3.6
7	5.6	4.9	4.2
8	6.4	5.6	4.8
9	7.2	6.3	5.4

→	L Sin *	d	L Tan *	c d	L Cot	L Cos *	
36° 00′	9.7692		9.8613		0.1387	9.9080	**54° 00′**
10′	.7710	18	.8639	26	.1361	.9070	53° 50′
20′	.7727	17	.8666	27	.1334	.9061	40′
30′	.7744	17	.8692	26	.1308	.9052	30′
40′	.7761	17	.8718	26	.1282	.9042	20′
36° 50′	.7778	17	.8745	27	.1255	.9033	10′
37° 00′	9.7795	17	9.8771	26	0.1229	9.9023	**53° 00′**
10′	.7811	16	.8797	26	.1203	.9014	52° 50′
20′	.7828	17	.8824	27	.1176	.9004	40′
30′	.7844	16	.8850	26	.1150	.8995	30′
40′	.7861	17	.8876	26	.1124	.8985	20′
37° 50′	.7877	16	.8902	26	.1098	.8975	10′
38° 00′	9.7893	16	9.8928	26	0.1072	9.8965	**52° 00′**
10′	.7910	17	.8954	26	.1046	.8955	51° 50′
20′	.7926	16	.8980	26	.1020	.8945	40′
30′	.7941	15	.9006	26	.0994	.8935	30′
40′	.7957	16	.9032	26	.0968	.8925	20′
38° 50′	.7973	16	.9058	26	.0942	.8915	10′
39° 00′	9.7989	16	9.9084	26	0.0916	9.8905	**51° 00′**
10′	.8004	15	.9110	26	.0890	.8895	50° 50′
20′	.8020	16	.9135	25	.0865	.8884	40′
30′	.8035	15	.9161	26	.0839	.8874	30′
40′	.8050	15	.9187	26	.0813	.8864	20′
39° 50′	.8066	16	.9212	25	.0788	.8853	10′
40° 00′	9.8081	15	9.9238	26	0.0762	9.8843	**50° 00′**
10′	.8096	15	.9264	26	.0736	.8832	49° 50′
20′	.8111	15	.9289	25	.0711	.8821	40′
30′	.8125	14	.9315	26	.0685	.8810	30′
40′	.8140	15	.9341	26	.0659	.8800	20′
40° 50′	.8155	15	.9366	25	.0634	.8789	10′
41° 00′	9.8169	14	9.9392	26	0.0608	9.8778	**49° 00′**
10′	.8184	15	.9417	25	.0583	.8767	48° 50′
20′	.8198	14	.9443	26	.0557	.8756	40′
30′	.8213	15	.9468	25	.0532	.8745	30′
40′	.8227	14	.9494	26	.0506	.8733	20′
41° 50′	.8241	14	.9519	25	.0481	.8722	10′
42° 00′	9.8255	14	9.9544	25	0.0456	9.8711	**48° 00′**
10′	.8269	14	.9570	26	.0430	.8699	47° 50′
20′	.8283	14	.9595	25	.0405	.8688	40′
30′	.8297	14	.9621	26	.0379	.8676	30′
40′	.8311	14	.9646	25	.0354	.8665	20′
42° 50′	.8324	13	.9671	25	.0329	.8653	10′
43° 00′	9.8338	14	9.9697	26	0.0303	9.8641	**47° 00′**
10′	.8351	13	.9722	25	.0278	.8629	46° 50′
20′	.8365	14	.9747	25	.0253	.8618	40′
30′	.8378	13	.9772	25	.0228	.8606	30′
40′	.8391	13	.9798	26	.0202	.8594	20′
43° 50′	.8405	14	.9823	25	.0177	.8582	10′
44° 00′	9.8418	13	9.9848	25	0.0152	9.8569	**46° 00′**
10′	.8431	13	.9874	26	.0126	.8557	45° 50′
20′	.8444	13	.9899	25	.0101	.8545	40′
30′	.8457	13	.9924	25	.0076	.8532	30′
40′	.8469	12	.9949	25	.0051	.8520	20′
44° 50′	.8482	13	.9975	26	.0025	.8507	10′
45° 00′	9.8495	13	10.0000	25	0.0000	9.8495	**45° 00′**
	L Cos *	d	L Cot *	c d	L Tan	L Sin *	←

* Subtract 10 from each entry in this column.

VII. FOUR–PLACE VALUES OF FUNCTIONS: 0° — 6°; 84° — 90°

→	Sin	Cos	Tan	Cot	Sec	Csc	
0° 00′	.0000	1.000	.0000	——	1.000	——	**90° 00′**
10′	029	000	029	343.8	000	343.8	89° 50′
20′	058	000	058	171.9	000	171.9	40′
30′	.0087	1.000	.0087	114.6	1.000	114.6	30′
40′	116	.9999	116	85.94	000	85.95	20′
0° 50′	145	999	145	68.75	000	68.76	10′
1° 00′	.0175	.9998	.0175	57.29	1.000	57.30	**89° 00′**
10′	204	998	204	49.10	000	49.11	88° 50′
20′	233	997	233	42.96	000	42.98	40′
30′	.0262	.9997	.0262	38.19	1.000	38.20	30′
40′	291	996	291	34.37	000	34.38	20′
1° 50′	320	995	320	31.24	001	31.26	10′
2° 00′	.0349	.9994	.0349	28.64	1.001	28.65	**88° 00′**
10′	378	993	378	26.43	001	26.45	87° 50′
20′	407	992	407	24.54	001	24.56	40′
30′	.0436	.9990	.0437	22.90	1.001	22.93	30′
40′	465	989	466	21.47	001	21.49	20′
2° 50′	494	988	495	20.21	001	20.23	10′
3° 00′	.0523	.9986	.0524	19.08	1.001	19.11	**87° 00′**
10′	552	985	553	18.07	002	18.10	86° 50′
20′	581	983	582	17.17	002	17.20	40′
30′	.0610	.9981	.0612	16.35	1.002	16.38	30′
40′	640	980	641	15.60	002	15.64	20′
3° 50′	669	978	670	14.92	002	14.96	10′
4° 00′	.0698	.9976	.0699	14.30	1.002	14.34	**86° 00′**
10′	727	974	729	13.73	003	13.76	85° 50′
20′	756	971	758	13.20	003	13.23	40′
30′	.0785	.9969	.0787	12.71	1.003	12.75	30′
40′	814	967	816	12.25	003	12.29	20′
4° 50′	843	964	846	11.83	004	11.87	10′
5° 00′	.0872	.9962	.0875	11.43	1.004	11.47	**85° 00′**
10′	901	959	904	11.06	004	11.10	84° 50′
20′	929	957	934	10.71	004	10.76	40′
30′	.0958	.9954	.0963	10.39	1.005	10.43	30′
40′	.0987	951	.0992	10.08	005	10.13	20′
5° 50′	.1016	948	.1022	9.788	005	9.839	10′
6° 00′	.1045	.9945	.1051	9.514	1.006	9.567	**84° 00′**
	Cos	Sin	Cot	Tan	Csc	Sec	←

Prop. Parts*

	28	**29**	**30**	**31**
1	2.8	2.9	3	3.1
2	5.6	5.8	6	6.2
3	8.4	8.7	9	9.3
4	11.2	11.6	12	12.4
5	14.0	14.5	15	15.5
6	16.8	17.4	18	18.6
7	19.6	20.3	21	21.7
8	22.4	23.2	24	24.8
9	25.2	26.1	27	27.9

	32	**33**	**34**	**35**
1	3.2	3.3	3.4	3.5
2	6.4	6.6	6.8	7.0
3	9.6	9.9	10.2	10.5
4	12.8	13.2	13.6	14.0
5	16.0	16.5	17.0	17.5
6	19.2	19.8	20.4	21.0
7	22.4	23.1	23.8	24.5
8	25.6	26.4	27.2	28.0
9	28.8	29.7	30.6	31.5

	48	**49**	**53**	**57**
1	4.8	4.9	5.3	5.7
2	9.6	9.8	10.6	11.4
3	14.4	14.7	15.9	17.1
4	19.2	19.6	21.2	22.8
5	24.0	24.5	26.5	28.5
6	28.8	29.4	31.8	34.2
7	33.6	34.3	37.1	39.9
8	38.4	39.2	42.4	45.6
9	43.2	44.1	47.7	51.3

	69	**70**	**71**	**72**
1	6.9	7	7.1	7.2
2	13.8	14	14.2	14.4
3	20.7	21	21.3	21.6
4	27.6	28	28.4	28.8
5	34.5	35	35.5	36.0
6	41.4	42	42.6	43.2
7	48.3	49	49.7	50.4
8	55.2	56	56.8	57.6
9	62.1	63	63.9	64.8

	79	**81**	**82**	**83**	**84**	**87**	**88**	**89**		**90**	**91**	**94**	**95**	**96**	**98**	**100**	**101**	
1	7.9	8.1	8.2	8.3	8.4	8.7	8.8	8.9	**1**	9	9.1	9.4	9.5	9.6	9.8	10	10.1	**1**
2	15.8	16.2	16.4	16.6	16.8	17.4	17.6	17.8	**2**	18	18.2	18.8	19.0	19.2	19.6	20	20.2	**2**
3	23.7	24.3	24.6	24.9	25.2	26.1	26.4	26.7	**3**	27	27.3	28.2	28.5	28.8	29.4	30	30.3	**3**
4	31.6	32.4	32.8	33.2	33.6	34.8	35.2	35.6	**4**	36	36.4	37.6	38.0	38.4	39.2	40	40.4	**4**
5	39.5	40.5	41.0	41.5	42.0	43.5	44.0	44.5	**5**	45	45.5	47.0	47.5	48.0	49.0	50	50.5	**5**
6	47.4	48.6	49.2	49.8	50.4	52.2	52.8	53.4	**6**	54	54.6	56.4	57.0	57.6	58.8	60	60.6	**6**
7	55.3	56.7	57.4	58.1	58.8	60.9	61.6	62.3	**7**	63	63.7	65.8	66.5	67.2	68.6	70	70.7	**7**
8	63.2	64.8	65.6	66.4	67.2	69.6	70.4	71.2	**8**	72	72.8	75.2	76.0	76.8	78.4	80	80.8	**8**
9	71.1	72.9	73.8	74.7	75.6	78.3	79.2	80.1	**9**	81	81.9	84.6	85.5	86.4	88.2	90	90.9	**9**

	102	**104**	**105**	**107**	**108**	**111**	**113**	**115**		**117**	**120**	**121**	**124**	**126**	**129**	**130**	**135**	
1	10.2	10.4	10.5	10.7	10.8	11	11	12	**1**	12	12	12	12	13	13	13	14	**1**
2	20.4	20.8	21.0	21.4	21.6	22	23	23	**2**	23	24	24	25	25	26	26	27	**2**
3	30.6	31.2	31.5	32.1	32.4	33	34	34	**3**	35	36	36	37	38	39	39	40	**3**
4	40.8	41.6	42.0	42.8	43.2	44	45	46	**4**	47	48	48	50	50	52	52	54	**4**
5	51.0	52.0	52.5	53.5	54.0	56	56	58	**5**	58	60	60	62	63	64	65	68	**5**
6	61.2	62.4	63.0	64.2	64.8	67	68	69	**6**	70	72	73	74	76	77	78	81	**6**
7	71.4	72.8	73.5	74.9	75.6	78	79	80	**7**	82	84	85	87	88	90	91	94	**7**
8	81.6	83.2	84.0	85.6	86.4	89	90	92	**8**	94	96	97	99	101	103	104	108	**8**
9	91.8	93.6	94.5	96.3	97.2	100	102	104	**9**	105	108	109	112	113	116	117	122	**9**

* If the difference is > 1.00, use Table XI to avoid interpolation.

VII. FOUR-PLACE VALUES OF FUNCTIONS: 6° — 12°; 78° — 84°

→	Sin	Cos	Tan	Cot	Sec	Csc	
6° 00′	.1045	.9945	.1051	9.514	1.006	9.567	**84° 00′**
10′	074	942	080	255	006	309	83° 50′
20′	103	939	110	9.010	006	9.065	40′
30′	.1132	.9936	.1139	8.777	1.006	8.834	30′
40	161	932	169	556	007	614	20′
6° 50′	190	929	198	345	007	405	10′
7° 00′	.1219	.9925	.1228	8.144	1.008	8.206	**83° 00′**
10′	248	922	257	7.953	008	8.016	82° 50′
20′	276	918	287	770	008	7.834	40′
30′	.1305	.9914	.1317	7.596	1.009	7.661	30′
40′	334	911	346	429	009	496	20′
7° 50′	363	907	376	269	009	337	10′
8° 00′	.1392	.9903	.1405	7.115	1.010	7.185	**82° 00′**
10′	421	899	435	6.968	010	7.040	81° 50′
20′	449	894	465	827	011	6.900	40′
30′	.1478	.9890	.1495	6.691	1.011	6.765	30′
40′	507	886	524	561	012	636	20′
8° 50′	536	881	554	435	012	512	10′
9° 00′	.1564	.9877	.1584	6.314	1.012	6.392	**81° 00′**
10′	593	872	614	197	013	277	80° 50′
20′	622	868	644	6.084	013	166	40′
30′	.1650	.9863	.1673	5.976	1.014	6.059	30′
40′	679	858	703	871	014	5.955	20′
9° 50′	708	853	733	769	015	855	10′
10° 00′	.1736	.9848	.1763	5.671	1.015	5.759	**80° 00′**
10′	765	843	793	576	016	665	79° 50′
20′	794	838	823	485	016	575	40′
30′	.1822	.9833	.1853	5.396	1.017	5.487	30′
40′	851	827	883	309	018	403	20′
10° 50′	880	822	914	226	018	320	10′
11° 00′	.1908	.9816	.1944	5.145	1.019	5.241	**79° 00′**
10′	937	811	.1974	5.066	019	164	78° 50′
20′	965	805	.2004	4.989	020	089	40′
30′	.1994	.9799	.2035	4.915	1.020	5.016	30′
40′	.2022	793	065	843	021	4.945	20′
11° 50′	051	787	095	773	022	876	10′
12° 00′	.2079	.9781	.2126	4.705	1.022	4.810	**78° 00′**
	Cos	Sin	Cot	Tan	Csc	Sec	←

Prop. Parts

	2	3	4	5	6
1	0.2	0.3	0.4	0.5	0.6
2	0.4	0.6	0.8	1.0	1.2
3	0.6	0.9	1.2	1.5	1.8
4	0.8	1.2	1.6	2 0	2.4
5	1.0	1.5	2.0	2.5	3.0
6	1.2	1.8	2.4	3.0	3.6
7	1.4	2.1	2.8	3.5	4.2
8	1.6	2.4	3.2	4.0	4.8
9	1.8	2.7	3.6	4.5	5.4

	37	40	42	46
1	3.7	4	4.2	4.6
2	7.4	8	8.4	9.2
3	11.1	12	12.6	13.8
4	14.8	16	16.8	18.4
5	18.5	20	21.0	23.0
6	22.2	24	25.2	27.6
7	25.9	28	29.4	32.2
8	29.6	32	33.6	36.8
9	33.3	36	37.8	41.4

	58	62	66	68
1	5.8	6.2	6.6	6.8
2	11.6	12.4	13.2	13.6
3	17.4	18.6	19.8	20.4
4	23.2	24.8	26.4	27.2
5	29.0	31.0	33.0	34.0
6	34.8	37.2	39.6	40.8
7	40.6	43.4	46.2	47.6
8	46.4	49.6	52.8	54.4
9	52.2	55.8	59.4	61.2

	73	74	75	77
1	7.3	7.4	7.5	7.7
2	14.6	14.8	15.0	15.4
3	21.9	22.2	22.5	23.1
4	29.2	29.6	30.0	30.8
5	36.5	37.0	37.5	38.5
6	43.8	44.4	45.0	46.2
7	51.1	51 8	52.5	53.9
8	58.4	59.2	60.0	61.6
9	65.7	66.6	67.5	69.3

	136	140	141	145	147	152	154	159		160	165	167	173	174	182	183	190	
1	14	14	14	14	15	15	15	16	**1**	16	16	17	17	17	18	18	19	**1**
2	27	28	28	29	29	30	31	32	**2**	32	33	33	35	35	36	37	38	**2**
3	41	42	42	44	44	46	46	48	**3**	48	50	50	52	52	55	55	57	**3**
4	54	56	56	58	59	61	62	64	**4**	64	66	67	69	70	73	73	76	**4**
5	68	70	70	72	74	76	77	80	**5**	80	82	84	86	87	91	92	95	**5**
6	82	84	85	87	88	91	92	95	**6**	96	99	100	104	104	109	110	114	**6**
7	95	98	99	102	103	106	108	111	**7**	112	116	117	121	122	127	128	133	**7**
8	109	112	113	116	118	122	123	127	**8**	128	132	134	138	139	146	146	152	**8**
9	122	126	127	130	132	137	139	143	**9**	144	148	150	156	157	164	165	171	**9**

	191	199	201	209	211	220	221	231		233	244	245	258	259	272	274	
1	19	20	20	21	21	22	22	23	**1**	23	24	24	26	26	27	27	**1**
2	38	40	40	42	42	44	44	46	**2**	47	49	49	52	52	54	55	**2**
3	57	60	60	63	63	66	66	69	**3**	70	73	74	77	78	82	82	**3**
4	76	80	80	84	84	88	88	92	**4**	93	98	98	103	104	109	110	**4**
5	96	100	100	104	106	110	110	116	**5**	116	122	122	129	130	136	137	**5**
6	115	119	121	125	127	132	133	139	**6**	140	146	147	155	155	163	164	**6**
7	134	139	141	146	148	154	155	162	**7**	163	171	172	181	181	190	192	**7**
8	153	159	161	167	169	176	177	185	**8**	186	195	196	206	207	218	219	**8**
9	172	179	181	188	190	198	199	208	**9**	210	220	220	232	233	245	247	**9**

→	Sin	Cos	Tan	Cot	Sec	Csc	
12° 00′	.2079	.9781	.2126	4.705	1.022	4.810	**78° 00′**
10′	108	775	156	638	023	745	77° 50′
20′	136	769	186	574	024	682	40′
30′	.2164	.9763	.2217	4.511	1.024	4.620	30′
40′	193	757	247	449	025	560	20′
12° 50′	221	750	278	390	026	502	10′
13° 00′	.2250	.9744	.2309	4.331	1.026	4.445	**77° 00′**
10′	278	737	339	275	027	390	76° 50′
20′	306	730	370	219	028	336	40′
30′	.2334	.9724	.2401	4.165	1.028	4.284	30′
40′	363	717	432	113	029	232	20′
13° 50′	391	710	462	061	030	182	10′
14° 00′	.2419	.9703	.2493	4.011	1.031	4.134	**76° 00′**
10′	447	696	524	3.962	031	086	75° 50′
20′	476	689	555	914	032	4.039	40′
30′	.2504	.9681	.2586	3.867	1.033	3.994	30′
40′	532	674	617	821	034	950	20′
14° 50′	560	667	648	776	034	906	10′
15° 00′	.2588	.9659	.2679	3.732	1.035	3.864	**75° 00′**
10′	616	652	711	689	036	822	74° 50′
20′	644	644	742	647	037	782	40′
30′	.2672	.9636	.2773	3.606	1.038	3.742	30′
40′	700	628	805	566	039	703	20′
15° 50′	728	621	836	526	039	665	10′
16° 00′	.2756	.9613	.2867	3.487	1.040	3.628	**74° 00′**
10′	784	605	899	450	041	592	73° 50′
20′	812	596	931	412	042	556	40′
30′	.2840	.9588	.2962	3.376	1.043	3.521	30′
40′	868	580	.2994	340	044	487	20′
16° 50′	896	572	.3026	305	045	453	10′
17° 00′	.2924	.9563	.3057	3.271	1.046	3.420	**73° 00′**
10′	952	555	089	237	047	388	72° 50′
20′	.2979	546	121	204	048	356	40′
30′	.3007	.9537	.3153	3.172	1.049	3.326	30′
40′	035	528	185	140	049	295	20′
17° 50′	062	520	217	108	050	265	10′
18° 00′	.3090	.9511	.3249	3.078	1.051	3.236	**72° 00′**
10′	118	502	281	047	052	207	71° 50′
20′	145	492	314	3.018	053	179	40′
30′	.3173	.9483	.3346	2.989	1.054	3.152	30′
40′	201	474	378	960	056	124	20′
18° 50′	228	465	411	932	057	098	10′
19° 00′	.3256	.9455	.3443	2.904	1.058	3.072	**71° 00′**
10′	283	446	476	877	059	046	70° 50′
20′	311	436	508	850	060	3.021	40′
30′	.3338	.9426	.3541	2.824	1.061	2.996	30′
40′	365	417	574	798	062	971	20′
19° 50′	393	407	607	773	063	947	10′
20° 00′	.3420	.9397	.3640	2.747	1.064	2.924	**70° 00′**
	Cos	Sin	Cot	Tan	Csc	Sec	←

Prop. Parts

	2	6	7	8
1	0.2	0.6	0.7	0.8
2	0.4	1.2	1.4	1.6
3	0.6	1.8	2.1	2.4
4	0.8	2.4	2.8	3.2
5	1.0	3.0	3.5	4.0
6	1.2	3.6	4.2	4.8
7	1.4	4.2	4.9	5.6
8	1.6	4.8	5.6	6.4
9	1.8	5.4	6.3	7.2

	13	14	15	16
1	1.3	1.4	1.5	1.6
2	2.6	2.8	3.0	3.2
3	3.9	4.2	4.5	4.8
4	5.2	5.6	6.0	6.4
5	6.5	7.0	7.5	8.0
6	7.8	8.4	9.0	9.6
7	9.1	9.8	10.5	11.2
8	10.4	11.2	12.0	12.8
9	11.7	12.6	13.5	14.4

	21	22	23	24
1	2.1	2.2	2.3	2.4
2	4.2	4.4	4.6	4.8
3	6.3	6.6	6.9	7.2
4	8.4	8.8	9.2	9.6
5	10.5	11.0	11.5	12.0
6	12.6	13.2	13.8	14.4
7	14.7	15.4	16.1	16.8
8	16.8	17.6	18.4	19.2
9	18.9	19.8	20.7	21.6

	29	30	31	32
1	2.9	3	3.1	3.2
2	5.8	6	6.2	6.4
3	8.7	9	9.3	9.6
4	11.6	12	12.4	12.8
5	14.5	15	15.5	16.0
6	17.4	18	18.6	19.2
7	20.3	21	21.7	22.4
8	23 2	24	24.8	25.6
9	26.1	27	27.9	28.8

	37	38	39	40	41	42	43		44	45	46	47	48	49	50	
1	3.7	3.8	3.9	4	4.1	4.2	4.3	**1**	4.4	4.5	4.6	4.7	4.8	4.9	5	**1**
2	7.4	7.6	7.8	8	8.2	8.4	8.6	**2**	8.8	9.0	9.2	9.4	9.6	9.8	10	**2**
3	11.1	11.4	11.7	12	12.3	12.6	12.9	**3**	13.2	13.5	13.8	14.1	14.4	14.7	15	**3**
4	14.8	15.2	15.6	16	16.4	16.8	17.2	**4**	17.6	18.0	18.4	18.8	19.2	19.6	20	**4**
5	18.5	19.0	19.5	20	20.5	21.0	21.5	**5**	22.0	22.5	23.0	23.5	24.0	24.5	25	**5**
6	22.2	22.8	23.4	24	24.6	25.2	25.8	**6**	26.4	27.0	27.6	28.2	28.8	29.4	30	**6**
7	25.9	26.6	27.3	28	28.7	29.4	30.1	**7**	30.8	31.5	32.2	32.9	33.6	34.3	35	**7**
8	29.6	30.4	31.2	32	32.8	33.6	34.4	**8**	35.2	36.0	36.8	37.6	38.4	39.2	40	**8**
9	33.3	34.2	35.1	36	36.9	37.8	38.7	**9**	39.6	40.5	41.4	42.3	43.2	44.1	45	**9**

VII. FOUR-PLACE VALUES OF FUNCTIONS: 20° — 28°; 62° — 70°

→	Sin	Cos	Tan	Cot	Sec	Csc	
20° 00′	.3420	.9397	.3640	2.747	1.064	2.924	**70° 00′**
10′	448	387	673	723	065	901	69° 50′
20′	475	377	706	699	066	878	40′
30′	.3502	.9367	.3739	2.675	1.068	2.855	30′
40′	529	356	772	651	069	833	20′
20° 50′	557	346	805	628	070	812	10′
21° 00′	.3584	.9336	.3839	2.605	1.071	2.790	**69° 00′**
10′	611	325	872	583	072	769	68° 50′
20′	638	315	906	560	074	749	40′
30′	.3665	.9304	.3939	2.539	1.075	2.729	30′
40′	692	293	.3973	517	076	709	20′
21° 50′	719	283	.4006	496	077	689	10′
22° 00′	.3746	.9272	.4040	2.475	1.079	2.669	**68° 00′**
10′	773	261	074	455	080	650	67° 50′
20′	800	250	108	434	081	632	40′
30′	.3827	.9239	.4142	2.414	1.082	2.613	30′
40′	854	228	176	394	084	595	20′
22° 50′	881	216	210	375	085	577	10′
23° 00′	.3907	.9205	.4245	2.356	1.086	2.559	**67° 00′**
10′	934	194	279	337	088	542	66° 50′
20′	961	182	314	318	089	525	40′
30′	.3987	.9171	.4348	2.300	1.090	2.508	30′
40′	.4014	159	383	282	092	491	20′
23° 50′	041	147	417	264	093	475	10′
24° 00′	.4067	.9135	.4452	2.246	1.095	2.459	**66° 00′**
10′	094	124	487	229	096	443	65° 50′
20′	120	112	522	211	097	427	40′
30′	.4147	.9100	.4557	2.194	1.099	2.411	30′
40′	173	088	592	177	100	396	20′
24° 50′	200	075	628	161	102	381	10′
25° 00′	.4226	.9063	.4663	2.145	1.103	2.366	**65° 00′**
10′	253	051	699	128	105	352	64° 50′
20′	279	038	734	112	106	337	40′
30′	.4305	.9026	.4770	2.097	1.108	2.323	30′
40′	331	013	806	081	109	309	20′
25° 50′	358	.9001	841	066	111	295	10′
26° 00′	.4384	.8988	.4877	2.050	1.113	2.281	**64° 00′**
10′	410	975	913	035	114	268	63° 50′
20′	436	962	950	020	116	254	40′
30′	.4462	.8949	.4986	2.006	1.117	2.241	30′
40′	488	936	.5022	1.991	119	228	20′
26° 50′	514	923	059	977	121	215	10′
27° 00′	.4540	.8910	.5095	1.963	1.122	2.203	**63° 00′**
10′	566	897	132	949	124	190	62° 50′
20′	592	884	169	935	126	178	40′
30′	.4617	.8870	.5206	1.921	1.127	2.166	30′
40′	643	857	243	907	129	154	20′
27° 50′	669	843	280	894	131	142	10′
28° 00′	.4695	.8829	.5317	1.881	1.133	2.130	**62° 00′**
	Cos	Sin	Cot	Tan	Csc	Sec	←

Prop. Parts

	9	10	11	12
1	0.9	1.0	1.1	1.2
2	1.8	2.0	2.2	2.4
3	2.7	3.0	3.3	3.6
4	3.6	4.0	4.4	4.8
5	4.5	5.0	5.5	6.0
6	5.4	6.0	6.6	7.2
7	6.3	7.0	7.7	8.4
8	7.2	8.0	8.8	9.6
9	8.1	9.0	9.9	10.8

	17	18	19	20
1	1.7	1.8	1.9	2
2	3.4	3.6	3.8	4
3	5.1	5.4	5.7	6
4	6.8	7.2	7.6	8
5	8.5	9.0	9.5	10
6	10.2	10.8	11.4	12
7	11.9	12.6	13.3	14
8	13.6	14.4	15.2	16
9	15.3	16.2	17.1	18

	25	26	27	28
1	2.5	2.6	2.7	2.8
2	5.0	5.2	5.4	5.6
3	7.5	7.8	8.1	8.4
4	10.0	10.4	10.8	11.2
5	12.5	13.0	13.5	14.0
6	15.0	15.6	16.2	16.8
7	17.5	18.2	18.9	19.6
8	20.0	20.8	21.6	22.4
9	22.5	23.4	24.3	25.2

	33	34	35	36
1	3.3	3.4	3.5	3.6
2	6.6	6.8	7.0	7.2
3	9.9	10.2	10.5	10.8
4	13.2	13.6	14.0	14.4
5	16.5	17.0	17.5	18.0
6	19.8	20.4	21.0	21.6
7	23.1	23.8	24.5	25.2
8	26.4	27.2	28.0	28.8
9	29.7	30.6	31.5	32.4

	52	54	55	56	57	58	59		60	62	63	64	65	67	
1	5.2	5.4	5.5	5.6	5.7	5.8	5.9	**1**	6	6.2	6.3	6.4	6.5	6.7	**1**
2	10.4	10.8	11.0	11.2	11.4	11.6	11.8	**2**	12	12.4	12.6	12.8	13.0	13.4	**2**
3	15.6	16.2	16.5	16.8	17.1	17.4	17.7	**3**	18	18.6	18.9	19.2	19.5	20.1	**3**
4	20.8	21.6	22.0	22.4	22.8	23.2	23.6	**4**	24	24.8	25.2	25.6	26.0	26.8	**4**
5	26.0	27.0	27.5	28.0	28.5	29.0	29.5	**5**	30	31.0	31.5	32.0	32.5	33.5	**5**
6	31.2	32.4	33.0	33.6	34.2	34.8	35.4	**6**	36	37.2	37.8	38.4	39.0	40.2	**6**
7	36.4	37.8	38.5	39.2	39.9	40.6	41.3	**7**	42	43.4	44.1	44.8	45.5	46.9	**7**
8	41.6	43.2	44.0	44.8	45.6	46.4	47.2	**8**	48	49.6	50.4	51.2	52.0	53.6	**8**
9	46.8	48.6	49.5	50.4	51.3	52.2	53.1	**9**	54	55.8	56.7	57.6	58.5	60.3	**9**

⟶	Sin	Cos	Tan	Cot	Sec	Csc	
28° 00′	.4695	.8829	.5317	1.881	1.133	2.130	**62° 00′**
10′	720	816	354	868	134	118	61° 50′
20′	746	802	392	855	136	107	40′
30′	.4772	.8788	.5430	1.842	1.138	2.096	30′
40′	797	774	467	829	140	085	20′
28° 50′	823	760	505	816	142	074	10′
29° 00′	.4848	.8746	.5543	1.804	1.143	2.063	**61° 00′**
10′	874	732	581	792	145	052	60° 50′
20′	899	718	619	780	147	041	40′
30′	.4924	.8704	.5658	1.767	1.149	2.031	30′
40′	950	689	696	756	151	020	20′
29° 50′	.4975	675	735	744	153	010	10′
30° 00′	.5000	.8660	.5774	1.732	1.155	2.000	**60° 00′**
10′	025	646	812	720	157	1.990	59° 50′
20′	050	631	851	709	159	980	40′
30′	.5075	.8616	.5890	1.698	1.161	1.970	30′
40′	100	601	930	686	163	961	20′
30° 50′	125	587	.5969	675	165	951	10′
31° 00′	.5150	.8572	.6009	1.664	1.167	1.942	**59° 00′**
10′	175	557	048	653	169	932	58° 50′
20′	200	542	088	643	171	923	40′
30′	.5225	.8526	.6128	1.632	1.173	1.914	30′
40′	250	511	168	621	175	905	20′
31° 50′	275	496	208	611	177	896	10′
32° 00′	.5299	.8480	.6249	1.600	1.179	1.887	**58° 00′**
10′	324	465	289	590	181	878	57° 50′
20′	348	450	330	580	184	870	40′
30′	.5373	.8434	.6371	1.570	1.186	1.861	30′
40′	398	418	412	560	188	853	20′
32° 50′	422	403	453	550	190	844	10′
33° 00′	.5446	.8387	.6494	1.540	1.192	1.836	**57° 00′**
10′	471	371	536	530	195	828	56° 50′
20′	495	355	577	520	197	820	40′
30′	.5519	.8339	.6619	1.511	1.199	1.812	30′
40′	544	323	661	501	202	804	20′
33° 50′	568	307	703	492	204	796	10′
34° 00′	.5592	.8290	.6745	1.483	1.206	1.788	**56° 00′**
10′	616	274	787	473	209	781	55° 50′
20′	640	258	830	464	211	773	40′
30	.5664	.8241	.6873	1.455	1.213	1.766	30′
40	688	225	916	446	216	758	20′
34° 50	712	208	.6959	437	218	751	10′
35° 00′	.5736	.8192	.7002	1.428	1.221	1.743	**55° 00′**
10′	760	175	046	419	223	736	54° 50′
20′	783	158	089	411	226	729	40′
30′	.5807	.8141	.7133	1.402	1.228	1.722	30′
40′	831	124	177	393	231	715	20′
35° 50′	854	107	221	385	233	708	10′
36° 00′	.5878	.8090	.7265	1.376	1.236	1.701	**54° 00′**
	Cos	Sin	Cot	Tan	Csc	Sec	⟵

Prop. Parts

	2	3	4	5	6
1	0.2	0.3	0.4	0.5	0.6
2	0.4	0.6	0.8	1.0	1.2
3	0.6	0.9	1.2	1.5	1.8
4	0.8	1.2	1.6	2.0	2.4
5	1.0	1.5	2.0	2.5	3.0
6	1.2	1.8	2.4	3.0	3.6
7	1.4	2.1	2.8	3.5	4.2
8	1.6	2.4	3.2	4.0	4.8
9	1.8	2.7	3.6	4.5	5.4

	11	12	13	14
1	1.1	1.2	1.3	1.4
2	2.2	2.4	2.6	2.8
3	3.3	3.6	3.9	4.2
4	4.4	4.8	5.2	5.6
5	5.5	6.0	6.5	7.0
6	6.6	7.2	7.8	8.4
7	7.7	8.4	9.1	9.8
8	8.8	9.6	10.4	11.2
9	9.9	10.8	11.7	12.6

	19	20	21	22
1	1.9	2	2.1	2.2
2	3.8	4	4.2	4.4
3	5.7	6	6.3	6.6
4	7.6	8	8.4	8.8
5	9.5	10	10.5	11.0
6	11.4	12	12.6	13.2
7	13.3	14	14.7	15.4
8	15.2	16	16.8	17.6
9	17.1	18	18.9	19.8

	37	38	39	40
1	3.7	3.8	3.9	4
2	7.4	7.6	7.8	8
3	11.1	11.4	11.7	12
4	14.8	15.2	15.6	16
5	18.5	19.0	19.5	20
6	22.2	22.8	23.4	24
7	25.9	26.6	27.3	28
8	29.6	30.4	31.2	32
9	33.3	34.2	35.1	36

	44	45	46	47	48	49		50	51	52	53	54	55	
1	4.4	4.5	4.6	4.7	4.8	4.9	1	5	5.1	5.2	5.3	5.4	5.5	1
2	8.8	9.0	9.2	9.4	9.6	9.8	2	10	10.2	10.4	10.6	10.8	11.0	2
3	13.2	13.5	13.8	14.1	14.4	14.7	3	15	15.3	15.6	15.9	16.2	16.5	3
4	17.6	18.0	18.4	18.8	19.2	19.6	4	20	20.4	20.8	21.2	21.6	22.0	4
5	22.0	22.5	23.0	23.5	24.0	24.5	5	25	25.5	26.0	26.5	27.0	27.5	5
6	26.4	27.0	27.6	28.2	28.8	29.4	6	30	30.6	31.2	31.8	32.4	33.0	6
7	30.8	31.5	32.2	32.9	33.6	34.3	7	35	35.7	36.4	37.1	37.8	38.5	7
8	35.2	36.0	36.8	37.6	38.4	39.2	8	40	40.8	41.6	42.4	43.2	44.0	8
9	39.6	40.5	41.4	42.3	43.2	44.1	9	45	45.9	46.8	47.7	48.6	49.5	9

→	Sin	Cos	Tan	Cot	Sec	Csc	
36° 00′	.5878	.8090	.7265	1.376	1.236	1.701	**54° 00′**
10′	901	073	310	368	239	695	53° 50′
20′	925	056	355	360	241	688	40′
30′	.5948	.8039	.7400	1.351	1.244	1.681	30′
40′	972	021	445	343	247	675	20′
36° 50′	.5995	.8004	490	335	249	668	10′
37° 00′	.6018	.7986	.7536	1.327	1.252	1.662	**53° 00′**
10′	041	969	581	319	255	655	52° 50′
20′	065	951	627	311	258	649	40′
30′	.6088	.7934	.7673	1.303	1.260	1.643	30′
40′	111	916	720	295	263	636	20′
37° 50′	134	898	766	288	266	630	10′
38° 00′	.6157	.7880	.7813	1.280	1.269	1.624	**52° 00′**
10′	180	862	860	272	272	618	51° 50′
20′	202	844	907	265	275	612	40′
30′	.6225	.7826	.7954	1.257	1.278	1.606	30′
40′	248	808	.8002	250	281	601	20′
38° 50′	271	790	050	242	284	595	10′
39° 00′	.6293	.7771	.8098	1.235	1.287	1.589	**51° 00′**
10′	316	753	146	228	290	583	50° 50′
20′	338	735	195	220	293	578	40′
30′	.6361	.7716	.8243	1.213	1.296	1.572	30′
40′	383	698	292	206	299	567	20′
39° 50′	406	679	342	199	302	561	10′
40° 00′	.6428	.7660	.8391	1.192	1.305	1.556	**50° 00**
10	450	642	441	185	309	550	49° 50′
20′	472	623	491	178	312	545	40′
30′	.6494	.7604	.8541	1.171	1.315	1.540	30′
40′	517	585	591	164	318	535	20′
40° 50′	539	566	642	157	322	529	10′
41° 00′	.6561	.7547	.8693	1.150	1.325	1.524	**49° 00′**
10′	583	528	744	144	328	519	48° 50′
20′	604	509	796	137	332	514	40′
30′	.6626	.7490	.8847	1.130	1.335	1.509	30′
40′	648	470	899	124	339	504	20′
41° 50′	670	451	.8952	117	342	499	10′
42° 00′	.6691	.7431	.9004	1.111	1.346	1.494	**48° 00′**
10′	713	412	057	104	349	490	47° 50′
20′	734	392	110	098	353	485	40′
30′	.6756	.7373	.9163	1.091	1.356	1.480	30′
40′	777	353	217	085	360	476	20′
42° 50′	799	333	271	079	364	471	10′
43° 00′	.6820	.7314	.9325	1.072	1.367	1.466	**47° 00′**
10′	841	294	380	066	371	462	46° 50′
20′	862	274	435	060	375	457	40′
30′	.6884	.7254	.9490	1.054	1.379	1.453	30′
40′	905	234	545	048	382	448	20′
43° 50′	926	214	601	042	386	444	10′
44° 00′	.6947	.7193	.9657	1.036	1.390	1.440	**46° 00′**
10′	967	173	713	030	394	435	45° 50′
20′	.6988	153	770	024	398	431	40′
30′	.7009	.7133	.9827	1.018	1.402	1.427	30′
40′	030	112	884	012	406	423	20′
44° 50′	050	092	.9942	006	410	418	10′
45° 00′	.7071	.7071	1.000	1.000	1.414	1.414	**45° 00′**
	Cos	Sin	Cot	Tan	Csc	Sec	←

Prop. Parts

	7	8	9	10
1	0.7	0.8	0.9	1.0
2	1.4	1.6	1.8	2.0
3	2.1	2.4	2.7	3.0
4	2.8	3.2	3.6	4.0
5	3.5	4.0	4.5	5.0
6	4.2	4.8	5.4	6.0
7	4.9	5.6	6.3	7.0
8	5.6	6.4	7.2	8.0
9	6.3	7.2	8.1	9.0

	15	16	17	18
1	1.5	1.6	1.7	1.8
2	3.0	3.2	3.4	3.6
3	4.5	4.8	5.1	5.4
4	6.0	6.4	6.8	7.2
5	7.5	8.0	8.5	9.0
6	9.0	9.6	10.2	10.8
7	10.5	11.2	11.9	12.6
8	12.0	12.8	13.6	14.4
9	13.5	14.4	15.3	16.2

	23	24	25	26
1	2.3	2.4	2.5	2.6
2	4.6	4.8	5.0	5.2
3	6.9	7.2	7.5	7.8
4	9.2	9.6	10.0	10.4
5	11.5	12.0	12.5	13.0
6	13.8	14.4	15.0	15.6
7	16.1	16.8	17.5	18.2
8	18.4	19.2	20.0	20.8
9	20.7	21.6	22.5	23.4

	41	42	43
1	4.1	4.2	4.3
2	8.2	8.4	8.6
3	12.3	12.6	12.9
4	16.4	16.8	17.2
5	20.5	21.0	21.5
6	24.6	25.2	25.8
7	28.7	29.4	30.1
8	32.8	33.6	34.4
9	36.9	37.8	38.7

	56	57	58
1	5.6	5.7	5.8
2	11.2	11.4	11.6
3	16.8	17.1	17.4
4	22.4	22.8	23.2
5	28.0	28.5	29.0
6	33.6	34.2	34.8
7	39.2	39.9	40.6
8	44.8	45.6	46.4
9	50.4	51.3	52.2

N	0	1	2	3	4	5	6	7	8	9
100	00 000	043	087	130	173	217	260	303	346	389
01	432	475	518	561	604	647	689	732	775	817
02	00 860	903	945	988	*030	*072	*115	*157	*199	*242
03	01 284	326	368	410	452	494	536	578	620	662
04	01 703	745	787	828	870	912	953	995	*036	*078
05	02 119	160	202	243	284	325	366	407	449	490
06	531	572	612	653	694	735	776	816	857	898
07	02 938	979	*019	*060	*100	*141	*181	*222	*262	*302
08	03 342	383	423	463	503	543	583	623	663	703
09	03 743	782	822	862	902	941	981	*021	*060	*100
110	04 139	179	218	258	297	336	376	415	454	493
11	532	571	610	650	689	727	766	805	844	883
12	04 922	961	999	*038	*077	*115	*154	*192	*231	*269
13	05 308	346	385	423	461	500	538	576	614	652
14	05 690	729	767	805	843	881	918	956	994	*032
15	06 070	108	145	183	221	258	296	333	371	408
16	446	483	521	558	595	633	670	707	744	781
17	06 819	856	893	930	967	*004	*041	*078	*115	*151
18	07 188	225	262	298	335	372	408	445	482	518
19	555	591	628	664	700	737	773	809	846	882
120	07 918	954	990	*027	*063	*099	*135	*171	*207	*243
21	08 279	314	350	386	422	458	493	529	565	600
22	636	672	707	743	778	814	849	884	920	955
23	08 991	*026	*061	*096	*132	*167	*202	*237	*272	*307
24	09 342	377	412	447	482	517	552	587	621	656
25	09 691	726	760	795	830	864	899	934	968	*003
26	10 037	072	106	140	175	209	243	278	312	346
27	380	415	449	483	517	551	585	619	653	687
28	10 721	755	789	823	857	890	924	958	992	*025
29	11 059	093	126	160	193	227	261	294	327	361
130	394	428	461	494	528	561	594	628	661	694
31	11 727	760	793	826	860	893	926	959	992	*024
32	12 057	090	123	156	189	222	254	287	320	352
33	385	418	450	483	516	548	581	613	646	678
34	12 710	743	775	808	840	872	905	937	969	*001
35	13 033	066	098	130	162	194	226	258	290	322
36	354	386	418	450	481	513	545	577	609	640
37	672	704	735	767	799	830	862	893	925	956
38	13 988	*019	*051	*082	*114	*145	*176	*208	*239	*270
39	14 301	333	364	395	426	457	489	520	551	582
140	613	644	675	706	737	768	799	829	860	891
41	14 922	953	983	*014	*045	*076	*106	*137	*168	*198
42	15 229	259	290	320	351	381	412	442	473	503
43	534	564	594	625	655	685	715	746	776	806
44	15 836	866	897	927	957	987	*017	*047	*077	*107
45	16 137	167	197	227	256	286	316	346	376	406
46	435	465	495	524	554	584	613	643	673	702
47	16 732	761	791	820	850	879	909	938	967	997
48	17 026	056	085	114	143	173	202	231	260	289
49	319	348	377	406	435	464	493	522	551	580
150	17 609	638	667	696	725	754	782	811	840	869
N	**0**	**1**	**2**	**3**	**4**	**5**	**6**	**7**	**8**	**9**

Prop. Parts

	44	43	42
1	4.4	4.3	4.2
2	8.8	8.6	8.4
3	13.2	12.9	12.6
4	17.6	17.2	16.8
5	22.0	21.5	21.0
6	26.4	25.8	25.2
7	30.8	30.1	29.4
8	35.2	34.4	33.6
9	39.6	38.7	37.8

	41	40	39
1	4.1	4	3.9
2	8.2	8	7.8
3	12.3	12	11.7
4	16.4	16	15.6
5	20.5	20	19.5
6	24.6	24	23.4
7	28.7	28	27.3
8	32.8	32	31.2
9	36.9	36	35.1

	38	37	36
1	3.8	3.7	3.6
2	7.6	7.4	7.2
3	11.4	11.1	10.8
4	15.2	14.8	14.4
5	19.0	18.5	18.0
6	22.8	22.2	21.6
7	26.6	25.9	25.2
8	30.4	29.6	28.8
9	34.2	33.3	32.4

	35	34	33
1	3.5	3.4	3.3
2	7.0	6.8	6.6
3	10.5	10.2	9.9
4	14.0	13.6	13.2
5	17.5	17.0	16.5
6	21.0	20.4	19.8
7	24.5	23.8	23.1
8	28.0	27.2	26.4
9	31.5	30.6	29.7

	32	31	30
1	3.2	3.1	3
2	6.4	6.2	6
3	9.6	9.3	9
4	12.8	12.4	12
5	16.0	15.5	15
6	19.2	18.6	18
7	22.4	21.7	21
8	25.6	24.8	24
9	28.8	27.9	27

Prop. Parts

N	0	1	2	3	4	5	6	7	8	9
150	17 609	638	667	696	725	754	782	811	840	869
51	17 898	926	955	984	*013	*041	*070	*099	*127	*156
52	18 184	213	241	270	298	327	355	384	412	441
53	469	498	526	554	583	611	639	667	696	724
54	18 752	780	808	837	865	893	921	949	977	*005
55	19 033	061	089	117	145	173	201	229	257	285
56	312	340	368	396	424	451	479	507	535	562
57	590	618	645	673	700	728	756	783	811	838
58	19 866	893	921	948	976	*003	*030	*058	*085	*112
59	20 140	167	194	222	249	276	303	330	358	385
160	412	439	466	493	520	548	575	602	629	656
61	683	710	737	763	790	817	844	871	898	925
62	20 952	978	*005	*032	*059	*085	*112	*139	*165	*192
63	21 219	245	272	299	325	352	378	405	431	458
64	484	511	537	564	590	617	643	669	696	722
65	21 748	775	801	827	854	880	906	932	958	985
66	22 011	037	063	089	115	141	167	194	220	246
67	272	298	324	350	376	401	427	453	479	505
68	531	557	583	608	634	660	686	712	737	763
69	22 789	814	840	866	891	917	943	968	994	*019
170	23 045	070	096	121	147	172	198	223	249	274
71	300	325	350	376	401	426	452	477	502	528
72	553	578	603	629	654	679	704	729	754	779
73	23 805	830	855	880	905	930	955	980	*005	*030
74	24 055	080	105	130	155	180	204	229	254	279
75	304	329	353	378	403	428	452	477	502	527
76	551	576	601	625	650	674	699	724	748	773
77	24 797	822	846	871	895	920	944	969	993	*018
78	25 042	066	091	115	139	164	188	212	237	261
79	285	310	334	358	382	406	431	455	479	503
180	527	551	575	600	624	648	672	696	720	744
81	25 768	792	816	840	864	888	912	935	959	983
82	26 007	031	055	079	102	126	150	174	198	221
83	245	269	293	316	340	364	387	411	435	458
84	482	505	529	553	576	600	623	647	670	694
85	717	741	764	788	811	834	858	881	905	928
86	26 951	975	998	*021	*045	*068	*091	*114	*138	*161
87	27 184	207	231	254	277	300	323	346	370	393
88	416	439	462	485	508	531	554	577	600	623
89	646	669	692	715	738	761	784	807	830	852
190	27 875	898	921	944	967	989	*012	*035	*058	*081
91	28 103	126	149	171	194	217	240	262	285	307
92	330	353	375	398	421	443	466	488	511	533
93	556	578	601	623	646	668	691	713	735	758
94	28 780	803	825	847	870	892	914	937	959	981
95	29 003	026	048	070	092	115	137	159	181	203
96	226	248	270	292	314	336	358	380	403	425
97	447	469	491	513	535	557	579	601	623	645
98	667	688	710	732	754	776	798	820	842	863
99	29 885	907	929	951	973	994	*016	*038	*060	*081
200	30 103	125	146	168	190	211	233	255	276	298
N	0	1	2	3	4	5	6	7	8	9

Prop. Parts

	29	28
1	2.9	2.8
2	5.8	5.6
3	8.7	8.4
4	11.6	11.2
5	14.5	14.0
6	17.4	16.8
7	20.3	19.6
8	23.2	22.4
9	26.1	25.2

	27	26
1	2.7	2.6
2	5.4	5.2
3	8.1	7.8
4	10.8	10.4
5	13.5	13.0
6	16.2	15.6
7	18.9	18.2
8	21.6	20.8
9	24.3	23.4

	25
1	2.5
2	5.0
3	7.5
4	10.0
5	12.5
6	15.0
7	17.5
8	20.0
9	22.5

	24	23
1	2.4	2.3
2	4.8	4.6
3	7.2	6.9
4	9.6	9.2
5	12.0	11.5
6	14.4	13.8
7	16.8	16.1
8	19.2	18.4
9	21.6	20.7

	22	21
1	2.2	2.1
2	4.4	4.2
3	6.6	6.3
4	8.8	8.4
5	11.0	10.5
6	13.2	12.6
7	15.4	14.7
8	17.6	16.8
9	19.8	18.9

Prop. Parts

VIII. FIVE-PLACE LOGARITHMS: 200 — 250

N	0	1	2	3	4	5	6	7	8	9
200	30 103	125	146	168	190	211	233	255	276	298
01	320	341	363	384	406	428	449	471	492	514
02	535	557	578	600	621	643	664	685	707	728
03	750	771	792	814	835	856	878	899	920	942
04	30 963	984	*006	*027	*048	*069	*091	*112	*133	*154
05	31 175	197	218	239	260	281	302	323	345	366
06	387	408	429	450	471	492	513	534	555	576
07	597	618	639	660	681	702	723	744	765	785
08	31 806	827	848	869	890	911	931	952	973	994
09	32 015	035	056	077	098	118	139	160	181	201
210	222	243	263	284	305	325	346	366	387	408
11	428	449	469	490	510	531	552	572	593	613
12	634	654	675	695	715	736	756	777	797	818
13	32 838	858	879	899	919	940	960	980	*001	*021
14	33 041	062	082	102	122	143	163	183	203	224
15	244	264	284	304	325	345	365	385	405	425
16	445	465	486	506	526	546	566	586	606	626
17	646	666	686	706	726	746	766	786	806	826
18	33 846	866	885	905	925	945	965	985	*005	*025
19	34 044	064	084	104	124	143	163	183	203	223
220	242	262	282	301	321	341	361	380	400	420
21	439	459	479	498	518	537	557	577	596	616
22	635	655	674	694	713	733	753	772	792	811
23	34 830	850	869	889	908	928	947	967	986	*005
24	35 025	044	064	083	102	122	141	160	180	199
25	218	238	257	276	295	315	334	353	372	392
26	411	430	449	468	488	507	526	545	564	583
27	603	622	641	660	679	698	717	736	755	774
28	793	813	832	851	870	889	908	927	946	965
29	35 984	*003	*021	*040	*059	*078	*097	*116	*135	*154
230	36 173	192	211	229	248	267	286	305	324	342
31	361	380	399	418	436	455	474	493	511	530
32	549	568	586	605	624	642	661	680	698	717
33	736	754	773	791	810	829	847	866	884	903
34	36 922	940	959	977	996	*014	*033	*051	*070	*088
35	37 107	125	144	162	181	199	218	236	254	273
36	291	310	328	346	365	383	401	420	438	457
37	475	493	511	530	548	566	585	603	621	639
38	658	676	694	712	731	749	767	785	803	822
39	37 840	858	876	894	912	931	949	967	985	*003
240	38 021	039	057	075	093	112	130	148	166	184
41	202	220	238	256	274	292	310	328	346	364
42	382	399	417	435	453	471	489	507	525	543
43	561	578	596	614	632	650	668	686	703	721
44	739	757	775	792	810	828	846	863	881	899
45	38 917	934	952	970	987	*005	*023	*041	*058	*076
46	39 094	111	129	146	164	182	199	217	235	252
47	270	287	305	322	340	358	375	393	410	428
48	445	463	480	498	515	533	550	568	585	602
49	620	637	655	672	690	707	724	742	759	777
250	39 794	811	829	846	863	881	898	915	933	950
N	0	1	2	3	4	5	6	7	8	9

Prop. Parts

	22	21
1	2.2	2.1
2	4.4	4.2
3	6.6	6.3
4	8.8	8.4
5	11.0	10.5
6	13.2	12.6
7	15.4	14.7
8	17.6	16.8
9	19.8	18.9

	20
1	2
2	4
3	6
4	8
5	10
6	12
7	14
8	16
9	18

	19
1	1.9
2	3.8
3	5.7
4	7.6
5	9.5
6	11.4
7	13.3
8	15.2
9	17.1

	18
1	1.8
2	3.6
3	5.4
4	7.2
5	9.0
6	10.8
7	12.6
8	14.4
9	16.2

	17
1	1.7
2	3.4
3	5.1
4	6.8
5	8.5
6	10.2
7	11.9
8	13.6
9	15.3

Prop. Parts

VIII. FIVE-PLACE LOGARITHMS: 250 — 300

N	0	1	2	3	4	5	6	7	8	9
250	39 794	811	829	846	863	881	898	915	933	950
51	39 967	985	*002	*019	*037	*054	*071	*088	*106	*123
52	40 140	157	175	192	209	226	243	261	278	295
53	312	329	346	364	381	398	415	432	449	466
54	483	500	518	535	552	569	586	603	620	637
55	654	671	688	705	722	739	756	773	790	807
56	824	841	858	875	892	909	926	943	960	976
57	40 993	*010	*027	*044	*061	*078	*095	*111	*128	*145
58	41 162	179	196	212	229	246	263	280	296	313
59	330	347	363	380	397	414	430	447	464	481
260	497	514	531	547	564	581	597	614	631	647
61	664	681	697	714	731	747	764	780	797	814
62	830	847	863	880	896	913	929	946	963	979
63	41 996	*012	*029	*045	*062	*078	*095	*111	*127	*144
64	42 160	177	193	210	226	243	259	275	292	308
65	325	341	357	374	390	406	423	439	455	472
66	488	504	521	537	553	570	586	602	619	635
67	651	667	684	700	716	732	749	765	781	797
68	813	830	846	862	878	894	911	927	943	959
69	42 975	991	*008	*024	*040	*056	*072	*088	*104	*120
270	43 136	152	169	185	201	217	233	249	265	281
71	297	313	329	345	361	377	393	409	425	441
72	457	473	489	505	521	537	553	569	584	600
73	616	632	648	664	680	696	712	727	743	759
74	775	791	807	823	838	854	870	886	902	917
75	43 933	949	965	981	996	*012	*028	*044	*059	*075
76	44 091	107	122	138	154	170	185	201	217	232
77	248	264	279	295	311	326	342	358	373	389
78	404	420	436	451	467	483	498	514	529	545
79	560	576	592	607	623	638	654	669	685	700
280	716	731	747	762	778	793	809	824	840	855
81	44 871	886	902	917	932	948	963	979	994	*010
82	45 025	040	056	071	086	102	117	133	148	163
83	179	194	209	225	240	255	271	286	301	317
84	332	347	362	378	393	408	423	439	454	469
85	484	500	515	530	545	561	576	591	606	621
86	637	652	667	682	697	712	728	743	758	773
87	788	803	818	834	849	864	879	894	909	924
88	45 939	954	969	984	*000	*015	*030	*045	*060	*075
89	46 090	105	120	135	150	165	180	195	210	225
290	240	255	270	285	300	315	330	345	359	374
91	389	404	419	434	449	464	479	494	509	523
92	538	553	568	583	598	613	627	642	657	672
93	687	702	716	731	746	761	776	790	805	820
94	835	850	864	879	894	909	923	938	953	967
95	46 982	997	*012	*026	*041	*056	*070	*085	*100	*114
96	47 129	144	159	173	188	202	217	232	246	261
97	276	290	305	319	334	349	363	378	392	407
98	422	436	451	465	480	494	509	524	538	553
99	567	582	596	611	625	640	654	669	683	698
300	47 712	727	741	756	770	784	799	813	828	842
N	0	1	2	3	4	5	6	7	8	9

Prop. Parts

	18
1	1.8
2	3.6
3	5.4
4	7.2
5	9.0
6	10.8
7	12.6
8	14.4
9	16.2

	17
1	1.7
2	3.4
3	5.1
4	6.8
5	8.5
6	10.2
7	11.9
8	13.6
9	15.3

	16
1	1.6
2	3.2
3	4.8
4	6.4
5	8.0
6	9.6
7	11.2
8	12.8
9	14.4

	15
1	1.5
2	3.0
3	4.5
4	6.0
5	7.5
6	9.0
7	10.5
8	12.0
9	13.5

	14
1	1.4
2	2.8
3	4.2
4	5.6
5	7.0
6	8.4
7	9.8
8	11.2
9	12.6

Prop. Parts

N	0	1	2	3	4	5	6	7	8	9
300	47 712	727	741	756	770	784	799	813	828	842
01	47 857	871	885	900	914	929	943	958	972	986
02	48 001	015	029	044	058	073	087	101	116	130
03	144	159	173	187	202	216	230	244	259	273
04	287	302	316	330	344	359	373	387	401	416
05	430	444	458	473	487	501	515	530	544	558
06	572	586	601	615	629	643	657	671	686	700
07	714	728	742	756	770	785	799	813	827	841
08	855	869	883	897	911	926	940	954	968	982
09	48 996	*010	*024	*038	*052	*066	*080	*094	*108	*122
310	49 136	150	164	178	192	206	220	234	248	262
11	276	290	304	318	332	346	360	374	388	402
12	415	429	443	457	471	485	499	513	527	541
13	554	568	582	596	610	624	638	651	665	679
14	693	707	721	734	748	762	776	790	803	817
15	831	845	859	872	886	900	914	927	941	955
16	49 969	982	996	*010	*024	*037	*051	*065	*079	*092
17	50 106	120	133	147	161	174	188	202	215	229
18	243	256	270	284	297	311	325	338	352	365
19	379	393	406	420	433	447	461	474	488	501
320	515	529	542	556	569	583	596	610	623	637
21	651	664	678	691	705	718	732	745	759	772
22	786	799	813	826	840	853	866	880	893	907
23	50 920	934	947	961	974	987	*001	*014	*028	*041
24	51 055	068	081	095	108	121	135	148	162	175
25	188	202	215	228	242	255	268	282	295	308
26	322	335	348	362	375	388	402	415	428	441
27	455	468	481	495	508	521	534	548	561	574
28	587	601	614	627	640	654	667	680	693	706
29	720	733	746	759	772	786	799	812	825	838
330	851	865	878	891	904	917	930	943	957	970
31	51 983	996	*009	*022	*035	*048	*061	*075	*088	*101
32	52 114	127	140	153	166	179	192	205	218	231
33	244	257	270	284	297	310	323	336	349	362
34	375	388	401	414	427	440	453	466	479	492
35	504	517	530	543	556	569	582	595	608	621
36	634	647	660	673	686	699	711	724	737	750
37	763	776	789	802	815	827	840	853	866	879
38	52 892	905	917	930	943	956	969	982	994	*007
39	53 020	033	046	058	071	084	097	110	122	135
340	148	161	173	186	199	212	224	237	250	263
41	275	288	301	314	326	339	352	364	377	390
42	403	415	428	441	453	466	479	491	504	517
43	529	542	555	567	580	593	605	618	631	643
44	656	668	681	694	706	719	732	744	757	769
45	782	794	807	820	832	845	857	870	882	895
46	53 908	920	933	945	958	970	983	995	*008	*020
47	54 033	045	058	070	083	095	108	120	133	145
48	158	170	183	195	208	220	233	245	258	270
49	283	295	307	320	332	345	357	370	382	394
350	54 407	419	432	444	456	469	481	494	506	518
N	0	1	2	3	4	5	6	7	8	9

Prop. Parts

	15
1	1.5
2	3.0
3	4.5
4	6.0
5	7.5
6	9.0
7	10.5
8	12.0
9	13.5

	14
1	1.4
2	2.8
3	4.2
4	5.6
5	7.0
6	8.4
7	9.8
8	11.2
9	12.6

	13
1	1.3
2	2.6
3	3.9
4	5.2
5	6.5
6	7.8
7	9.1
8	10.4
9	11.7

	12
1	1.2
2	2.4
3	3.6
4	4.8
5	6.0
6	7.2
7	8.4
8	9.6
9	10.8

Prop. Parts

VIII. FIVE-PLACE LOGARITHMS: 350 — 400

N	0	1	2	3	4	5	6	7	8	9
350	54 407	419	432	444	456	469	481	494	506	518
51	531	543	555	568	580	593	605	617	630	642
52	654	667	679	691	704	716	728	741	753	765
53	777	790	802	814	827	839	851	864	876	888
54	54 900	913	925	937	949	962	974	986	998	*011
55	55 023	035	047	060	072	084	096	108	121	133
56	145	157	169	182	194	206	218	230	242	255
57	267	279	291	303	315	328	340	352	364	376
58	388	400	413	425	437	449	461	473	485	497
59	509	522	534	546	558	570	582	594	606	618
360	630	642	654	666	678	691	703	715	727	739
61	751	763	775	787	799	811	823	835	847	859
62	871	883	895	907	919	931	943	955	967	979
63	55 991	*003	*015	*027	*038	*050	*062	*074	*086	*098
64	56 110	122	134	146	158	170	182	194	205	217
65	229	241	253	265	277	289	301	312	324	336
66	348	360	372	384	396	407	419	431	443	455
67	467	478	490	502	514	526	538	549	561	573
68	585	597	608	620	632	644	656	667	679	691
69	703	714	726	738	750	761	773	785	797	808
370	820	832	844	855	867	879	891	902	914	926
71	56 937	949	961	972	984	996	*008	*019	*031	*043
72	57 054	066	078	089	101	113	124	136	148	159
73	171	183	194	206	217	229	241	252	264	276
74	287	299	310	322	334	345	357	368	380	392
75	403	415	426	438	449	461	473	484	496	507
76	519	530	542	553	565	576	588	600	611	623
77	634	646	657	669	680	692	703	715	726	738
78	749	761	772	784	795	807	818	830	841	852
79	864	875	887	898	910	921	933	944	955	967
380	57 978	990	*001	*013	*024	*035	*047	*058	*070	*081
81	58 092	104	115	127	138	149	161	172	184	195
82	206	218	229	240	252	263	274	286	297	309
83	320	331	343	354	365	377	388	399	410	422
84	433	444	456	467	478	490	501	512	524	535
85	546	557	569	580	591	602	614	625	636	647
86	659	670	681	692	704	715	726	737	749	760
87	771	782	794	805	816	827	838	850	861	872
88	883	894	906	917	928	939	950	961	973	984
89	58 995	*006	*017	*028	*040	*051	*062	*073	*084	*095
390	59 106	118	129	140	151	162	173	184	195	207
91	218	229	240	251	262	273	284	295	306	318
92	329	340	351	362	373	384	395	406	417	428
93	439	450	461	472	483	494	506	517	528	539
94	550	561	572	583	594	605	616	627	638	649
95	660	671	682	693	704	715	726	737	748	759
96	770	780	791	802	813	824	835	846	857	868
97	879	890	901	912	923	934	945	956	966	977
98	59 988	999	*010	*021	*032	*043	*054	*065	*076	*086
99	60 097	108	119	130	141	152	163	173	184	195
400	60 206	217	228	239	249	260	271	282	293	304
N	0	1	2	3	4	5	6	7	8	9

Prop. Parts

	13	12	11	10
1	1.3	1.2	1.1	1.0
2	2.6	2.4	2.2	2.0
3	3.9	3.6	3.3	3.0
4	5.2	4.8	4.4	4.0
5	6.5	6.0	5.5	5.0
6	7.8	7.2	6.6	6.0
7	9.1	8.4	7.7	7.0
8	10.4	9.6	8.8	8.0
9	11.7	10.8	9.9	9.0

N	0	1	2	3	4	5	6	7	8	9
400	60 206	217	228	239	249	260	271	282	293	304
01	314	325	336	347	358	369	379	390	401	412
02	423	433	444	455	466	477	487	498	509	520
03	531	541	552	563	574	584	595	606	617	627
04	638	649	660	670	681	692	703	713	724	735
05	746	756	767	778	788	799	810	821	831	842
06	853	863	874	885	895	906	917	927	938	949
07	60 959	970	981	991	*002	*013	*023	*034	*045	*055
08	61 066	077	087	098	109	119	130	140	151	162
09	172	183	194	204	215	225	236	247	257	268
410	278	289	300	310	321	331	342	352	363	374
11	384	395	405	416	426	437	448	458	469	479
12	490	500	511	521	532	542	553	563	574	584
13	595	606	616	627	637	648	658	669	679	690
14	700	711	721	731	742	752	763	773	784	794
15	805	815	826	836	847	857	868	878	888	899
16	61 909	920	930	941	951	962	972	982	993	*003
17	62 014	024	034	045	055	066	076	086	097	107
18	118	128	138	149	159	170	180	190	201	211
19	221	232	242	252	263	273	284	294	304	315
420	325	335	346	356	366	377	387	397	408	418
21	428	439	449	459	469	480	490	500	511	521
22	531	542	552	562	572	583	593	603	613	624
23	634	644	655	665	675	685	696	706	716	726
24	737	747	757	767	778	788	798	808	818	829
25	839	849	859	870	880	890	900	910	921	931
26	62 941	951	961	972	982	992	*002	*012	*022	*033
27	63 043	053	063	073	083	094	104	114	124	134
28	144	155	165	175	185	195	205	215	225	236
29	246	256	266	276	286	296	306	317	327	337
430	347	357	367	377	387	397	407	417	428	438
31	448	458	468	478	488	498	508	518	528	538
32	548	558	568	579	589	599	609	619	629	639
33	649	659	669	679	689	699	709	719	729	739
34	749	759	769	779	789	799	809	819	829	839
35	849	859	869	879	889	899	909	919	929	939
36	63 949	959	969	979	988	998	*008	*018	*028	*038
37	64 048	058	068	078	088	098	108	118	128	137
38	147	157	167	177	187	197	207	217	227	237
39	246	256	266	276	286	296	306	316	326	335
440	345	355	365	375	385	395	404	414	424	434
41	444	454	464	473	483	493	503	513	523	532
42	542	552	562	572	582	591	601	611	621	631
43	640	650	660	670	680	689	699	709	719	729
44	738	748	758	768	777	787	797	807	816	826
45	836	846	856	865	875	885	895	904	914	924
46	64 933	943	953	963	972	982	992	*002	*011	*021
47	65 031	040	050	060	070	079	089	099	108	118
48	128	137	147	157	167	176	186	196	205	215
49	225	234	244	254	263	273	283	292	302	312
450	65 321	331	341	350	360	369	379	389	398	408
N	**0**	**1**	**2**	**3**	**4**	**5**	**6**	**7**	**8**	**9**

Prop. Parts

	11
1	1.1
2	2.2
3	3.3
4	4.4
5	5.5
6	6.6
7	7.7
8	8.8
9	9.9

	10
1	1.0
2	2.0
3	3.0
4	4.0
5	5.0
6	6.0
7	7.0
8	8.0
9	9.0

	9
1	0.9
2	1.8
3	2.7
4	3.6
5	4.5
6	5.4
7	6.3
8	7.2
9	8.1

Prop. Parts

VIII. FIVE-PLACE LOGARITHMS: 450 — 500

N	0	1	2	3	4	5	6	7	8	9
450	65 321	331	341	350	360	369	379	389	398	408
51	418	427	437	447	456	466	475	485	495	504
52	514	523	533	543	552	562	571	581	591	600
53	610	619	629	639	648	658	667	677	686	696
54	706	715	725	734	744	753	763	772	782	792
55	801	811	820	830	839	849	858	868	877	887
56	896	906	916	925	935	944	954	963	973	982
57	65 992	*001	*011	*020	*030	*039	*049	*058	*068	*077
58	66 087	096	106	115	124	134	143	153	162	172
59	181	191	200	210	219	229	238	247	257	266
460	276	285	295	304	314	323	332	342	351	361
61	370	380	389	398	408	417	427	436	445	455
62	464	474	483	492	502	511	521	530	539	549
63	558	567	577	586	596	605	614	624	633	642
64	652	661	671	680	689	699	708	717	727	736
65	745	755	764	773	783	792	801	811	820	829
66	839	848	857	867	876	885	894	904	913	922
67	66 932	941	950	960	969	978	987	997	*006	*015
68	67 025	034	043	052	062	071	080	089	099	108
69	117	127	136	145	154	164	173	182	191	201
470	210	219	228	237	247	256	265	274	284	293
71	302	311	321	330	339	348	357	367	376	385
72	394	403	413	422	431	440	449	459	468	477
73	486	495	504	514	523	532	541	550	560	569
74	578	587	596	605	614	624	633	642	651	660
75	669	679	688	697	706	715	724	733	742	752
76	761	770	779	788	797	806	815	825	834	843
77	852	861	870	879	888	897	906	916	925	934
78	67 943	952	961	970	979	988	997	*006	*015	*024
79	68 034	043	052	061	070	079	088	097	106	115
480	124	133	142	151	160	169	178	187	196	205
81	215	224	233	242	251	260	269	278	287	296
82	305	314	323	332	341	350	359	368	377	386
83	395	404	413	422	431	440	449	458	467	476
84	485	494	502	511	520	529	538	547	556	565
85	574	583	592	601	610	619	628	637	646	655
86	664	673	681	690	699	708	717	726	735	744
87	753	762	771	780	789	797	806	815	824	833
88	842	851	860	869	878	886	895	904	913	922
89	68 931	940	949	958	966	975	984	993	*002	*011
490	69 020	028	037	046	055	064	073	082	090	099
91	108	117	126	135	144	152	161	170	179	188
92	197	205	214	223	232	241	249	258	267	276
93	285	294	302	311	320	329	338	346	355	364
94	373	381	390	399	408	417	425	434	443	452
95	461	469	478	487	496	504	513	522	531	539
96	548	557	566	574	583	592	601	609	618	627
97	636	644	653	662	671	679	688	697	705	714
98	723	732	740	749	758	767	775	784	793	801
99	810	819	827	836	845	854	862	871	880	888
500	69 897	906	914	923	932	940	949	958	966	975
N	0	1	2	3	4	5	6	7	8	9

Prop. Parts

	10
1	1.0
2	2.0
3	3.0
4	4.0
5	5.0
6	6.0
7	7.0
8	8.0
9	9.0

	9
1	0.9
2	1 8
3	2.7
4	3.6
5	4.5
6	5.4
7	6.3
8	7.2
9	8.1

	8
1	0.8
2	1.6
3	2.4
4	3.2
5	4.0
6	4.8
7	5.6
8	6.4
9	7.2

Prop. Parts

N	0	1	2	3	4	5	6	7	8	9
500	69 897	906	914	923	932	940	949	958	966	975
01	69 984	992	*001	*010	*018	*027	*036	*044	*053	*062
02	70 070	079	088	096	105	114	122	131	140	148
03	157	165	174	183	191	200	209	217	226	234
04	243	252	260	269	278	286	295	303	312	321
05	329	338	346	355	364	372	381	389	398	406
06	415	424	432	441	449	458	467	475	484	492
07	501	509	518	526	535	544	552	561	569	578
08	586	595	603	612	621	629	638	646	655	663
09	672	680	689	697	706	714	723	731	740	749
510	757	766	774	783	791	800	808	817	825	834
11	842	851	859	868	876	885	893	902	910	919
12	70 927	935	944	952	961	969	978	986	995	*003
13	71 012	020	029	037	046	054	063	071	079	088
14	096	105	113	122	130	139	147	155	164	172
15	181	189	198	206	214	223	231	240	248	257
16	265	273	282	290	299	307	315	324	332	341
17	349	357	366	374	383	391	399	408	416	425
18	433	441	450	458	466	475	483	492	500	508
19	517	525	533	542	550	559	567	575	584	592
520	600	609	617	625	634	642	650	659	667	675
21	684	692	700	709	717	725	734	742	750	759
22	767	775	784	792	800	809	817	825	834	842
23	850	858	867	875	883	892	900	908	917	925
24	71 933	941	950	958	966	975	983	991	999	*008
25	72 016	024	032	041	049	057	066	074	082	090
26	099	107	115	123	132	140	148	156	165	173
27	181	189	198	206	214	222	230	239	247	255
28	263	272	280	288	296	304	313	321	329	337
29	346	354	362	370	378	387	395	403	411	419
530	428	436	444	452	460	469	477	485	493	501
31	509	518	526	534	542	550	558	567	575	583
32	591	599	607	616	624	632	640	648	656	665
33	673	681	689	697	705	713	722	730	738	746
34	754	762	770	779	787	795	803	811	819	827
35	835	843	852	860	868	876	884	892	900	908
36	916	925	933	941	949	957	965	973	981	989
37	72 997	*006	*014	*022	*030	*038	*046	*054	*062	*070
38	73 078	086	094	102	111	119	127	135	143	151
39	159	167	175	183	191	199	207	215	223	231
540	239	247	255	263	272	280	288	296	304	312
41	320	328	336	344	352	360	368	376	384	392
42	400	408	416	424	432	440	448	456	464	472
43	480	488	496	504	512	520	528	536	544	552
44	560	568	576	584	592	600	608	616	624	632
45	640	648	656	664	672	679	687	695	703	711
46	719	727	735	743	751	759	767	775	783	791
47	799	807	815	823	830	838	846	854	862	870
48	878	886	894	902	910	918	926	933	941	949
49	73 957	965	973	981	989	997	*005	*013	*020	*028
550	74 036	044	052	060	068	076	084	092	099	107
N	0	1	2	3	4	5	6	7	8	9

Prop. Parts

	9
1	0.9
2	1.8
3	2.7
4	3.6
5	4.5
6	5.4
7	6.3
8	7.2
9	8.1

	8
1	0.8
2	1.6
3	2.4
4	3.2
5	4.0
6	4.8
7	5.6
8	6.4
9	7.2

	7
1	0.7
2	1.4
3	2.1
4	2.8
5	3.5
6	4.2
7	4.9
8	5.6
9	6.3

Prop. Parts

N	0	1	2	3	4	5	6	7	8	9
550	74 036	044	052	060	068	076	084	092	099	107
51	115	123	131	139	147	155	162	170	178	186
52	194	202	210	218	225	233	241	249	257	265
53	273	280	288	296	304	312	320	327	335	343
54	351	359	367	374	382	390	398	406	414	421
55	429	437	445	453	461	468	476	484	492	500
56	507	515	523	531	539	547	554	562	570	578
57	586	593	601	609	617	624	632	640	648	656
58	663	671	679	687	695	702	710	718	726	733
59	741	749	757	764	772	780	788	796	803	811
560	819	827	834	842	850	858	865	873	881	889
61	896	904	912	920	927	935	943	950	958	966
62	74 974	981	989	997	*005	*012	*020	*028	*035	*043
63	75 051	059	066	074	082	089	097	105	113	120
64	128	136	143	151	159	166	174	182	189	197
65	205	213	220	228	236	243	251	259	266	274
66	282	289	297	305	312	320	328	335	343	351
67	358	366	374	381	389	397	404	412	420	427
68	435	442	450	458	465	473	481	488	496	504
69	511	519	526	534	542	549	557	565	572	580
570	587	595	603	610	618	626	633	641	648	656
71	664	671	679	686	694	702	709	717	724	732
72	740	747	755	762	770	778	785	793	800	808
73	815	823	831	838	846	853	861	868	876	884
74	891	899	906	914	921	929	937	944	952	959
75	75 967	974	982	989	997	*005	*012	*020	*027	*035
76	76 042	050	057	065	072	080	087	095	103	110
77	118	125	133	140	148	155	163	170	178	185
78	193	200	208	215	223	230	238	245	253	260
79	268	275	283	290	298	305	313	320	328	335
580	343	350	358	365	373	380	388	395	403	410
81	418	425	433	440	448	455	462	470	477	485
82	492	500	507	515	522	530	537	545	552	559
83	567	574	582	589	597	604	612	619	626	634
84	641	649	656	664	671	678	686	693	701	708
85	716	723	730	738	745	753	760	768	775	782
86	790	797	805	812	819	827	834	842	849	856
87	864	871	879	886	893	901	908	916	923	930
88	76 938	945	953	960	967	975	982	989	997	*004
89	77 012	019	026	034	041	048	056	063	070	078
590	085	093	100	107	115	122	129	137	144	151
91	159	166	173	181	188	195	203	210	217	225
92	232	240	247	254	262	269	276	283	291	298
93	305	313	320	327	335	342	349	357	364	371
94	379	386	393	401	408	415	422	430	437	444
95	452	459	466	474	481	488	495	503	510	517
96	525	532	539	546	554	561	568	576	583	590
97	597	605	612	619	627	634	641	648	656	663
98	670	677	685	692	699	706	714	721	728	735
99	743	750	757	764	772	779	786	793	801	808
600	77 815	822	830	837	844	851	859	866	873	880
N	**0**	**1**	**2**	**3**	**4**	**5**	**6**	**7**	**8**	**9**

Prop. Parts

	8
1	0.8
2	1.6
3	2.4
4	3.2
5	4.0
6	4.8
7	5.6
8	6.4
9	7.2

	7
1	0.7
2	1.4
3	2.1
4	2.8
5	3.5
6	4.2
7	4.9
8	5.6
9	6.3

Prop. Parts

VIII. FIVE-PLACE LOGARITHMS: 600 — 650

N	0	1	2	3	4	5	6	7	8	9
600	77 815	822	830	837	844	851	859	866	873	880
01	887	895	902	909	916	924	931	938	945	952
02	77 960	967	974	981	988	996	*003	*010	*017	*025
03	78 032	039	046	053	061	068	075	082	089	097
04	104	111	118	125	132	140	147	154	161	168
05	176	183	190	197	204	211	219	226	233	240
06	247	254	262	269	276	283	290	297	305	312
07	319	326	333	340	347	355	362	369	376	383
08	390	398	405	412	419	426	433	440	447	455
09	462	469	476	483	490	497	504	512	519	526
610	533	540	547	554	561	569	576	583	590	597
11	604	611	618	625	633	640	647	654	661	668
12	675	682	689	696	704	711	718	725	732	739
13	746	753	760	767	774	781	789	796	803	810
14	817	824	831	838	845	852	859	866	873	880
15	888	895	902	909	916	923	930	937	944	951
16	78 958	965	972	979	986	993	*000	*007	*014	*021
17	79 029	036	043	050	057	064	071	078	085	092
18	099	106	113	120	127	134	141	148	155	162
19	169	176	183	190	197	204	211	218	225	232
620	239	246	253	260	267	274	281	288	295	302
21	309	316	323	330	337	344	351	358	365	372
22	379	386	393	400	407	414	421	428	435	442
23	449	456	463	470	477	484	491	498	505	511
24	518	525	532	539	546	553	560	567	574	581
25	588	595	602	609	616	623	630	637	644	650
26	657	664	671	678	685	692	699	706	713	720
27	727	734	741	748	754	761	768	775	782	789
28	796	803	810	817	824	831	837	844	851	858
29	865	872	879	886	893	900	906	913	920	927
630	79 934	941	948	955	962	969	975	982	989	996
31	80 003	010	017	024	030	037	044	051	058	065
32	072	079	085	092	099	106	113	120	127	134
33	140	147	154	161	168	175	182	188	195	202
34	209	216	223	229	236	243	250	257	264	271
35	277	284	291	298	305	312	318	325	332	339
36	346	353	359	366	373	380	387	393	400	407
37	414	421	428	434	441	448	455	462	468	475
38	482	489	496	502	509	516	523	530	536	543
39	550	557	564	570	577	584	591	598	604	611
640	618	625	632	638	645	652	659	665	672	679
41	686	693	699	706	713	720	726	733	740	747
42	754	760	767	774	781	787	794	801	808	814
43	821	828	835	841	848	855	862	868	875	882
44	889	895	902	909	916	922	929	936	943	949
45	80 956	963	969	976	983	990	996	*003	*010	*017
46	81 023	030	037	043	050	057	064	070	077	084
47	090	097	104	111	117	124	131	137	144	151
48	158	164	171	178	184	191	198	204	211	218
49	224	231	238	245	251	258	265	271	278	285
650	81 291	298	305	311	318	325	331	338	345	351
N	0	1	2	3	4	5	6	7	8	9

Prop. Parts

	8
1	0.8
2	1.6
3	2.4
4	3.2
5	4.0
6	4.8
7	5 6
8	6.4
9	7.2

	7
1	0.7
2	1.4
3	2.1
4	2.8
5	3.5
6	4.2
7	4.9
8	5.6
9	6.3

	6
1	0.6
2	1.2
3	1.8
4	2.4
5	3.0
6	3.6
7	4.2
8	4.8
9	5.4

Prop. Parts

N	0	1	2	3	4	5	6	7	8	9
650	81 291	298	305	311	318	325	331	338	345	351
51	358	365	371	378	385	391	398	405	411	418
52	425	431	438	445	451	458	465	471	478	485
53	491	498	505	511	518	525	531	538	544	551
54	558	564	571	578	584	591	598	604	611	617
55	624	631	637	644	651	657	664	671	677	684
56	690	697	704	710	717	723	730	737	743	750
57	757	763	770	776	783	790	796	803	809	816
58	823	829	836	842	849	856	862	869	875	882
59	889	895	902	908	915	921	928	935	941	948
660	81 954	961	968	974	981	987	994	*000	*007	*014
61	82 020	027	033	040	046	053	060	066	073	079
62	086	092	099	105	112	119	125	132	138	145
63	151	158	164	171	178	184	191	197	204	210
64	217	223	230	236	243	249	256	263	269	276
65	282	289	295	302	308	315	321	328	334	341
66	347	354	360	367	373	380	387	393	400	406
67	413	419	426	432	439	445	452	458	465	471
68	478	484	491	497	504	510	517	523	530	536
69	543	549	556	562	569	575	582	588	595	601
670	607	614	620	627	633	640	646	653	659	666
71	672	679	685	692	698	705	711	718	724	730
72	737	743	750	756	763	769	776	782	789	795
73	802	808	814	821	827	834	840	847	853	860
74	866	872	879	885	892	898	905	911	918	924
75	930	937	943	950	956	963	969	975	982	988
76	82 995	*001	*008	*014	*020	*027	*033	*040	*046	*052
77	83 059	065	072	078	085	091	097	104	110	117
78	123	129	136	142	149	155	161	168	174	181
79	187	193	200	206	213	219	225	232	238	245
680	251	257	264	270	276	283	289	296	302	308
81	315	321	327	334	340	347	353	359	366	372
82	378	385	391	398	404	410	417	423	429	436
83	442	448	455	461	467	474	480	487	493	499
84	506	512	518	525	531	537	544	550	556	563
85	569	575	582	588	594	601	607	613	620	626
86	632	639	645	651	658	664	670	677	683	689
87	696	702	708	715	721	727	734	740	746	753
88	759	765	771	778	784	790	797	803	809	816
89	822	828	835	841	847	853	860	866	872	879
690	885	891	897	904	910	916	923	929	935	942
91	83 948	954	960	967	973	979	985	992	998	*004
92	84 011	017	023	029	036	042	048	055	061	067
93	073	080	086	092	098	105	111	117	123	130
94	136	142	148	155	161	167	173	180	186	192
95	198	205	211	217	223	230	236	242	248	255
96	261	267	273	280	286	292	298	305	311	317
97	323	330	336	342	348	354	361	367	373	379
98	386	392	398	404	410	417	423	429	435	442
99	448	454	460	466	473	479	485	491	497	504
700	84 510	516	522	528	535	541	547	553	559	566
N	0	1	2	3	4	5	6	7	8	9

Prop. Parts

	7
1	0.7
2	1.4
3	2.1
4	2.8
5	3.5
6	4.2
7	4.9
8	5.6
9	6.3

	6
1	0.6
2	1.2
3	1.8
4	2.4
5	3.0
6	3.6
7	4.2
8	4.8
9	5.4

Prop. Parts

N	0	1	2	3	4	5	6	7	8	9
700	84 510	516	522	528	535	541	547	553	559	566
01	572	578	584	590	597	603	609	615	621	628
02	634	640	646	652	658	665	671	677	683	689
03	696	702	708	714	720	726	733	739	745	751
04	757	763	770	776	782	788	794	800	807	813
05	819	825	831	837	844	850	856	862	868	874
06	880	887	893	899	905	911	917	924	930	936
07	84 942	948	954	960	967	973	979	985	991	997
08	85 003	009	016	022	028	034	040	046	052	058
09	065	071	077	083	089	095	101	107	114	120
710	126	132	138	144	150	156	163	169	175	181
11	187	193	199	205	211	217	224	230	236	242
12	248	254	260	266	272	278	285	291	297	303
13	309	315	321	327	333	339	345	352	358	364
14	370	376	382	388	394	400	406	412	418	425
15	431	437	443	449	455	461	467	473	479	485
16	491	497	503	509	516	522	528	534	540	546
17	552	558	564	570	576	582	588	594	600	606
18	612	618	625	631	637	643	649	655	661	667
19	673	679	685	691	697	703	709	715	721	727
720	733	739	745	751	757	763	769	775	781	788
21	794	800	806	812	818	824	830	836	842	848
22	854	860	866	872	878	884	890	896	902	908
23	914	920	926	932	938	944	950	956	962	968
24	85 974	980	986	992	998	*004	*010	*016	*022	*028
25	86 034	040	046	052	058	064	070	076	082	088
26	094	100	106	112	118	124	130	136	141	147
27	153	159	165	171	177	183	189	195	201	207
28	213	219	225	231	237	243	249	255	261	267
29	273	279	285	291	297	303	308	314	320	326
730	332	338	344	350	356	362	368	374	380	386
31	392	398	404	410	415	421	427	433	439	445
32	451	457	463	469	475	481	487	493	499	504
33	510	516	522	528	534	540	546	552	558	564
34	570	576	581	587	593	599	605	611	617	623
35	629	635	641	646	652	658	664	670	676	682
36	688	694	700	705	711	717	723	729	735	741
37	747	753	759	764	770	776	782	788	794	800
38	806	812	817	823	829	835	841	847	853	859
39	864	870	876	882	888	894	900	906	911	917
740	923	929	935	941	947	953	958	964	970	976
41	86 982	988	994	999	*005	*011	*017	*023	*029	*035
42	87 040	046	052	058	064	070	075	081	087	093
43	099	105	111	116	122	128	134	140	146	151
44	157	163	169	175	181	186	192	198	204	210
45	216	221	227	233	239	245	251	256	262	268
46	274	280	286	291	297	303	309	315	320	326
47	332	338	344	349	355	361	367	373	379	384
48	390	396	402	408	413	419	425	431	437	442
49	448	454	460	466	471	477	483	489	495	500
750	87 506	512	518	523	529	535	541	547	552	558
N	0	1	2	3	4	5	6	7	8	9

Prop. Parts

	7
1	0.7
2	1.4
3	2.1
4	2.8
5	3.5
6	4.2
7	4.9
8	5.6
9	6.3

	6
1	0.6
2	1.2
3	1.8
4	2.4
5	3.0
6	3.6
7	4.2
8	4.8
9	5.4

	5
1	0.5
2	1.0
3	1.5
4	2.0
5	2.5
6	3.0
7	3.5
8	4.0
9	4.5

Prop. Parts

Prop. Parts

	6
1	0.6
2	1.2
3	1.8
4	2.4
5	3.0
6	3.6
7	4.2
8	4.8
9	5.4

	5
1	0.5
2	1.0
3	1.5
4	2.0
5	2.5
6	3.0
7	3.5
8	4.0
9	4.5

N	0	1	2	3	4	5	6	7	8	9
750	87 506	512	518	523	529	535	541	547	552	558
51	564	570	576	581	587	593	599	604	610	616
52	622	628	633	639	645	651	656	662	668	674
53	679	685	691	697	703	708	714	720	726	731
54	737	743	749	754	760	766	772	777	783	789
55	795	800	806	812	818	823	829	835	841	846
56	852	858	864	869	875	881	887	892	898	904
57	910	915	921	927	933	938	944	950	955	961
58	87 967	973	978	984	990	996	*001	*007	*013	*018
59	88 024	030	036	041	047	053	058	064	070	076
760	081	087	093	098	104	110	116	121	127	133
61	138	144	150	156	161	167	173	178	184	190
62	195	201	207	213	218	224	230	235	241	247
63	252	258	264	270	275	281	287	292	298	304
64	309	315	321	326	332	338	343	349	355	360
65	366	372	377	383	389	395	400	406	412	417
66	423	429	434	440	446	451	457	463	468	474
67	480	485	491	497	502	508	513	519	525	530
68	536	542	547	553	559	564	570	576	581	587
69	593	598	604	610	615	621	627	632	638	643
770	649	655	660	666	672	677	683	689	694	700
71	705	711	717	722	728	734	739	745	750	756
72	762	767	773	779	784	790	795	801	807	812
73	818	824	829	835	840	846	852	857	863	868
74	874	880	885	891	897	902	908	913	919	925
75	930	936	941	947	953	958	964	969	975	981
76	88 986	992	997	*003	*009	*014	*020	*025	*031	*037
77	89 042	048	053	059	064	070	076	081	087	092
78	098	104	109	115	120	126	131	137	143	148
79	154	159	165	170	176	182	187	193	198	204
780	209	215	221	226	232	237	243	248	254	260
81	265	271	276	282	287	293	298	304	310	315
82	321	326	332	337	343	348	354	360	365	371
83	376	382	387	393	398	404	409	415	421	426
84	432	437	443	448	454	459	465	470	476	481
85	487	492	498	504	509	515	520	526	531	537
86	542	548	553	559	564	570	575	581	586	592
87	597	603	609	614	620	625	631	636	642	647
88	653	658	664	669	675	680	686	691	697	702
89	708	713	719	724	730	735	741	746	752	757
790	763	768	774	779	785	790	796	801	807	812
91	818	823	829	834	840	845	851	856	862	867
92	873	878	883	889	894	900	905	911	916	922
93	927	933	938	944	949	955	960	966	971	977
94	89 982	988	993	998	*004	*009	*015	*020	*026	*031
95	90 037	042	048	053	059	064	069	075	080	086
96	091	097	102	108	113	119	124	129	135	140
97	146	151	157	162	168	173	179	184	189	195
98	200	206	211	217	222	227	233	238	244	249
99	255	260	266	271	276	282	287	293	298	304
800	90 309	314	320	325	331	336	342	347	352	358
N	0	1	2	3	4	5	6	7	8	9

Prop. Parts

N	0	1	2	3	4	5	6	7	8	9
800	90 309	314	320	325	331	336	342	347	352	358
01	363	369	374	380	385	390	396	401	407	412
02	417	423	428	434	439	445	450	455	461	466
03	472	477	482	488	493	499	504	509	515	520
04	526	531	536	542	547	553	558	563	569	574
05	580	585	590	596	601	607	612	617	623	628
06	634	639	644	650	655	660	666	671	677	682
07	687	693	698	703	709	714	720	725	730	736
08	741	747	752	757	763	768	773	779	784	789
09	795	800	806	811	816	822	827	832	838	843
810	849	854	859	865	870	875	881	886	891	897
11	902	907	913	918	924	929	934	940	945	950
12	90 956	961	966	972	977	982	988	993	998	*004
13	91 009	014	020	025	030	036	041	046	052	057
14	062	068	073	078	084	089	094	100	105	110
15	116	121	126	132	137	142	148	153	158	164
16	169	174	180	185	190	196	201	206	212	217
17	222	228	233	238	243	249	254	259	265	270
18	275	281	286	291	297	302	307	312	318	323
19	328	334	339	344	350	355	360	365	371	376
820	381	387	392	397	403	408	413	418	424	429
21	434	440	445	450	455	461	466	471	477	482
22	487	492	498	503	508	514	519	524	529	535
23	540	545	551	556	561	566	572	577	582	587
24	593	598	603	609	614	619	624	630	635	640
25	645	651	656	661	666	672	677	682	687	693
26	698	703	709	714	719	724	730	735	740	745
27	751	756	761	766	772	777	782	787	793	798
28	803	808	814	819	824	829	834	840	845	850
29	855	861	866	871	876	882	887	892	897	903
830	908	913	918	924	929	934	939	944	950	955
31	91 960	965	971	976	981	986	991	997	*002	*007
32	92 012	018	023	028	033	038	044	049	054	059
33	065	070	075	080	085	091	096	101	106	111
34	117	122	127	132	137	143	148	153	158	163
35	169	174	179	184	189	195	200	205	210	215
36	221	226	231	236	241	247	252	257	262	267
37	273	278	283	288	293	298	304	309	314	319
38	324	330	335	340	345	350	355	361	366	371
39	376	381	387	392	397	402	407	412	418	423
840	428	433	438	443	449	454	459	464	469	474
41	480	485	490	495	500	505	511	516	521	526
42	531	536	542	547	552	557	562	567	572	578
43	583	588	593	598	603	609	614	619	624	629
44	634	639	645	650	655	660	665	670	675	681
45	686	691	696	701	706	711	716	722	727	732
46	737	742	747	752	758	763	768	773	778	783
47	788	793	799	804	809	814	819	824	829	834
48	840	845	850	855	860	865	870	875	881	886
49	891	896	901	906	911	916	921	927	932	937
850	92 942	947	952	957	962	967	973	978	983	988
N	0	1	2	3	4	5	6	7	8	9

Prop. Parts

	6
1	0.6
2	1.2
3	1.8
4	2.4
5	3.0
6	3.6
7	4.2
8	4.8
9	5.4

	5
1	0.5
2	1.0
3	1.5
4	2.0
5	2.5
6	3.0
7	3.5
8	4.0
9	4.5

Prop. Parts

VIII. FIVE-PLACE LOGARITHMS: 850 — 900

N	0	1	2	3	4	5	6	7	8	9
850	92 942	947	952	957	962	967	973	978	983	988
51	92 993	998	*003	*008	*013	*018	*024	*029	*034	*039
52	93 044	049	054	059	064	069	075	080	085	090
53	095	100	105	110	115	120	125	131	136	141
54	146	151	156	161	166	171	176	181	186	192
55	197	202	207	212	217	222	227	232	237	242
56	247	252	258	263	268	273	278	283	288	293
57	298	303	308	313	318	323	328	334	339	344
58	349	354	359	364	369	374	379	384	389	394
59	399	404	409	414	420	425	430	435	440	445
860	450	455	460	465	470	475	480	485	490	495
61	500	505	510	515	520	526	531	536	541	546
62	551	556	561	566	571	576	581	586	591	596
63	601	606	611	616	621	626	631	636	641	646
64	651	656	661	666	671	676	682	687	692	697
65	702	707	712	717	722	727	732	737	742	747
66	752	757	762	767	772	777	782	787	792	797
67	802	807	812	817	822	827	832	837	842	847
68	852	857	862	867	872	877	882	887	892	897
69	902	907	912	917	922	927	932	937	942	947
870	93 952	957	962	967	972	977	982	987	992	997
71	94 002	007	012	017	022	027	032	037	042	047
72	052	057	062	067	072	077	082	086	091	096
73	101	106	111	116	121	126	131	136	141	146
74	151	156	161	166	171	176	181	186	191	196
75	201	206	211	216	221	226	231	236	240	245
76	250	255	260	265	270	275	280	285	290	295
77	300	305	310	315	320	325	330	335	340	345
78	349	354	359	364	369	374	379	384	389	394
79	399	404	409	414	419	424	429	433	438	443
880	448	453	458	463	468	473	478	483	488	493
81	498	503	507	512	517	522	527	532	537	542
82	547	552	557	562	567	571	576	581	586	591
83	596	601	606	611	616	621	626	630	635	640
84	645	650	655	660	665	670	675	680	685	689
85	694	699	704	709	714	719	724	729	734	738
86	743	748	753	758	763	768	773	778	783	787
87	792	797	802	807	812	817	822	827	832	836
88	841	846	851	856	861	866	871	876	880	885
89	890	895	900	905	910	915	919	924	929	934
890	939	944	949	954	959	963	968	973	978	983
91	94 988	993	998	*002	*007	*012	*017	*022	*027	*032
92	95 036	041	046	051	056	061	066	071	075	080
93	085	090	095	100	105	109	114	119	124	129
94	134	139	143	148	153	158	163	168	173	177
95	182	187	192	197	202	207	211	216	221	226
96	231	236	240	245	250	255	260	265	270	274
97	279	284	289	294	299	303	308	313	318	323
98	328	332	337	342	347	352	357	361	366	371
99	376	381	386	390	395	400	405	410	415	419
900	95 424	429	434	439	444	448	453	458	463	468
N	0	1	2	3	4	5	6	7	8	9

Prop. Parts

	6
1	0.6
2	1.2
3	1.8
4	2.4
5	3.0
6	3.6
7	4.2
8	4.8
9	5.4

	5
1	0.5
2	1.0
3	1.5
4	2.0
5	2.5
6	3.0
7	3.5
8	4.0
9	4.5

	4
1	0.4
2	0.8
3	1.2
4	1.6
5	2.0
6	2.4
7	2.8
8	3.2
9	3.6

N	0	1	2	3	4	5	6	7	8	9
900	95 424	429	434	439	444	448	453	458	463	468
01	472	477	482	487	492	497	501	506	511	516
02	521	525	530	535	540	545	550	554	559	564
03	569	574	578	583	588	593	598	602	607	612
04	617	622	626	631	636	641	646	650	655	660
05	665	670	674	679	684	689	694	698	703	708
06	713	718	722	727	732	737	742	746	751	756
07	761	766	770	775	780	785	789	794	799	804
08	809	813	818	823	828	832	837	842	847	852
09	856	861	866	871	875	880	885	890	895	899
910	904	909	914	918	923	928	933	938	942	947
11	952	957	961	966	971	976	980	985	990	995
12	95 999	*004	*009	*014	*019	*023	*028	*033	*038	*042
13	96 047	052	057	061	066	071	076	080	085	090
14	095	099	104	109	114	118	123	128	133	137
15	142	147	152	156	161	166	171	175	180	185
16	190	194	199	204	209	213	218	223	227	232
17	237	242	246	251	256	261	265	270	275	280
18	284	289	294	298	303	308	313	317	322	327
19	332	336	341	346	350	355	360	365	369	374
920	379	384	388	393	398	402	407	412	417	421
21	426	431	435	440	445	450	454	459	464	468
22	473	478	483	487	492	497	501	506	511	515
23	520	525	530	534	539	544	548	553	558	562
24	567	572	577	581	586	591	595	600	605	609
25	614	619	624	628	633	638	642	647	652	656
26	661	666	670	675	680	685	689	694	699	703
27	708	713	717	722	727	731	736	741	745	750
28	755	759	764	769	774	778	783	788	792	797
29	802	806	811	816	820	825	830	834	839	844
930	848	853	858	862	867	872	876	881	886	890
31	895	900	904	909	914	918	923	928	932	937
32	942	946	951	956	960	965	970	974	979	984
33	96 988	993	997	*002	*007	*011	*016	*021	*025	*030
34	97 035	039	044	049	053	058	063	067	072	077
35	081	086	090	095	100	104	109	114	118	123
36	128	132	137	142	146	151	155	160	165	169
37	174	179	183	188	192	197	202	206	211	216
38	220	225	230	234	239	243	248	253	257	262
39	267	271	276	280	285	290	294	299	304	308
940	313	317	322	327	331	336	340	345	350	354
41	359	364	368	373	377	382	387	391	396	400
42	405	410	414	419	424	428	433	437	442	447
43	451	456	460	465	470	474	479	483	488	493
44	497	502	506	511	516	520	525	529	534	539
45	543	548	552	557	562	566	571	575	580	585
46	589	594	598	603	607	612	617	621	626	630
47	635	640	644	649	653	658	663	667	672	676
48	681	685	690	695	699	704	708	713	717	722
49	727	731	736	740	745	749	754	759	763	768
950	97 772	777	782	786	791	795	800	804	809	813
N	0	1	2	3	4	5	6	7	8	9

Prop. Parts

	5
1	0.5
2	1.0
3	1.5
4	2.0
5	2.5
6	3.0
7	3.5
8	4.0
9	4.5

	4
1	0.4
2	0.8
3	1.2
4	1.6
5	2.0
6	2.4
7	2.8
8	3.2
9	3.6

Prop. Parts

VIII. FIVE–PLACE LOGARITHMS: 950 — 1000

N	0	1	2	3	4	5	6	7	8	9
950	97 772	777	782	786	791	795	800	804	809	813
51	818	823	827	832	836	841	845	850	855	859
52	864	868	873	877	882	886	891	896	900	905
53	909	914	918	923	928	932	937	941	946	950
54	97 955	959	964	968	973	978	982	987	991	996
55	98 000	005	009	014	019	023	028	032	037	041
56	046	050	055	059	064	068	073	078	082	087
57	091	096	100	105	109	114	118	123	127	132
58	137	141	146	150	155	159	164	168	173	177
59	182	186	191	195	200	204	209	214	218	223
960	227	232	236	241	245	250	254	259	263	268
61	272	277	281	286	290	295	299	304	308	313
62	318	322	327	331	336	340	345	349	354	358
63	363	367	372	376	381	385	390	394	399	403
64	408	412	417	421	426	430	435	439	444	448
65	453	457	462	466	471	475	480	484	489	493
66	498	502	507	511	516	520	525	529	534	538
67	543	547	552	556	561	565	570	574	579	583
68	588	592	597	601	605	610	614	619	623	628
69	632	637	641	646	650	655	659	664	668	673
970	677	682	686	691	695	700	704	709	713	717
71	722	726	731	735	740	744	749	753	758	762
72	767	771	776	780	784	789	793	798	802	807
73	811	816	820	825	829	834	838	843	847	851
74	856	860	865	869	874	878	883	887	892	896
75	900	905	909	914	918	923	927	932	936	941
76	945	949	954	958	963	967	972	976	981	985
77	98 989	994	998	*003	*007	*012	*016	*021	*025	*029
78	99 034	038	043	047	052	056	061	065	069	074
79	078	083	087	092	096	100	105	109	114	118
980	123	127	131	136	140	145	149	154	158	162
81	167	171	176	180	185	189	193	198	202	207
82	211	216	220	224	229	233	238	242	247	251
83	255	260	264	269	273	277	282	286	291	295
84	300	304	308	313	317	322	326	330	335	339
85	344	348	352	357	361	366	370	374	379	383
86	388	392	396	401	405	410	414	419	423	427
87	432	436	441	445	449	454	458	463	467	471
88	476	480	484	489	493	498	502	506	511	515
89	520	524	528	533	537	542	546	550	555	559
990	564	568	572	577	581	585	590	594	599	603
91	607	612	616	621	625	629	634	638	642	647
92	651	656	660	664	669	673	677	682	686	691
93	695	699	704	708	712	717	721	726	730	734
94	739	743	747	752	756	760	765	769	774	778
95	782	787	791	795	800	804	808	813	817	822
96	826	830	835	839	843	848	852	856	861	865
97	870	874	878	883	887	891	896	900	904	909
98	913	917	922	926	930	935	939	944	948	952
99	99 957	961	965	970	974	978	983	987	991	996
1000	00 000	004	009	013	017	022	026	030	035	039
N	**0**	**1**	**2**	**3**	**4**	**5**	**6**	**7**	**8**	**9**

Prop. Parts

	5
1	0.5
2	1.0
3	1.5
4	2.0
5	2.5
6	3.0
7	3.5
8	4.0
9	4.5

	4
1	0.4
2	0.8
3	1.2
4	1.6
5	2.0
6	2.4
7	2.8
8	3.2
9	3.6

Prop. Parts

′	L Sin *	d	L Tan *	c d	L Cot	L Cos *	
0	. . . .		. . . .		. . . .	10.00 000	**60**
1	6.46 373		6.46 373		3.53 627	000	59
2	6.76 476		6.76 476		3.23 524	000	58
3	6.94 085		6.94 085		3.05 915	000	57
4	7.06 579		7.06 579		2.93 421	000	56
5	7.16 270		7.16 270		2.83 730	10.00 000	**55**
6	7.24 188		7.24 188		2.75 812	000	54
7	7.30 882		7.30 882		2.69 118	000	53
8	7.36 682		7.36 682		2.63 318	000	52
9	7.41 797		7.41 797		2.58 203	000	51
10	7.46 373		7.46 373		2.53 627	10.00 000	**50**
11	7.50 512		7.50 512		2.49 488	000	49
12	7.54 291		7.54 291		2.45 709	000	48
13	7.57 767		7.57 767		2.42 233	000	47
14	7.60 985		7.60 986		2.39 014	000	46
15	7.63 982		7.63 982		2.36 018	10.00 000	**45**
16	7.66 784		7.66 785		2.33 215	10.00 000	44
17	7.69 417		7.69 418		2.30 582	9.99 999	43
18	7.71 900		7.71 900		2.28 100	999	42
19	7.74 248		7.74 248		2.25 752	999	41
20	7.76 475		7.76 476		2.23 524	9.99 999	**40**
21	7.78 594		7.78 595		2.21 405	999	39
22	7.80 615		7.80 615		2.19 385	999	38
23	7.82 545		7.82 546		2.17 454	999	37
24	7.84 393		7.84 394		2.15 606	999	36
25	7.86 166		7.86 167		2.13 833	9.99 999	**35**
26	7.87 870		7.87 871		2.12 129	999	34
27	7.89 509		7.89 510		2.10 490	999	33
28	7.91 088		7.91 089		2.08 911	999	32
29	7.92 612		7.92 613		2.07 387	998	31
30	7.94 084		7.94 086		2.05 914	9.99 998	**30**
31	7.95 508		7.95 510		2.04 490	998	29
32	7.96 887		7.96 889		2.03 111	998	28
33	7.98 223		7.98 225		2.01 775	998	27
34	7.99 520		7.99 522		2.00 478	998	26
35	8.00 779		8.00 781		1.99 219	9.99 998	**25**
36	8.02 002		8.02 004		1.97 996	998	24
37	8.03 192		8.03 194		1.96 806	997	23
38	8.04 350		8.04 353		1.95 647	997	22
39	8.05 478		8.05 481		1.94 519	997	21
40	8.06 578		8.06 581		1.93 419	9.99 997	**20**
41	8.07 650		8.07 653		1.92 347	997	19
42	8.08 696		8.08 700		1.91 300	997	18
43	8.09 718	999	8.09 722	998	1.90 278	997	17
44	8.10 717	976	8.10 720	976	1.89 280	996	16
45	8.11 693	954	8.11 696	955	1.88 304	9.99 996	**15**
46	8.12 647	934	8.12 651	934	1.87 349	996	14
47	8.13 581	914	8.13 585	915	1.86 415	996	13
48	8.14 495	896	8.14 500	895	1.85 500	996	12
49	8.15 391	877	8.15 395	878	1.84 605	996	11
50	8.16 268	860	8.16 273	860	1.83 727	9.99 995	**10**
51	8.17 128	843	8.17 133	843	1.82 867	995	9
52	8.17 971	827	8.17 976	828	1.82 024	995	8
53	8.18 798	812	8.18 804	812	1.81 196	995	7
54	8.19 610	797	8.19 616	797	1.80 384	995	6
55	8.20 407	782	8.20 413	782	1.79 587	9.99 994	**5**
56	8.21 189	769	8.21 195	769	1.78 805	994	4
57	8.21 958	755	8.21 964	756	1.78 036	994	3
58	8.22 713	743	8.22 720	742	1.77 280	994	2
59	8.23 456	730	8.23 462	730	1.76 538	994	1
60	8.24 186		8.24 192		1.75 808	9.99 993	**0**
	L Cos *	d	L Cot *	c d	L Tan	L Sin *	′

Prop. Parts

Avoid inaccurate interpolation by using Table X on page 83.

Subtract 10 *from each entry in the columns marked with "*" in the table.*

	717	706	695	684	673
1	72	71	70	68	67
2	143	141	139	137	135
3	215	212	208	205	202
4	287	282	278	274	269
5	358	353	348	342	336
6	430	424	417	410	404
7	502	494	486	479	471
8	574	565	556	547	538
9	645	635	626	616	606

	663	653	643	634	625
1	66	65	64	63	62
2	133	130	129	127	125
3	199	196	193	190	188
4	265	261	257	254	250
5	332	326	322	317	312
6	398	392	386	380	375
7	464	457	450	444	438
8	530	522	514	507	500
9	597	588	579	571	562

	616	608	599	590	583
1	62	61	60	59	58
2	123	122	120	118	117
3	185	182	180	177	175
4	246	243	240	236	233
5	308	304	300	295	292
6	370	365	359	354	350
7	431	426	419	413	408
8	493	486	479	472	466
9	554	547	539	531	525

	575	568	560	553	546
1	58	57	56	55	55
2	115	114	112	111	109
3	172	170	168	166	164
4	230	227	224	221	218
5	288	284	280	276	273
6	345	341	336	332	328
7	402	398	392	387	382
8	460	454	448	442	437
9	518	511	504	498	491

	540	533	526	520	514
1	54	53	53	52	51
2	108	107	105	104	103
3	162	160	158	156	154
4	216	213	210	208	206
5	270	266	263	260	257
6	324	320	316	312	308
7	378	373	368	364	360
8	432	426	421	416	411
9	486	480	473	468	463

	508	502	496	491	485
1	51	50	50	49	48
2	102	100	99	98	97
3	152	151	149	147	146
4	203	201	198	196	194
5	254	251	248	246	242
6	305	301	298	295	291
7	356	351	347	344	340
8	406	402	397	393	388
9	457	452	446	442	436

	480	475	470	464	460
1	48	48	47	46	46
2	96	95	94	93	92
3	144	142	141	139	138
4	192	190	188	186	184
5	240	238	235	232	230
6	288	285	282	278	276
7	336	332	329	325	322
8	384	380	376	371	368
9	432	428	423	418	414

89°

Prop. Parts

Use the proportional parts of the number below or at the left which is ***nearest*** *to the actual tabular difference; the error will be at most 2 units in the last place. For greater accuracy, use Table X on page 83.*

	455	450	446	445	441
1	46	45	45	44	44
2	91	90	89	89	88
3	136	135	134	134	132
4	182	180	178	178	176
5	228	225	223	222	220
6	273	270	268	267	265
7	318	315	312	312	309
8	364	360	357	356	353
9	410	405	401	400	397

	437	436	433	432	428
1	44	44	43	43	43
2	87	87	87	86	86
3	131	131	130	130	128
4	175	174	173	173	171
5	218	218	216	216	214
6	262	262	260	259	257
7	306	305	303	302	300
8	350	349	346	346	342
9	393	392	390	389	385

	427	424	420	419	416
1	43	42	42	42	42
2	85	85	84	84	83
3	128	127	126	126	125
4	171	170	168	168	166
5	214	212	210	210	208
6	256	254	252	251	250
7	299	297	294	293	291
8	342	339	336	335	333
9	384	382	378	377	374

	412	411	408	404	401
1	41	41	41	40	40
2	82	82	82	81	80
3	124	123	122	121	120
4	165	164	163	162	160
5	206	206	204	202	200
6	247	247	245	242	241
7	288	288	286	283	281
8	330	329	326	323	321
9	371	370	367	364	361

	397	396	393	390	386
1	40	40	39	39	39
2	79	79	79	78	77
3	119	119	118	117	116
4	159	158	157	156	154
5	198	198	196	195	193
6	238	238	236	234	232
7	278	277	275	273	270
8	318	317	314	312	309
9	357	356	354	351	347

	383	382	380	379	376
1	38	38	38	38	38
2	77	76	76	76	75
3	115	115	114	114	113
4	153	153	152	152	150
5	192	191	190	190	188
6	230	229	228	227	226
7	268	267	266	265	263
8	306	306	304	303	301
9	345	344	342	341	338

	373	370	369	367	363
1	37	37	37	37	36
2	75	74	74	73	73
3	112	111	111	110	109
4	149	148	148	147	145
5	186	185	184	184	182
6	224	222	221	220	218
7	261	259	258	257	254
8	298	296	295	294	290
9	336	333	332	330	327

′	L Sin *	d	L Tan *	c d	L Cot	L Cos *	
0	8.24 186		8.24 192		1.75 808	9.99 993	**60**
1	8.24 903	717	8.24 910	718	1.75 090	993	59
2	8.25 609	706	8.25 616	706	1.74 384	993	58
3	8.26 304	695	8.26 312	696	1.73 688	993	57
4	8.26 988	684	8.26 996	684	1.73 004	992	56
5	8.27 661	673	8.27 669	673	1.72 331	9.99 992	**55**
6	8.28 324	663	8.28 332	663	1.71 668	992	54
7	8.28 977	653	8.28 986	654	1.71 014	992	53
8	8.29 621	644	8.29 629	643	1.70 371	992	52
9	8.30 255	634	8.30 263	634	1.69 737	991	51
10	8.30 879	624	8.30 888	625	1.69 112	9.99 991	**50**
11	8.31 495	616	8.31 505	617	1.68 495	991	49
12	8.32 103	608	8.32 112	607	1.67 888	990	48
13	8.32 702	599	8.32 711	599	1.67 289	990	47
14	8.33 292	590	8.33 302	591	1.66 698	990	46
15	8.33 875	583	8.33 886	584	1.66 114	9.99 990	**45**
16	8.34 450	575	8.34 461	575	1.65 539	989	44
17	8.35 018	568	8.35 029	568	1.64 971	989	43
18	8.35 578	560	8.35 590	561	1.64 410	989	42
19	8.36 131	553	8.36 143	553	1.63 857	989	41
20	8.36 678	547	8.36 689	546	1.63 311	9.99 988	**40**
21	8.37 217	539	8.37 229	540	1.62 771	988	39
22	8.37 750	533	8.37 762	533	1.62 238	988	38
23	8.38 276	526	8.38 289	527	1.61 711	987	37
24	8.38 796	520	8.38 809	520	1.61 191	987	36
25	8.39 310	514	8.39 323	514	1.60 677	9.99 987	**35**
26	8.39 818	508	8.39 832	509	1.60 168	986	34
27	8.40 320	502	8.40 334	502	1.59 666	986	33
28	8.40 816	496	8.40 830	496	1.59 170	986	32
29	8.41 307	491	8.41 321	491	1.58 679	985	31
30	8.41 792	485	8.41 807	486	1.58 193	9.99 985	**30**
31	8.42 272	480	8.42 287	480	1.57 713	985	29
32	8.42 746	474	8.42 762	475	1.57 238	984	28
33	8.43 216	470	8.43 232	470	1.56 768	984	27
34	8.43 680	464	8.43 696	464	1.56 304	984	26
35	8.44 139	459	8.44 156	460	1.55 844	9.99 983	**25**
36	8.44 594	455	8.44 611	455	1.55 389	983	24
37	8.45 044	450	8.45 061	450	1.54 939	983	23
38	8.45 489	445	8.45 507	446	1.54 493	982	22
39	8.45 930	441	8.45 948	441	1.54 052	982	21
40	8.46 366	436	8.46 385	437	1.53 615	9.99 982	**20**
41	8.46 799	433	8.46 817	432	1.53 183	981	19
42	8.47 226	427	8.47 245	428	1.52 755	981	18
43	8.47 650	424	8.47 669	424	1.52 331	981	17
44	8.48 069	419	8.48 089	420	1.51 911	980	16
45	8.48 485	416	8.48 505	416	1.51 495	9.99 980	**15**
46	8.48 896	411	8.48 917	412	1.51 083	979	14
47	8.49 304	408	8.49 325	408	1.50 675	979	13
48	8.49 708	404	8.49 729	404	1.50 271	979	12
49	8.50 108	400	8.50 130	401	1.49 870	978	11
50	8.50 504	396	8.50 527	397	1.49 473	9.99 978	**10**
51	8.50 897	393	8.50 920	393	1.49 080	977	9
52	8.51 287	390	8.51 310	390	1.48 690	977	8
53	8.51 673	386	8.51 696	386	1.48 304	977	7
54	8.52 055	382	8.52 079	383	1.47 921	976	6
55	8.52 434	379	8.52 459	380	1.47 541	9.99 976	**5**
56	8.52 810	376	8.52 835	376	1.47 165	975	4
57	8.53 183	373	8.53 208	373	1.46 792	975	3
58	8.53 552	369	8.53 578	370	1.46 422	974	2
59	8.53 919	367	8.53 945	367	1.46 055	974	1
60	8.54 282	363	8.54 308	363	1.45 692	9.99 974	**0**
	L Cos *	d	L Cot *	c d	L Tan	L Sin *	′

88°

′	L Sin *	d	L Tan *	c d	L Cot	L Cos *	
0	8.54 282		8.54 308		1.45 692	9.99 974	**60**
1	8.54 642	360	8.54 669	361	1.45 331	973	59
2	8.54 999	357	8.55 027	358	1.44 973	973	58
3	8.55 354	355	382	355	618	972	57
4	8.55 705	351	8.55 734	352	1.44 266	972	56
5	8.56 054	349	8.56 083	349	1.43 917	9.99 971	**55**
6	400	346	429	346	571	971	54
7	8.56 743	343	8.56 773	344	1.43 227	970	53
8	8.57 084	341	8.57 114	341	1.42 886	970	52
9	421	337	452	338	548	969	51
10	8.57 757	336	8.57 788	336	1.42 212	9.99 969	**50**
11	8.58 089	332	8.58 121	333	1.41 879	968	49
12	419	330	451	330	549	968	48
13	8.58 747	328	8.58 779	328	1.41 221	967	47
14	8.59 072	325	8.59 105	326	1.40 895	967	46
15	8.59 395	323	8.59 428	323	1.40 572	9.99 967	**45**
16	8.59 715	320	8.59 749	321	1.40 251	966	44
17	8.60 033	318	8.60 068	319	1.39 932	966	43
18	349	316	384	316	616	965	42
19	662	313	8.60 698	314	1.39 302	964	41
20	8.60 973	311	8.61 009	311	1.38 991	9.99 964	**40**
21	8.61 282	309	319	310	681	963	39
22	589	307	626	307	374	963	38
23	8.61 894	305	8.61 931	305	1.38 069	962	37
24	8.62 196	302	8.62 234	303	1.37 766	962	36
25	8.62 497	301	8.62 535	301	1.37 465	9.99 961	**35**
26	8.62 795	298	8.62 834	299	1.37 166	961	34
27	8.63 091	296	8.63 131	297	1.36 869	960	33
28	385	294	426	295	574	960	32
29	678	293	8.63 718	292	1.36 282	959	31
30	8.63 968	290	8.64 009	291	1.35 991	9.99 959	**30**
31	8.64 256	288	298	289	702	958	29
32	543	287	585	287	415	958	28
33	8.64 827	284	8.64 870	285	1.35 130	957	27
34	8.65 110	283	8.65 154	284	1.34 846	956	26
35	8.65 391	281	8.65 435	281	1.34 565	9.99 956	**25**
36	670	279	715	280	285	955	24
37	8.65 947	277	8.65 993	278	1.34 007	955	23
38	8.66 223	276	8.66 269	276	1.33 731	954	22
39	497	274	543	274	457	954	21
40	8.66 769	272	8.66 816	273	1.33 184	9.99 953	**20**
41	8.67 039	270	8.67 087	271	1.32 913	952	19
42	308	269	356	269	644	952	18
43	575	267	624	268	376	951	17
44	8.67 841	266	8.67 890	266	1.32 110	951	16
45	8.68 104	263	8.68 154	264	1.31 846	9.99 950	**15**
46	367	263	417	263	583	949	14
47	627	260	678	261	322	949	13
48	8.68 886	259	8.68 938	260	1.31 062	948	12
49	8.69 144	258	8.69 196	258	1.30 804	948	11
50	8.69 400	256	8.69 453	257	1.30 547	9.99 947	**10**
51	654	254	708	255	292	946	9
52	8.69 907	253	8.69 962	254	1.30 038	946	8
53	8.70 159	252	8.70 214	252	1.29 786	945	7
54	409	250	465	251	535	944	6
55	8.70 658	249	8.70 714	249	1.29 286	9.99 944	**5**
56	8.70 905	247	8.70 962	248	1.29 038	943	4
57	8.71 151	246	8.71 208	246	1.28 792	942	3
58	395	244	453	245	547	942	2
59	638	243	697	244	303	941	1
60	8.71 880	242	8.71 940	243	1.28 060	9.99 940	**0**
	L Cos *	d	L Cot *	c d	L Tan	L Sin *	′

Prop. Parts

Subtract 10 *from each entry in the columns marked with "*."*

See opposite page for additional tables.

	361	360	358
1	36	36	36
2	72	72	72
3	108	108	107
4	144	144	143
5	180	180	179
6	217	216	215
7	253	252	251
8	289	288	286
9	325	324	322

	357	355	352
1	36	36	35
2	71	71	70
3	107	106	106
4	143	142	141
5	178	178	176
6	214	213	211
7	250	248	246
8	286	284	282
9	321	320	317

	351	349	346
1	35	35	35
2	70	70	69
3	105	105	104
4	140	140	138
5	176	174	173
6	211	209	208
7	246	244	242
8	281	279	277
9	316	314	311

	344	343	341
1	34	34	34
2	69	69	68
3	103	103	102
4	138	137	136
5	172	172	170
6	206	206	205
7	241	240	239
8	275	274	273
9	310	309	307

	338	337	336
1	34	34	34
2	68	67	67
3	101	101	101
4	135	135	134
5	169	168	168
6	203	202	202
7	237	236	235
8	270	270	269
9	304	303	302

	333	332	330
1	33	33	33
2	67	66	66
3	100	100	99
4	133	133	132
5	166	166	165
6	200	199	198
7	233	232	231
8	266	266	264
9	300	299	297

87°

IX. FIVE-PLACE LOGARITHMS OF FUNCTIONS

Proportional Parts for 2° and 87°

	328	326	325	323	321	320		319	318	316	314	313	311	
1	33	33	32	32	32	32	1	32	32	32	31	31	31	1
2	66	65	65	65	64	64	2	64	64	63	63	63	62	2
3	98	98	98	97	96	96	3	96	95	95	94	94	93	3
4	131	130	130	129	128	128	4	128	127	126	126	125	124	4
5	164	163	162	162	160	160	5	160	159	158	157	156	156	5
6	197	196	195	194	193	192	6	191	191	190	188	188	187	6
7	230	228	228	226	225	224	7	223	223	221	220	219	218	7
8	262	261	260	258	257	256	8	255	254	253	251	250	249	8
9	295	293	292	291	289	288	9	287	286	284	283	282	280	9

	310	309	307	305	303	302		301	299	298	297	296	295	
1	31	31	31	30	30	30	1	30	30	30	30	30	30	1
2	62	62	61	61	61	60	2	60	60	60	59	59	59	2
3	93	93	92	92	91	91	3	90	90	89	89	89	88	3
4	124	124	123	122	121	121	4	120	120	119	119	118	118	4
5	155	154	154	152	152	151	5	150	150	149	148	148	148	5
6	186	185	184	183	182	181	6	181	179	179	178	178	177	6
7	217	216	215	214	212	211	7	211	209	209	208	207	206	7
8	248	247	246	244	242	242	8	241	239	238	238	237	236	8
9	279	278	276	274	273	272	9	271	269	268	267	266	266	9

	294	293	292	291	290	289		288	287	285	284	283	281	
1	29	29	29	29	29	29	1	29	29	28	28	28	28	1
2	59	59	58	58	58	58	2	58	57	57	57	57	56	2
3	88	88	88	87	87	87	3	86	86	86	85	85	84	3
4	118	117	117	116	116	116	4	115	115	114	114	113	112	4
5	147	146	146	146	145	144	5	144	144	142	142	142	140	5
6	176	176	175	175	174	173	6	173	172	171	170	170	169	6
7	206	205	204	204	203	202	7	202	201	200	199	198	197	7
8	235	234	234	233	232	231	8	230	230	228	227	226	225	8
9	265	264	263	262	261	260	9	259	258	256	256	255	253	9

	280	279	278	277	276	274		273	272	271	270	269	268	
1	28	28	28	28	28	27	1	27	27	27	27	27	27	1
2	56	56	56	55	55	55	2	55	54	54	54	54	54	2
3	84	84	83	83	83	82	3	82	82	81	81	81	80	3
4	112	112	111	111	110	110	4	109	109	108	108	108	107	4
5	140	140	139	138	138	137	5	136	136	136	135	134	134	5
6	168	167	167	166	166	164	6	164	163	163	162	161	161	6
7	196	195	195	194	193	192	7	191	190	190	189	188	188	7
8	224	223	222	222	221	219	8	218	218	217	216	215	214	8
9	252	251	250	249	248	247	9	246	245	244	243	242	241	9

	267	266	264	263	261	260		259	258	257	256	255	254	
1	27	27	26	26	26	26	1	26	26	26	26	26	25	1
2	53	53	53	53	52	52	2	52	52	51	51	51	51	2
3	80	80	79	79	78	78	3	78	77	77	77	76	76	3
4	107	106	106	105	104	104	4	104	103	103	102	102	102	4
5	134	133	132	132	130	130	5	130	129	128	128	128	127	5
6	160	160	158	158	157	156	6	155	155	154	154	153	152	6
7	187	186	185	184	183	182	7	181	181	180	179	178	178	7
8	214	213	211	210	209	208	8	207	206	206	205	204	203	8
9	240	239	238	237	235	234	9	233	232	231	230	230	229	9

	253	252	251	250	249	248		247	246	245	244	243	242	
1	25	25	25	25	25	25	1	25	25	24	24	24	24	1
2	51	50	50	50	50	50	2	49	49	49	49	49	48	2
3	76	76	75	75	75	74	3	74	74	74	73	73	73	3
4	101	101	100	100	100	99	4	99	98	98	98	97	97	4
5	126	126	126	125	124	124	5	124	123	122	122	122	121	5
6	152	151	151	150	149	149	6	148	148	147	146	146	145	6
7	177	176	176	175	174	174	7	173	172	172	171	170	169	7
8	202	202	201	200	199	198	8	198	197	196	195	194	194	8
9	228	227	226	225	224	223	9	222	221	220	220	219	218	9

′	L Sin *	d	L Tan *	c d	L Cot	L Cos *	
0	8.71 880		8.71 940		1.28 060	9.99 940	**60**
1	8.72 120	240	8.72 181	241	1.27 819	940	59
2	359	239	420	239	580	939	58
3	597	238	659	239	341	938	57
4	8.72 834	237	8.72 896	237	1.27 104	938	56
5	8.73 069	235	8.73 132	236	1.26 868	9.99 937	**55**
6	303	234	366	234	634	936	54
7	535	232	600	234	400	936	53
8	767	232	8.73 832	232	1.26 168	935	52
9	8.73 997	230	8.74 063	231	1.25 937	934	51
10	8.74 226	229	8.74 292	229	1.25 708	9.99 934	**50**
11	454	228	521	229	479	933	49
12	680	226	748	227	252	932	48
13	8.74 906	226	8.74 974	226	1.25 026	932	47
14	8.75 130	224	8.75 199	225	1.24 801	931	46
15	8.75 353	223	8.75 423	224	1.24 577	9.99 930	**45**
16	575	222	645	222	355	929	44
17	8.75 795	220	8.75 867	222	1.24 133	929	43
18	8.76 015	220	8.76 087	220	1.23 913	928	42
19	234	219	306	219	694	927	41
20	8.76 451	217	8.76 525	219	1.23 475	9.99 926	**40**
21	667	216	742	217	258	926	39
22	8.76 883	216	8.76 958	216	1.23 042	925	38
23	8.77 097	214	8.77 173	215	1.22 827	924	37
24	310	213	387	214	613	923	36
25	8.77 522	212	8.77 600	213	1.22 400	9.99 923	**35**
26	733	211	8.77 811	211	1.22 189	922	34
27	8.77 943	210	8.78 022	211	1.21 978	921	33
28	8.78 152	209	232	210	768	920	32
29	360	208	441	209	559	920	31
30	8.78 568	208	8.78 649	208	1.21 351	9.99 919	**30**
31	774	206	8.78 855	206	1.21 145	918	29
32	8.78 979	205	8.79 061	206	1.20 939	917	28
33	8.79 183	204	266	205	734	917	27
34	386	203	470	204	530	916	26
35	8.79 588	202	8.79 673	203	1.20 327	9.99 915	**25**
36	789	201	8.79 875	202	1.20 125	914	24
37	8.79 990	201	8.80 076	201	1.19 924	913	23
38	8.80 189	199	277	201	723	913	22
39	388	199	476	199	524	912	21
40	8.80 585	197	8.80 674	198	1.19 326	9.99 911	**20**
41	782	197	8.80 872	198	1.19 128	910	19
42	8.80 978	196	8.81 068	196	1.18 932	909	18
43	8.81 173	195	264	196	736	909	17
44	367	194	459	195	541	908	16
45	8.81 560	193	8.81 653	194	1.18 347	9.99 907	**15**
46	752	192	8.81 846	193	1.18 154	906	14
47	8.81 944	192	8.82 038	192	1.17 962	905	13
48	8.82 134	190	230	192	770	904	12
49	324	190	420	190	580	904	11
50	8.82 513	189	8.82 610	190	1.17 390	9.99 903	**10**
51	701	188	799	189	201	902	9
52	8.82 888	187	8.82 987	188	1.17 013	901	8
53	8.83 075	187	8.83 175	188	1.16 825	900	7
54	261	186	361	186	639	899	6
55	8.83 446	185	8.83 547	186	1.16 453	9.99 898	**5**
56	630	184	732	185	268	898	4
57	813	183	8.83 916	184	1.16 084	897	3
58	8.83 996	183	8.84 100	184	1.15 900	896	2
59	8.84 177	181	282	182	718	895	1
60	8.84 358	181	8.84 464	182	1.15 536	9.99 894	**0**
	L Cos *	d	L Cot *	c d	L Tan	L Sin *	′

Prop. Parts

Subtract 10 from each entry in the columns marked with "."*

See opposite page for additional tables.

	241	**240**
1	24.1	24
2	48.2	48
3	72.3	72
4	96.4	96
5	120.5	120
6	144.6	144
7	168.7	168
8	192.8	192
9	216.9	216

	239	**238**
1	23.9	23.8
2	47.8	47.6
3	71.7	71.4
4	95.6	95.2
5	119.5	119.0
6	143.4	142.8
7	167.3	166.6
8	191.2	190.4
9	215.1	214.2

	237
1	23.7
2	47.4
3	71.1
4	94.8
5	118.5
6	142.2
7	165.9
8	189.6
9	213.3

	236	**235**
1	23.6	23.5
2	47.2	47.0
3	70.8	70.5
4	94.4	94.0
5	118.0	117.5
6	141.6	141.0
7	165.2	164.5
8	188.8	188.0
9	212.4	211.5

86°

IX. FIVE-PLACE LOGARITHMS OF FUNCTIONS

Proportional Parts for 3° and 86°

	234	232	231	230		229	228	227	226	
1	23.4	23.2	23.1	23	1	22.9	22.8	22.7	22.6	1
2	46.8	46.4	46.2	46	2	45.8	45.6	45.4	45.2	2
3	70.2	69.6	69.3	69	3	68.7	68.4	68.1	67.8	3
4	93.6	92.8	92.4	92	4	91.6	91.2	90.8	90.4	4
5	117.0	116.0	115.5	115	5	114.5	114.0	113.5	113.0	5
6	140.4	139.2	138.6	138	6	137.4	136.8	136.2	135.6	6
7	163.8	162.4	161.7	161	7	160.3	159.6	158.9	158.2	7
8	187.2	185.6	184.8	184	8	183.2	182.4	181.6	180.8	8
9	210.6	208.8	207.9	207	9	206.1	205.2	204.3	203.4	9

	225	224	223	222		220	219	217	216	
1	22.5	22.4	22.3	22.2	1	22	21.9	21.7	21.6	1
2	45.0	44.8	44.6	44.4	2	44	43.8	43.4	43.2	2
3	67.5	67.2	66.9	66.6	3	66	65.7	65.1	64.8	3
4	90.0	89.6	89.2	88.8	4	88	87.6	86.8	86.4	4
5	112.5	112.0	111.5	111.0	5	110	109.5	108.5	108.0	5
6	135.0	134.4	133.8	133.2	6	132	131.4	130.2	129.6	6
7	157.5	156.8	156.1	155.4	7	154	153.3	151.9	151.2	7
8	180.0	179.2	178.4	177.6	8	176	175.2	173.6	172.8	8
9	202.5	201.6	200.7	199.8	9	198	197.1	195.3	194.4	9

	215	214	213	212		211	210	209	208	
1	21.5	21.4	21.3	21.2	1	21.1	21	20.9	20.8	1
2	43.0	42.8	42.6	42.4	2	42.2	42	41.8	41.6	2
3	64.5	64.2	63.9	63.6	3	63.3	63	62.7	62.4	3
4	86.0	85.6	85.2	84.8	4	84.4	84	83.6	83.2	4
5	107.5	107.0	106.5	106.0	5	105.5	105	104.5	104.0	5
6	129.0	128.4	127.8	127.2	6	126.6	126	125.4	124.8	6
7	150.5	149.8	149.1	148.4	7	147.7	147	146.3	145.6	7
8	172.0	171.2	170.4	169.6	8	168.8	168	167.2	166.4	8
9	193.5	192.6	191.7	190.8	9	189.9	189	188.1	187.2	9

	206	205	204	203		202	201	199	198	
1	20.6	20.5	20.4	20.3	1	20.2	20.1	19.9	19.8	1
2	41.2	41.0	40.8	40.6	2	40.4	40.2	39.8	39.6	2
3	61.8	61.5	61.2	60.9	3	60.6	60.3	59.7	59.4	3
4	82.4	82.0	81.6	81.2	4	80.8	80.4	79.6	79.2	4
5	103.0	102.5	102.0	101.5	5	101.0	100.5	99.5	99.0	5
6	123.6	123.0	122.4	121.8	6	121.2	120.6	119.4	118.8	6
7	144.2	143.5	142.8	142.1	7	141.4	140.7	139.3	138.6	7
8	164.8	164.0	163.2	162.4	8	161.6	160.8	159.2	158.4	8
9	185.4	184.5	183.6	182.7	9	181.8	180.9	179.1	178.2	9

	197	196	195	194		193	192	190	189	
1	19.7	19.6	19.5	19.4	1	19.3	19.2	19	18.9	1
2	39.4	39.2	39.0	38.8	2	38.6	38.4	38	37.8	2
3	59.1	58.8	58.5	58.2	3	57.9	57.6	57	56.7	3
4	78.8	78.4	78.0	77.6	4	77.2	76.8	76	75.6	4
5	98.5	98.0	97.5	97.0	5	96.5	96.0	95	94.5	5
6	118.2	117.6	117.0	116.4	6	115.8	115.2	114	113.4	6
7	137.9	137.2	136.5	135.8	7	135.1	134.4	133	132.3	7
8	157.6	156.8	156.0	155.2	8	154.4	153.6	152	151.2	8
9	177.3	176.4	175.5	174.6	9	173.7	172.8	171	170.1	9

	188	187	186	185		184	183	182	181	
1	18.8	18.7	18.6	18.5	1	18.4	18.3	18.2	18.1	1
2	37.6	37.4	37.2	37.0	2	36.8	36.6	36.4	36.2	2
3	56.4	56.1	55.8	55.5	3	55.2	54.9	54.6	54.3	3
4	75.2	74.8	74.4	74.0	4	73.6	73.2	72.8	72.4	4
5	94.0	93.5	93.0	92.5	5	92.0	91.5	91.0	90.5	5
6	112.8	112.2	111.6	111.0	6	110.4	109.8	109.2	108.6	6
7	131.6	130.9	130.2	129.5	7	128.8	128.1	127.4	126.7	7
8	150.4	149.6	148.8	148.0	8	147.2	146.4	145.6	144.8	8
9	169.2	168.3	167.4	166.5	9	165.6	164.7	163.8	162.9	9

IX. FIVE-PLACE LOGARITHMS OF FUNCTIONS — 4°

′	L Sin *	d	L Tan *	c d	L Cot	L Cos *	
0	8.84 358		8.84 464		1.15 536	9.99 894	**60**
1	539	181	646	182	354	893	59
2	718	179	8.84 826	180	1.15 174	892	58
3	8.84 897	179	8.85 006	180	1.14 994	891	57
4	8.85 075	178	185	179	815	891	56
5	8.85 252	177	8.85 363	178	1.14 637	9.99 890	**55**
6	429	177	540	177	460	889	54
7	605	176	717	177	283	888	53
8	780	175	8.85 893	176	1.14 107	887	52
9	8.85 955	175	8.86 069	176	1.13 931	886	51
10	8.86 128	173	8.86 243	174	1.13 757	9.99 885	**50**
11	301	173	417	174	583	884	49
12	474	173	591	174	409	883	48
13	645	171	763	172	237	882	47
14	816	171	8.86 935	172	1.13 065	881	46
15	8.86 987	171	8.87 106	171	1.12 894	9.99 880	**45**
16	8.87 156	169	277	171	723	879	44
17	325	169	447	170	553	879	43
18	494	169	616	169	384	878	42
19	661	167	785	169	215	877	41
20	8.87 829	168	8.87 953	168	1.12 047	9.99 876	**40**
21	8.87 995	166	8.88 120	167	1.11 880	875	39
22	8.88 161	166	287	167	713	874	38
23	326	165	453	166	547	873	37
24	490	164	618	165	382	872	36
25	8.88 654	164	8.88 783	165	1.11 217	9.99 871	**35**
26	817	163	8.88 948	165	1.11 052	870	34
27	8.88 980	163	8.89 111	163	1.10 889	869	33
28	8.89 142	162	274	163	726	868	32
29	304	162	437	163	563	867	31
30	8.89 464	160	8.89 598	161	1.10 402	9.99 866	**30**
31	625	161	760	162	240	865	29
32	784	159	8.89 920	160	1.10 080	864	28
33	8.89 943	159	8.90 080	160	1.09 920	863	27
34	8.90 102	159	240	160	760	862	26
35	8.90 260	158	8.90 399	159	1.09 601	9.99 861	**25**
36	417	157	557	158	443	860	24
37	574	157	715	158	285	859	23
38	730	156	8.90 872	157	1.09 128	858	22
39	8.90 885	155	8.91 029	157	1.08 971	857	21
40	8.91 040	155	8.91 185	156	1.08 815	9.99 856	**20**
41	195	155	340	155	660	855	19
42	349	154	495	155	505	854	18
43	502	153	650	155	350	853	17
44	655	153	803	153	197	852	16
45	8.91 807	152	8.91 957	154	1.08 043	9.99 851	**15**
46	8.91 959	152	8.92 110	153	1.07 890	850	14
47	8.92 110	151	262	152	738	848	13
48	261	151	414	152	586	847	12
49	411	150	565	151	435	846	11
50	8.92 561	150	8.92 716	151	1.07 284	9.99 845	**10**
51	710	149	8.92 866	150	1.07 134	844	9
52	8.92 859	149	8.93 016	150	1.06 984	843	8
53	8.93 007	148	165	149	835	842	7
54	154	147	313	148	687	841	6
55	8.93 301	147	8.93 462	149	1.06 538	9.99 840	**5**
56	448	147	609	147	391	839	4
57	594	146	756	147	244	838	3
58	740	146	8.93 903	147	1.06 097	837	2
59	8.93 885	145	8.94 049	146	1.05 951	836	1
60	8.94 030	145	8.94 195	146	1.05 805	9.99 834	**0**
	L Cos *	d	L Cot *	c d	L Tan	L Sin *	′

Prop. Parts

	182	181	180	179
1	18.2	18.1	18	17.9
2	36.4	36.2	36	35.8
3	54.6	54.3	54	53.7
4	72.8	72.4	72	71.6
5	91.0	90.5	90	89.5
6	109.2	108.6	108	107.4
7	127.4	126.7	126	125.3
8	145.6	144.8	144	143.2
9	163.8	162.9	162	161.1

	178	177	176	175
1	17.8	17.7	17.6	17.5
2	35.6	35.4	35.2	35.0
3	53.4	53.1	52.8	52.5
4	71.2	70.8	70.4	70.0
5	89.0	88.5	88.0	87.5
6	106.8	106.2	105.6	105.0
7	124.6	123.9	123.2	122.5
8	142.4	141.6	140.8	140.0
9	160.2	159.3	158.4	157.5

	174	173	172	171
1	17.4	17.3	17.2	17.1
2	34.8	34.6	34.4	34.2
3	52.2	51.9	51.6	51.3
4	69.6	69.2	68.8	68.4
5	87.0	86.5	86.0	85.5
6	104.4	103.8	103.2	102.6
7	121.8	121.1	120.4	119.7
8	139.2	138.4	137.6	136.8
9	156.6	155.7	154.8	153.9

	170	169	168	167
1	17	16.9	16.8	16.7
2	34	33.8	33.6	33.4
3	51	50.7	50.4	50.1
4	68	67.6	67.2	66.8
5	85	84.5	84.0	83.5
6	102	101.4	100.8	100.2
7	119	118.3	117.6	116.9
8	136	135.2	134.4	133.6
9	153	152.1	151.2	150.3

	166	165	164	163
1	16.6	16.5	16.4	16.3
2	33.2	33.0	32.8	32.6
3	49.8	49.5	49.2	48.9
4	66.4	66.0	65.6	65.2
5	83.0	82.5	82.0	81.5
6	99.6	99.0	98.4	97.8
7	116.2	115.5	114.8	114.1
8	132.8	132.0	131.2	130.4
9	149.4	148.5	147.6	146.7

	162	161	160	159
1	16.2	16.1	16	15.9
2	32.4	32.2	32	31.8
3	48.6	48.3	48	47.7
4	64.8	64.4	64	63.6
5	81.0	80.5	80	79.5
6	97.2	96.6	96	95.4
7	113.4	112.7	112	111.3
8	129.6	128.8	128	127.2
9	145.8	144.9	144	143.1

	158	157	156	155
1	15.8	15.7	15.6	15.5
2	31.6	31.4	31.2	31.0
3	47.4	47.1	46.8	46.5
4	63.2	62.8	62.4	62.0
5	79.0	78.5	78.0	77.5
6	94.8	94.2	93.6	93.0
7	110.6	109.9	109.2	108.5
8	126.4	125.6	124.8	124.0
9	142.2	141.3	140.4	139.5

	154	153	152	151
1	15.4	15.3	15.2	15.1
2	30.8	30.6	30.4	30.2
3	46.2	45.9	45.6	45.3
4	61.6	61.2	60.8	60.4
5	77.0	76.5	76.0	75.5
6	92.4	91.8	91.2	90.6
7	107.8	107.1	106.4	105.7
8	123.2	122.4	121.6	120.8
9	138.6	137.7	136.8	135.9

85°

′	L Sin *	d	L Tan *	c d	L Cot	L Cos *	
0	8.94 030		8.94 195		1.05 805	9.99 834	**60**
1	174	144	340	145	660	833	59
2	317	143	485	145	515	832	58
3	461	144	630	145	370	831	57
4	603	142	773	143	227	830	56
5	8.94 746	143	8.94 917	144	1.05 083	9.99 829	**55**
6	8.94 887	141	8.95 060	143	1.04 940	828	54
7	8.95 029	142	202	142	798	827	53
8	170	141	344	142	656	825	52
9	310	140	486	142	514	824	51
10	8.95 450	140	8.95 627	141	1.04 373	9.99 823	**50**
11	589	139	767	140	233	822	49
12	728	139	8.95 908	141	1.04 092	821	48
13	8.95 867	139	8.96 047	139	1.03 953	820	47
14	8.96 005	138	187	140	813	819	46
15	8.96 143	138	8.96 325	138	1.03 675	9.99 817	**45**
16	280	137	464	139	536	816	44
17	417	137	602	138	398	815	43
18	553	136	739	137	261	814	42
19	689	136	8.96 877	138	1.03 123	813	41
20	8.96 825	136	8.97 013	136	1.02 987	9.99 812	**40**
21	8.96 960	135	150	137	850	810	39
22	8.97 095	135	285	135	715	809	38
23	229	134	421	136	579	808	37
24	363	134	556	135	444	807	36
25	8.97 496	133	8.97 691	135	1.02 309	9.99 806	**35**
26	629	133	825	134	175	804	34
27	762	133	8.97 959	134	1.02 041	803	33
28	8.97 894	132	8.98 092	133	1.01 908	802	32
29	8.98 026	132	225	133	775	801	31
30	8.98 157	131	8.98 358	133	1.01 642	9.99 800	**30**
31	288	131	490	132	510	798	29
32	419	131	622	132	378	797	28
33	549	130	753	131	247	796	27
34	679	130	8.98 884	131	1.01 116	795	26
35	8.98 808	129	8.99 015	131	1.00 985	9.99 793	**25**
36	8.98 937	129	145	130	855	792	24
37	8.99 066	129	275	130	725	791	23
38	194	128	405	130	595	790	22
39	322	128	534	129	466	788	21
40	8.99 450	128	8.99 662	128	1.00 338	9.99 787	**20**
41	577	127	791	129	209	786	19
42	704	127	8.99 919	128	1.00 081	785	18
43	830	126	9.00 046	127	0.99 954	783	17
44	8.99 956	126	174	128	826	782	16
45	9.00 082	126	9.00 301	127	0.99 699	9.99 781	**15**
46	207	125	427	126	573	780	14
47	332	125	553	126	447	778	13
48	456	124	679	126	321	777	12
49	581	125	805	126	195	776	11
50	9.00 704	123	9.00 930	125	0.99 070	9.99 775	**10**
51	828	124	9.01 055	125	0.98 945	773	9
52	9.00 951	123	179	124	821	772	8
53	9.01 074	123	303	124	697	771	7
54	196	122	427	124	573	769	6
55	9.01 318	122	9.01 550	123	0.98 450	9.99 768	**5**
56	440	122	673	123	327	767	4
57	561	121	796	123	204	765	3
58	682	121	9.01 918	122	0.98 082	764	2
59	803	121	9.02 040	122	0.97 960	763	1
60	9.01 923	120	9.02 162	122	0.97 838	9.99 761	**0**
	L Cos *	d	L Cot *	c d	L Tan	L Sin *	′

Prop. Parts

	150	149	148	147
1	15	14.9	14.8	14.7
2	30	29.8	29.6	29.4
3	45	44.7	44.4	44.1
4	60	59.6	59.2	58.8
5	75	74.5	74.0	73.5
6	90	89.4	88.8	88.2
7	105	104.3	103.6	102.9
8	120	119.2	118.4	117.6
9	135	134.1	133.2	132.3

	146	145	144	143
1	14.6	14.5	14.4	14.3
2	29.2	29.0	28.8	28.6
3	43.8	43.5	43.2	42.9
4	58.4	58.0	57.6	57.2
5	73.0	72.5	72.0	71.5
6	87.6	87.0	86.4	85.8
7	102.2	101.5	100.8	100.1
8	116.8	116.0	115.2	114.4
9	131.4	130.5	129.6	128.7

	142	141	140	139
1	14.2	14.1	14	13.9
2	28.4	28.2	28	27.8
3	42.6	42.3	42	41.7
4	56.8	56.4	56	55.6
5	71.0	70.5	70	69.5
6	85.2	84.6	84	83.4
7	99.4	98.7	98	97.3
8	113.6	112.8	112	111.2
9	127.8	126.9	126	125.1

	138	137	136	135
1	13.8	13.7	13.6	13.5
2	27.6	27.4	27.2	27.0
3	41.4	41.1	40.8	40.5
4	55.2	54.8	54.4	54.0
5	69.0	68.5	68.0	67.5
6	82.8	82.2	81.6	81.0
7	96.6	95.9	95.2	94.5
8	110.4	109.6	108.8	108.0
9	124.2	123.3	122.4	121.5

	134	133	132	131
1	13.4	13.3	13.2	13.1
2	26.8	26.6	26.4	26.2
3	40.2	39.9	39.6	39.3
4	53.6	53.2	52.8	52.4
5	67.0	66.5	66.0	65.5
6	80.4	79.8	79.2	78.6
7	93.8	93.1	92.4	91.7
8	107.2	106.4	105.6	104.8
9	120.6	119.7	118.8	117.9

	130	129	128	127
1	13	12.9	12.8	12.7
2	26	25.8	25.6	25.4
3	39	38.7	38.4	38.1
4	52	51.6	51.2	50.8
5	65	64.5	64.0	63.5
6	78	77.4	76.8	76.2
7	91	90.3	89.6	88.9
8	104	103.2	102.4	101.6
9	117	116.1	115.2	114.3

	126	125	124	123
1	12.6	12.5	12.4	12.3
2	25.2	25.0	24.8	24.6
3	37.8	37.5	37.2	36.9
4	50.4	50.0	49.6	49.2
5	63.0	62.5	62.0	61.5
6	75.6	75.0	74.4	73.8
7	88.2	87.5	86.8	86.1
8	100.8	100.0	99.2	98.4
9	113.4	112.5	111.6	110.7

	122	121	120
1	12.2	12.1	12
2	24.4	24.2	24
3	36.6	36.3	36
4	48.8	48.4	48
5	61.0	60.5	60
6	73.2	72.6	72
7	85.4	84.7	84
8	97.6	96.8	96
9	109.8	108.9	108

84°

IX. FIVE-PLACE LOGARITHMS OF FUNCTIONS — 6°

′	L Sin *	d	L Tan *	c d	L Cot	L Cos *	
0	9.01 923		9.02 162		0.97 838	9.99 761	**60**
1	9.02 043	120	283	121	717	760	59
2	163	120	404	121	596	759	58
3	283	120	525	121	475	757	57
4	402	119	645	120	355	756	56
5	9.02 520	118	9.02 766	121	0.97 234	9.99 755	**55**
6	639	119	9.02 885	119	0.97 115	753	54
7	757	118	9.03 005	120	0.96 995	752	53
8	874	117	124	119	876	751	52
9	9.02 992	118	242	118	758	749	51
10	9.03 109	117	9.03 361	119	0.96 639	9.99 748	**50**
11	226	117	479	118	521	747	49
12	342	116	597	118	403	745	48
13	458	116	714	117	286	744	47
14	574	116	832	118	168	742	46
15	9.03 690	116	9.03 948	116	0.96 052	9.99 741	**45**
16	805	115	9.04 065	117	0.95 935	740	44
17	9.03 920	115	181	116	819	738	43
18	9.04 034	114	297	116	703	737	42
19	149	115	413	116	587	736	41
20	9.04 262	113	9.04 528	115	0.95 472	9.99 734	**40**
21	376	114	643	115	357	733	39
22	490	114	758	115	242	731	38
23	603	113	873	115	127	730	37
24	715	112	9.04 987	114	0.95 013	728	36
25	9.04 828	113	9.05 101	114	0.94 899	9.99 727	**35**
26	9.04 940	112	214	113	786	726	34
27	9.05 052	112	328	114	672	724	33
28	164	112	441	113	559	723	32
29	275	111	553	112	447	721	31
30	9.05 386	111	9.05 666	113	0.94 334	9.99 720	**30**
31	497	111	778	112	222	718	29
32	607	110	9.05 890	112	0.94 110	717	28
33	717	110	9.06 002	112	0.93 998	716	27
34	827	110	113	111	887	714	26
35	9.05 937	110	9.06 224	111	0.93 776	9.99 713	**25**
36	9.06 046	109	335	111	665	711	24
37	155	109	445	110	555	710	23
38	264	109	556	111	444	708	22
39	372	108	666	110	334	707	21
40	9.06 481	109	9.06 775	109	0.93 225	9.99 705	**20**
41	589	108	885	110	115	704	**19**
42	696	107	9.06 994	109	0.93 006	702	18
43	804	108	9.07 103	109	0.92 897	701	17
44	9.06 911	107	211	108	789	699	16
45	9.07 018	107	9.07 320	109	0.92 680	9.99 698	**15**
46	124	106	428	108	572	696	14
47	231	107	536	108	464	695	13
48	337	106	643	107	357	693	12
49	442	105	751	108	249	692	11
50	9.07 548	106	9.07 858	107	0.92 142	9.99 690	**10**
51	653	105	9.07 964	106	0.92 036	689	9
52	758	105	9.08 071	107	0.91 929	687	8
53	863	105	177	106	823	686	7
54	9.07 968	105	283	106	717	684	6
55	9.08 072	104	9.08 389	106	0.91 611	9.99 683	**5**
56	176	104	495	106	505	681	4
57	280	104	600	105	400	680	3
58	383	103	705	105	295	678	2
59	486	103	810	105	190	677	1
60	9.08 589	103	9.08 914	104	0.91 086	9.99 675	**0**
	L Cos *	d	L Cot *	c d	L Tan	L Sin *	′

83°

Prop. Parts

Subtract 10 *from each entry in the columns marked with "*."*

	121	**120**	**119**
1	12.1	12	11.9
2	24.2	24	23.8
3	36.3	36	35.7
4	48.4	48	47.6
5	60.5	60	59.5
6	72.6	72	71.4
7	84.7	84	83.3
8	96.8	96	95.2
9	108.9	108	107.1

	118	**117**	**116**
1	11.8	11.7	11.6
2	23.6	23.4	23.2
3	35.4	35.1	34.8
4	47.2	46.8	46.4
5	59.0	58.5	58.0
6	70.8	70.2	69.6
7	82.6	81.9	81.2
8	94.4	93.6	92.8
9	106.2	105.3	104.4

	115	**114**	**113**
1	11.5	11.4	11.3
2	23.0	22.8	22.6
3	34.5	34.2	33.9
4	46.0	45.6	45.2
5	57.5	57.0	56.5
6	69.0	68.4	67.8
7	80.5	79.8	79.1
8	92.0	91.2	90.4
9	103.5	102.6	101.7

	112	**111**	**110**
1	11.2	11.1	11
2	22.4	22.2	22
3	33.6	33.3	33
4	44.8	44.4	44
5	56.0	55.5	55
6	67.2	66.6	66
7	78.4	77.7	77
8	89.6	88.8	88
9	100.8	99.9	99

	109	**108**	**107**	**106**
1	10.9	10.8	10.7	10.6
2	21.8	21.6	21.4	21.2
3	32.7	32.4	32.1	31.8
4	43.6	43.2	42.8	42.4
5	54.5	54.0	53.5	53.0
6	65.4	64.8	64.2	63.6
7	76.3	75.6	74.9	74.2
8	87.2	86.4	85.6	84.8
9	98.1	97.2	96.3	95.4

Prop. Parts

	105	104	103
1	10.5	10.4	10.3
2	21.0	20.8	20.6
3	31.5	31.2	30.9
4	42.0	41.6	41.2
5	52.5	52.0	51.5
6	63.0	62.4	61.8
7	73.5	72.8	72.1
8	84.0	83.2	82.4
9	94.5	93.6	92.7

	102	101	99
1	10.2	10.1	9.9
2	20.4	20.2	19.8
3	30.6	30.3	29.7
4	40.8	40.4	39.6
5	51.0	50.5	49.5
6	61.2	60.6	59.4
7	71.4	70.7	69.3
8	81.6	80.8	79.2
9	91.8	90.9	89.1

	98	97	96
1	9.8	9.7	9.6
2	19.6	19.4	19.2
3	29.4	29.1	28.8
4	39.2	38.8	38.4
5	49.0	48.5	48.0
6	58.8	58.2	57.6
7	68.6	67.9	67.2
8	78.4	77.6	76.8
9	88.2	87.3	86.4

	95	94	93
1	9.5	9.4	9.3
2	19.0	18.8	18.6
3	28.5	28.2	27.9
4	38.0	37.6	37.2
5	47.5	47.0	46.5
6	57.0	56.4	55.8
7	66.5	65.8	65.1
8	76.0	75.2	74.4
9	85.5	84.6	83.7

	92	91	90
1	9.2	9.1	9
2	18.4	18.2	18
3	27.6	27.3	27
4	36.8	36.4	36
5	46.0	45.5	45
6	55.2	54.6	54
7	64.4	63.7	63
8	73.6	72.8	72
9	82.8	81.9	81

′	L Sin *	d	L Tan *	c d	L Cot	L Cos *	
0	9.08 589		9.08 914		0.91 086	9.99 675	**60**
1	692	103	9.09 019	105	0.90 981	674	59
2	795	103	123	104	877	672	58
3	897	102	227	104	773	670	57
4	9.08 999	102	330	103	670	669	56
5	9.09 101	102	9.09 434	104	0.90 566	9.99 667	**55**
6	202	101	537	103	463	666	54
7	304	102	640	103	360	664	53
8	405	101	742	102	258	663	52
9	506	101	845	103	155	661	51
10	9.09 606	100	9.09 947	102	0.90 053	9.99 659	**50**
11	707	101	9.10 049	102	0.89 951	658	49
12	807	100	150	101	850	656	48
13	9.09 907	100	252	102	748	655	47
14	9.10 006	99	353	101	647	653	46
15	9.10 106	100	9.10 454	101	0.89 546	9.99 651	**45**
16	205	99	555	101	445	650	44
17	304	99	656	101	344	648	43
18	402	98	756	100	244	647	42
19	501	99	856	100	144	645	41
20	9.10 599	98	9.10 956	100	0.89 044	9.99 643	**40**
21	697	98	9.11 056	100	0.88 944	642	39
22	795	98	155	99	845	640	38
23	893	98	254	99	746	638	37
24	9.10 990	97	353	99	647	637	36
25	9.11 087	97	9.11 452	99	0.88 548	9.99 635	**35**
26	184	97	551	99	449	633	34
27	281	97	649	98	351	632	33
28	377	96	747	98	253	630	32
29	474	97	845	98	155	629	31
30	9.11 570	96	9.11 943	98	0.88 057	9.99 627	**30**
31	666	96	9.12 040	97	0.87 960	625	29
32	761	95	138	98	862	624	28
33	857	96	235	97	765	622	27
34	9.11 952	95	332	97	668	620	26
35	9.12 047	95	9.12 428	96	0.87 572	9.99 618	**25**
36	142	95	525	97	475	617	24
37	236	94	621	96	379	615	23
38	331	95	717	96	283	613	22
39	425	94	813	96	187	612	21
40	9.12 519	94	9.12 909	96	0.87 091	9.99 610	**20**
41	612	93	9.13 004	95	0.86 996	608	19
42	706	94	099	95	901	607	18
43	799	93	194	95	806	605	17
44	892	93	289	95	711	603	16
45	9.12 985	93	9.13 384	95	0.86 616	9.99 601	**15**
46	9.13 078	93	478	94	522	600	14
47	171	93	573	95	427	598	13
48	263	92	667	94	333	596	12
49	355	92	761	94	239	595	11
50	9.13 447	92	9.13 854	93	0.86 146	9.99 593	**10**
51	539	92	9.13 948	94	0.86 052	591	9
52	630	91	9.14 041	93	0.85 959	589	8
53	722	92	134	93	866	588	7
54	813	91	227	93	773	586	6
55	9.13 904	91	9.14 320	93	0.85 680	9.99 584	**5**
56	9.13 994	90	412	92	588	582	4
57	9.14 085	91	504	92	496	581	3
58	175	90	597	93	403	579	2
59	266	91	688	91	312	577	1
60	9.14 356	90	9.14 780	92	0.85 220	9.99 575	**0**
	L Cos *	d	L Cot *	c d	L Tan	L Sin *	′

82°

′	L Sin *	d	L Tan *	c d	L Cot	L Cos *	
0	9.14 356		9.14 780		0.85 220	9.99 575	**60**
1	445	89	872	92	128	574	59
2	535	90	9.14 963	91	0.85 037	572	58
3	624	89	9.15 054	91	0.84 946	570	57
4	714	90	145	91	855	568	56
5	9.14 803	89	9.15 236	91	0.84 764	9.99 566	**55**
6	891	88	327	91	673	565	54
7	9.14 980	89	417	90	583	563	53
8	9.15 069	89	508	91	492	561	52
9	157	88	598	90	402	559	51
10	9.15 245	88	9.15 688	90	0.84 312	9.99 557	**50**
11	333	88	777	89	223	556	49
12	421	88	867	90	133	554	48
13	508	87	9.15 956	89	0.84 044	552	47
14	596	88	9.16 046	90	0.83 954	550	46
15	9.15 683	87	9.16 135	89	0.83 865	9.99 548	**45**
16	770	87	224	89	776	546	44
17	857	87	312	88	688	545	43
18	9.15 944	87	401	89	599	543	42
19	9.16 030	86	489	88	511	541	41
20	9.16 116	86	9.16 577	88	0.83 423	9.99 539	**40**
21	203	87	665	88	335	537	39
22	289	86	753	88	247	535	38
23	374	85	841	88	159	533	37
24	460	86	9.16 928	87	0.83 072	532	36
25	9.16 545	85	9.17 016	88	0.82 984	9.99 530	**35**
26	631	86	103	87	897	528	34
27	716	85	190	87	810	526	33
28	801	85	277	87	723	524	32
29	886	85	363	86	637	522	31
30	9.16 970	84	9.17 450	87	0.82 550	9.99 520	**30**
31	9.17 055	85	536	86	464	518	29
32	139	84	622	86	378	517	28
33	223	84	708	86	292	515	27
34	307	84	794	86	206	513	26
35	9.17 391	84	9.17 880	86	0.82 120	9.99 511	**25**
36	474	83	9.17 965	85	0.82 035	509	24
37	558	84	9.18 051	86	0.81 949	507	23
38	641	83	136	85	864	505	22
39	724	83	221	85	779	503	21
40	9.17 807	83	9.18 306	85	0.81 694	9.99 501	**20**
41	890	83	391	85	609	499	19
42	9.17 973	83	475	84	525	497	18
43	9.18 055	82	560	85	440	495	17
44	137	82	644	84	356	494	16
45	9.18 220	83	9.18 728	84	0.81 272	9.99 492	**15**
46	302	82	812	84	188	490	14
47	383	81	896	84	104	488	13
48	465	82	9.18 979	83	0.81 021	486	12
49	547	82	9.19 063	84	0.80 937	484	11
50	9.18 628	81	9.19 146	83	0.80 854	9.99 482	**10**
51	709	81	229	83	771	480	9
52	790	81	312	83	688	478	8
53	871	81	395	83	605	476	7
54	9.18 952	81	478	83	522	474	6
55	9.19 033	81	9.19 561	83	0.80 439	9.99 472	**5**
56	113	80	643	82	357	470	4
57	193	80	725	82	275	468	3
58	273	80	807	82	193	466	2
59	353	80	889	82	111	464	1
60	9.19 433	80	9.19 971	82	0.80 029	9.99 462	**0**
	L Cos *	d	L Cot *	c d	L Tan	L Sin *	′

81°

Prop. Parts

Subtract 10 *from each entry in the columns marked with "*."*

	92	91	90	89
1	9.2	9.1	9	8.9
2	18.4	18.2	18	17.8
3	27.6	27.3	27	26.7
4	36.8	36.4	36	35.6
5	46.0	45.5	45	44.5
6	55.2	54.6	54	53.4
7	64.4	63.7	63	62.3
8	73.6	72.8	72	71.2
9	82.8	81.9	81	80.1

	88	87	86
1	8.8	8.7	8.6
2	17.6	17.4	17.2
3	26.4	26.1	25.8
4	35.2	34.8	34.4
5	44.0	43.5	43.0
6	52.8	52.2	51.6
7	61.6	60.9	60.2
8	70.4	69.6	68.8
9	79.2	78.3	77.4

	85	84	83
1	8.5	8.4	8.3
2	17.0	16.8	16.6
3	25.5	25.2	24.9
4	34.0	33.6	33.2
5	42.5	42.0	41.5
6	51.0	50.4	49.8
7	59.5	58.8	58.1
8	68.0	67.2	66.4
9	76.5	75.6	74.7

	82	81	80
1	8.2	8.1	8
2	16.4	16.2	16
3	24.6	24.3	24
4	32.8	32.4	32
5	41.0	40.5	40
6	49.2	48.6	48
7	57.4	56.7	56
8	65.6	64.8	64
9	73.8	72.9	72

′	L Sin *	d	L Tan *	c d	L Cot	L Cos *	d	
0	9.19 433		9.19 971		0.80 029	9.99 462		60
1	513	80	9.20 053	82	0.79 947	460	2	59
2	592	79	134	81	866	458	2	58
3	672	80	216	82	784	456	2	57
4	751	79	297	81	703	454	2	56
5	9.19 830	79	9.20 378	81	0.79 622	9.99 452	2	55
6	909	79	459	81	541	450	2	54
7	9.19 988	79	540	81	460	448	2	53
8	9.20 067	79	621	81	379	446	2	52
9	145	78	701	80	299	444	2	51
10	9.20 223	78	9.20 782	81	0.79 218	9.99 442	2	50
11	302	79	862	80	138	440	2	49
12	380	78	9.20 942	80	0.79 058	438	2	48
13	458	78	9.21 022	80	0.78 978	436	2	47
14	535	77	102	80	898	434	2	46
15	9.20 613	78	9.21 182	80	0.78 818	9.99 432	2	45
16	691	78	261	79	739	429	3	44
17	768	77	341	80	659	427	2	43
18	845	77	420	79	580	425	2	42
19	922	77	499	79	501	423	2	41
20	9.20 999	77	9.21 578	79	0.78 422	9.99 421	2	40
21	9.21 076	77	657	79	343	419	2	39
22	153	77	736	79	264	417	2	38
23	229	76	814	78	186	415	2	37
24	306	77	893	79	107	413	2	36
25	9.21 382	76	9.21 971	78	0.78 029	9.99 411	2	35
26	458	76	9.22 049	78	0.77 951	409	2	34
27	534	76	127	78	873	407	2	33
28	610	76	205	78	795	404	3	32
29	685	75	283	78	717	402	2	31
30	9.21 761	76	9.22 361	78	0.77 639	9.99 400	2	30
31	836	75	438	77	562	398	2	29
32	912	76	516	78	484	396	2	28
33	9.21 987	75	593	77	407	394	2	27
34	9.22 062	75	670	77	330	392	2	26
35	9.22 137	75	9.22 747	77	0.77 253	9.99 390	2	25
36	211	74	824	77	176	388	2	24
37	286	75	901	77	099	385	3	23
38	361	75	9.22 977	76	0.77 023	383	2	22
39	435	74	9.23 054	77	0.76 946	381	2	21
40	9.22 509	74	9.23 130	76	0.76 870	9.99 379	2	20
41	583	74	206	76	794	377	2	19
42	657	74	283	77	717	375	2	18
43	731	74	359	76	641	372	3	17
44	805	74	435	76	565	370	2	16
45	9.22 878	73	9.23 510	75	0.76 490	9.99 368	2	15
46	9.22 952	74	586	76	414	366	2	14
47	9.23 025	73	661	75	339	364	2	13
48	098	73	737	76	263	362	2	12
49	171	73	812	75	188	359	3	11
50	9.23 244	73	9.23 887	75	0.76 113	9.99 357	2	10
51	317	73	9.23 962	75	0.76 038	355	2	9
52	390	73	9.24 037	75	0.75 963	353	2	8
53	462	72	112	75	888	351	2	7
54	535	73	186	74	814	348	3	6
55	9.23 607	72	9.24 261	75	0.75 739	9.99 346	2	5
56	679	72	335	74	665	344	2	4
57	752	73	410	75	590	342	2	3
58	823	71	484	74	516	340	2	2
59	895	72	558	74	442	337	3	1
60	9.23 967	72	9.24 632	74	0.75 368	9.99 335	2	0
	L Cos *	d	L Cot *	c d	L Tan	L Sin *	d	′

Prop. Parts

	82	81	80
1	8.2	8.1	8
2	16.4	16.2	16
3	24.6	24.3	24
4	32.8	32.4	32
5	41.0	40.5	40
6	49.2	48.6	48
7	57.4	56.7	56
8	65.6	64.8	64
9	73.8	72.9	72

	79	78	77
1	7.9	7.8	7.7
2	15.8	15.6	15.4
3	23.7	23.4	23.1
4	31.6	31.2	30.8
5	39.5	39.0	38.5
6	47.4	46.8	46.2
7	55.3	54.6	53.9
8	63.2	62.4	61.6
9	71.1	70.2	69.3

	76	75	74
1	7.6	7.5	7.4
2	15.2	15.0	14.8
3	22.8	22.5	22.2
4	30.4	30.0	29.6
5	38.0	37.5	37.0
6	45.6	45.0	44.4
7	53.2	52.5	51.8
8	60.8	60.0	59.2
9	68.4	67.5	66.6

	73	72	71
1	7.3	7.2	7.1
2	14.6	14.4	14.2
3	21.9	21.6	21.3
4	29.2	28.8	28.4
5	36.5	36.0	35.5
6	43.8	43.2	42.6
7	51.1	50.4	49.7
8	58.4	57.6	56.8
9	65.7	64.8	63.9

80°

′	L Sin *	d	L Tan *	c d	L Cot	L Cos *	d	
0	9.23 967		9.24 632		0.75 368	9.99 335		**60**
1	9.24 039	72	706	74	294	333	2	59
2	110	71	779	73	221	331	2	58
3	181	71	853	74	147	328	3	57
4	253	72	9.24 926	73	074	326	2	56
5	9.24 324	71	9.25 000	74	0.75 000	9.99 324	2	**55**
6	395	71	073	73	0.74 927	322	2	54
7	466	71	146	73	854	319	3	53
8	536	70	219	73	781	317	2	52
9	607	71	292	73	708	315	2	51
10	9.24 677	70	9.25 365	73	0.74 635	9.99 313	2	**50**
11	748	71	437	72	563	310	3	49
12	818	70	510	73	490	308	2	48
13	888	70	582	72	418	306	2	47
14	9.24 958	70	655	73	345	304	2	46
15	9.25 028	70	9.25 727	72	0.74 273	9.99 301	3	**45**
16	098	70	799	72	201	299	2	44
17	168	70	871	72	129	297	2	43
18	237	69	9.25 943	72	0.74 057	294	3	42
19	307	70	9.26 015	72	0.73 985	292	2	41
20	9.25 376	69	9.26 086	71	0.73 914	9.99 290	2	**40**
21	445	69	158	72	842	288	2	39
22	514	69	229	71	771	285	3	38
23	583	69	301	72	699	283	2	37
24	652	69	372	71	628	281	2	36
25	9.25 721	69	9.26 443	71	0.73 557	9.99 278	3	**35**
26	790	69	514	71	486	276	2	34
27	858	68	585	71	415	274	2	33
28	927	69	655	70	345	271	3	32
29	9.25 995	68	726	71	274	269	2	31
30	9.26 063	68	9.26 797	71	0.73 203	9.99 267	2	**30**
31	131	68	867	70	133	264	3	29
32	199	68	9.26 937	70	0.73 063	262	2	28
33	267	68	9.27 008	71	0.72 992	260	2	27
34	335	68	078	70	922	257	3	26
35	9.26 403	68	9.27 148	70	0.72 852	9.99 255	2	**25**
36	470	67	218	70	782	252	3	24
37	538	68	288	70	712	250	2	23
38	605	67	357	69	643	248	2	22
39	672	67	427	70	573	245	3	21
40	9.26 739	67	9.27 496	69	0.72 504	9.99 243	2	**20**
41	806	67	566	70	434	241	2	19
42	873	67	635	69	365	238	3	18
43	9.26 940	67	704	69	296	236	2	17
44	9.27 007	67	773	69	227	233	3	16
45	9.27 073	66	9.27 842	69	0.72 158	9.99 231	2	**15**
46	140	67	911	69	089	229	2	14
47	206	66	9.27 980	69	0.72 020	226	3	13
48	273	67	9.28 049	69	0.71 951	224	2	12
49	339	66	117	68	883	221	3	11
50	9.27 405	66	9.28 186	69	0.71 814	9.99 219	2	**10**
51	471	66	254	68	746	217	2	9
52	537	66	323	69	677	214	3	8
53	602	65	391	68	609	212	2	7
54	668	66	459	68	541	209	3	6
55	9.27 734	66	9.28 527	68	0.71 473	9.99 207	2	**5**
56	799	65	595	68	405	204	3	4
57	864	65	662	67	338	202	2	3
58	930	66	730	68	270	200	2	2
59	9.27 995	65	798	68	202	197	3	1
60	9.28 060	65	9.28 865	67	0.71 135	9.99 195	2	**0**
	L Cos *	d	L Cot *	c d	L Tan	L Sin *	d	′

Prop. Parts

	74	**73**	**72**
1	7.4	7.3	7.2
2	14.8	14.6	14.4
3	22.2	21.9	21.6
4	29.6	29.2	28.8
5	37.0	36.5	36.0
6	44.4	43.8	43.2
7	51.8	51.1	50.4
8	59.2	58.4	57.6
9	66.6	65.7	64.8

	71	**70**	**69**
1	7.1	7	6.9
2	14.2	14	13.8
3	21.3	21	20.7
4	28.4	28	27.6
5	35.5	35	34.5
6	42.6	42	41.4
7	49.7	49	48.3
8	56.8	56	55.2
9	63.9	63	62.1

	68	**67**	**66**
1	6.8	6.7	6.6
2	13.6	13.4	13.2
3	20.4	20.1	19.8
4	27.2	26.8	26.4
5	34.0	33.5	33.0
6	40.8	40.2	39.6
7	47.6	46.9	46.2
8	54.4	53.6	52.8
9	61.2	60.3	59.4

	65	**3**	**2**
1	6.5	0.3	0.2
2	13.0	0.6	0.4
3	19.5	0.9	0.6
4	26.0	1.2	0.8
5	32.5	1.5	1.0
6	39.0	1.8	1.2
7	45.5	2.1	1.4
8	52.0	2.4	1.6
9	58.5	2.7	1.8

79°

Prop. Parts

	68	67	66
1	6.8	6.7	6.6
2	13.6	13.4	13.2
3	20.4	20.1	19.8
4	27.2	26.8	26.4
5	34.0	33.5	33.0
6	40.8	40.2	39.6
7	47.6	46.9	46.2
8	54.4	53.6	52.8
9	61.2	60.3	59.4

	65	64	63
1	6.5	6.4	6.3
2	13.0	12.8	12.6
3	19.5	19.2	18.9
4	26.0	25.6	25.2
5	32.5	32.0	31.5
6	39.0	38.4	37.8
7	45.5	44.8	44.1
8	52.0	51.2	50.4
9	58.5	57.6	56.7

	62	61	60
1	6.2	6.1	6
2	12.4	12.2	12
3	18.6	18.3	18
4	24.8	24.4	24
5	31.0	30.5	30
6	37.2	36.6	36
7	43.4	42.7	42
8	49.6	48.8	48
9	55.8	54.9	54

	59	3	2
1	5.9	0.3	0.2
2	11.8	0.6	0.4
3	17.7	0.9	0.6
4	23.6	1.2	0.8
5	29.5	1.5	1.0
6	35.4	1.8	1.2
7	41.3	2.1	1.4
8	47.2	2.4	1.6
9	53.1	2.7	1.8

′	L Sin *	d	L Tan *	c d	L Cot	L Cos *	d	
0	9.28 060		9.28 865		0.71 135	9.99 195		**60**
1	125	65	9.28 933	68	067	192	3	59
2	190	65	9.29 000	67	0.71 000	190	2	58
3	254	64	067	67	0.70 933	187	3	57
4	319	65	134	67	866	185	2	56
5	9.28 384	65	9.29 201	67	0.70 799	9.99 182	3	**55**
6	448	64	268	67	732	180	2	54
7	512	64	335	67	665	177	3	53
8	577	65	402	67	598	175	2	52
9	641	64	468	66	532	172	3	51
10	9.28 705	64	9.29 535	67	0.70 465	9.99 170	2	**50**
11	769	64	601	66	399	167	3	49
12	833	64	668	67	332	165	2	48
13	896	63	734	66	266	162	3	47
14	9.28 960	64	800	66	200	160	2	46
15	9.29 024	64	9.29 866	66	0.70 134	9.99 157	3	**45**
16	087	63	932	66	068	155	2	44
17	150	63	9.29 998	66	0.70 002	152	3	43
18	214	64	9.30 064	66	0.69 936	150	2	42
19	277	63	130	66	870	147	3	41
20	9.29 340	63	9.30 195	65	0.69 805	9.99 145	2	**40**
21	403	63	261	66	739	142	3	39
22	466	63	326	65	674	140	2	38
23	529	63	391	65	609	137	3	37
24	591	62	457	66	543	135	2	36
25	9.29 654	63	9.30 522	65	0.69 478	9.99 132	3	**35**
26	716	62	587	65	413	130	2	34
27	779	63	652	65	348	127	3	33
28	841	62	717	65	283	124	3	32
29	903	62	782	65	218	122	2	31
30	9.29 966	63	9.30 846	64	0.69 154	9.99 119	3	**30**
31	9.30 028	62	911	65	089	117	2	29
32	090	62	9.30 975	64	0.69 025	114	3	28
33	151	61	9.31 040	65	0.68 960	112	2	27
34	213	62	104	64	896	109	3	26
35	9.30 275	62	9.31 168	64	0.68 832	9.99 106	3	**25**
36	336	61	233	65	767	104	2	24
37	398	62	297	64	703	101	3	23
38	459	61	361	64	639	099	2	22
39	521	62	425	64	575	096	3	21
40	9.30 582	61	9.31 489	64	0.68 511	9.99 093	3	**20**
41	643	61	552	63	448	091	2	19
42	704	61	616	64	384	088	3	18
43	765	61	679	63	321	086	2	17
44	826	61	743	64	257	083	3	16
45	9.30 887	61	9.31 806	63	0.68 194	9.99 080	3	**15**
46	9.30 947	60	870	64	130	078	2	14
47	9.31 008	61	933	63	067	075	3	13
48	068	60	9.31 996	63	0.68 004	072	3	12
49	129	61	9.32 059	63	0.67 941	070	2	11
50	9.31 189	60	9.32 122	63	0.67 878	9.99 067	3	**10**
51	250	61	185	63	815	064	3	9
52	310	60	248	63	752	062	2	8
53	370	60	311	63	689	059	3	7
54	430	60	373	62	627	056	3	6
55	9.31 490	60	9.32 436	63	0.67 564	9.99 054	2	**5**
56	549	59	498	62	502	051	3	4
57	609	60	561	63	439	048	3	3
58	669	60	623	62	377	046	2	2
59	728	59	685	62	315	043	3	1
60	9.31 788	60	9.32 747	62	0.67 253	9.99 040	3	**0**
	L Cos *	d	L Cot *	c d	L Tan	L Sin *	d	′

78°

′	L Sin *	d	L Tan *	c d	L Cot	L Cos *	d	
0	9.31 788		9.32 747		0.67 253	9.99 040		**60**
1	847	59	810	63	190	038	2	59
2	907	60	872	62	128	035	3	58
3	9.31 966	59	933	61	067	032	3	57
4	9.32 025	59	9.32 995	62	0.67 005	030	2	56
5	9.32 084	59	9.33 057	62	0.66 943	9.99 027	3	**55**
6	143	59	119	62	881	024	3	54
7	202	59	180	61	820	022	2	53
8	261	59	242	62	758	019	3	52
9	319	58	303	61	697	016	3	51
10	9.32 378	59	9.33 365	62	0.66 635	9.99 013	3	**50**
11	437	59	426	61	574	011	2	49
12	495	58	487	61	513	008	3	48
13	553	58	548	61	452	005	3	47
14	612	59	609	61	391	002	3	46
15	9.32 670	58	9.33 670	61	0.66 330	9.99 000	2	**45**
16	728	58	731	61	269	9.98 997	3	44
17	786	58	792	61	208	994	3	43
18	844	58	853	61	147	991	3	42
19	902	58	913	60	087	989	2	41
20	9.32 960	58	9.33 974	61	0.66 026	9.98 986	3	**40**
21	9.33 018	58	9.34 034	60	0.65 966	983	3	39
22	075	57	095	61	905	980	3	38
23	133	58	155	60	845	978	2	37
24	190	57	215	60	785	975	3	36
25	9.33 248	58	9.34 276	61	0.65 724	9.98 972	3	**35**
26	305	57	336	60	664	969	3	34
27	362	57	396	60	604	967	2	33
28	420	58	456	60	544	964	3	32
29	477	57	516	60	484	961	3	31
30	9.33 534	57	9.34 576	60	0.65 424	9.98 958	3	**30**
31	591	57	635	59	365	955	3	29
32	647	56	695	60	305	953	2	28
33	704	57	755	60	245	950	3	27
34	761	57	814	59	186	947	3	26
35	9.33 818	57	9.34 874	60	0.65 126	9.98 944	3	**25**
36	874	56	933	59	067	941	3	24
37	931	57	9.34 992	59	0.65 008	938	3	23
38	9.33 987	56	9.35 051	59	0.64 949	936	2	22
39	9.34 043	56	111	60	889	933	3	21
40	9.34 100	57	9.35 170	59	0.64 830	9.98 930	3	**20**
41	156	56	229	59	771	927	3	19
42	212	56	288	59	712	924	3	18
43	268	56	347	59	653	921	3	17
44	324	56	405	58	595	919	2	16
45	9.34 380	56	9.35 464	59	0.64 536	9.98 916	3	**15**
46	436	56	523	59	477	913	3	14
47	491	55	581	58	419	910	3	13
48	547	56	640	59	360	907	3	12
49	602	55	698	58	302	904	3	11
50	9.34 658	56	9.35 757	59	0.64 243	9.98 901	3	**10**
51	713	55	815	58	185	898	3	9
52	769	56	873	58	127	896	2	8
53	824	55	931	58	069	893	3	7
54	879	55	9.35 989	58	0.64 011	890	3	6
55	9.34 934	55	9.36 047	58	0.63 953	9.98 887	3	**5**
56	9.34 989	55	105	58	895	884	3	4
57	9.35 044	55	163	58	837	881	3	3
58	099	55	221	58	779	878	3	2
59	154	55	279	58	721	875	3	1
60	9.35 209	55	9.36 336	57	0.63 664	9.98 872	3	**0**
	L Cos *	d	L Cot *	c d	L Tan	L Sin *	d	′

Prop. Parts

	63	62	61
1	6.3	6.2	6.1
2	12.6	12.4	12.2
3	18.9	18.6	18.3
4	25.2	24.8	24.4
5	31.5	31.0	30.5
6	37.8	37.2	36.6
7	44.1	43.4	42.7
8	50.4	49.6	48.8
9	56.7	55.8	54.9

	60	59	58
1	6	5.9	5.8
2	12	11.8	11.6
3	18	17.7	17.4
4	24	23.6	23.2
5	30	29.5	29.0
6	36	35.4	34.8
7	42	41.3	40.6
8	48	47.2	46.4
9	54	53.1	52.2

	57	56	55
1	5.7	5.6	5.5
2	11.4	11.2	11.0
3	17.1	16.8	16.5
4	22.8	22.4	22.0
5	28.5	28.0	27.5
6	34.2	33.6	33.0
7	39.9	39.2	38.5
8	45.6	44.8	44.0
9	51.3	50.4	49.5

	3	2
1	0.3	0.2
2	0.6	0.4
3	0.9	0.6
4	1.2	0.8
5	1.5	1.0
6	1.8	1.2
7	2.1	1.4
8	2.4	1.6
9	2.7	1.8

77°

Prop. Parts

Subtract 10 *from each entry in the columns marked with "*."*

	58	57	56
1	5.8	5.7	5.6
2	11.6	11.4	11.2
3	17.4	17.1	16.8
4	23.2	22.8	22.4
5	29.0	28.5	28.0
6	34.8	34.2	33.6
7	40.6	39.9	39.2
8	46.4	45.6	44.8
9	52.2	51.3	50.4

	55	54	53
1	5.5	5.4	5.3
2	11.0	10.8	10.6
3	16.5	16.2	15.9
4	22.0	21.6	21.2
5	27.5	27.0	26.5
6	33.0	32.4	31.8
7	38.5	37.8	37.1
8	44.0	43.2	42.4
9	49.5	48.6	47.7

	52	51
1	5.2	5.1
2	10.4	10.2
3	15.6	15.3
4	20.8	20.4
5	26.0	25.5
6	31.2	30.6
7	36.4	35.7
8	41.6	40.8
9	46.8	45.9

	4	3	2
1	0.4	0.3	0.2
2	0.8	0.6	0.4
3	1.2	0.9	0.6
4	1.6	1.2	0.8
5	2.0	1.5	1.0
6	2.4	1.8	1.2
7	2.8	2.1	1.4
8	3.2	2.4	1.6
9	3.6	2.7	1.8

′	L Sin *	d	L Tan *	c d	L Cot	L Cos *	d	
0	9.35 209		9.36 336		0.63 664	9.98 872		**60**
1	263	54	394	58	606	869	3	59
2	318	55	452	58	548	867	2	58
3	373	55	509	57	491	864	3	57
4	427	54	566	57	434	861	3	56
5	9.35 481	54	9.36 624	58	0.63 376	9.98 858	3	**55**
6	536	55	681	57	319	855	3	54
7	590	54	738	57	262	852	3	53
8	644	54	795	57	205	849	3	52
9	698	54	852	57	148	846	3	51
10	9.35 752	54	9.36 909	57	0.63 091	9.98 843	3	**50**
11	806	54	9.36 966	57	0.63 034	840	3	49
12	860	54	9.37 023	57	0.62 977	837	3	48
13	914	54	080	57	920	834	3	47
14	9.35 968	54	137	57	863	831	3	46
15	9.36 022	54	9.37 193	56	0.62 807	9.98 828	3	**45**
16	075	53	250	57	750	825	3	44
17	129	54	306	56	694	822	3	43
18	182	53	363	57	637	819	3	42
19	236	54	419	56	581	816	3	41
20	9.36 289	53	9.37 476	57	0.62 524	9.98 813	3	**40**
21	342	53	532	56	468	810	3	39
22	395	53	588	56	412	807	3	38
23	449	54	644	56	356	804	3	37
24	502	53	700	56	300	801	3	36
25	9.36 555	53	9.37 756	56	0.62 244	9.98 798	3	**35**
26	608	53	812	56	188	795	3	34
27	660	52	868	56	132	792	3	33
28	713	53	924	56	076	789	3	32
29	766	53	9.37 980	56	0.62 020	786	3	31
30	9.36 819	53	9.38 035	55	0.61 965	9.98 783	3	**30**
31	871	52	091	56	909	780	3	29
32	924	53	147	56	853	777	3	28
33	9.36 976	52	202	55	798	774	3	27
34	9.37 028	52	257	55	743	771	3	26
35	9.37 081	53	9.38 313	56	0.61 687	9.98 768	3	**25**
36	133	52	368	55	632	765	3	24
37	185	52	423	55	577	762	3	23
38	237	52	479	56	521	759	3	22
39	289	52	534	55	466	756	3	21
40	9.37 341	52	9.38 589	55	0.61 411	9.98 753	3	**20**
41	393	52	644	55	356	750	3	19
42	445	52	699	55	301	746	4	18
43	497	52	754	55	246	743	3	17
44	549	52	808	54	192	740	3	16
45	9.37 600	51	9.38 863	55	0.61 137	9.98 737	3	**15**
46	652	52	918	55	082	734	3	14
47	703	51	9.38 972	54	0.61 028	731	3	13
48	755	52	9.39 027	55	0.60 973	728	3	12
49	806	51	082	55	918	725	3	11
50	9.37 858	52	9.39 136	54	0.60 864	9.98 722	3	**10**
51	909	51	190	54	810	719	3	9
52	9.37 960	51	245	55	755	715	4	8
53	9.38 011	51	299	54	701	712	3	7
54	062	51	353	54	647	709	3	6
55	9.38 113	51	9.39 407	54	0.60 593	9.98 706	3	**5**
56	164	51	461	54	539	703	3	4
57	215	51	515	54	485	700	3	3
58	266	51	569	54	431	697	3	2
59	317	51	623	54	377	694	3	1
60	9.38 368	51	9.39 677	54	0.60 323	9.98 690	4	**0**
	L Cos *	d	L Cot *	c d	L Tan	L Sin *	d	′

76°

′	L Sin *	d	L Tan *	c d	L Cot	L Cos *	d	
0	9.38 368		9.39 677		0.60 323	9.98 690		**60**
1	418	50	731	54	269	687	3	59
2	469	51	785	54	215	684	3	58
3	519	50	838	53	162	681	3	57
4	570	51	892	54	108	678	3	56
5	9.38 620	50	9.39 945	53	0.60 055	9.98 675	3	**55**
6	670	50	9.39 999	54	0.60 001	671	4	54
7	721	51	9.40 052	53	0.59 948	668	3	53
8	771	50	106	54	894	665	3	52
9	821	50	159	53	841	662	3	51
10	9.38 871	50	9.40 212	53	0.59 788	9.98 659	3	**50**
11	921	50	266	54	734	656	3	49
12	9.38 971	50	319	53	681	652	4	48
13	9.39 021	50	372	53	628	649	3	47
14	071	50	425	53	575	646	3	46
15	9.39 121	50	9.40 478	53	0.59 522	9.98 643	3	**45**
16	170	49	531	53	469	640	3	44
17	220	50	584	53	416	636	4	43
18	270	50	636	52	364	633	3	42
19	319	49	689	53	311	630	3	41
20	9.39 369	50	9.40 742	53	0.59 258	9.98 627	3	**40**
21	418	49	795	53	205	623	4	39
22	467	49	847	52	153	620	3	38
23	517	50	900	53	100	617	3	37
24	566	49	9.40 952	52	0.59 048	614	3	36
25	9.39 615	49	9.41 005	53	0.58 995	9.98 610	4	**35**
26	664	49	057	52	943	607	3	34
27	713	49	109	52	891	604	3	33
28	762	49	161	52	839	601	3	32
29	811	49	214	53	786	597	4	31
30	9.39 860	49	9.41 266	52	0.58 734	9.98 594	3	**30**
31	909	49	318	52	682	591	3	29
32	9.39 958	49	370	52	630	588	3	28
33	9.40 006	48	422	52	578	584	4	27
34	055	49	474	52	526	581	3	26
35	9.40 103	48	9.41 526	52	0.58 474	9.98 578	3	**25**
36	152	49	578	52	422	574	4	24
37	200	48	629	51	371	571	3	23
38	249	49	681	52	319	568	3	22
39	297	48	733	52	267	565	3	21
40	9.40 346	49	9.41 784	51	0.58 216	9.98 561	4	**20**
41	394	48	836	52	164	558	3	19
42	442	48	887	51	113	555	3	18
43	490	48	939	52	061	551	4	17
44	538	48	9.41 990	51	0.58 010	548	3	16
45	9.40 586	48	9.42 041	51	0.57 959	9.98 545	3	**15**
46	634	48	093	52	907	541	4	14
47	682	48	144	51	856	538	3	13
48	730	48	195	51	805	535	3	12
49	778	48	246	51	754	531	4	11
50	9.40 825	47	9.42 297	51	0.57 703	9.98 528	3	**10**
51	873	48	348	51	652	525	3	9
52	921	48	399	51	601	521	4	8
53	9.40 968	47	450	51	550	518	3	7
54	9.41 016	48	501	51	499	515	3	6
55	9.41 063	47	9.42 552	51	0.57 448	9.98 511	4	**5**
56	111	48	603	51	397	508	3	4
57	158	47	653	50	347	505	3	3
58	205	47	704	51	296	501	4	2
59	252	47	755	51	245	498	3	1
60	9.41 300	48	9.42 805	50	0.57 195	9.98 494	4	**0**
	L Cos *	d	L Cot *	c d	L Tan	L Sin *	d	′

Prop. Parts

Subtract 10 *from each entry in the columns marked with "*."*

	54	53	52
1	5.4	5.3	5.2
2	10.8	10.6	10.4
3	16.2	15.9	15.6
4	21.6	21.2	20.8
5	27.0	26.5	26.0
6	32.4	31.8	31.2
7	37.8	37.1	36.4
8	43.2	42.4	41.6
9	48.6	47.7	46.8

	51	50	49
1	5.1	5	4.9
2	10.2	10	9.8
3	15.3	15	14.7
4	20.4	20	19.6
5	25.5	25	24.5
6	30.6	30	29.4
7	35.7	35	34.3
8	40.8	40	39.2
9	45.9	45	44.1

	48	47
1	4.8	4.7
2	9.6	9.4
3	14.4	14.1
4	19.2	18.8
5	24.0	23.5
6	28.8	28.2
7	33.6	32.9
8	38.4	37.6
9	43.2	42.3

	4	3
1	0.4	0.3
2	0.8	0.6
3	1.2	0.9
4	1.6	1.2
5	2.0	1.5
6	2.4	1.8
7	2.8	2.1
8	3.2	2.4
9	3.6	2.7

75°

′	L Sin *	d	L Tan *	c d	L Cot	L Cos *	d	
0	9.41 300		9.42 805		0.57 195	9.98 494		60
1	347	47	856	51	144	491	3	59
2	394	47	906	50	094	488	3	58
3	441	47	9.42 957	51	0.57 043	484	4	57
4	488	47	9.43 007	50	0.56 993	481	3	56
5	9.41 535	47	9.43 057	50	0.56 943	9.98 477	4	55
6	582	47	108	51	892	474	3	54
7	628	46	158	50	842	471	3	53
8	675	47	208	50	792	467	4	52
9	722	47	258	50	742	464	3	51
10	9.41 768	46	9.43 308	50	0.56 692	9.98 460	4	50
11	815	47	358	50	642	457	3	49
12	861	46	408	50	592	453	4	48
13	908	47	458	50	542	450	3	47
14	9.41 954	46	508	50	492	447	3	46
15	9.42 001	47	9.43 558	50	0.56 442	9.98 443	4	45
16	047	46	607	49	393	440	3	44
17	093	46	657	50	343	436	4	43
18	140	47	707	50	293	433	3	42
19	186	46	756	49	244	429	4	41
20	9.42 232	46	9.43 806	50	0.56 194	9.98 426	3	40
21	278	46	855	49	145	422	4	39
22	324	46	905	50	095	419	3	38
23	370	46	9.43 954	49	0.56 046	415	4	37
24	416	46	9.44 004	50	0.55 996	412	3	36
25	9.42 461	45	9.44 053	49	0.55 947	9.98 409	3	35
26	507	46	102	49	898	405	4	34
27	553	46	151	49	849	402	3	33
28	599	46	201	50	799	398	4	32
29	644	45	250	49	750	395	3	31
30	9.42 690	46	9.44 299	49	0.55 701	9.98 391	4	30
31	735	45	348	49	652	388	3	29
32	781	46	397	49	603	384	4	28
33	826	45	446	49	554	381	3	27
34	872	46	495	49	505	377	4	26
35	9.42 917	45	9.44 544	49	0.55 456	9.98 373	4	25
36	9.42 962	45	592	48	408	370	3	24
37	9.43 008	46	641	49	359	366	4	23
38	053	45	690	49	310	363	3	22
39	098	45	738	48	262	359	4	21
40	9.43 143	45	9.44 787	49	0.55 213	9.98 356	3	20
41	188	45	836	49	164	352	4	19
42	233	45	884	48	116	349	3	18
43	278	45	933	49	067	345	4	17
44	323	45	9.44 981	48	0.55 019	342	3	16
45	9.43 367	44	9.45 029	48	0.54 971	9.98 338	4	15
46	412	45	078	49	922	334	4	14
47	457	45	126	48	874	331	3	13
48	502	45	174	48	826	327	4	12
49	546	44	222	48	778	324	3	11
50	9.43 591	45	9.45 271	49	0.54 729	9.98 320	4	10
51	635	44	319	48	681	317	3	9
52	680	45	367	48	633	313	4	8
53	724	44	415	48	585	309	4	7
54	769	45	463	48	537	306	3	6
55	9.43 813	44	9.45 511	48	0.54 489	9.98 302	4	5
56	857	44	559	48	441	299	3	4
57	901	44	606	47	394	295	4	3
58	946	45	654	48	346	291	4	2
59	9.43 990	44	702	48	298	288	3	1
60	9.44 034	44	9.45 750	48	0.54 250	9.98 284	4	0
	L Cos *	d	L Cot *	c d	L Tan	L Sin *	d	′

Prop. Parts

	51	50	49
1	5.1	5	4.9
2	10.2	10	9.8
3	15.3	15	14.7
4	20.4	20	19.6
5	25.5	25	24.5
6	30.6	30	29.4
7	35.7	35	34.3
8	40.8	40	39.2
9	45.9	45	44.1

	48	47	46
1	4.8	4.7	4.6
2	9.6	9.4	9.2
3	14.4	14.1	13.8
4	19.2	18.8	18.4
5	24.0	23.5	23.0
6	28.8	28.2	27.6
7	33.6	32.9	32.2
8	38.4	37.6	36.8
9	43.2	42.3	41.4

	45	44
1	4.5	4.4
2	9.0	8.8
3	13.5	13.2
4	18.0	17.6
5	22.5	22.0
6	27.0	26.4
7	31.5	30.8
8	36.0	35.2
9	40.5	39.6

	4	3
1	0.4	0.3
2	0.8	0.6
3	1.2	0.9
4	1.6	1.2
5	2.0	1.5
6	2.4	1.8
7	2.8	2.1
8	3.2	2.4
9	3.6	2.7

74°

′	L Sin *	d	L Tan *	c d	L Cot	L Cos *	d	
0	9.44 034		9.45 750		0.54 250	9.98 284		**60**
1	078	44	797	47	203	281	3	59
2	122	44	845	48	155	277	4	58
3	166	44	892	47	108	273	4	57
4	210	44	940	48	060	270	3	56
5	9.44 253	43	9.45 987	47	0.54 013	9.98 266	4	**55**
6	297	44	9.46 035	48	0.53 965	262	4	54
7	341	44	082	47	918	259	3	53
8	385	44	130	48	870	255	4	52
9	428	43	177	47	823	251	4	51
10	9.44 472	44	9.46 224	47	0.53 776	9.98 248	3	**50**
11	516	44	271	47	729	244	4	49
12	559	43	319	48	681	240	4	48
13	602	43	366	47	634	237	3	47
14	646	44	413	47	587	233	4	46
15	9.44 689	43	9.46 460	47	0.53 540	9.98 229	4	**45**
16	733	44	507	47	493	226	3	44
17	776	43	554	47	446	222	4	43
18	819	43	601	47	399	218	4	42
19	862	43	648	47	352	215	3	41
20	9.44 905	43	9.46 694	46	0.53 306	9.98 211	4	**40**
21	948	43	741	47	259	207	4	39
22	9.44 992	44	788	47	212	204	3	38
23	9.45 035	43	835	47	165	200	4	37
24	077	42	881	46	119	196	4	36
25	9.45 120	43	9.46 928	47	0.53 072	9.98 192	4	**35**
26	163	43	9.46 975	47	0.53 025	189	3	34
27	206	43	9.47 021	46	0.52 979	185	4	33
28	249	43	068	47	932	181	4	32
29	292	43	114	46	886	177	4	31
30	9.45 334	42	9.47 160	46	0.52 840	9.98 174	3	**30**
31	377	43	207	47	793	170	4	29
32	419	42	253	46	747	166	4	28
33	462	43	299	46	701	162	4	27
34	504	42	346	47	654	159	3	26
35	9.45 547	43	9.47 392	46	0.52 608	9.98 155	4	**25**
36	589	42	438	46	562	151	4	24
37	632	43	484	46	516	147	4	23
38	674	42	530	46	470	144	3	22
39	716	42	576	46	424	140	4	21
40	9.45 758	42	9.47 622	46	0.52 378	9.98 136	4	**20**
41	801	43	668	46	332	132	4	19
42	843	42	714	46	286	129	3	18
43	885	42	760	46	240	125	4	17
44	927	42	806	46	194	121	4	16
45	9.45 969	42	9.47 852	46	0.52 148	9.98 117	4	**15**
46	9.46 011	42	897	45	103	113	4	14
47	053	42	943	46	057	110	3	13
48	095	42	9.47 989	46	0.52 011	106	4	12
49	136	41	9.48 035	46	0.51 965	102	4	11
50	9.46 178	42	9.48 080	45	0.51 920	9.98 098	4	**10**
51	220	42	126	46	874	094	4	9
52	262	42	171	45	829	090	4	8
53	303	41	217	46	783	087	3	7
54	345	42	262	45	738	083	4	6
55	9.46 386	41	9.48 307	45	0.51 693	9.98 079	4	**5**
56	428	42	353	46	647	075	4	4
57	469	41	398	45	602	071	4	3
58	511	42	443	45	557	067	4	2
59	552	41	489	46	511	063	4	1
60	9.46 594	42	9.48 534	45	0.51 466	9.98 060	3	**0**
	L Cos *	d	L Cot *	c d	L Tan	L Sin *	d	′

Prop. Parts

	48	47	46
1	4.8	4.7	4.6
2	9.6	9.4	9.2
3	14.4	14.1	13.8
4	19.2	18.8	18.4
5	24.0	23.5	23.0
6	28.8	28.2	27.6
7	33.6	32.9	32.2
8	38.4	37.6	36.8
9	43.2	42.3	41.4

	45	44	43
1	4.5	4.4	4.3
2	9.0	8.8	8.6
3	13.5	13.2	12.9
4	18.0	17.6	17.2
5	22.5	22.0	21.5
6	27.0	26.4	25.8
7	31.5	30.8	30.1
8	36.0	35.2	34.4
9	40.5	39.6	38.7

	42	41
1	4.2	4.1
2	8.4	8.2
3	12.6	12.3
4	16.8	16.4
5	21.0	20.5
6	25.2	24.6
7	29.4	28.7
8	33.6	32.8
9	37.8	36.9

	4	3
1	0.4	0.3
2	0.8	0.6
3	1.2	0.9
4	1.6	1.2
5	2.0	1.5
6	2.4	1.8
7	2.8	2.1
8	3.2	2.4
9	3.6	2.7

73°

Prop. Parts

Subtract 10 *from each entry in the columns marked with "*."*

	45	44	43
1	4.5	4.4	4.3
2	9.0	8.8	8.6
3	13.5	13.2	12.9
4	18.0	17.6	17.2
5	22.5	22.0	21.5
6	27.0	26.4	25.8
7	31.5	30.8	30.1
8	36.0	35.2	34.4
9	40.5	39.6	38.7

	42	41
1	4.2	4.1
2	8.4	8.2
3	12.6	12.3
4	16.8	16.4
5	21.0	20.5
6	25.2	24.6
7	29.4	28.7
8	33.6	32.8
9	37.8	36.9

	40	39
1	4	3.9
2	8	7.8
3	12	11.7
4	16	15.6
5	20	19.5
6	24	23.4
7	28	27.3
8	32	31.2
9	36	35.1

	5	4	3
1	0.5	0.4	0.3
2	1.0	0.8	0.6
3	1.5	1.2	0.9
4	2.0	1.6	1.2
5	2.5	2.0	1.5
6	3.0	2.4	1.8
7	3.5	2.8	2.1
8	4.0	3.2	2.4
9	4.5	3.6	2.7

′	L Sin *	d	L Tan *	c d	L Cot	L Cos *	d	
0	9.46 594	41	9.48 534	45	0.51 466	9.98 060	4	**60**
1	635	41	579	45	421	056	4	59
2	676	41	624	45	376	052	4	58
3	717	41	669	45	331	048	4	57
4	758	42	714	45	286	044	4	56
5	9.46 800	41	9.48 759	45	0.51 241	9.98 040	4	**55**
6	841	41	804	45	196	036	4	54
7	882	41	849	45	151	032	3	53
8	923	41	894	45	106	029	4	52
9	9.46 964	41	939	45	061	025	4	51
10	9.47 005	40	9.48 984	45	0.51 016	9.98 021	4	**50**
11	045	41	9.49 029	44	0.50 971	017	4	49
12	086	41	073	45	927	013	4	48
13	127	41	118	45	882	009	4	47
14	168	41	163	44	837	005	4	46
15	9.47 209	40	9.49 207	45	0.50 793	9.98 001	4	**45**
16	249	41	252	44	748	9.97 997	4	44
17	290	40	296	45	704	993	4	43
18	330	41	341	44	659	989	3	42
19	371	40	385	45	615	986	4	41
20	9.47 411	41	9.49 430	44	0.50 570	9.97 982	4	**40**
21	452	40	474	45	526	978	4	39
22	492	41	519	44	481	974	4	38
23	533	40	563	44	437	970	4	37
24	573	40	607	45	393	966	4	36
25	9.47 613	41	9.49 652	44	0.50 348	9.97 962	4	**35**
26	654	40	696	44	304	958	4	34
27	694	40	740	44	260	954	4	33
28	734	40	784	44	216	950	4	32
29	774	40	828	44	172	946	4	31
30	9.47 814	40	9.49 872	44	0.50 128	9.97 942	4	**30**
31	854	40	916	44	084	938	4	29
32	894	40	9.49 960	44	0.50 040	934	4	28
33	934	40	9.50 004	44	0.49 996	930	4	27
34	9.47 974	40	048	44	952	926	4	26
35	9.48 014	40	9.50 092	44	0.49 908	9.97 922	4	**25**
36	054	40	136	44	864	918	4	24
37	094	39	180	43	820	914	4	23
38	133	40	223	44	777	910	4	22
39	173	40	267	44	733	906	4	21
40	9.48 213	39	9.50 311	44	0.49 689	9.97 902	4	**20**
41	252	40	355	43	645	898	4	19
42	292	40	398	44	602	894	4	18
43	332	39	442	43	558	890	4	17
44	371	40	485	44	515	886	4	16
45	9.48 411	39	9.50 529	43	0.49 471	9.97 882	4	**15**
46	450	40	572	44	428	878	4	14
47	490	39	616	43	384	874	4	13
48	529	39	659	44	341	870	4	12
49	568	39	703	43	297	866	5	11
50	9.48 607	40	9.50 746	43	0.49 254	9.97 861	4	**10**
51	647	39	789	44	211	857	4	9
52	686	39	833	43	167	853	4	8
53	725	39	876	43	124	849	4	7
54	764	39	919	43	081	845	4	6
55	9.48 803	39	9.50 962	43	0.49 038	9.97 841	4	**5**
56	842	39	9.51 005	43	0.48 995	837	4	4
57	881	39	048	44	952	833	4	3
58	920	39	092	43	908	829	4	2
59	959	39	135	43	865	825	4	1
60	9.48 998		9.51 178		0.48 822	9.97 821		**0**
	L Cos *	d	L Cot *	c d	L Tan	L Sin *	d	′

72°

′	L Sin *	d	L Tan *	c d	L Cot	L Cos *	d	
0	9.48 998		9.51 178		0.48 822	9.97 821		60
1	9.49 037	39	221	43	779	817	4	59
2	076	39	264	43	736	812	5	58
3	115	39	306	42	694	808	4	57
4	153	38	349	43	651	804	4	56
5	9.49 192	39	9.51 392	43	0.48 608	9.97 800	4	55
6	231	39	435	43	565	796	4	54
7	269	38	478	43	522	792	4	53
8	308	39	520	42	480	788	4	52
9	347	39	563	43	437	784	4	51
10	9.49 385	38	9.51 606	43	0.48 394	9.97 779	5	50
11	424	39	648	42	352	775	4	49
12	462	38	691	43	309	771	4	48
13	500	38	734	43	266	767	4	47
14	539	39	776	42	224	763	4	46
15	9.49 577	38	9.51 819	43	0.48 181	9.97 759	4	45
16	615	38	861	42	139	754	5	44
17	654	39	903	42	097	750	4	43
18	692	38	946	43	054	746	4	42
19	730	38	9.51 988	42	0.48 012	742	4	41
20	9.49 768	38	9.52 031	43	0.47 969	9.97 738	4	40
21	806	38	073	42	927	734	4	39
22	844	38	115	42	885	729	5	38
23	882	38	157	42	843	725	4	37
24	920	38	200	43	800	721	4	36
25	9.49 958	38	9.52 242	42	0.47 758	9.97 717	4	35
26	9.49 996	38	284	42	716	713	4	34
27	9.50 034	38	326	42	674	708	5	33
28	072	38	368	42	632	704	4	32
29	110	38	410	42	590	700	4	31
30	9.50 148	38	9.52 452	42	0.47 548	9.97 696	4	30
31	185	37	494	42	506	691	5	29
32	223	38	536	42	464	687	4	28
33	261	38	578	42	422	683	4	27
34	298	37	620	42	380	679	4	26
35	9.50 336	38	9.52 661	41	0.47 339	9.97 674	5	25
36	374	38	703	42	297	670	4	24
37	411	37	745	42	255	666	4	23
38	449	38	787	42	213	662	4	22
39	486	37	829	42	171	657	5	21
40	9.50 523	37	9.52 870	41	0.47 130	9.97 653	4	20
41	561	38	912	42	088	649	4	19
42	598	37	953	41	047	645	4	18
43	635	37	9.52 995	42	0.47 005	640	5	17
44	673	38	9.53 037	42	0.46 963	636	4	16
45	9.50 710	37	9.53 078	41	0.46 922	9.97 632	4	15
46	747	37	120	42	880	628	4	14
47	784	37	161	41	839	623	5	13
48	821	37	202	41	798	619	4	12
49	858	37	244	42	756	615	4	11
50	9.50 896	38	9.53 285	41	0.46 715	9.97 610	5	10
51	933	37	327	42	673	606	4	9
52	9.50 970	37	368	41	632	602	4	8
53	9.51 007	37	409	41	591	597	5	7
54	043	36	450	41	550	593	4	6
55	9.51 080	37	9.53 492	42	0.46 508	9.97 589	4	5
56	117	37	533	41	467	584	5	4
57	154	37	574	41	426	580	4	3
58	191	37	615	41	385	576	4	2
59	227	36	656	41	344	571	5	1
60	9.51 264	37	9.53 697	41	0.46 303	9.97 567	4	0
	L Cos *	d	L Cot *	c d	L Tan	L Sin *	d	′

71°

Prop. Parts

	43	42	41
1	4.3	4.2	4.1
2	8.6	8.4	8.2
3	12.9	12.6	12.3
4	17.2	16.8	16.4
5	21.5	21.0	20.5
6	25.8	25.2	24.6
7	30.1	29.4	28.7
8	34.4	33.6	32.8
9	38.7	37.8	36.9

	39	38
1	3.9	3.8
2	7.8	7.6
3	11.7	11.4
4	15.6	15.2
5	19.5	19.0
6	23.4	22.8
7	27.3	26.6
8	31.2	30.4
9	35.1	34.2

	37	36
1	3.7	3.6
2	7.4	7.2
3	11.1	10.8
4	14.8	14.4
5	18.5	18.0
6	22.2	21.6
7	25.9	25.2
8	29.6	28.8
9	33.3	32.4

	5	4
1	0.5	0.4
2	1.0	0.8
3	1.5	1.2
4	2.0	1.6
5	2.5	2.0
6	3.0	2.4
7	3.5	2.8
8	4.0	3.2
9	4.5	3.6

Prop. Parts

	41	40	39
1	4.1	4	3.9
2	8.2	8	7.8
3	12.3	12	11.7
4	16.4	16	15.6
5	20.5	20	19.5
6	24.6	24	23.4
7	28.7	28	27.3
8	32.8	32	31.2
9	36.9	36	35.1

	37	36
1	3.7	3.6
2	7.4	7.2
3	11.1	10.8
4	14.8	14.4
5	18.5	18.0
6	22.2	21.6
7	25.9	25.2
8	29.6	28.8
9	33.3	32.4

	35	34
1	3.5	3.4
2	7.0	6.8
3	10.5	10.2
4	14.0	13.6
5	17.5	17.0
6	21.0	20.4
7	24.5	23.8
8	28.0	27.2
9	31.5	30.6

	5	4
1	0.5	0.4
2	1.0	0.8
3	1.5	1.2
4	2.0	1.6
5	2.5	2.0
6	3.0	2.4
7	3.5	2.8
8	4.0	3.2
9	4.5	3.6

′	L Sin *	d	L Tan *	c d	L Cot	L Cos *	d	
0	9.51 264		9.53 697		0.46 303	9.97 567		**60**
1	301	37	738	41	262	563	4	59
2	338	37	779	41	221	558	5	58
3	374	36	820	41	180	554	4	57
4	411	37	861	41	139	550	4	56
5	9.51 447	36	9.53 902	41	0.46 098	9.97 545	5	**55**
6	484	37	943	41	057	541	4	54
7	520	36	9.53 984	41	0.46 016	536	5	53
8	557	37	9.54 025	41	0.45 975	532	4	52
9	593	36	065	40	935	528	4	51
10	9.51 629	36	9.54 106	41	0.45 894	9.97 523	5	**50**
11	666	37	147	41	853	519	4	49
12	702	36	187	40	813	515	4	48
13	738	36	228	41	772	510	5	47
14	774	36	269	41	731	506	4	46
15	9.51 811	37	9.54 309	40	0.45 691	9.97 501	5	**45**
16	847	36	350	41	650	497	4	44
17	883	36	390	40	610	492	5	43
18	919	36	431	41	569	488	4	42
19	955	36	471	40	529	484	4	41
20	9.51 991	36	9.54 512	41	0.45 488	9.97 479	5	**40**
21	9.52 027	36	552	40	448	475	4	39
22	063	36	593	41	407	470	5	38
23	099	36	633	40	367	466	4	37
24	135	36	673	40	327	461	5	36
25	9.52 171	36	9.54 714	41	0.45 286	9.97 457	4	**35**
26	207	36	754	40	246	453	4	34
27	242	35	794	40	206	448	5	33
28	278	36	835	41	165	444	4	32
29	314	36	875	40	125	439	5	31
30	9.52 350	36	9.54 915	40	0.45 085	9.97 435	4	**30**
31	385	35	955	40	045	430	5	29
32	421	36	9.54 995	40	0.45 005	426	4	28
33	456	35	9.55 035	40	0.44 965	421	5	27
34	492	36	075	40	925	417	4	26
35	9.52 527	35	9.55 115	40	0.44 885	9.97 412	5	**25**
36	563	36	155	40	845	408	4	24
37	598	35	195	40	805	403	5	23
38	634	36	235	40	765	399	4	22
39	669	35	275	40	725	394	5	21
40	9.52 705	36	9.55 315	40	0.44 685	9.97 390	4	**20**
41	740	35	355	40	645	385	5	19
42	775	35	395	40	605	381	4	18
43	811	36	434	39	566	376	5	17
44	846	35	474	40	526	372	4	16
45	9.52 881	35	9.55 514	40	0.44 486	9.97 367	5	**15**
46	916	35	554	40	446	363	4	14
47	951	35	593	39	407	358	5	13
48	9.52 986	35	633	40	367	353	5	12
49	9.53 021	35	673	40	327	349	4	11
50	9.53 056	35	9.55 712	39	0.44 288	9.97 344	5	**10**
51	092	36	752	40	248	340	4	9
52	126	34	791	39	209	335	5	8
53	161	35	831	40	169	331	4	7
54	196	35	870	39	130	326	5	6
55	9.53 231	35	9.55 910	40	0.44 090	9.97 322	4	**5**
56	266	35	949	39	051	317	5	4
57	301	35	9.55 989	40	0.44 011	312	5	3
58	336	35	9.56 028	39	0.43 972	308	4	2
59	370	34	067	39	933	303	5	1
60	9.53 405	35	9.56 107	40	0.43 893	9.97 299	4	**0**
	L Cos *	d	L Cot *	c d	L Tan	L Sin *	d	′

70°

′	L Sin *	d	L Tan *	c d	L Cot	L Cos *	d	
0	9.53 405		9.56 107		0.43 893	9.97 299		**60**
1	440	35	146	39	854	294	5	59
2	475	35	185	39	815	289	5	58
3	509	34	224	39	776	285	4	57
4	544	35	264	40	736	280	5	56
5	9.53 578	34	9.56 303	39	0.43 697	9.97 276	4	**55**
6	613	35	342	39	658	271	5	54
7	647	34	381	39	619	266	5	53
8	682	35	420	39	580	262	4	52
9	716	34	459	39	541	257	5	51
10	9.53 751	35	9.56 498	39	0.43 502	9.97 252	5	**50**
11	785	34	537	39	463	248	4	49
12	819	34	576	39	424	243	5	48
13	854	35	615	39	385	238	5	47
14	888	34	654	39	346	234	4	46
15	9.53 922	34	9.56 693	39	0.43 307	9.97 229	5	**45**
16	957	35	732	39	268	224	5	44
17	9.53 991	34	771	39	229	220	4	43
18	9.54 025	34	810	39	190	215	5	42
19	059	34	849	39	151	210	5	41
20	9.54 093	34	9.56 887	38	0.43 113	9.97 206	4	**40**
21	127	34	926	39	074	201	5	39
22	161	34	9.56 965	39	0.43 035	196	5	38
23	195	34	9.57 004	39	0.42 996	192	4	37
24	229	34	042	38	958	187	5	36
25	9.54 263	34	9.57 081	39	0.42 919	9.97 182	5	**35**
26	297	34	120	39	880	178	4	34
27	331	34	158	38	842	173	5	33
28	365	34	197	39	803	168	5	32
29	399	34	235	38	765	163	5	31
30	9.54 433	34	9.57 274	39	0.42 726	9.97 159	4	**30**
31	466	33	312	38	688	154	5	29
32	500	34	351	39	649	149	5	28
33	534	34	389	38	611	145	4	27
34	567	33	428	39	572	140	5	26
35	9.54 601	34	9.57 466	38	0.42 534	9.97 135	5	**25**
36	635	34	504	38	496	130	5	24
37	668	33	543	39	457	126	4	23
38	702	34	581	38	419	121	5	22
39	735	33	619	38	381	116	5	21
40	9.54 769	34	9.57 658	39	0.42 342	9.97 111	5	**20**
41	802	33	696	38	304	107	4	19
42	836	34	734	38	266	102	5	18
43	869	33	772	38	228	097	5	17
44	903	34	810	38	190	092	5	16
45	9.54 936	33	9.57 849	39	0.42 151	9.97 087	5	**15**
46	9.54 969	33	887	38	113	083	4	14
47	9.55 003	34	925	38	075	078	5	13
48	036	33	9.57 963	38	0.42 037	073	5	12
49	069	33	9.58 001	38	0.41 999	068	5	11
50	9.55 102	33	9.58 039	38	0.41 961	9.97 063	5	**10**
51	136	34	077	38	923	059	4	9
52	169	33	115	38	885	054	5	8
53	202	33	153	38	847	049	5	7
54	235	33	191	38	809	044	5	6
55	9.55 268	33	9.58 229	38	0.41 771	9.97 039	5	**5**
56	301	33	267	38	733	035	4	4
57	334	33	304	37	696	030	5	3
58	367	33	342	38	658	025	5	2
59	400	33	380	38	620	020	5	1
60	9.55 433	33	9.58 418	38	0.41 582	9.97 015	5	**0**
	L Cos *	d	L Cot *	c d	L Tan	L Sin *	d	′

Prop. Parts

Subtract 10 *from each entry in the columns marked with "*."*

	40	**39**	**38**
1	4	3.9	3.8
2	8	7.8	7.6
3	12	11.7	11.4
4	16	15.6	15.2
5	20	19.5	19.0
6	24	23.4	22.8
7	28	27.3	26.6
8	32	31.2	30.4
9	36	35.1	34.2

	37	**35**
1	3.7	3.5
2	7.4	7.0
3	11.1	10.5
4	14.8	14.0
5	18.5	17.5
6	22.2	21.0
7	25.9	24.5
8	29.6	28.0
9	33.3	31.5

	34	**33**
1	3.4	3.3
2	6.8	6.6
3	10.2	9.9
4	13.6	13.2
5	17.0	16.5
6	20.4	19.8
7	23.8	23.1
8	27.2	26.4
9	30.6	29.7

	5	**4**
1	0.5	0.4
2	1.0	0.8
3	1.5	1.2
4	2.0	1.6
5	2.5	2.0
6	3.0	2.4
7	3.5	2.8
8	4.0	3.2
9	4.5	3.6

69°

′	L Sin *	d	L Tan *	c d	L Cot	L Cos *	d	
0	9.55 433		9.58 418		0.41 582	9.97 015		**60**
1	466	33	455	37	545	010	5	59
2	499	33	493	38	507	005	5	58
3	532	33	531	38	469	9.97 001	4	57
4	564	32	569	38	431	9.96 996	5	56
5	9.55 597	33	9.58 606	37	0.41 394	9.96 991	5	**55**
6	630	33	644	38	356	986	5	54
7	663	33	681	37	319	981	5	53
8	695	32	719	38	281	976	5	52
9	728	33	757	38	243	971	5	51
10	9.55 761	33	9.58 794	37	0.41 206	9.96 966	5	**50**
11	793	32	832	38	168	962	4	49
12	826	33	869	37	131	957	5	48
13	858	32	907	38	093	952	5	47
14	891	33	944	37	056	947	5	46
15	9.55 923	32	9.58 981	37	0.41 019	9.96 942	5	**45**
16	956	33	9.59 019	38	0.40 981	937	5	44
17	9.55 988	32	056	37	944	932	5	43
18	9.56 021	33	094	38	906	927	5	42
19	053	32	131	37	869	922	5	41
20	9.56 085	32	9.59 168	37	0.40 832	9.96 917	5	**40**
21	118	33	205	37	795	912	5	39
22	150	32	243	38	757	907	5	38
23	182	32	280	37	720	903	4	37
24	215	33	317	37	683	898	5	36
25	9.56 247	32	9.59 354	37	0.40 646	9.96 893	5	**35**
26	279	32	391	37	609	888	5	34
27	311	32	429	38	571	883	5	33
28	343	32	466	37	534	878	5	32
29	375	32	503	37	497	873	5	31
30	9.56 408	33	9.59 540	37	0.40 460	9.96 868	5	**30**
31	440	32	577	37	423	863	5	29
32	472	32	614	37	386	858	5	28
33	504	32	651	37	349	853	5	27
34	536	32	688	37	312	848	5	26
35	9.56 568	32	9.59 725	37	0.40 275	9.96 843	5	**25**
36	599	31	762	37	238	838	5	24
37	631	32	799	37	201	833	5	23
38	663	32	835	36	165	828	5	22
39	695	32	872	37	128	823	5	21
40	9.56 727	32	9.59 909	37	0.40 091	9.96 818	5	**20**
41	759	32	946	37	054	813	5	19
42	790	31	9.59 983	37	0.40 017	808	5	18
43	822	32	9.60 019	36	0.39 981	803	5	17
44	854	32	056	37	944	798	5	16
45	9.56 886	32	9.60 093	37	0.39 907	9.96 793	5	**15**
46	917	31	130	37	870	788	5	14
47	949	32	166	36	834	783	5	13
48	9.56 980	31	203	37	797	778	5	12
49	9.57 012	32	240	37	760	772	6	11
50	9.57 044	32	9.60 276	36	0.39 724	9.96 767	5	**10**
51	075	31	313	37	687	762	5	9
52	107	32	349	36	651	757	5	8
53	138	31	386	37	614	752	5	7
54	169	31	422	36	578	747	5	6
55	9.57 201	32	9.60 459	37	0.39 541	9.96 742	5	**5**
56	232	31	495	36	505	737	5	4
57	264	32	532	37	468	732	5	3
58	295	31	568	36	432	727	5	2
59	326	31	605	37	395	722	5	1
60	9.57 358	32	9.60 641	36	0.39 359	9.96 717	5	**0**
	L Cos *	d	L Cot *	c d	L Tan	L Sin *	d	′

Prop. Parts

	38	**37**	**36**
1	3.8	3.7	3.6
2	7.6	7.4	7.2
3	11.4	11.1	10.8
4	15.2	14.8	14.4
5	19.0	18.5	18.0
6	22.8	22.2	21.6
7	26.6	25.9	25.2
8	30.4	29.6	28.8
9	34.2	33.3	32.4

	33	**32**	**31**
1	3.3	3.2	3.1
2	6 6	6.4	6.2
3	9.9	9.6	9.3
4	13.2	12.8	12.4
5	16.5	16.0	15.5
6	19.8	19.2	18.6
7	23.1	22.4	21.7
8	26.4	25.6	24.8
9	29.7	28.8	27.9

	6	**5**	**4**
1	0.6	0.5	0.4
2	1.2	1.0	0.8
3	1.8	1.5	1.2
4	2.4	2.0	1.6
5	3.0	2.5	2.0
6	3.6	3.0	2.4
7	4.2	3.5	2.8
8	4.8	4.0	3.2
9	5.4	4.5	3.6

68°

′	L Sin *	d	L Tan *	c d	L Cot	L Cos *	d	
0	9.57 358		9.60 641		0.39 359	9.96 717		**60**
1	389	31	677	36	323	711	6	59
2	420	31	714	37	286	706	5	58
3	451	31	750	36	250	701	5	57
4	482	31	786	36	214	696	5	56
5	9.57 514	32	9.60 823	37	0.39 177	9.96 691	5	**55**
6	545	31	859	36	141	686	5	54
7	576	31	895	36	105	681	5	53
8	607	31	931	36	069	676	5	52
9	638	31	9.60 967	36	0.39 033	670	6	51
10	9.57 669	31	9.61 004	37	0.38 996	9.96 665	5	**50**
11	700	31	040	36	960	660	5	49
12	731	31	076	36	924	655	5	48
13	762	31	112	36	888	650	5	47
14	793	31	148	36	852	645	5	46
15	9.57 824	31	9.61 184	36	0.38 816	9.96 640	5	**45**
16	855	31	220	36	780	634	6	44
17	885	30	256	36	744	629	5	43
18	916	31	292	36	708	624	5	42
19	947	31	328	36	672	619	5	41
20	9.57 978	31	9.61 364	36	0.38 636	9.96 614	5	**40**
21	9.58 008	30	400	36	600	608	6	39
22	039	31	436	36	564	603	5	38
23	070	31	472	36	528	598	5	37
24	101	31	508	36	492	593	5	36
25	9.58 131	30	9.61 544	36	0.38 456	9.96 588	5	**35**
26	162	31	579	35	421	582	6	34
27	192	30	615	36	385	577	5	33
28	223	31	651	36	349	572	5	32
29	253	30	687	36	313	567	5	31
30	9.58 284	31	9.61 722	35	0.38 278	9.96 562	5	**30**
31	314	30	758	36	242	556	6	29
32	345	31	794	36	206	551	5	28
33	375	30	830	36	170	546	5	27
34	406	31	865	35	135	541	5	26
35	9.58 436	30	9.61 901	36	0.38 099	9.96 535	6	**25**
36	467	31	936	35	064	530	5	24
37	497	30	9.61 972	36	0.38 028	525	5	23
38	527	30	9.62 008	36	0.37 992	520	5	22
39	557	30	043	35	957	514	6	21
40	9.58 588	31	9.62 079	36	0.37 921	9.96 509	5	**20**
41	618	30	114	35	886	504	5	19
42	648	30	150	36	850	498	6	18
43	678	30	185	35	815	493	5	17
44	709	31	221	36	779	488	5	16
45	9.58 739	30	9.62 256	35	0.37 744	9.96 483	5	**15**
46	769	30	292	36	708	477	6	14
47	799	30	327	35	673	472	5	13
48	829	30	362	35	638	467	5	12
49	859	30	398	36	602	461	6	11
50	9.58 889	30	9.62 433	35	0.37 567	9.96 456	5	**10**
51	919	30	468	35	532	451	5	9
52	949	30	504	36	496	445	6	8
53	9.58 979	30	539	35	461	440	5	7
54	9.59 009	30	574	35	426	435	5	6
55	9.59 039	30	9.62 609	35	0.37 391	9.96 429	6	**5**
56	069	30	645	36	355	424	5	4
57	098	29	680	35	320	419	5	3
58	128	30	715	35	285	413	6	2
59	158	30	750	35	250	408	5	1
60	9.59 188	30	9.62 785	35	0.37 215	9.96 403	5	**0**
	L Cos *	d	L Cot *	c d	L Tan	L Sin *	d	′

Prop. Parts

	37	**36**	**35**
1	3.7	3.6	3.5
2	7.4	7.2	7.0
3	11.1	10.8	10.5
4	14.8	14.4	14.0
5	18.5	18.0	17.5
6	22.2	21.6	21.0
7	25.9	25.2	24.5
8	29.6	28.8	28.0
9	33.3	32.4	31.5

	32	**31**
1	3.2	3.1
2	6.4	6.2
3	9.6	9.3
4	12.8	12.4
5	16.0	15.5
6	19.2	18.6
7	22.4	21.7
8	25.6	24.8
9	28.8	27.9

	30	**29**
1	3	2.9
2	6	5.8
3	9	8.7
4	12	11.6
5	15	14.5
6	18	17.4
7	21	20.3
8	24	23.2
9	27	26.1

	6	**5**
1	0.6	0.5
2	1.2	1.0
3	1.8	1.5
4	2.4	2.0
5	3.0	2.5
6	3.6	3.0
7	4.2	3.5
8	4.8	4.0
9	5.4	4.5

67°

′	L Sin *	d	L Tan *	c d	L Cot	L Cos *	d	
0	9.59 188		9.62 785		0.37 215	9.96 403		**60**
1	218	30	820	35	180	397	6	59
2	247	29	855	35	145	392	5	58
3	277	30	890	35	110	387	5	57
4	307	30	926	36	074	381	6	56
5	9.59 336	29	9.62 961	35	0.37 039	9.96 376	5	**55**
6	366	30	9.62 996	35	0.37 004	370	6	54
7	396	30	9.63 031	35	0.36 969	365	5	53
8	425	29	066	35	934	360	5	52
9	455	30	101	35	899	354	6	51
10	9.59 484	29	9.63 135	34	0.36 865	9.96 349	5	**50**
11	514	30	170	35	830	343	6	49
12	543	29	205	35	795	338	5	48
13	573	30	240	35	760	333	5	47
14	602	29	275	35	725	327	6	46
15	9.59 632	30	9.63 310	35	0.36 690	9.96 322	5	**45**
16	661	29	345	35	655	316	6	44
17	690	29	379	34	621	311	5	43
18	720	30	414	35	586	305	6	42
19	749	29	449	35	551	300	5	41
20	9.59 778	29	9.63 484	35	0.36 516	9.96 294	6	**40**
21	808	30	519	35	481	289	5	39
22	837	29	553	34	447	284	5	38
23	866	29	588	35	412	278	6	37
24	895	29	623	35	377	273	5	36
25	9.59 924	29	9.63 657	34	0.36 343	9.96 267	6	**35**
26	954	30	692	35	308	262	5	34
27	9.59 983	29	726	34	274	256	6	33
28	9.60 012	29	761	35	239	251	5	32
29	041	29	796	35	204	245	6	31
30	9.60 070	29	9.63 830	34	0.36 170	9.96 240	5	**30**
31	099	29	865	35	135	234	6	29
32	128	29	899	34	101	229	5	28
33	157	29	934	35	066	223	6	27
34	186	29	9.63 968	34	0.36 032	218	5	26
35	9.60 215	29	9.64 003	35	0.35 997	9.96 212	6	**25**
36	244	29	037	34	963	207	5	24
37	273	29	072	35	928	201	6	23
38	302	29	106	34	894	196	5	22
39	331	29	140	34	860	190	6	21
40	9.60 359	28	9.64 175	35	0.35 825	9.96 185	5	**20**
41	388	29	209	34	791	179	6	19
42	417	29	243	34	757	174	5	18
43	446	29	278	35	722	168	6	17
44	474	28	312	34	688	162	6	16
45	9.60 503	29	9.64 346	34	0.35 654	9.96 157	5	**15**
46	532	29	381	35	619	151	6	14
47	561	29	415	34	585	146	5	13
48	589	28	449	34	551	140	6	12
49	618	29	483	34	517	135	5	11
50	9.60 646	28	9.64 517	34	0.35 483	9.96 129	6	**10**
51	675	29	552	35	448	123	6	9
52	704	29	586	34	414	118	5	8
53	732	28	620	34	380	112	6	7
54	761	29	654	34	346	107	5	6
55	9.60 789	28	9.64 688	34	0.35 312	9.96 101	6	**5**
56	818	29	722	34	278	095	6	4
57	846	28	756	34	244	090	5	3
58	875	29	790	34	210	084	6	2
59	903	28	824	34	176	079	5	1
60	9.60 931	28	9.64 858	34	0.35 142	9.96 073	6	**0**
	L Cos *	d	L Cot *	c d	L Tan	L Sin *	d	′

Prop. Parts

	36	35	34
1	3.6	3.5	3.4
2	7.2	7.0	6.8
3	10.8	10.5	10.2
4	14.4	14.0	13.6
5	18.0	17.5	17.0
6	21.6	21.0	20.4
7	25.2	24.5	23.8
8	28.8	28.0	27.2
9	32.4	31.5	30.6

	30	29	28
1	3	2.9	2.8
2	6	5.8	5.6
3	9	8.7	8.4
4	12	11.6	11.2
5	15	14.5	14.0
6	18	17.4	16.8
7	21	20.3	19.6
8	24	23.2	22.4
9	27	26.1	25.2

	6	5
1	0.6	0.5
2	1.2	1.0
3	1.8	1.5
4	2.4	2.0
5	3.0	2.5
6	3.6	3.0
7	4.2	3.5
8	4.8	4.0
9	5.4	4.5

66°

′	L Sin *	d	L Tan *	c d	L Cot	L Cos *	d	
0	9.60 931		9.64 858		0.35 142	9.96 073		**60**
1	960	29	892	34	108	067	6	59
2	9.60 988	28	926	34	074	062	5	58
3	9.61 016	28	960	34	040	056	6	57
4	045	29	9.64 994	34	0.35 006	050	6	56
5	9.61 073	28	9.65 028	34	0.34 972	9.96 045	5	**55**
6	101	28	062	34	938	039	6	54
7	129	28	096	34	904	034	5	53
8	158	29	130	34	870	028	6	52
9	186	28	164	34	836	022	6	51
10	9.61 214	28	9.65 197	33	0.34 803	9.96 017	5	**50**
11	242	28	231	34	769	011	6	49
12	270	28	265	34	735	005	6	48
13	298	28	299	34	701	9.96 000	5	47
14	326	28	333	34	667	9.95 994	6	46
15	9.61 354	28	9.65 366	33	0.34 634	9.95 988	6	**45**
16	382	28	400	34	600	982	6	44
17	411	29	434	34	566	977	5	43
18	438	27	467	33	533	971	6	42
19	466	28	501	34	499	965	6	41
20	9.61 494	28	9.65 535	34	0.34 465	9.95 960	5	**40**
21	522	28	568	33	432	954	6	39
22	550	28	602	34	398	948	6	38
23	578	28	636	34	364	942	6	37
24	606	28	669	33	331	937	5	36
25	9 61 634	28	9.65 703	34	0.34 297	9.95 931	6	**35**
26	662	28	736	33	264	925	6	34
27	689	27	770	34	230	920	5	33
28	717	28	803	33	197	914	6	32
29	745	28	837	34	163	908	6	31
30	9.61 773	28	9.65 870	33	0.34 130	9.95 902	6	**30**
31	800	27	904	34	096	897	5	29
32	828	28	937	33	063	891	6	28
33	856	28	9.65 971	34	0.34 029	885	6	27
34	883	27	9.66 004	33	0.33 996	879	6	26
35	9.61 911	28	9.66 038	34	0.33 962	9.95 873	6	**25**
36	939	28	071	33	929	868	5	24
37	966	27	104	33	896	862	6	23
38	9.61 994	28	138	34	862	856	6	22
39	9.62 021	27	171	33	829	850	6	21
40	9.62 049	28	9.66 204	33	0.33 796	9.95 844	6	**20**
41	076	27	238	34	762	839	5	19
42	104	28	271	33	729	833	6	18
43	131	27	304	33	696	827	6	17
44	159	28	337	33	663	821	6	16
45	9.62 186	27	9.66 371	34	0.33 629	9.95 815	6	**15**
46	214	28	404	33	596	810	5	14
47	241	27	437	33	563	804	6	13
48	268	27	470	33	530	798	6	12
49	296	28	503	33	497	792	6	11
50	9.62 323	27	9.66 537	34	0.33 463	9.95 786	6	**10**
51	350	27	570	33	430	780	6	9
52	377	27	603	33	397	775	5	8
53	405	28	636	33	364	769	6	7
54	432	27	669	33	331	763	6	6
55	9.62 459	27	9.66 702	33	0.33 298	9.95 757	6	**5**
56	486	27	735	33	265	751	6	4
57	513	27	768	33	232	745	6	3
58	541	28	801	33	199	739	6	2
59	568	27	834	33	166	733	6	1
60	9.62 595	27	9.66 867	33	0.33 133	9.95 728	5	**0**
	L Cos *	d	L Cot *	c d	L Tan	L Sin *	d	′

Prop. Parts

Subtract 10 *from each entry in the columns marked with* "*."

	34	33
1	3.4	3.3
2	6.8	6.6
3	10.2	9.9
4	13.6	13.2
5	17.0	16.5
6	20.4	19.8
7	23.8	23.1
8	27.2	26.4
9	30.6	29.7

	29	28	27
1	2.9	2.8	2.7
2	5.8	5.6	5.4
3	8.7	8.4	8.1
4	11.6	11.2	10.8
5	14.5	14.0	13.5
6	17.4	16.8	16.2
7	20.3	19.6	18.9
8	23.2	22.4	21.6
9	26.1	25.2	24.3

	6	5
1	0.6	0.5
2	1.2	1.0
3	1.8	1.5
4	2.4	2.0
5	3.0	2.5
6	3.6	3.0
7	4.2	3.5
8	4.8	4.0
9	5.4	4.5

65°

′	L Sin *	d	L Tan *	c d	L Cot	L Cos *	d	
0	9.62 595		9.66 867		0.33 133	9.95 728		**60**
1	622	27	900	33	100	722	6	59
2	649	27	933	33	067	716	6	58
3	676	27	966	33	034	710	6	57
4	703	27	9.66 999	33	0.33 001	704	6	56
5	9.62 730	27	9.67 032	33	0.32 968	9.95 698	6	**55**
6	757	27	065	33	935	692	6	54
7	784	27	098	33	902	686	6	53
8	811	27	131	33	869	680	6	52
9	838	27	163	32	837	674	6	51
10	9.62 865	27	9.67 196	33	0.32 804	9.95 668	6	**50**
11	892	27	229	33	771	663	5	49
12	918	26	262	33	738	657	6	48
13	945	27	295	33	705	651	6	47
14	972	27	327	32	673	645	6	46
15	9.62 999	27	9.67 360	33	0.32 640	9.95 639	6	**45**
16	9.63 026	27	393	33	607	633	6	44
17	052	26	426	33	574	627	6	43
18	079	27	458	32	542	621	6	42
19	106	27	491	33	509	615	6	41
20	9.63 133	27	9.67 524	33	0.32 476	9.95 609	6	**40**
21	159	26	556	32	444	603	6	39
22	186	27	589	33	411	597	6	38
23	213	27	622	33	378	591	6	37
24	239	26	654	32	346	585	6	36
25	9.63 266	27	9.67 687	33	0.32 313	9.95 579	6	**35**
26	292	26	719	32	281	573	6	34
27	319	27	752	33	248	567	6	33
28	345	26	785	33	215	561	6	32
29	372	27	817	32	183	555	6	31
30	9.63 398	26	9.67 850	33	0.32 150	9.95 549	6	**30**
31	425	27	882	32	118	543	6	29
32	451	26	915	33	085	537	6	28
33	478	27	947	32	053	531	6	27
34	504	26	9.67 980	33	0.32 020	525	6	26
35	9.63 531	27	9.68 012	32	0.31 988	9.95 519	6	**25**
36	557	26	044	32	956	513	6	24
37	583	26	077	33	923	507	6	23
38	610	27	109	32	891	500	7	22
39	636	26	142	33	858	494	6	21
40	9.63 662	26	9.68 174	32	0.31 826	9.95 488	6	**20**
41	689	27	206	32	794	482	6	19
42	715	26	239	33	761	476	6	18
43	741	26	271	32	729	470	6	17
44	767	26	303	32	697	464	6	16
45	9.63 794	27	9.68 336	33	0.31 664	9.95 458	6	**15**
46	820	26	368	32	632	452	6	14
47	846	26	400	32	600	446	6	13
48	872	26	432	32	568	440	6	12
49	898	26	465	33	535	434	6	11
50	9.63 924	26	9.68 497	32	0.31 503	9.95 427	7	**10**
51	950	26	529	32	471	421	6	9
52	9.63 976	26	561	32	439	415	6	8
53	9.64 002	26	593	32	407	409	6	7
54	028	26	626	33	374	403	6	6
55	9.64 054	26	9.68 658	32	0.31 342	9.95 397	6	**5**
56	080	26	690	32	310	391	6	4
57	106	26	722	32	278	384	7	3
58	132	26	754	32	246	378	6	2
59	158	26	786	32	214	372	6	1
60	9.64 184	26	9.68 818	32	0.31 182	9.95 366	6	**0**
	L Cos *	d	L Cot *	c d	L Tan	L Sin *	d	′

Prop. Parts

	33	**32**
1	3.3	3.2
2	6.6	6.4
3	9.9	9.6
4	13.2	12.8
5	16.5	16.0
6	19.8	19.2
7	23.1	22.4
8	26.4	25.6
9	29.7	28.8

	27	**26**
1	2.7	2.6
2	5.4	5.2
3	8.1	7.8
4	10.8	10.4
5	13.5	13.0
6	16.2	15.6
7	18.9	18.2
8	21.6	20.8
9	24.3	23.4

	7	**6**	**5**
1	0.7	0.6	0.5
2	1.4	1.2	1.0
3	2.1	1.8	1.5
4	2.8	2.4	2.0
5	3.5	3.0	2.5
6	4.2	3.6	3.0
7	4.9	4.2	3.5
8	5.6	4.8	4.0
9	6.3	5.4	4.5

64°

′	L Sin *	d	L Tan *	c d	L Cot	L Cos *	d	
0	9.64 184		9.68 818		0.31 182	9.95 366		**60**
1	210	26	850	32	150	360	6	59
2	236	26	882	32	118	354	6	58
3	262	26	914	32	086	348	6	57
4	288	26	946	32	054	341	7	56
5	9.64 313	25	9.68 978	32	0.31 022	9.95 335	6	**55**
6	339	26	9.69 010	32	0.30 990	329	6	54
7	365	26	042	32	958	323	6	53
8	391	26	074	32	926	317	6	52
9	417	26	106	32	894	310	7	51
10	9.64 442	25	9.69 138	32	0.30 862	9.95 304	6	**50**
11	468	26	170	32	830	298	6	49
12	494	26	202	32	798	292	6	48
13	519	25	234	32	766	286	6	47
14	545	26	266	32	734	279	7	46
15	9.64 571	26	9.69 298	32	0.30 702	9.95 273	6	**45**
16	596	25	329	31	671	267	6	44
17	622	26	361	32	639	261	6	43
18	647	25	393	32	607	254	7	42
19	673	26	425	32	575	248	6	41
20	9.64 698	25	9.69 457	32	0.30 543	9.95 242	6	**40**
21	724	26	488	31	512	236	6	39
22	749	25	520	32	480	229	7	38
23	775	26	552	32	448	223	6	37
24	800	25	584	32	416	217	6	36
25	9.64 826	26	9.69 615	31	0.30 385	9.95 211	6	**35**
26	851	25	647	32	353	204	7	34
27	877	26	679	32	321	198	6	33
28	902	25	710	31	290	192	6	32
29	927	25	742	32	258	185	7	31
30	9.64 953	26	9.69 774	32	0.30 226	9.95 179	6	**30**
31	9.64 978	25	805	31	195	173	6	29
32	9.65 003	25	837	32	163	167	6	28
33	029	26	868	31	132	160	7	27
34	054	25	900	32	100	154	6	26
35	9.65 079	25	9.69 932	32	0.30 068	9.95 148	6	**25**
36	104	25	963	31	037	141	7	24
37	130	26	9.69 995	32	0.30 005	135	6	23
38	155	25	9.70 026	31	0.29 974	129	6	22
39	180	25	058	32	942	122	7	21
40	9.65 205	25	9.70 089	31	0.29 911	9.95 116	6	**20**
41	230	25	121	32	879	110	6	19
42	255	25	152	31	848	103	7	18
43	281	26	184	32	816	097	6	17
44	306	25	215	31	785	090	7	16
45	9.65 331	25	9.70 247	32	0.29 753	9.95 084	6	**15**
46	356	25	278	31	722	078	6	14
47	381	25	309	31	691	071	7	13
48	406	25	341	32	659	065	6	12
49	431	25	372	31	628	059	6	11
50	9.65 456	25	9.70 404	32	0.29 596	9.95 052	7	**10**
51	481	25	435	31	565	046	6	9
52	506	25	466	31	534	039	7	8
53	531	25	498	32	502	033	6	7
54	556	25	529	31	471	027	6	6
55	9.65 580	24	9.70 560	31	0.29 440	9.95 020	7	**5**
56	605	25	592	32	408	014	6	4
57	630	25	623	31	377	007	7	3
58	655	25	654	31	346	9.95 001	6	2
59	680	25	685	31	315	9.94 995	6	1
60	9.65 705	25	9.70 717	32	0.29 283	9.94 988	7	**0**
	L Cos *	d	L Cot *	c d	L Tan	L Sin *	d	′

Prop. Parts

	32	31
1	3.2	3.1
2	6.4	6.2
3	9.6	9.3
4	12.8	12.4
5	16.0	15.5
6	19.2	18.6
7	22.4	21.7
8	25.6	24.8
9	28.8	27.9

	26	25	24
1	2.6	2.5	2.4
2	5.2	5.0	4.8
3	7.8	7.5	7.2
4	10.4	10.0	9.6
5	13.0	12.5	12.0
6	15.6	15.0	14.4
7	18.2	17.5	16.8
8	20.8	20.0	19.2
9	23.4	22.5	21.6

	7	6
1	0.7	0.6
2	1.4	1.2
3	2.1	1.8
4	2.8	2.4
5	3.5	3.0
6	4.2	3.6
7	4.9	4.2
8	5.6	4.8
9	6.3	5.4

63°

′	L Sin *	d	L Tan *	c d	L Cot	L Cos *	d	
0	9.65 705		9.70 717		0.29 283	9.94 988		**60**
1	729	24	748	31	252	982	6	59
2	754	25	779	31	221	975	7	58
3	779	25	810	31	190	969	6	57
4	804	25	841	31	159	962	7	56
5	9.65 828	24	9.70 873	32	0.29 127	9.94 956	6	**55**
6	853	25	904	31	096	949	7	54
7	878	25	935	31	065	943	6	53
8	902	24	966	31	034	936	7	52
9	927	25	9.70 997	31	0.29 003	930	6	51
10	9.65 952	25	9.71 028	31	0.28 972	9.94 923	7	**50**
11	9.65 976	24	059	31	941	917	6	49
12	9.66 001	25	090	31	910	911	6	48
13	025	24	121	31	879	904	7	47
14	050	25	153	32	847	898	6	46
15	9.66 075	25	9.71 184	31	0.28 816	9.94 891	7	**45**
16	099	24	215	31	785	885	6	44
17	124	25	246	31	754	878	7	43
18	148	24	277	31	723	871	7	42
19	173	25	308	31	692	865	6	41
20	9.66 197	24	9.71 339	31	0.28 661	9.94 858	7	**40**
21	221	24	370	31	630	852	6	39
22	246	25	401	31	599	845	7	38
23	270	24	431	30	569	839	6	37
24	295	25	462	31	538	832	7	36
25	9.66 319	24	9.71 493	31	0.28 507	9.94 826	6	**35**
26	343	24	524	31	476	819	7	34
27	368	25	555	31	445	813	6	33
28	392	24	586	31	414	806	7	32
29	416	24	617	31	383	799	7	31
30	9.66 441	25	9.71 648	31	0.28 352	9.94 793	6	**30**
31	465	24	679	31	321	786	7	29
32	489	24	709	30	291	780	6	28
33	513	24	740	31	260	773	7	27
34	537	24	771	31	229	767	6	26
35	9.66 562	25	9.71 802	31	0.28 198	9.94 760	7	**25**
36	586	24	833	31	167	753	7	24
37	610	24	863	30	137	747	6	23
38	634	24	894	31	106	740	7	22
39	658	24	925	31	075	734	6	21
40	9.66 682	24	9.71 955	30	0.28 045	9.94 727	7	**20**
41	706	24	9.71 986	31	0.28 014	720	7	19
42	731	25	9.72 017	31	0.27 983	714	6	18
43	755	24	048	31	952	707	7	17
44	779	24	078	30	922	700	7	16
45	9.66 803	24	9.72 109	31	0.27 891	9.94 694	6	**15**
46	827	24	140	31	860	687	7	14
47	851	24	170	30	830	680	7	13
48	875	24	201	31	799	674	6	12
49	899	24	231	30	769	667	7	11
50	9.66 922	23	9.72 262	31	0.27 738	9.94 660	7	**10**
51	946	24	293	31	707	654	6	9
52	970	24	323	30	677	647	7	8
53	9.66 994	24	354	31	646	640	7	7
54	9.67 018	24	384	30	616	634	6	6
55	9.67 042	24	9.72 415	31	0.27 585	9.94 627	7	**5**
56	066	24	445	30	555	620	7	4
57	090	24	476	31	524	614	6	3
58	113	23	506	30	494	607	7	2
59	137	24	537	31	463	600	7	1
60	9.67 161	24	9.72 567	30	0.27 433	9.94 593	7	**0**
	L Cos *	d	L Cot *	c d	L Tan	L Sin *	d	′

Prop. Parts

	32	31	30
1	3.2	3.1	3
2	6.4	6.2	6
3	9.6	9.3	9
4	12.8	12.4	12
5	16.0	15.5	15
6	19.2	18.6	18
7	22.4	21.7	21
8	25.6	24.8	24
9	28.8	27.9	27

	25	24	23
1	2.5	2.4	2.3
2	5.0	4.8	4.6
3	7.5	7.2	6.9
4	10.0	9.6	9.2
5	12.5	12.0	11.5
6	15.0	14.4	13.8
7	17.5	16.8	16.1
8	20.0	19.2	18.4
9	22.5	21.6	20.7

	7	6
1	0.7	0.6
2	1.4	1.2
3	2.1	1.8
4	2.8	2.4
5	3.5	3.0
6	4.2	3.6
7	4.9	4.2
8	5.6	4.8
9	6.3	5.4

62°

′	L Sin *	d	L Tan *	c d	L Cot	L Cos *	d	
0	9.67 161		9.72 567		0.27 433	9.94 593		**60**
1	185	24	598	31	402	587	6	59
2	208	23	628	30	372	580	7	58
3	232	24	659	31	341	573	7	57
4	256	24	689	30	311	567	6	56
5	9.67 280	24	9.72 720	31	0.27 280	9.94 560	7	**55**
6	303	23	750	30	250	553	7	54
7	327	24	780	30	220	546	7	53
8	350	23	811	31	189	540	6	52
9	374	24	841	30	159	533	7	51
10	9.67 398	24	9.72 872	31	0.27 128	9.94 526	7	**50**
11	421	23	902	30	098	519	7	49
12	445	24	932	30	068	513	6	48
13	468	23	963	31	037	506	7	47
14	492	24	9.72 993	30	0.27 007	499	7	46
15	9.67 515	23	9.73 023	30	0.26 977	9.94 492	7	**45**
16	539	24	054	31	946	485	7	44
17	562	23	084	30	916	479	6	43
18	586	24	114	30	886	472	7	42
19	609	23	144	30	856	465	7	41
20	9.67 633	24	9.73 175	31	0.26 825	9.94 458	7	**40**
21	656	23	205	30	795	451	7	39
22	680	24	235	30	765	445	6	38
23	703	23	265	30	735	438	7	37
24	726	23	295	30	705	431	7	36
25	9.67 750	24	9.73 326	31	0.26 674	9.94 424	7	**35**
26	773	23	356	30	644	417	7	34
27	796	23	386	30	614	410	7	33
28	820	24	416	30	584	404	6	32
29	843	23	446	30	554	397	7	31
30	9.67 866	23	9.73 476	30	0.26 524	9.94 390	7	**30**
31	890	24	507	31	493	383	7	29
32	913	23	537	30	463	376	7	28
33	936	23	567	30	433	369	7	27
34	959	23	597	30	403	362	7	26
35	9.67 982	23	9.73 627	30	0.26 373	9.94 355	7	**25**
36	9.68 006	24	657	30	343	349	6	24
37	029	23	687	30	313	342	7	23
38	052	23	717	30	283	335	7	22
39	075	23	747	30	253	328	7	21
40	9.68 098	23	9.73 777	30	0.26 223	9.94 321	7	**20**
41	121	23	807	30	193	314	7	19
42	144	23	837	30	163	307	7	18
43	167	23	867	30	133	300	7	17
44	190	23	897	30	103	293	7	16
45	9.68 213	23	9.73 927	30	0.26 073	9.94 286	7	**15**
46	237	24	957	30	043	279	7	14
47	260	23	9.73 987	30	0.26 013	273	6	13
48	283	23	9.74 017	30	0.25 983	266	7	12
49	305	22	047	30	953	259	7	11
50	9.68 328	23	9.74 077	30	0.25 923	9.94 252	7	**10**
51	351	23	107	30	893	245	7	9
52	374	23	137	30	863	238	7	8
53	397	23	166	29	834	231	7	7
54	420	23	196	30	804	224	7	6
55	9.68 443	23	9.74 226	30	0.25 774	9.94 217	7	**5**
56	466	23	256	30	744	210	7	4
57	489	23	286	30	714	203	7	3
58	512	23	316	30	684	196	7	2
59	534	22	345	29	655	189	7	1
60	9.68 557	23	9.74 375	30	0.25 625	9.94 182	7	**0**
	L Cos *	d	L Cot *	c d	L Tan	L Sin *	d	′

Prop. Parts

Subtract 10 *from each entry in the columns marked with "*."*

	31	30	29
1	3.1	3	2.9
2	6.2	6	5.8
3	9.3	9	8.7
4	12.4	12	11.6
5	15.5	15	14.5
6	18.6	18	17.4
7	21.7	21	20.3
8	24.8	24	23.2
9	27.9	27	26.1

	24	23	22
1	2.4	2.3	2.2
2	4.8	4.6	4.4
3	7.2	6.9	6.6
4	9.6	9.2	8.8
5	12.0	11.5	11.0
6	14.4	13.8	13.2
7	16.8	16.1	15.4
8	19.2	18.4	17.6
9	21.6	20.7	19.8

	7	6
1	0.7	0.6
2	1.4	1.2
3	2.1	1.8
4	2.8	2.4
5	3.5	3.0
6	4.2	3.6
7	4.9	4.2
8	5.6	4.8
9	6.3	5.4

61°

'	L Sin *	d	L Tan *	c d	L Cot	L Cos *	d	
0	9.68 557		9.74 375		0.25 625	9.94 182		**60**
1	580	23	405	30	595	175	7	59
2	603	23	435	30	565	168	7	58
3	625	22	465	30	535	161	7	57
4	648	23	494	29	506	154	7	56
5	9.68 671	23	9.74 524	30	0.25 476	9.94 147	7	**55**
6	694	23	554	30	446	140	7	54
7	716	22	583	29	417	133	7	53
8	739	23	613	30	387	126	7	52
9	762	23	643	30	357	119	7	51
10	9.68 784	22	9.74 673	30	0.25 327	9.94 112	7	**50**
11	807	23	702	29	298	105	7	49
12	829	22	732	30	268	098	7	48
13	852	23	762	30	238	090	8	47
14	875	23	791	29	209	083	7	46
15	9.68 897	22	9.74 821	30	0.25 179	9.94 076	7	**45**
16	920	23	851	30	149	069	7	44
17	942	22	880	29	120	062	7	43
18	965	23	910	30	090	055	7	42
19	9.68 987	22	939	29	061	048	7	41
20	9.69 010	23	9.74 969	30	0.25 031	9.94 041	7	**40**
21	032	22	9.74 998	29	0.25 002	034	7	39
22	055	23	9.75 028	30	0.24 972	027	7	38
23	077	22	058	30	942	020	7	37
24	100	23	087	29	913	012	8	36
25	9.69 122	22	9.75 117	30	0.24 883	9.94 005	7	**35**
26	144	22	146	29	854	9.93 998	7	34
27	167	23	176	30	824	991	7	33
28	189	22	205	29	795	984	7	32
29	212	23	235	30	765	977	7	31
30	9.69 234	22	9.75 264	29	0.24 736	9.93 970	7	**30**
31	256	22	294	30	706	963	7	29
32	279	23	323	29	677	955	8	28
33	301	22	353	30	647	948	7	27
34	323	22	382	29	618	941	7	26
35	9.69 345	22	9.75 411	29	0.24 589	9.93 934	7	**25**
36	368	23	441	30	559	927	7	24
37	390	22	470	29	530	920	7	23
38	412	22	500	30	500	912	8	22
39	434	22	529	29	471	905	7	21
40	9.69 456	22	9.75 558	29	0.24 442	9.93 898	7	**20**
41	479	23	588	30	412	891	7	19
42	501	22	617	29	383	884	7	18
43	523	22	647	30	353	876	8	17
44	545	22	676	29	324	869	7	16
45	9.69 567	22	9.75 705	29	0.24 295	9.93 862	7	**15**
46	589	22	735	30	265	855	7	14
47	611	22	764	29	236	847	8	13
48	633	22	793	29	207	840	7	12
49	655	22	822	29	178	833	7	11
50	9.69 677	22	9.75 852	30	0.24 148	9.93 826	7	**10**
51	699	22	881	29	119	819	7	9
52	721	22	910	29	090	811	8	8
53	743	22	939	29	061	804	7	7
54	765	22	969	30	031	797	7	6
55	9.69 787	22	9.75 998	29	0.24 002	9.93 789	8	**5**
56	809	22	9.76 027	29	0.23 973	782	7	4
57	831	22	056	29	944	775	7	3
58	853	22	086	30	914	768	7	2
59	875	22	115	29	885	760	8	1
60	9.69 897	22	9.76 144	29	0.23 856	9.93 753	7	**0**
	L Cos *	d	L Cot *	c d	L Tan	L Sin *	d	'

Prop. Parts

	30	**29**
1	3	2.9
2	6	5.8
3	9	8.7
4	12	11.6
5	15	14.5
6	18	17.4
7	21	20.3
8	24	23.2
9	27	26.1

	23	**22**
1	2.3	2.2
2	4.6	4.4
3	6.9	6.6
4	9.2	8.8
5	11.5	11.0
6	13.8	13.2
7	16.1	15.4
8	18.4	17.6
9	20.7	19.8

	8	**7**
1	0.8	0.7
2	1.6	1.4
3	2.4	2.1
4	3.2	2.8
5	4.0	3.5
6	4.8	4.2
7	5.6	4.9
8	6.4	5.6
9	7.2	6.3

′	L Sin *	d	L Tan *	c d	L Cot	L Cos *	d	
0	9.69 897		9.76 144		0.23 856	9.93 753		**60**
1	919	22	173	29	827	746	7	59
2	941	22	202	29	798	738	8	58
3	963	22	231	29	769	731	7	57
4	9.69 984	21	261	30	739	724	7	56
5	9.70 006	22	9.76 290	29	0.23 710	9.93 717	7	**55**
6	028	22	319	29	681	709	8	54
7	050	22	348	29	652	702	7	53
8	072	22	377	29	623	695	7	52
9	093	21	406	29	594	687	8	51
10	9.70 115	22	9.76 435	29	0.23 565	9.93 680	7	**50**
11	137	22	464	29	536	673	7	49
12	159	22	493	29	507	665	8	48
13	180	21	522	29	478	658	7	47
14	202	22	551	29	449	650	8	46
15	9.70 224	22	9.76 580	29	0.23 420	9.93 643	7	**45**
16	245	21	609	29	391	636	7	44
17	267	22	639	30	361	628	8	43
18	288	21	668	29	332	621	7	42
19	310	22	697	29	303	614	7	41
20	9.70 332	22	9.76 725	28	0.23 275	9.93 606	8	**40**
21	353	21	754	29	246	599	7	39
22	375	22	783	29	217	591	8	38
23	396	21	812	29	188	584	7	37
24	418	22	841	29	159	577	7	36
25	9.70 439	21	9.76 870	29	0.23 130	9.93 569	8	**35**
26	461	22	899	29	101	562	7	34
27	482	21	928	29	072	554	8	33
28	504	22	957	29	043	547	7	32
29	525	21	9.76 986	29	0.23 014	539	8	31
30	9.70 547	22	9.77 015	29	0.22 985	9.93 532	7	**30**
31	568	21	044	29	956	525	7	29
32	590	22	073	29	927	517	8	28
33	611	21	101	28	899	510	7	27
34	633	22	130	29	870	502	8	26
35	9.70 654	21	9.77 159	29	0.22 841	9.93 495	7	**25**
36	675	21	188	29	812	487	8	24
37	697	22	217	29	783	480	7	23
38	718	21	246	29	754	472	8	22
39	739	21	274	28	726	465	7	21
40	9.70 761	22	9.77 303	29	0.22 697	9.93 457	8	**20**
41	782	21	332	29	668	450	7	19
42	803	21	361	29	639	442	8	18
43	824	21	390	29	610	435	7	17
44	846	22	418	28	582	427	8	16
45	9.70 867	21	9.77 447	29	0.22 553	9.93 420	7	**15**
46	888	21	476	29	524	412	8	14
47	909	21	505	29	495	405	7	13
48	931	22	533	28	467	397	8	12
49	952	21	562	29	438	390	7	11
50	9.70 973	21	9.77 591	29	0.22 409	9.93 382	8	**10**
51	9.70 994	21	619	28	381	375	7	9
52	9.71 015	21	648	29	352	367	8	8
53	036	21	677	29	323	360	7	7
54	058	22	706	29	294	352	8	6
55	9.71 079	21	9.77 734	28	0.22 266	9.93 344	8	**5**
56	100	21	763	29	237	337	7	4
57	121	21	791	28	209	329	8	3
58	142	21	820	29	180	322	7	2
59	163	21	849	29	151	314	8	1
60	9.71 184	21	9.77 877	28	0.22 123	9.93 307	7	**0**
	L Cos *	d	L Cot *	c d	L Tan	L Sin *	d	′

Prop. Parts

	30	29	28
1	3	2.9	2.8
2	6	5.8	5.6
3	9	8.7	8.4
4	12	11.6	11.2
5	15	14.5	14.0
6	18	17.4	16.8
7	21	20.3	19.6
8	24	23.2	22.4
9	27	26.1	25.2

	22	21
1	2.2	2.1
2	4.4	4.2
3	6.6	6.3
4	8.8	8.4
5	11.0	10.5
6	13.2	12.6
7	15.4	14.7
8	17.6	16.8
9	19.8	18.9

	8	7
1	0.8	0.7
2	1.6	1.4
3	2.4	2.1
4	3.2	2.8
5	4.0	3.5
6	4.8	4.2
7	5.6	4.9
8	6.4	5.6
9	7.2	6.3

Prop. Parts

Subtract 10 *from each entry in the columns marked with "*."*

	29	28
1	2.9	2.8
2	5.8	5.6
3	8.7	8.4
4	11.6	11.2
5	14.5	14.0
6	17.4	16.8
7	20.3	19.6
8	23.2	22.4
9	26.1	25.2

	21	20
1	2.1	2
2	4.2	4
3	6.3	6
4	8.4	8
5	10.5	10
6	12.6	12
7	14.7	14
8	16 8	16
9	18.9	18

	8	7
1	0.8	0.7
2	1.6	1.4
3	2.4	2.1
4	3.2	2.8
5	4.0	3.5
6	4.8	4.2
7	5.6	4.9
8	6.4	5.6
9	7.2	6.3

′	L Sin *	d	L Tan *	c d	L Cot	L Cos *	d	
0	9.71 184		9.77 877		0.22 123	9.93 307		60
1	205	21	906	29	094	299	8	59
2	226	21	935	29	065	291	8	58
3	247	21	963	28	037	284	7	57
4	268	21	9.77 992	29	0.22 008	276	8	56
5	9.71 289	21	9.78 020	28	0.21 980	9.93 269	7	55
6	310	21	049	29	951	261	8	54
7	331	21	077	28	923	253	8	53
8	352	21	106	29	894	246	7	52
9	373	21	135	29	865	238	8	51
10	9.71 393	20	9.78 163	28	0.21 837	9.93 230	8	50
11	414	21	192	29	808	223	7	49
12	435	21	220	28	780	215	8	48
13	456	21	249	29	751	207	8	47
14	477	21	277	28	723	200	7	46
15	9.71 498	21	9.78 306	29	0.21 694	9.93 192	8	45
16	519	21	334	28	666	184	8	44
17	539	20	363	29	637	177	7	43
18	560	21	391	28	609	169	8	42
19	581	21	419	28	581	161	8	41
20	9.71 602	21	9.78 448	29	0.21 552	9.93 154	7	40
21	622	20	476	28	524	146	8	39
22	643	21	505	29	495	138	8	38
23	664	21	533	28	467	131	7	37
24	685	21	562	29	438	123	8	36
25	9.71 705	20	9.78 590	28	0.21 410	9.93 115	8	35
26	726	21	618	28	382	108	7	34
27	747	21	647	29	353	100	8	33
28	767	20	675	28	325	092	8	32
29	788	21	704	29	296	084	8	31
30	9.71 809	21	9.78 732	28	0.21 268	9.93 077	7	30
31	829	20	760	28	240	069	8	29
32	850	21	789	29	211	061	8	28
33	870	20	817	28	183	053	8	27
34	891	21	845	28	155	046	7	26
35	9.71 911	20	9.78 874	29	0.21 126	9.93 038	8	25
36	932	21	902	28	098	030	8	24
37	952	20	930	28	070	022	8	23
38	973	21	959	29	041	014	8	22
39	9.71 994	21	9.78 987	28	0.21 013	9.93 007	7	21
40	9.72 014	20	9.79 015	28	0.20 985	9.92 999	8	20
41	034	20	043	28	957	991	8	19
42	055	21	072	29	928	983	8	18
43	075	20	100	28	900	976	7	17
44	096	21	128	28	872	968	8	16
45	9.72 116	20	9.79 156	28	0.20 844	9.92 960	8	15
46	137	21	185	29	815	952	8	14
47	157	20	213	28	787	944	8	13
48	177	20	241	28	759	936	8	12
49	198	21	269	28	731	929	7	11
50	9.72 218	20	9.79 297	28	0.20 703	9.92 921	8	10
51	238	20	326	29	674	913	8	9
52	259	21	354	28	646	905	8	8
53	279	20	382	28	618	897	8	7
54	299	20	410	28	590	889	8	6
55	9.72 320	21	9.79 438	28	0.20 562	9.92 881	8	5
56	340	20	466	28	534	874	7	4
57	360	20	495	29	505	866	8	3
58	381	21	523	28	477	858	8	2
59	401	20	551	28	449	850	8	1
60	9.72 421	20	9.79 579	28	0.20 421	9.92 842	8	0
	L Cos *	d	L Cot *	c d	L Tan	L Sin *	d	′

58°

′	L Sin *	d	L Tan *	c d	L Cot	L Cos *	d	
0	9.72 421		9.79 579		0.20 421	9.92 842		**60**
1	441	20	607	28	393	834	8	59
2	461	20	635	28	365	826	8	58
3	482	21	663	28	337	818	8	57
4	502	20	691	28	309	810	8	56
5	9.72 522	20	9.79 719	28	0.20 281	9.92 803	7	**55**
6	542	20	747	28	253	795	8	54
7	562	20	776	29	224	787	8	53
8	582	20	804	28	196	779	8	52
9	602	20	832	28	168	771	8	51
10	9.72 622	20	9.79 860	28	0.20 140	9.92 763	8	**50**
11	643	21	888	28	112	755	8	49
12	663	20	916	28	084	747	8	48
13	683	20	944	28	056	739	8	47
14	703	20	9.79 972	28	028	731	8	46
15	9.72 723	20	9.80 000	28	0.20 000	9.92 723	8	**45**
16	743	20	028	28	0.19 972	715	8	44
17	763	20	056	28	944	707	8	43
18	783	20	084	28	916	699	8	42
19	803	20	112	28	888	691	8	41
20	9.72 823	20	9.80 140	28	0.19 860	9.92 683	8	**40**
21	843	20	168	28	832	675	8	39
22	863	20	195	27	805	667	8	38
23	883	20	223	28	777	659	8	37
24	902	19	251	28	749	651	8	36
25	9.72 922	20	9.80 279	28	0.19 721	9.92 643	8	**35**
26	942	20	307	28	693	635	8	34
27	962	20	335	28	665	627	8	33
28	9.72 982	20	363	28	637	619	8	32
29	9.73 002	20	391	28	609	611	8	31
30	9.73 022	20	9.80 419	28	0.19 581	9.92 603	8	**30**
31	041	19	447	28	553	595	8	29
32	061	20	474	27	526	587	8	28
33	081	20	502	28	498	579	8	27
34	101	20	530	28	470	571	8	26
35	9.73 121	20	9.80 558	28	0.19 442	9.92 563	8	**25**
36	140	19	586	28	414	555	8	24
37	160	20	614	28	386	546	9	23
38	180	20	642	28	358	538	8	22
39	200	20	669	27	331	530	8	21
40	9.73 219	19	9.80 697	28	0.19 303	9.92 522	8	**20**
41	239	20	725	28	275	514	8	19
42	259	20	753	28	247	506	8	18
43	278	19	781	28	219	498	8	17
44	298	20	808	27	192	490	8	16
45	9.73 318	20	9.80 836	28	0.19 164	9.92 482	8	**15**
46	337	19	864	28	136	473	9	14
47	357	20	892	28	108	465	8	13
48	377	20	919	27	081	457	8	12
49	396	19	947	28	053	449	8	11
50	9.73 416	20	9.80 975	28	0.19 025	9.92 441	8	**10**
51	435	19	9.81 003	28	0.18 997	433	8	9
52	455	20	030	27	970	425	8	8
53	474	19	058	28	942	416	9	7
54	494	20	086	28	914	408	8	6
55	9.73 513	19	9.81 113	27	0.18 887	9.92 400	8	**5**
56	533	20	141	28	859	392	8	4
57	552	19	169	28	831	384	8	3
58	572	20	196	27	804	376	8	2
59	591	19	224	28	776	367	9	1
60	9.73 611	20	9.81 252	28	0.18 748	9.92 359	8	**0**
	L Cos *	d	L Cot *	c d	L Tan	L Sin *	d	′

Prop. Parts

	29	28	27
1	2.9	2.8	2.7
2	5.8	5.6	5.4
3	8.7	8.4	8.1
4	11.6	11.2	10.8
5	14.5	14.0	13.5
6	17.4	16.8	16.2
7	20.3	19.6	18.9
8	23.2	22.4	21.6
9	26.1	25.2	24.3

	21	20	19
1	2.1	2	1.9
2	4.2	4	3.8
3	6.3	6	5.7
4	8.4	8	7.6
5	10.5	10	9.5
6	12.6	12	11.4
7	14.7	14	13.3
8	16.8	16	15.2
9	18.9	18	17.1

	9	8	7
1	0.9	0.8	0.7
2	1.8	1.6	1.4
3	2.7	2.4	2.1
4	3.6	3.2	2.8
5	4.5	4.0	3.5
6	5.4	4.8	4.2
7	6.3	5.6	4.9
8	7.2	6.4	5.6
9	8.1	7.2	6.3

57°

′	L Sin *	d	L Tan *	c d	L Cot	L Cos *	d	
0	9.73 611		9.81 252		0.18 748	9.92 359		**60**
1	630	19	279	27	721	351	8	59
2	650	20	307	28	693	343	8	58
3	669	19	335	28	665	335	8	57
4	689	20	362	27	638	326	9	56
5	9.73 708	19	9.81 390	28	0.18 610	9.92 318	8	**55**
6	727	19	418	28	582	310	8	54
7	747	20	445	27	555	302	8	53
8	766	19	473	28	527	293	9	52
9	785	19	500	27	500	285	8	51
10	9.73 805	20	9.81 528	28	0.18 472	9.92 277	8	**50**
11	824	19	556	28	444	269	8	49
12	843	19	583	27	417	260	9	48
13	863	20	611	28	389	252	8	47
14	882	19	638	27	362	244	8	46
15	9.73 901	19	9.81 666	28	0.18 334	9.92 235	9	**45**
16	921	20	693	27	307	227	8	44
17	940	19	721	28	279	219	8	43
18	959	19	748	27	252	211	8	42
19	978	19	776	28	224	202	9	41
20	9.73 997	19	9.81 803	27	0.18 197	9.92 194	8	**40**
21	9.74 017	20	831	28	169	186	8	39
22	036	19	858	27	142	177	9	38
23	055	19	886	28	114	169	8	37
24	074	19	913	27	087	161	8	36
25	9.74 093	19	9.81 941	28	0.18 059	9.92 152	9	**35**
26	113	20	968	27	032	144	8	34
27	132	19	9.81 996	28	0.18 004	136	8	33
28	151	19	9.82 023	27	0.17 977	127	9	32
29	170	19	051	28	949	119	8	31
30	9.74 189	19	9.82 078	27	0.17 922	9.92 111	8	**30**
31	208	19	106	28	894	102	9	29
32	227	19	133	27	867	094	8	28
33	246	19	161	28	839	086	8	27
34	265	19	188	27	812	077	9	26
35	9.74 284	19	9.82 215	27	0.17 785	9.92 069	8	**25**
36	303	19	243	28	757	060	9	24
37	322	19	270	27	730	052	8	23
38	341	19	298	28	702	044	8	22
39	360	19	325	27	675	035	9	21
40	9.74 379	19	9.82 352	27	0.17 648	9.92 027	8	**20**
41	398	19	380	28	620	018	9	19
42	417	19	407	27	593	010	8	18
43	436	19	435	28	565	9.92 002	8	17
44	455	19	462	27	538	9.91 993	9	16
45	9.74 474	19	9.82 489	27	0.17 511	9.91 985	8	**15**
46	493	19	517	28	483	976	9	14
47	512	19	544	27	456	968	8	13
48	531	19	571	27	429	959	9	12
49	549	18	599	28	401	951	8	11
50	9.74 568	19	9.82 626	27	0.17 374	9.91 942	9	**10**
51	587	19	653	27	347	934	8	9
52	606	19	681	28	319	925	9	8
53	625	19	708	27	292	917	8	7
54	644	19	735	27	265	908	9	6
55	9.74 662	18	9.82 762	27	0.17 238	9.91 900	8	**5**
56	681	19	790	28	210	891	9	4
57	700	19	817	27	183	883	8	3
58	719	19	844	27	156	874	9	2
59	737	18	871	27	129	866	8	1
60	9.74 756	19	9.82 899	28	0.17 101	9.91 857	9	**0**
	L Cos *	d	L Cot *	c d	L Tan	L Sin *	d	′

Prop. Parts

	28	27
1	2.8	2.7
2	5.6	5.4
3	8.4	8.1
4	11.2	10.8
5	14.0	13.5
6	16.8	16.2
7	19.6	18.9
8	22.4	21.6
9	25.2	24.3

	20	19	18
1	2	1.9	1.8
2	4	3.8	3.6
3	6	5.7	5.4
4	8	7.6	7.2
5	10	9.5	9.0
6	12	11.4	10.8
7	14	13.3	12.6
8	16	15.2	14.4
9	18	17.1	16.2

	9	8
1	0.9	0.8
2	1.8	1.6
3	2.7	2.4
4	3.6	3.2
5	4.5	4.0
6	5.4	4.8
7	6.3	5.6
8	7.2	6.4
9	8.1	7.2

56°

′	L Sin *	d	L Tan *	c d	L Cot	L Cos *	d	
0	9.74 756		9.82 899		0.17 101	9.91 857		**60**
1	775	19	926	27	074	849	8	59
2	794	19	953	27	047	840	9	58
3	812	18	9.82 980	27	0.17 020	832	8	57
4	831	19	9.83 008	28	0.16 992	823	9	56
5	9.74 850	19	9.83 035	27	0.16 965	9.91 815	8	**55**
6	868	18	062	27	938	806	9	54
7	887	19	089	27	911	798	8	53
8	906	19	117	28	883	789	9	52
9	924	18	144	27	856	781	8	51
10	9.74 943	19	9.83 171	27	0.16 829	9.91 772	9	**50**
11	961	18	198	27	802	763	9	49
12	980	19	225	27	775	755	8	48
13	9.74 999	19	252	27	748	746	9	47
14	9.75 017	18	280	28	720	738	8	46
15	9.75 036	19	9.83 307	27	0.16 693	9.91 729	9	**45**
16	054	18	334	27	666	720	9	44
17	073	19	361	27	639	712	8	43
18	091	18	388	27	612	703	9	42
19	110	19	415	27	585	695	8	41
20	9.75 128	18	9.83 442	27	0.16 558	9.91 686	9	**40**
21	147	19	470	28	530	677	9	39
22	165	18	497	27	503	669	8	38
23	184	19	524	27	476	660	9	37
24	202	18	551	27	449	651	9	36
25	9.75 221	19	9.83 578	27	0.16 422	9.91 643	8	**35**
26	239	18	605	27	395	634	9	34
27	258	19	632	27	368	625	9	33
28	276	18	659	27	341	617	8	32
29	294	18	686	27	314	608	9	31
30	9.75 313	19	9.83 713	27	0.16 287	9.91 599	9	**30**
31	331	18	740	27	260	591	8	29
32	350	19	768	28	232	582	9	28
33	368	18	795	27	205	573	9	27
34	386	18	822	27	178	565	8	26
35	9.75 405	19	9.83 849	27	0.16 151	9.91 556	9	**25**
36	423	18	876	27	124	547	9	24
37	441	18	903	27	097	538	9	23
38	459	18	930	27	070	530	8	22
39	478	19	957	27	043	521	9	21
40	9.75 496	18	9.83 984	27	0.16 016	9.91 512	9	**20**
41	514	18	9.84 011	27	0.15 989	504	8	19
42	533	19	038	27	962	495	9	18
43	551	18	065	27	935	486	9	17
44	569	18	092	27	908	477	9	16
45	9.75 587	18	9.84 119	27	0.15 881	9.91 469	8	**15**
46	605	18	146	27	854	460	9	14
47	624	19	173	27	827	451	9	13
48	642	18	200	27	800	442	9	12
49	660	18	227	27	773	433	9	11
50	9.75 678	18	9.84 254	27	0.15 746	9.91 425	8	**10**
51	696	18	280	26	720	416	9	9
52	714	18	307	27	693	407	9	8
53	733	19	334	27	666	398	9	7
54	751	18	361	27	639	389	9	6
55	9.75 769	18	9.84 388	27	0.15 612	9.91 381	8	**5**
56	787	18	415	27	585	372	9	4
57	805	18	442	27	558	363	9	3
58	823	18	469	27	531	354	9	2
59	841	18	496	27	504	345	9	1
60	9.75 859	18	9.84 523	27	0.15 477	9.91 336	9	**0**
	L Cos *	d	L Cot *	c d	L Tan	L Sin *	d	′

Prop. Parts

	28	27	26
1	2.8	2.7	2.6
2	5.6	5.4	5.2
3	8.4	8.1	7.8
4	11.2	10.8	10.4
5	14.0	13.5	13.0
6	16.8	16.2	15.6
7	19.6	18.9	18.2
8	22.4	21.6	20.8
9	25.2	24.3	23.4

	19	18
1	1.9	1.8
2	3.8	3.6
3	5.7	5.4
4	7.6	7.2
5	9.5	9.0
6	11.4	10.8
7	13.3	12.6
8	15.2	14.4
9	17.1	16.2

	9	8
1	0.9	0.8
2	1.8	1.6
3	2.7	2.4
4	3.6	3.2
5	4.5	4.0
6	5.4	4.8
7	6.3	5.6
8	7.2	6.4
9	8.1	7.2

Prop. Parts

	27	26
1	2.7	2.6
2	5.4	5.2
3	8.1	7.8
4	10.8	10.4
5	13.5	13.0
6	16.2	15.6
7	18.9	18.2
8	21.6	20.8
9	24.3	23.4

	18	17
1	1.8	1.7
2	3.6	3.4
3	5.4	5.1
4	7.2	6.8
5	9.0	8.5
6	10.8	10.2
7	12.6	11.9
8	14.4	13.6
9	16.2	15.3

	10	9	8
1	1.0	0.9	0.8
2	2.0	1.8	1.6
3	3.0	2.7	2.4
4	4.0	3.6	3.2
5	5.0	4.5	4.0
6	6.0	5.4	4.8
7	7.0	6.3	5.6
8	8.0	7.2	6.4
9	9.0	8.1	7.2

′	L Sin *	d	L Tan *	c d	L Cot	L Cos *	d	
0	9.75 859		9.84 523		0.15 477	9.91 336		**60**
1	877	18	550	27	450	328	8	59
2	895	18	576	26	424	319	9	58
3	913	18	603	27	397	310	9	57
4	931	18	630	27	370	301	9	56
5	9.75 949	18	9.84 657	27	0.15 343	9.91 292	9	**55**
6	967	18	684	27	316	283	9	54
7	9.75 985	18	711	27	289	274	9	53
8	9.76 003	18	738	27	262	266	8	52
9	021	18	764	26	236	257	9	51
10	9.76 039	18	9.84 791	27	0.15 209	9.91 248	9	**50**
11	057	18	818	27	182	239	9	49
12	075	18	845	27	155	230	9	48
13	093	18	872	27	128	221	9	47
14	111	18	899	27	101	212	9	46
15	9.76 129	18	9.84 925	26	0.15 075	9.91 203	9	**45**
16	146	17	952	27	048	194	9	44
17	164	18	9.84 979	27	0.15 021	185	9	43
18	182	18	9.85 006	27	0.14 994	176	9	42
19	200	18	033	27	967	167	9	41
20	9.76 218	18	9.85 059	26	0.14 941	9.91 158	9	**40**
21	236	18	086	27	914	149	9	39
22	253	17	113	27	887	141	8	38
23	271	18	140	27	860	132	9	37
24	289	18	166	26	834	123	9	36
25	9.76 307	18	9.85 193	27	0.14 807	9.91 114	9	**35**
26	324	17	220	27	780	105	9	34
27	342	18	247	27	753	096	9	33
28	360	18	273	26	727	087	9	32
29	378	18	300	27	700	078	9	31
30	9.76 395	17	9.85 327	27	0.14 673	9.91 069	9	**30**
31	413	18	354	27	646	060	9	29
32	431	18	380	26	620	051	9	28
33	448	17	407	27	593	042	9	27
34	466	18	434	27	566	033	9	26
35	9.76 484	18	9.85 460	26	0.14 540	9.91 023	10	**25**
36	501	17	487	27	513	014	9	24
37	519	18	514	27	486	9.91 005	9	23
38	537	18	540	26	460	9.90 996	9	22
39	554	17	567	27	433	987	9	21
40	9.76 572	18	9.85 594	27	0.14 406	9.90 978	9	**20**
41	590	18	620	26	380	969	9	19
42	607	17	647	27	353	960	9	18
43	625	18	674	27	326	951	9	17
44	642	17	700	26	300	942	9	16
45	9.76 660	18	9.85 727	27	0.14 273	9.90 933	9	**15**
46	677	17	754	27	246	924	9	14
47	695	18	780	26	220	915	9	13
48	712	17	807	27	193	906	9	12
49	730	18	834	27	166	896	10	11
50	9.76 747	17	9.85 860	26	0.14 140	9.90 887	9	**10**
51	765	18	887	27	113	878	9	9
52	782	17	913	26	087	869	9	8
53	800	18	940	27	060	860	9	7
54	817	17	967	27	033	851	9	6
55	9.76 835	18	9.85 993	26	0.14 007	9.90 842	9	**5**
56	852	17	9.86 020	27	0.13 980	832	10	4
57	870	18	046	26	954	823	9	3
58	887	17	073	27	927	814	9	2
59	904	17	100	27	900	805	9	1
60	9.76 922	18	9.86 126	26	0.13 874	9.90 796	9	**0**
	L Cos *	d	L Cot *	c d	L Tan	L Sin *	d	′

54°

′	L Sin *	d	L Tan *	c d	L Cot	L Cos *	d	
0	9.76 922		9.86 126		0.13 874	9.90 796		**60**
1	939	17	153	27	847	787	9	59
2	957	18	179	26	821	777	10	58
3	974	17	206	27	794	768	9	57
4	9.76 991	17	232	26	768	759	9	56
5	9.77 009	18	9.86 259	27	0.13 741	9.90 750	9	**55**
6	026	17	285	26	715	741	9	54
7	043	17	312	27	688	731	10	53
8	061	18	338	26	662	722	9	52
9	078	17	365	27	635	713	9	51
10	9.77 095	17	9.86 392	27	0.13 608	9.90 704	9	**50**
11	112	17	418	26	582	694	10	49
12	130	18	445	27	555	685	9	48
13	147	17	471	26	529	676	9	47
14	164	17	498	27	502	667	9	46
15	9.77 181	17	9.86 524	26	0.13 476	9.90 657	10	**45**
16	199	18	551	27	449	648	9	44
17	216	17	577	26	423	639	9	43
18	233	17	603	26	397	630	9	42
19	250	17	630	27	370	620	10	41
20	9.77 268	18	9.86 656	26	0.13 344	9.90 611	9	**40**
21	285	17	683	27	317	602	9	39
22	302	17	709	26	291	592	10	38
23	319	17	736	27	264	583	9	37
24	336	17	762	26	238	574	9	36
25	9.77 353	17	9.86 789	27	0.13 211	9.90 565	9	**35**
26	370	17	815	26	185	555	10	34
27	387	17	842	27	158	546	9	33
28	405	18	868	26	132	537	9	32
29	422	17	894	26	106	527	10	31
30	9.77 439	17	9.86 921	27	0.13 079	9.90 518	9	**30**
31	456	17	947	26	053	509	9	29
32	473	17	9.86 974	27	026	499	10	28
33	490	17	9.87 000	26	0.13 000	490	9	27
34	507	17	027	27	0.12 973	480	10	26
35	9.77 524	17	9.87 053	26	0.12 947	9.90 471	9	**25**
36	541	17	079	26	921	462	9	24
37	558	17	106	27	894	452	10	23
38	575	17	132	26	868	443	9	22
39	592	17	158	26	842	434	9	21
40	9.77 609	17	9.87 185	27	0.12 815	9.90 424	10	**20**
41	626	17	211	26	789	415	9	19
42	643	17	238	27	762	405	10	18
43	660	17	264	26	736	396	9	17
44	677	17	290	26	710	386	10	16
45	9.77 694	17	9.87 317	27	0.12 683	9.90 377	9	**15**
46	711	17	343	26	657	368	9	14
47	728	17	369	26	631	358	10	13
48	744	16	396	27	604	349	9	12
49	761	17	422	26	578	339	10	11
50	9.77 778	17	9.87 448	26	0.12 552	9.90 330	9	**10**
51	795	17	475	27	525	320	10	9
52	812	17	501	26	499	311	9	8
53	829	17	527	26	473	301	10	7
54	846	17	554	27	446	292	9	6
55	9.77 862	16	9.87 580	26	0.12 420	9.90 282	10	**5**
56	879	17	606	26	394	273	9	4
57	896	17	633	27	367	263	10	3
58	913	17	659	26	341	254	9	2
59	930	17	685	26	315	244	10	1
60	9.77 946	16	9.87 711	26	0.12 289	9.90 235	9	**0**
	L Cos *	d	L Cot *	c d	L Tan	L Sin *	d	′

53°

Prop. Parts

Subtract 10 from each entry in the columns marked with "."*

	27	**26**
1	2.7	2.6
2	5.4	5.2
3	8.1	7.8
4	10.8	10.4
5	13.5	13.0
6	16.2	15.6
7	18.9	18.2
8	21.6	20.8
9	24.3	23.4

	18	**17**	**16**
1	1.8	1.7	1.6
2	3.6	3.4	3.2
3	5.4	5.1	4.8
4	7.2	6.8	6.4
5	9.0	8.5	8.0
6	10.8	10.2	9.6
7	12.6	11.9	11.2
8	14.4	13.6	12.8
9	16.2	15.3	14.4

	10	**9**
1	1.0	0.9
2	2.0	1.8
3	3.0	2.7
4	4.0	3.6
5	5.0	4.5
6	6.0	5.4
7	7.0	6.3
8	8.0	7.2
9	9.0	8.1

′	L Sin *	d	L Tan *	c d	L Cot	L Cos *	d	
0	9.77 946		9.87 711		0.12 289	9.90 235		**60**
1	963	17	738	27	262	225	10	59
2	980	17	764	26	236	216	9	58
3	9.77 997	17	790	26	210	206	10	57
4	9.78 013	16	817	27	183	197	9	56
5	9.78 030	17	9.87 843	26	0.12 157	9.90 187	10	**55**
6	047	17	869	26	131	178	9	54
7	063	16	895	26	105	168	10	53
8	080	17	922	27	078	159	9	52
9	097	17	948	26	052	149	10	51
10	9.78 113	16	9.87 974	26	0.12 026	9.90 139	10	**50**
11	130	17	9.88 000	26	0.12 000	130	9	49
12	147	17	027	27	0.11 973	120	10	48
13	163	16	053	26	947	111	9	47
14	180	17	079	26	921	101	10	46
15	9.78 197	17	9.88 105	26	0.11 895	9.90 091	10	**45**
16	213	16	131	26	869	082	9	44
17	230	17	158	27	842	072	10	43
18	246	16	184	26	816	063	9	42
19	263	17	210	26	790	053	10	41
20	9.78 280	17	9.88 236	26	0.11 764	9.90 043	10	**40**
21	296	16	262	26	738	034	9	39
22	313	17	289	27	711	024	10	38
23	329	16	315	26	685	014	10	37
24	346	17	341	26	659	9.90 005	9	36
25	9.78 362	16	9.88 367	26	0.11 633	9.89 995	10	**35**
26	379	17	393	26	607	985	10	34
27	395	16	420	27	580	976	9	33
28	412	17	446	26	554	966	10	32
29	428	16	472	26	528	956	10	31
30	9.78 445	17	9.88 498	26	0.11 502	9.89 947	9	**30**
31	461	16	524	26	476	937	10	29
32	478	17	550	26	450	927	10	28
33	494	16	577	27	423	918	9	27
34	510	16	603	26	397	908	10	26
35	9.78 527	17	9.88 629	26	0.11 371	9.89 898	10	**25**
36	543	16	655	26	345	888	10	24
37	560	17	681	26	319	879	9	23
38	576	16	707	26	293	869	10	22
39	592	16	733	26	267	859	10	21
40	9.78 609	17	9.88 759	26	0.11 241	9.89 849	10	**20**
41	625	16	786	27	214	840	9	19
42	642	17	812	26	188	830	10	18
43	658	16	838	26	162	820	10	17
44	674	16	864	26	136	810	10	16
45	9.78 691	17	9.88 890	26	0.11 110	9.89 801	9	**15**
46	707	16	916	26	084	791	10	14
47	723	16	942	26	058	781	10	13
48	739	16	968	26	032	771	10	12
49	756	17	9.88 994	26	0.11 006	761	10	11
50	9.78 772	16	9.89 020	26	0.10 980	9.89 752	9	**10**
51	788	16	046	26	954	742	10	9
52	805	17	073	27	927	732	10	8
53	821	16	099	26	901	722	10	7
54	837	16	125	26	875	712	10	6
55	9.78 853	16	9.89 151	26	0.10 849	9.89 702	10	**5**
56	869	16	177	26	823	693	9	4
57	886	17	203	26	797	683	10	3
58	902	16	229	26	771	673	10	2
59	918	16	255	26	745	663	10	1
60	9.78 934	16	9.89 281	26	0.10 719	9.89 653	10	**0**
	L Cos *	d	L Cot *	c d	L Tan	L Sin *	d	′

Prop. Parts

	27	26
1	2.7	2.6
2	5.4	5.2
3	8.1	7.8
4	10.8	10.4
5	13.5	13.0
6	16.2	15.6
7	18.9	18.2
8	21.6	20.8
9	24.3	23.4

	17	16
1	1.7	1.6
2	3.4	3.2
3	5.1	4.8
4	6.8	6.4
5	8.5	8.0
6	10.2	9.6
7	11.9	11.2
8	13.6	12.8
9	15.3	14.4

	10	9
1	1.0	0.9
2	2.0	1.8
3	3.0	2.7
4	4.0	3.6
5	5.0	4.5
6	6.0	5.4
7	7.0	6.3
8	8.0	7.2
9	9.0	8.1

52°

′	L Sin *	d	L Tan *	c d	L Cot	L Cos *	d	
0	9.78 934		9.89 281		0.10 719	9.89 653		**60**
1	950	16	307	26	693	643	10	59
2	967	17	333	26	667	633	10	58
3	983	16	359	26	641	624	9	57
4	9.78 999	16	385	26	615	614	10	56
5	9.79 015	16	9.89 411	26	0.10 589	9.89 604	10	**55**
6	031	16	437	26	563	594	10	54
7	047	16	463	26	537	584	10	53
8	063	16	489	26	511	574	10	52
9	079	16	515	26	485	564	10	51
10	9.79 095	16	9.89 541	26	0.10 459	9.89 554	10	**50**
11	111	16	567	26	433	544	10	49
12	128	17	593	26	407	534	10	48
13	144	16	619	26	381	524	10	47
14	160	16	645	26	355	514	10	46
15	9.79 176	16	9.89 671	26	0.10 329	9.89 504	10	**45**
16	192	16	697	26	303	495	9	44
17	208	16	723	26	277	485	10	43
18	224	16	749	26	251	475	10	42
19	240	16	775	26	225	465	10	41
20	9.79 256	16	9.89 801	26	0.10 199	9.89 455	10	**40**
21	272	16	827	26	173	445	10	39
22	288	16	853	26	147	435	10	38
23	304	16	879	26	121	425	10	37
24	319	15	905	26	095	415	10	36
25	9.79 335	16	9.89 931	26	0.10 069	9.89 405	10	**35**
26	351	16	957	26	043	395	10	34
27	367	16	9.89 983	26	0.10 017	385	10	33
28	383	16	9.90 009	26	0.09 991	375	10	32
29	399	16	035	26	965	364	11	31
30	9.79 415	16	9.90 061	26	0.09 939	9.89 354	10	**30**
31	431	16	086	25	914	344	10	29
32	447	16	112	26	888	334	10	28
33	463	16	138	26	862	324	10	27
34	478	15	164	26	836	314	10	26
35	9.79 494	16	9.90 190	26	0.09 810	9.89 304	10	**25**
36	510	16	216	26	784	294	10	24
37	526	16	242	26	758	284	10	23
38	542	16	268	26	732	274	10	22
39	558	16	294	26	706	264	10	21
40	9.79 573	15	9.90 320	26	0.09 680	9.89 254	10	**20**
41	589	16	346	26	654	244	10	19
42	605	16	371	25	629	233	11	18
43	621	16	397	26	603	223	10	17
44	636	15	423	26	577	213	10	16
45	9.79 652	16	9.90 449	26	0.09 551	9.89 203	10	**15**
46	668	16	475	26	525	193	10	14
47	684	16	501	26	499	183	10	13
48	699	15	527	26	473	173	10	12
49	715	16	553	26	447	162	11	11
50	9.79 731	16	9.90 578	25	0.09 422	9.89 152	10	**10**
51	746	15	604	26	396	142	10	9
52	762	16	630	26	370	132	10	8
53	778	16	656	26	344	122	10	7
54	793	15	682	26	318	112	10	6
55	9.79 809	16	9.90 708	26	0.09 292	9.89 101	11	**5**
56	825	16	734	26	266	091	10	4
57	840	15	759	25	241	081	10	3
58	856	16	785	26	215	071	10	2
59	872	16	811	26	189	060	11	1
60	9.79 887	15	9.90 837	26	0.09 163	9.89 050	10	**0**
	L Cos *	d	L Cot *	c d	L Tan	L Sin *	d	′

51°

Prop. Parts

	26	25
1	2.6	2.5
2	5.2	5.0
3	7.8	7.5
4	10.4	10.0
5	13.0	12.5
6	15.6	15.0
7	18.2	17.5
8	20.8	20.0
9	23.4	22.5

	17	16	15
1	1.7	1.6	1.5
2	3.4	3.2	3.0
3	5.1	4.8	4.5
4	6.8	6.4	6.0
5	8.5	8.0	7.5
6	10.2	9.6	9.0
7	11.9	11.2	10.5
8	13.6	12.8	12.0
9	15.3	14.4	13.5

	11	10	9
1	1.1	1.0	0.9
2	2.2	2.0	1.8
3	3.3	3.0	2.7
4	4.4	4.0	3.6
5	5.5	5.0	4.5
6	6.6	6.0	5.4
7	7.7	7.0	6.3
8	8.8	8.0	7.2
9	9.9	9.0	8.1

Prop. Parts

	26	25
1	2.6	2.5
2	5.2	5.0
3	7.8	7.5
4	10.4	10.0
5	13.0	12.5
6	15.6	15.0
7	18.2	17.5
8	20.8	20.0
9	23.4	22.5

	16	15
1	1.6	1.5
2	3.2	3.0
3	4.8	4.5
4	6.4	6.0
5	8.0	7.5
6	9.6	9.0
7	11.2	10.5
8	12.8	12.0
9	14.4	13.5

	11	10
1	1.1	1.0
2	2.2	2.0
3	3.3	3.0
4	4.4	4.0
5	5.5	5.0
6	6.6	6.0
7	7.7	7.0
8	8.8	8.0
9	9.9	9.0

′	L Sin *	d	L Tan *	c d	L Cot	L Cos *	d	
0	9.79 887		9.90 837		0.09 163	9.89 050		**60**
1	903	16	863	26	137	040	10	59
2	918	15	889	26	111	030	10	58
3	934	16	914	25	086	020	10	57
4	950	16	940	26	060	9.89 009	11	56
5	9.79 965	15	9.90 966	26	0.09 034	9.88 999	10	**55**
6	981	16	9.90 992	26	0.09 008	989	10	54
7	9.79 996	15	9.91 018	26	0.08 982	978	11	53
8	9.80 012	16	043	25	957	968	10	52
9	027	15	069	26	931	958	10	51
10	9.80 043	16	9.91 095	26	0.08 905	9.88 948	10	**50**
11	058	15	121	26	879	937	11	49
12	074	16	147	26	853	927	10	48
13	089	15	172	25	828	917	10	47
14	105	16	198	26	802	906	11	46
15	9.80 120	15	9.91 224	26	0.08 776	9.88 896	10	**45**
16	136	16	250	26	750	886	10	44
17	151	15	276	26	724	875	11	43
18	166	15	301	25	699	865	10	42
19	182	16	327	26	673	855	10	41
20	9.80 197	15	9.91 353	26	0.08 647	9.88 844	11	**40**
21	213	16	379	26	621	834	10	39
22	228	15	404	25	596	824	10	38
23	244	16	430	26	570	813	11	37
24	259	15	456	26	544	803	10	36
25	9.80 274	15	9.91 482	26	0.08 518	9.88 793	10	**35**
26	290	16	507	25	493	782	11	34
27	305	15	533	26	467	772	10	33
28	320	15	559	26	441	761	11	32
29	336	16	585	26	415	751	10	31
30	9.80 351	15	9.91 610	25	0.08 390	9.88 741	10	**30**
31	366	15	636	26	364	730	11	29
32	382	16	662	26	338	720	10	28
33	397	15	688	26	312	709	11	27
34	412	15	713	25	287	699	10	26
35	9.80 428	16	9.91 739	26	0.08 261	9.88 688	11	**25**
36	443	15	765	26	235	678	10	24
37	458	15	791	26	209	668	10	23
38	473	15	816	25	184	657	11	22
39	489	16	842	26	158	647	10	21
40	9.80 504	15	9.91 868	26	0.08 132	9.88 636	11	**20**
41	519	15	893	25	107	626	10	19
42	534	15	919	26	081	615	11	18
43	550	16	945	26	055	605	10	17
44	565	15	971	26	029	594	11	16
45	9.80 580	15	9.91 996	25	0.08 004	9.88 584	10	**15**
46	595	15	9.92 022	26	0.07 978	573	11	14
47	610	15	048	26	952	563	10	13
48	625	15	073	25	927	552	11	12
49	641	16	099	26	901	542	10	11
50	9.80 656	15	9.92 125	26	0.07 875	9.88 531	11	**10**
51	671	15	150	25	850	521	10	9
52	686	15	176	26	824	510	11	8
53	701	15	202	26	798	499	11	7
54	716	15	227	25	773	489	10	6
55	9.80 731	15	9.92 253	26	0.07 747	9.88 478	11	**5**
56	746	15	279	26	721	468	10	4
57	762	16	304	25	696	457	11	3
58	777	15	330	26	670	447	10	2
59	792	15	356	26	644	436	11	1
60	9.80 807	15	9.92 381	25	0.07 619	9.88 425	11	**0**
	L Cos *	d	L Cot *	c d	L Tan	L Sin *	d	′

50°

′	L Sin *	d	L Tan *	c d	L Cot	L Cos *	d	
0	9.80 807		9.92 381		0.07 619	9.88 425		**60**
1	822	15	407	26	593	415	10	59
2	837	15	433	26	567	404	11	58
3	852	15	458	25	542	394	10	57
4	867	15	484	26	516	383	11	56
5	9.80 882	15	9.92 510	26	0.07 490	9.88 372	11	**55**
6	897	15	535	25	465	362	10	54
7	912	15	561	26	439	351	11	53
8	927	15	587	26	413	340	11	52
9	942	15	612	25	388	330	10	51
10	9.80 957	15	9.92 638	26	0.07 362	9.88 319	11	**50**
11	972	15	663	25	337	308	11	49
12	9.80 987	15	689	26	311	298	10	48
13	9.81 002	15	715	26	285	287	11	47
14	017	15	740	25	260	276	11	46
15	9.81 032	15	9.92 766	26	0.07 234	9.88 266	10	**45**
16	047	15	792	26	208	255	11	44
17	061	14	817	25	183	244	11	43
18	076	15	843	26	157	234	10	42
19	091	15	868	25	132	223	11	41
20	9.81 106	15	9.92 894	26	0.07 106	9.88 212	11	**40**
21	121	15	920	26	080	201	11	39
22	136	15	945	25	055	191	10	38
23	151	15	971	26	029	180	11	37
24	166	15	9.92 996	25	0.07 004	169	11	36
25	9.81 180	14	9.93 022	26	0.06 978	9.88 158	11	**35**
26	195	15	048	26	952	148	10	34
27	210	15	073	25	927	137	11	33
28	225	15	099	26	901	126	11	32
29	240	15	124	25	876	115	11	31
30	9.81 254	14	9.93 150	26	0.06 850	9.88 105	10	**30**
31	269	15	175	25	825	094	11	29
32	284	15	201	26	799	083	11	28
33	299	15	227	26	773	072	11	27
34	314	15	252	25	748	061	11	26
35	9.81 328	14	9.93 278	26	0.06 722	9.88 051	10	**25**
36	343	15	303	25	697	040	11	24
37	358	15	329	26	671	029	11	23
38	372	14	354	25	646	018	11	22
39	387	15	380	26	620	9.88 007	11	21
40	9.81 402	15	9.93 406	26	0.06 594	9.87 996	11	**20**
41	417	15	431	25	569	985	11	19
42	431	14	457	26	543	975	10	18
43	446	15	482	25	518	964	11	17
44	461	15	508	26	492	953	11	16
45	9.81 475	14	9.93 533	25	0.06 467	9.87 942	11	**15**
46	490	15	559	26	441	931	11	14
47	505	15	584	25	416	920	11	13
48	519	14	610	26	390	909	11	12
49	534	15	636	26	364	898	11	11
50	9.81 549	15	9.93 661	25	0.06 339	9.87 887	11	**10**
51	563	14	687	26	313	877	10	9
52	578	15	712	25	288	866	11	8
53	592	14	738	26	262	855	11	7
54	607	15	763	25	237	844	11	6
55	9.81 622	15	9.93 789	26	0.06 211	9.87 833	11	**5**
56	636	14	814	25	186	822	11	4
57	651	15	840	26	160	811	11	3
58	665	14	865	25	135	800	11	2
59	680	15	891	26	109	789	11	1
60	9.81 694	14	9.93 916	25	0.06 084	9.87 778	11	**0**
	L Cos *	d	L Cot *	c d	L Tan	L Sin *	d	′

Prop. Parts

Subtract 10 *from each entry in the columns marked with "*".*

	26	25
1	2.6	2.5
2	5.2	5.0
3	7.8	7.5
4	10.4	10.0
5	13.0	12.5
6	15.6	15.0
7	18.2	17.5
8	20.8	20.0
9	23.4	22.5

	15	14
1	1.5	1.4
2	3.0	2.8
3	4.5	4.2
4	6.0	5.6
5	7.5	7.0
6	9.0	8.4
7	10.5	9.8
8	12.0	11.2
9	13.5	12.6

	11	10
1	1.1	1.0
2	2.2	2.0
3	3.3	3.0
4	4.4	4.0
5	5.5	5.0
6	6.6	6.0
7	7.7	7.0
8	8.8	8.0
9	9.9	9.0

49°

Prop. Parts

	26	25
1	2.6	2.5
2	5.2	5.0
3	7.8	7.5
4	10.4	10.0
5	13.0	12.5
6	15.6	15.0
7	18.2	17.5
8	20.8	20.0
9	23.4	22.5

	15	14
1	1.5	1.4
2	3.0	2.8
3	4.5	4.2
4	6.0	5.6
5	7.5	7.0
6	9.0	8.4
7	10.5	9.8
8	12.0	11.2
9	13.5	12.6

	12	11
1	1.2	1.1
2	2.4	2.2
3	3.6	3.3
4	4.8	4.4
5	6.0	5.5
6	7.2	6.6
7	8.4	7.7
8	9.6	8.8
9	10.8	9.9

′	L Sin *	d	L Tan *	c d	L Cot	L Cos *	d	
0	9.81 694		9.93 916		0.06 084	9.87 778		**60**
1	709	15	942	26	058	767	11	59
2	723	14	967	25	033	756	11	58
3	738	15	9.93 993	26	0.06 007	745	11	57
4	752	14	9.94 018	25	0.05 982	734	11	56
5	9.81 767	15	9.94 044	26	0.05 956	9.87 723	11	**55**
6	781	14	069	25	931	712	11	54
7	796	15	095	26	905	701	11	53
8	810	14	120	25	880	690	11	52
9	825	15	146	26	854	679	11	51
10	9.81 839	14	9.94 171	25	0.05 829	9.87 668	11	**50**
11	854	15	197	26	803	657	11	49
12	868	14	222	25	778	646	11	48
13	882	14	248	26	752	635	11	47
14	897	15	273	25	727	624	11	46
15	9.81 911	14	9.94 299	26	0.05 701	9.87 613	11	**45**
16	926	15	324	25	676	601	12	44
17	940	14	350	26	650	590	11	43
18	955	15	375	25	625	579	11	42
19	969	14	401	26	599	568	11	41
20	9.81 983	14	9.94 426	25	0.05 574	9.87 557	11	**40**
21	9.81 998	15	452	26	548	546	11	39
22	9.82 012	14	477	25	523	535	11	38
23	026	14	503	26	497	524	11	37
24	041	15	528	25	472	513	11	36
25	9.82 055	14	9.94 554	26	0.05 446	9.87 501	12	**35**
26	069	14	579	25	421	490	11	34
27	084	15	604	25	396	479	11	33
28	098	14	630	26	370	468	11	32
29	112	14	655	25	345	457	11	31
30	9.82 126	14	9.94 681	26	0.05 319	9.87 446	11	**30**
31	141	15	706	25	294	434	12	29
32	155	14	732	26	268	423	11	28
33	169	14	757	25	243	412	11	27
34	184	15	783	26	217	401	11	26
35	9.82 198	14	9.94 808	25	0.05 192	9.87 390	11	**25**
36	212	14	834	26	166	378	12	24
37	226	14	859	25	141	367	11	23
38	240	14	884	25	116	356	11	22
39	255	15	910	26	090	345	11	21
40	9.82 269	14	9.94 935	25	0.05 065	9.87 334	11	**20**
41	283	14	961	26	039	322	12	19
42	297	14	9.94 986	25	0.05 014	311	11	18
43	311	14	9.95 012	26	0.04 988	300	11	17
44	326	15	037	25	963	288	12	16
45	9.82 340	14	9.95 062	25	0.04 938	9.87 277	11	**15**
46	354	14	088	26	912	266	11	14
47	368	14	113	25	887	255	11	13
48	382	14	139	26	861	243	12	12
49	396	14	164	25	836	232	11	11
50	9.82 410	14	9.95 190	26	0.04 810	9.87 221	11	**10**
51	424	14	215	25	785	209	12	9
52	439	15	240	25	760	198	11	8
53	453	14	266	26	734	187	11	7
54	467	14	291	25	709	175	12	6
55	9.82 481	14	9.95 317	26	0.04 683	9.87 164	11	**5**
56	495	14	342	25	658	153	11	4
57	509	14	368	26	632	141	12	3
58	523	14	393	25	607	130	11	2
59	537	14	418	25	582	119	11	1
60	9.82 551	14	9.95 444	26	0.04 556	9.87 107	12	**0**
	L Cos *	d	L Cot *	c d	L Tan	L Sin *	d	′

48°

′	L Sin *	d	L Tan *	c d	L Cot	L Cos *	d	
0	9.82 551		9.95 444		0.04 556	9.87 107		**60**
1	565	14	469	25	531	096	11	59
2	579	14	495	26	505	085	11	58
3	593	14	520	25	480	073	12	57
4	607	14	545	25	455	062	11	56
5	9.82 621	14	9.95 571	26	0.04 429	9.87 050	12	**55**
6	635	14	596	25	404	039	11	54
7	649	14	622	26	378	028	11	53
8	663	14	647	25	353	016	12	52
9	677	14	672	25	328	9.87 005	11	51
10	9.82 691	14	9.95 698	26	0.04 302	9.86 993	12	**50**
11	705	14	723	25	277	982	11	49
12	719	14	748	25	252	970	12	48
13	733	14	774	26	226	959	11	47
14	747	14	799	25	201	947	12	46
15	9.82 761	14	9.95 825	26	0.04 175	9.86 936	11	**45**
16	775	14	850	25	150	924	12	44
17	788	13	875	25	125	913	11	43
18	802	14	901	26	099	902	11	42
19	816	14	926	25	074	890	12	41
20	9.82 830	14	9.95 952	26	0.04 048	9.86 879	11	**40**
21	844	14	9.95 977	25	0.04 023	867	12	39
22	858	14	9.96 002	25	0.03 998	855	12	38
23	872	14	028	26	972	844	11	37
24	885	13	053	25	947	832	12	36
25	9.82 899	14	9.96 078	25	0.03 922	9.86 821	11	**35**
26	913	14	104	26	896	809	12	34
27	927	14	129	25	871	798	11	33
28	941	14	155	26	845	786	12	32
29	955	14	180	25	820	775	11	31
30	9.82 968	13	9.96 205	25	0.03 795	9.86 763	12	**30**
31	982	14	231	26	769	752	11	29
32	9.82 996	14	256	25	744	740	12	28
33	9.83 010	14	281	25	719	728	12	27
34	023	13	307	26	693	717	11	26
35	9.83 037	14	9.96 332	25	0.03 668	9.86 705	12	**25**
36	051	14	357	25	643	694	11	24
37	065	14	383	26	617	682	12	23
38	078	13	408	25	592	670	12	22
39	092	14	433	25	567	659	11	21
40	9.83 106	14	9.96 459	26	0.03 541	9.86 647	12	**20**
41	120	14	484	25	516	635	12	19
42	133	13	510	26	490	624	11	18
43	147	14	535	25	465	612	12	17
44	161	14	560	25	440	600	12	16
45	9.83 174	13	9.96 586	26	0.03 414	9.86 589	11	**15**
46	188	14	611	25	389	577	12	14
47	202	14	636	25	364	565	12	13
48	215	13	662	26	338	554	11	12
49	229	14	687	25	313	542	12	11
50	9.83 242	13	9.96 712	25	0.03 288	9.86 530	12	**10**
51	256	14	738	26	262	518	12	9
52	270	14	763	25	237	507	11	8
53	283	13	788	25	212	495	12	7
54	297	14	814	26	186	483	12	6
55	9.83 310	13	9.96 839	25	0.03 161	9.86 472	11	**5**
56	324	14	864	25	136	460	12	4
57	338	14	890	26	110	448	12	3
58	351	13	915	25	085	436	12	2
59	365	14	940	25	060	425	11	1
60	9.83 378	13	9.96 966	26	0.03 034	9.86 413	12	**0**
	L Cos *	d	L Cot *	c d	L Tan	L Sin *	d	′

Prop. Parts

	26	25
1	2.6	2.5
2	5.2	5.0
3	7.8	7.5
4	10.4	10.0
5	13.0	12.5
6	15.6	15.0
7	18.2	17.5
8	20.8	20.0
9	23.4	22.5

	14	13
1	1.4	1.3
2	2.8	2.6
3	4.2	3.9
4	5.6	5.2
5	7.0	6.5
6	8.4	7.8
7	9.8	9.1
8	11.2	10.4
9	12.6	11.7

	12	11
1	1.2	1.1
2	2.4	2.2
3	3.6	3.3
4	4.8	4.4
5	6.0	5.5
6	7.2	6.6
7	8.4	7.7
8	9.6	8.8
9	10.8	9.9

47°

Prop. Parts

	26	25
1	2.6	2.5
2	5.2	5.0
3	7.8	7.5
4	10.4	10.0
5	13.0	12.5
6	15.6	15.0
7	18.2	17.5
8	20.8	20.0
9	23.4	22.5

	14	13
1	1.4	1.3
2	2.8	2.6
3	4.2	3.9
4	5.6	5.2
5	7.0	6.5
6	8.4	7.8
7	9.8	9.1
8	11.2	10.4
9	12.6	11.7

	12	11
1	1.2	1.1
2	2.4	2.2
3	3.6	3.3
4	4.8	4.4
5	6.0	5.5
6	7.2	6.6
7	8.4	7.7
8	9.6	8.8
9	10.8	9.9

′	L Sin *	d	L Tan *	c d	L Cot	L Cos *	d	
0	9.83 378		9.96 966		0.03 034	9.86 413		**60**
1	392	14	9.96 991	25	0.03 009	401	12	59
2	405	13	9.97 016	25	0.02 984	389	12	58
3	419	14	042	26	958	377	12	57
4	432	13	067	25	933	366	11	56
5	9.83 446	14	9.97 092	25	0.02 908	9.86 354	12	**55**
6	459	13	118	26	882	342	12	54
7	473	14	143	25	857	330	12	53
8	486	13	168	25	832	318	12	52
9	500	14	193	25	807	306	12	51
10	9.83 513	13	9.97 219	26	0.02 781	9.86 295	11	**50**
11	527	14	244	25	756	283	12	49
12	540	13	269	25	731	271	12	48
13	554	14	295	26	705	259	12	47
14	567	13	320	25	680	247	12	46
15	9.83 581	14	9.97 345	25	0.02 655	9.86 235	12	**45**
16	594	13	371	26	629	223	12	44
17	608	14	396	25	604	211	12	43
18	621	13	421	25	579	200	11	42
19	634	13	447	26	553	188	12	41
20	9.83 648	14	9.97 472	25	0.02 528	9.86 176	12	**40**
21	661	13	497	25	503	164	12	39
22	674	13	523	26	477	152	12	38
23	688	14	548	25	452	140	12	37
24	701	13	573	25	427	128	12	36
25	9.83 715	14	9.97 598	25	0.02 402	9.86 116	12	**35**
26	728	13	624	26	376	104	12	34
27	741	13	649	25	351	092	12	33
28	755	14	674	25	326	080	12	32
29	768	13	700	26	300	068	12	31
30	9.83 781	13	9.97 725	25	0.02 275	9.86 056	12	**30**
31	795	14	750	25	250	044	12	29
32	808	13	776	26	224	032	12	28
33	821	13	801	25	199	020	12	27
34	834	13	826	25	174	9.86 008	12	26
35	9.83 848	14	9.97 851	25	0.02 149	9.85 996	12	**25**
36	861	13	877	26	123	984	12	24
37	874	13	902	25	098	972	12	23
38	887	13	927	25	073	960	12	22
39	901	14	953	26	047	948	12	21
40	9.83 914	13	9.97 978	25	0.02 022	9.85 936	12	**20**
41	927	13	9.98 003	25	0.01 997	924	12	19
42	940	13	029	26	971	912	12	18
43	954	14	054	25	946	900	12	17
44	967	13	079	25	921	888	12	16
45	9.83 980	13	9.98 104	25	0.01 896	9.85 876	12	**15**
46	9.83 993	13	130	26	870	864	12	14
47	9.84 006	13	155	25	845	851	13	13
48	020	14	180	25	820	839	12	12
49	033	13	206	26	794	827	12	11
50	9.84 046	13	9.98 231	25	0.01 769	9.85 815	12	**10**
51	059	13	256	25	744	803	12	9
52	072	13	281	25	719	791	12	8
53	085	13	307	26	693	779	12	7
54	098	13	332	25	668	766	13	6
55	9.84 112	14	9.98 357	25	0.01 643	9.85 754	12	**5**
56	125	13	383	26	617	742	12	4
57	138	13	408	25	592	730	12	3
58	151	13	433	25	567	718	12	2
59	164	13	458	25	542	706	12	1
60	9.84 177	13	9.98 484	26	0.01 516	9.85 693	13	**0**
	L Cos *	d	L Cot *	c d	L Tan	L Sin *	d	′

46°

′	L Sin *	d	L Tan *	c d	L Cot	L Cos *	d	
0	9.84 177		9.98 484		0.01 516	9.85 693		60
1	190	13	509	25	491	681	12	59
2	203	13	534	25	466	669	12	58
3	216	13	560	26	440	657	12	57
4	229	13	585	25	415	645	12	56
5	9.84 242	13	9.98 610	25	0.01 390	9.85 632	13	55
6	255	13	635	25	365	620	12	54
7	269	14	661	26	339	608	12	53
8	282	13	686	25	314	596	12	52
9	295	13	711	25	289	583	13	51
10	9.84 308	13	9.98 737	26	0.01 263	9.85 571	12	50
11	321	13	762	25	238	559	12	49
12	334	13	787	25	213	547	12	48
13	347	13	812	25	188	534	13	47
14	360	13	838	26	162	522	12	46
15	9.84 373	13	9.98 863	25	0.01 137	9.85 510	12	45
16	385	12	888	25	112	497	13	44
17	398	13	913	25	087	485	12	43
18	411	13	939	26	061	473	12	42
19	424	13	964	25	036	460	13	41
20	9.84 437	13	9.98 989	25	0.01 011	9.85 448	12	40
21	450	13	9.99 015	26	0.00 985	436	12	39
22	463	13	040	25	960	423	13	38
23	476	13	065	25	935	411	12	37
24	489	13	090	25	910	399	12	36
25	9.84 502	13	9.99 116	26	0.00 884	9.85 386	13	35
26	515	13	141	25	859	374	12	34
27	528	13	166	25	834	361	13	33
28	540	12	191	25	809	349	12	32
29	553	13	217	26	783	337	12	31
30	9.84 566	13	9.99 242	25	0.00 758	9.85 324	13	30
31	579	13	267	25	733	312	12	29
32	592	13	293	26	707	299	13	28
33	605	13	318	25	682	287	12	27
34	618	13	343	25	657	274	13	26
35	9.84 630	12	9.99 368	25	0.00 632	9.85 262	12	25
36	643	13	394	26	606	250	12	24
37	656	13	419	25	581	237	13	23
38	669	13	444	25	556	225	12	22
39	682	13	469	25	531	212	13	21
40	9.84 694	12	9.99 495	26	0.00 505	9.85 200	12	20
41	707	13	520	25	480	187	13	19
42	720	13	545	25	455	175	12	18
43	733	13	570	25	430	162	13	17
44	745	12	596	26	404	150	12	16
45	9.84 758	13	9.99 621	25	0.00 379	9.85 137	13	15
46	771	13	646	25	354	125	12	14
47	784	13	672	26	328	112	13	13
48	796	12	697	25	303	100	12	12
49	809	13	722	25	278	087	13	11
50	9.84 822	13	9.99 747	25	0.00 253	9.85 074	13	10
51	835	13	773	26	227	062	12	9
52	847	12	798	25	202	049	13	8
53	860	13	823	25	177	037	12	7
54	873	13	848	25	152	024	13	6
55	9.84 885	12	9.99 874	26	0.00 126	9.85 012	12	5
56	898	13	899	25	101	9.84 999	13	4
57	911	13	924	25	076	986	13	3
58	923	12	949	25	051	974	12	2
59	936	13	9.99 975	26	025	961	13	1
60	9.84 949	13	10.00 000	25	0.00 000	9.84 949	12	0
	L Cos *	d	L Cot *	c d	L Tan	L Sin *	d	′

Prop. Parts

Subtract 10 *from each entry in the columns marked with* "*."

	26	25
1	2.6	2.5
2	5.2	5.0
3	7.8	7.5
4	10.4	10.0
5	13.0	12.5
6	15.6	15.0
7	18.2	17.5
8	20.8	20.0
9	23.4	22.5

	14
1	1.4
2	2.8
3	4.2
4	5.6
5	7.0
6	8.4
7	9.8
8	11.2
9	12.6

	13	12
1	1.3	1.2
2	2.6	2.4
3	3.9	3.6
4	5.2	4.8
5	6.5	6.0
6	7.8	7.2
7	9.1	8.4
8	10.4	9.6
9	11.7	10.8

45°

X. AUXILIARY TABLES FOR ANGLES NEAR 0° OR 90°

Note 1. On account of large tabular differences, results obtained by interpolation in the preceding table are particularly inaccurate if we are determining **log sin, log tan,** or **log cot** for an angle near 0°, or **log cos, log tan,** or **log cot** for an angle near 90°. To avoid such interpolation in Table IX, we use Table X*a* or Table X*b*.

Table X*b* applies without interpolation *if the angle is expressed to the nearest tenth of a minute,* and if the angle differs from 0°, or 90°, by at most 2°. If angles are expressible to the nearest *second,* interpolation in Table X*b* is sufficiently accurate except on the upper parts of pages 84 and 85.

Table X*a* applies for the indicated values of the angle M in connection with the following formulas.*

A. Angle α near 0°. Let M be the number of **minutes** in α. Then,

$$\log \sin \alpha = S + \log M; \qquad \log \tan \alpha = T + \log M. \qquad (1)$$

B. Angle α near 90°. Let M be the number of **minutes** in $(90° - \alpha)$. Then,

$$\log \cos \alpha = S + \log M; \qquad \log \cot \alpha = T + \log M. \qquad (2)$$

In using (1) and (2), we find S and T from Table X*a* below and log M from Table VIII.

Note 2. If log cot α is desired in (A), or log tan α in (B), recall that $\tan \alpha = \frac{1}{\cot \alpha}$.

Table X*a*. Auxiliary Table for S and T

To find S or T, subtract 10 from the given entry.

M	$S + 10$
0′ — 13′	6.46373
14′ — 42′	72
43′ — 58′	71
59′ — 71′	6.46370
72′ — 81′	69
82′ — 91′	68
92′ — 99′	6.46367
100′ — 107′	66
108′ — 115′	65
116′ — 121′	6.46364
122′ — 128′	63
129′ — 134′	62
135′ — 140′	6.46361
141′ — 146′	60
147′ — 151′	59
152′ — 157′	6.46358
158′ — 162′	57
163′ — 167′	56
168′ — 171′	6.46355
172′ — 176′	54
177′ — 180′	53

M	$T + 10$	M	$T + 10$
0′ — 26′	6.46373	131′ — 133′	6.46394
27′ — 39′	74	134′ — 136′	95
40′ — 48′	75	137′ — 139′	96
49′ — 56′	6.46376	140′ — 142′	6.46397
57′ — 63′	77	143′ — 145′	98
64′ — 69′	78	146′ — 148′	99
70′ — 74′	6.46379	149′ — 150′	6.46400
75′ — 80′	80	151′ — 153′	01
81′ — 85′	81	154′ — 156′	02
86′ — 89′	6.46382	157′ — 158′	6.46403
90′ — 94′	83	159′ — 161′	04
95′ — 98′	84	162′ — 163′	05
99′ — 102′	6.46385	164′ — 166′	6.46406
103′ — 106′	86	167′ — 168′	07
107′ — 110′	87	169′ — 171′	08
111′ — 113′	6.46388	172′ — 173′	6.46409
114′ — 117′	89	174′ — 175′	10
118′ — 120′	90	176′ — 178′	11
121′ — 124′	6.46391	179′ — 180′	6.46412
125′ — 127′	92	181′ — 182′	13
128′ — 130′	93	183′ — 184′	14

* For an explanation of these formulas, see page 176 of William L. Hart's *Plane Trigonometry,* or page 176 of William L. Hart's *Plane and Spherical Trigonometry,* or page 166 of William L. Hart's *College Trigonometry,* all published by D. C. Heath and Company.

↓	10 + log sin:						0°					
′	.0	.1	.2	.3	.4	.5	.6	.7	.8	.9	1.0	
0	5. ———	46373	76476	94085	*06579	*16270	*24188	*30882	*36682	*41797	*46373	59
1	6. 46373	50512	54291	57767	60985	63982	66785	69418	71900	74248	76476	58
2	6. 76476	78595	80615	82545	84394	86167	87870	89509	91088	92612	94085	57
3	6. 94085	95509	96888	98224	99520	*00779	*02003	*03193	*04351	*05479	*06579	56
4	7. 06579	07651	08698	09719	10718	11694	12648	13582	14497	15392	16270	**55**
5	7. 16270	17130	17973	18800	19612	20409	21191	21960	22715	23458	24188	54
6	7. 24188	24906	25612	26307	26991	27664	28327	28980	29623	30257	30882	53
7	7. 30882	31498	32106	32705	33296	33879	34454	35022	35582	36135	36682	52
8	7. 36682	37221	37754	38280	38800	39314	39822	40324	40821	41312	41797	51
9	7. 41797	42277	42751	43221	43685	44145	44600	45050	45495	45936	46373	**50**
10	7. 46373	46805	47233	47656	48076	48491	48903	49311	49715	50115	50512	49
11	7. 50512	50905	51294	51680	52063	52442	52818	53191	53561	53927	54291	48
12	7. 54291	54651	55009	55363	55715	56064	56410	56753	57094	57431	57767	47
13	7. 57767	58100	58430	58758	59083	59406	59726	60045	60360	60674	60985	46
14	7. 60985	61294	61601	61906	62209	62509	62808	63104	63399	63691	63982	**45**
15	7. 63982	64270	64557	64842	65125	65406	65685	65962	66238	66512	66784	44
16	7. 66784	67055	67324	67591	67857	68121	68383	68644	68903	69161	69417	43
17	7. 69417	69672	69925	70177	70427	70676	70924	71170	71414	71658	71900	42
18	7. 71900	72140	72380	72618	72854	73090	73324	73557	73788	74019	74248	41
19	7. 74248	74476	74703	74928	75153	75376	75598	75819	76039	76258	76475	**40**
20	7.7 6475	6692	6907	7122	7335	7548	7759	7969	8179	8387	8594	39
21	7.7 8594	8801	9006	9210	9414	9616	9818	*0018	*0218	*0417	*0615	38
22	7.8 0615	0812	1008	1203	1397	1591	1783	1975	2166	2356	2545	37
23	7.8 2545	2733	2921	3108	3294	3479	3663	3847	4030	4212	4393	36
24	7.8 4393	4574	4754	4933	5111	5289	5466	5642	5817	5992	6166	**35**
25	7.8 6166	6340	6512	6684	6856	7026	7196	7366	7534	7702	7870	34
26	7.8 7870	8036	8202	8368	8533	8697	8860	9023	9186	9347	9509	33
27	7.8 9509	9669	9829	9988	*0147	*0305	*0463	*0620	*0777	*0933	*1088	32
28	7.9 1088	1243	1397	1551	1704	1857	2009	2160	2311	2462	2612	31
29	7.9 2612	2761	2910	3059	3207	3354	3501	3648	3794	3939	4084	**30**
30	7.9 4084	4229	4373	4516	4659	4802	4944	5086	5227	5368	5508	29
31	7.9 5508	5648	5787	5926	6065	6203	6341	6478	6615	6751	6887	28
32	7.9 6887	7022	7158	7292	7426	7560	7694	7827	7959	8092	8223	27
33	7.9 8223	8355	8486	8616	8747	8876	9006	9135	9264	9392	9520	26
34	7.9 9520	9647	9775	9901	*0028	*0154	*0279	*0405	*0530	*0654	*0779	**25**
35	8.0 0779	0903	1026	1149	1272	1395	1517	1639	1760	1881	2002	24
36	8.0 2002	2123	2243	2362	2482	2601	2720	2838	2957	3074	3192	23
37	8.0 3192	3309	3426	3543	3659	3775	3891	4006	4121	4236	4350	22
38	8.0 4350	4464	4578	4692	4805	4918	5030	5143	5255	5367	5478	21
39	8.0 5478	5589	5700	5811	5921	6031	6141	6251	6360	6469	6578	**20**
40	8.0 6578	6686	6794	6902	7010	7117	7224	7331	7438	7544	7650	19
41	8.0 7650	7756	7861	7967	8072	8176	8281	8385	8489	8593	8696	18
42	8.0 8696	8800	8903	9006	9108	9210	9312	9414	9516	9617	9718	17
43	8.0 9718	9819	9920	*0020	*0120	*0220	*0320	*0420	*0519	*0618	*0717	16
44	8.1 0717	0815	0914	1012	1110	1207	1305	1402	1499	1596	1693	**15**
45	8.1 1693	1789	1885	1981	2077	2172	2268	2363	2458	2553	2647	14
46	8.1 2647	2741	2836	2929	3023	3117	3210	3303	3396	3489	3581	13
47	8.1 3581	3673	3765	3857	3949	4041	4132	4223	4314	4405	4495	12
48	8.1 4495	4586	4676	4766	4856	4945	5035	5124	5213	5302	5391	11
49	8.1 5391	5479	5568	5656	5744	5832	5919	6007	6094	6181	6268	**10**
50	8.1 6268	6355	6441	6528	6614	6700	6786	6872	6957	7043	7128	9
51	8.1 7128	7213	7298	7383	7467	7552	7636	7720	7804	7888	7971	8
52	8.1 7971	8055	8138	8221	8304	8387	8469	8552	8634	8716	8798	7
53	8.1 8798	8880	8962	9044	9125	9206	9287	9368	9449	9530	9610	6
54	8.1 9610	9691	9771	9851	9931	*0010	*0090	*0170	*0249	*0328	*0407	**5**
55	8.2 0407	0486	0565	0643	0722	0800	0878	0956	1034	1112	1189	4
56	8.2 1189	1267	1344	1422	1499	1576	1652	1729	1805	1882	1958	3
57	8.2 1958	2034	2110	2186	2262	2337	2413	2488	2563	2638	2713	2
58	8.2 2713	2788	2863	2937	3012	3086	3160	3234	3308	3382	3456	1
59	8.2 3456	3529	3603	3676	3749	3822	3895	3968	4041	4113	4186	**0**
	1.0	.9	.8	.7	.6	.5	.4	.3	.2	.1	.0	′
	10 + log cos:						89°					↑

X*b*. ANGLES NEAR TO 0° OR 90°

	10 + log tan: 0°											
′	.0	.1	.2	.3	.4	.5	.6	.7	.8	.9	1.0	
0	5. ———	46373	76476	94085	*06579	*16270	*24188	*30882	*36682	*41797	*46373	59
1	6. 46373	50512	54291	57767	60985	63982	66785	69418	71900	74248	76476	58
2	6. 76476	78595	80615	82545	84394	86167	87870	89509	91088	92612	94085	57
3	6. 94085	95509	96888	98224	99521	*00779	*02003	*03193	*04351	*05479	*06579	56
4	7. 06579	07651	08698	09719	10718	11694	12648	13582	14497	15392	16270	**55**
5	7. 16270	17130	17973	18800	19612	20409	21191	21960	22715	23458	24188	54
6	7. 24188	24906	25612	26307	26991	27664	28327	28980	29624	30258	30882	53
7	7. 30882	31499	32106	32705	33296	33879	34454	35022	35582	36135	36682	52
8	7. 36682	37221	37754	38281	38801	39315	39823	40325	40821	41312	41797	51
9	7. 41797	42277	42751	43221	43686	44145	44600	45050	45495	45936	46373	**50**
10	7. 46373	46805	47233	47656	48076	48492	48903	49311	49715	50115	50512	49
11	7. 50512	50905	51295	51681	52063	52443	52819	53191	53561	53927	54291	48
12	7. 54291	54651	55009	55363	55715	56064	56410	56753	57094	57432	57767	47
13	7. 57767	58100	58430	58758	59083	59406	59727	60045	60361	60674	60986	46
14	7. 60986	61295	61602	61906	62209	62510	62808	63105	63399	63692	63982	**45**
15	7. 63982	64271	64557	64842	65125	65406	65685	65963	66239	66513	66785	44
16	7. 66785	67056	67324	67592	67857	68121	68384	68645	68904	69162	69418	43
17	7. 69418	69673	69926	70178	70428	70677	70924	71170	71415	71658	71900	42
18	7. 71900	72141	72380	72618	72855	73090	73324	73557	73789	74019	74248	41
19	7. 74248	74476	74703	74929	75153	75377	75599	75820	76040	76258	76476	**40**
20	7.7 6476	6693	6908	7123	7336	7549	7760	7970	8179	8388	8595	39
21	7.7 8595	8801	9007	9211	9415	9617	9819	*0019	*0219	*0418	*0615	38
22	7.8 0615	0812	1009	1204	1398	1591	1784	1976	2167	2357	2546	37
23	7.8 2546	2734	2922	3109	3295	3480	3664	3848	4031	4213	4394	36
24	7.8 4394	4575	4755	4934	5112	5290	5467	5643	5819	5993	6167	**35**
25	7.8 6167	6341	6513	6685	6857	7027	7197	7367	7535	7703	7871	34
26	7.8 7871	8037	8204	8369	8534	8698	8862	9025	9187	9349	9510	33
27	7.8 9510	9670	9830	9990	*0149	*0307	*0464	*0622	*0778	*0934	*1089	32
28	7.9 1089	1244	1398	1552	1705	1858	2010	2162	2313	2463	2613	31
29	7.9 2613	2763	2912	3060	3208	3356	3503	3649	3795	3941	4086	**30**
30	7.9 4086	4230	4374	4518	4661	4804	4946	5088	5229	5370	5510	29
31	7.9 5510	5650	5789	5928	6067	6205	6343	6480	6617	6753	6889	28
32	7.9 6889	7024	7159	7294	7428	7562	7696	7829	7961	8094	8225	27
33	7.9 8225	8357	8488	8618	8749	8878	9008	9137	9266	9394	9522	26
34	7.9 9522	9649	9777	9903	*0030	*0156	*0282	*0407	*0532	*0657	*0781	**25**
35	8.0 0781	0905	1028	1152	1274	1397	1519	1641	1762	1884	2004	24
36	8.0 2004	2125	2245	2365	2484	2604	2722	2841	2959	3077	3194	23
37	8.0 3194	3312	3429	3545	3661	3777	3893	4008	4124	4238	4353	22
38	8.0 4353	4467	4581	4694	4808	4921	5033	5146	5258	5369	5481	21
39	8.0 5481	5592	5703	5814	5924	6034	6144	6254	6363	6472	6581	**20**
40	8.0 6581	6689	6797	6905	7013	7120	7227	7334	7441	7547	7653	19
41	8.0 7653	7759	7864	7970	8075	8180	8284	8388	8492	8596	8700	18
42	8.0 8700	8803	8906	9009	9111	9214	9316	9418	9519	9621	9722	17
43	8.0 9722	9823	9923	*0024	*0124	*0224	*0324	*0423	*0522	*0621	*0720	16
44	8.1 0720	0819	0917	1015	1113	1211	1309	1406	1503	1600	1696	**15**
45	8.1 1696	1793	1889	1985	2081	2176	2272	2367	2462	2556	2651	14
46	8.1 2651	2745	2839	2933	3027	3121	3214	3307	3400	3493	3585	13
47	8.1 3585	3677	3770	3861	3953	4045	4136	4227	4318	4409	4500	12
48	8.1 4500	4590	4680	4770	4860	4950	5039	5128	5218	5306	5395	11
49	8.1 5395	5484	5572	5660	5748	5836	5924	6011	6099	6186	6273	**10**
50	8.1 6273	6359	6446	6533	6619	6705	6791	6877	6962	7048	7133	9
51	8.1 7133	7218	7303	7388	7472	7557	7641	7725	7809	7893	7976	8
52	8.1 7976	8060	8143	8226	8309	8392	8475	8557	8639	8722	8804	7
53	8.1 8804	8886	8967	9049	9130	9211	9293	9374	9454	9535	9616	6
54	8.1 9616	9696	9776	9856	9936	*0016	*0096	*0175	*0254	*0334	*0413	**5**
55	8.2 0413	0491	0570	0649	0727	0806	0884	0962	1040	1118	1195	4
56	8.2 1195	1273	1350	1427	1504	1581	1658	1735	1811	1888	1964	3
57	8.2 1964	2040	2116	2192	2268	2343	2419	2494	2569	2645	2720	2
58	8.2 2720	2794	2869	2944	3018	3092	3167	3241	3315	3388	3462	1
59	8.2 3462	3536	3609	3682	3756	3829	3902	3974	4047	4120	4192	**0**
	1.0	.9	.8	.7	.6	.5	.4	.3	.2	.1	.0	′
	10 + log cot: 89°											

ψ	10 + log sin: 1°											
′	.0	.1	.2	.3	.4	.5	.6	.7	.8	.9	1.0	
0	8.2 4186	4258	4330	4402	4474	4546	4618	4689	4761	4832	4903	59
1	8.2 4903	4974	5045	5116	5187	5258	5328	5399	5469	5539	5609	58
2	8.2 5609	5679	5749	5819	5889	5958	6028	6097	6166	6235	6304	57
3	8.2 6304	6373	6442	6511	6579	6648	6716	6784	6852	6920	6988	56
4	8.2 6988	7056	7124	7191	7259	7326	7393	7460	7528	7595	7661	**55**
5	8.2 7661	7728	7795	7861	7928	7994	8060	8127	8193	8258	8324	54
6	8.2 8324	8390	8456	8521	8587	8652	8717	8782	8848	8912	8977	53
7	8.2 8977	9042	9107	9171	9236	9300	9364	9429	9493	9557	9621	52
8	8.2 9621	9684	9748	9812	9875	9939	*0002	*0065	*0129	*0192	*0255	51
9	8.3 0255	0317	0380	0443	0506	0568	0631	0693	0755	0817	0879	**50**
10	8.3 0879	0941	1003	1065	1127	1188	1250	1311	1373	1434	1495	49
11	8.3 1495	1556	1618	1678	1739	1800	1861	1921	1982	2042	2103	48
12	8.3 2103	2163	2223	2283	2343	2403	2463	2523	2583	2642	2702	47
13	8.3 2702	2761	2820	2880	2939	2998	3057	3116	3175	3234	3292	46
14	8.3 3292	3351	3410	3468	3527	3585	3643	3701	3759	3817	3875	**45**
15	8.3 3875	3933	3991	4049	4106	4164	4221	4279	4336	4393	4450	44
16	8.3 4450	4508	4565	4621	4678	4735	4792	4849	4905	4962	5018	43
17	8.3 5018	5074	5131	5187	5243	5299	5355	5411	5467	5523	5578	42
18	8.3 5578	5634	5690	5745	5800	5856	5911	5966	6021	6076	6131	41
19	8.3 6131	6186	6241	6296	6351	6405	6460	6515	6569	6623	6678	**40**
20	8.3 6678	6732	6786	6840	6894	6948	7002	7056	7110	7163	7217	39
21	8.3 7217	7271	7324	7378	7431	7484	7538	7591	7644	7697	7750	38
22	8.3 7750	7803	7856	7908	7961	8014	8066	8119	8171	8224	8276	37
23	8.3 8276	8328	8381	8433	8485	8537	8589	8641	8693	8744	8796	36
24	8.3 8796	8848	8899	8951	9002	9054	9105	9157	9208	9259	9310	**35**
25	8.3 9310	9361	9412	9463	9514	9565	9616	9666	9717	9767	9818	34
26	8.3 9818	9868	9919	9969	*0019	*0070	*0120	*0170	*0220	*0270	*0320	33
27	8.4 0320	0370	0420	0469	0519	0569	0618	0668	0717	0767	0816	32
28	8.4 0816	0865	0915	0964	1013	1062	1111	1160	1209	1258	1307	31
29	8.4 1307	1356	1404	1453	1501	1550	1598	1647	1695	1744	1792	**30**
30	8.4 1792	1840	1888	1936	1984	2032	2080	2128	2176	2224	2272	29
31	8.4 2272	2319	2367	2415	2462	2510	2557	2604	2652	2699	2746	28
32	8.4 2746	2793	2840	2888	2935	2982	3028	3075	3122	3169	3216	27
33	8.4 3216	3262	3309	3355	3402	3448	3495	3541	3588	3634	3680	26
34	8.4 3680	3726	3772	3818	3864	3910	3956	4002	4048	4094	4139	**25**
35	8.4 4139	4185	4231	4276	4322	4367	4413	4458	4504	4549	4594	24
36	8.4 4594	4639	4684	4730	4775	4820	4865	4910	4954	4999	5044	23
37	8.4 5044	5089	5133	5178	5223	5267	5312	5356	5401	5445	5489	22
38	8.4 5489	5534	5578	5622	5666	5710	5754	5798	5842	5886	5930	21
39	8.4 5930	5974	6018	6061	6105	6149	6192	6236	6280	6323	6366	**20**
40	8.4 6366	6410	6453	6497	6540	6583	6626	6669	6712	6755	6799	19
41	8.4 6799	6841	6884	6927	6970	7013	7056	7098	7141	7184	7226	18
42	8.4 7226	7269	7311	7354	7396	7439	7481	7523	7565	7608	7650	17
43	8.4 7650	7692	7734	7776	7818	7860	7902	7944	7986	8028	8069	16
44	8.4 8069	8111	8153	8194	8236	8278	8319	8361	8402	8443	8485	**15**
45	8.4 8485	8526	8567	8609	8650	8691	8732	8773	8814	8855	8896	14
46	8.4 8896	8937	8978	9019	9060	9101	9141	9182	9223	9263	9304	13
47	8.4 9304	9345	9385	9426	9466	9506	9547	9587	9627	9668	9708	12
48	8.4 9708	9748	9788	9828	9868	9908	9948	9988	*0028	*0068	*0108	11
49	8.5 0108	0148	0188	0227	0267	0307	0346	0386	0425	0465	0504	**10**
50	8.5 0504	0544	0583	0623	0662	0701	0741	0780	0819	0858	0897	9
51	8.5 0897	0936	0976	1015	1054	1092	1131	1170	1209	1248	1287	8
52	8.5 1287	1325	1364	1403	1442	1480	1519	1557	1596	1634	1673	7
53	8.5 1673	1711	1749	1788	1826	1864	1903	1941	1979	2017	2055	6
54	8.5 2055	2093	2131	2169	2207	2245	2283	2321	2359	2397	2434	**5**
55	8.5 2434	2472	2510	2547	2585	2623	2660	2698	2735	2773	2810	4
56	8.5 2810	2848	2885	2922	2960	2997	3034	3071	3109	3146	3183	3
57	8.5 3183	3220	3257	3294	3331	3368	3405	3442	3479	3515	3552	2
58	8.5 3552	3589	3626	3663	3699	3736	3772	3809	3846	3882	3919	1
59	8.5 3919	3955	3992	4028	4064	4101	4137	4173	4210	4246	4282	**0**
	1.0	.9	.8	.7	.6	.5	.4	.3	.2	.1	.0	′
	10 + log cos: 88°											ψ

Xb. ANGLES NEAR TO 0° OR 90°

↓	10 + log tan: 1°											
′	.0	.1	.2	.3	.4	.5	.6	.7	.8	.9	1.0	
0	8.2 4192	4264	4337	4409	4481	4553	4624	4696	4767	4839	4910	59
1	8.2 4910	4981	5052	5123	5194	5265	5335	5406	5476	5546	5616	58
2	8.2 5616	5686	5756	5826	5896	5965	6035	6104	6173	6243	6312	57
3	8.2 6312	6380	6449	6518	6586	6655	6723	6792	6860	6928	6996	56
4	8.2 6996	7063	7131	7199	7266	7334	7401	7468	7535	7602	7669	**55**
5	8.2 7669	7736	7803	7869	7936	8002	8068	8134	8201	8266	8332	54
6	8.2 8332	8398	8464	8529	8595	8660	8725	8791	8856	8921	8986	53
7	8.2 8986	9050	9115	9180	9244	9309	9373	9437	9501	9565	9629	52
8	8.2 9629	9693	9757	9820	9884	9947	*0011	*0074	*0137	*0200	*0263	51
9	8.3 0263	0326	0389	0452	0514	0577	0639	0702	0764	0826	0888	**50**
10	8.3 0888	0950	1012	1074	1136	1198	1259	1321	1382	1443	1505	49
11	8.3 1505	1566	1627	1688	1749	1809	1870	1931	1991	2052	2112	48
12	8.3 2112	2173	2233	2293	2353	2413	2473	2533	2592	2652	2711	47
13	8.3 2711	2771	2830	2890	2949	3008	3067	3126	3185	3244	3302	46
14	8.3 3302	3361	3420	3478	3537	3595	3653	3712	3770	3828	3886	**45**
15	8.3 3886	3944	4001	4059	4117	4174	4232	4289	4347	4404	4461	44
16	8.3 4461	4518	4575	4632	4689	4746	4803	4859	4916	4972	5029	43
17	8.3 5029	5085	5142	5198	5254	5310	5366	5422	5478	5534	5590	42
18	8.3 5590	5645	5701	5756	5812	5867	5922	5978	6033	6088	6143	41
19	8.3 6143	6198	6253	6308	6362	6417	6472	6526	6581	6635	6689	**40**
20	8.3 6689	6744	6798	6852	6906	6960	7014	7068	7122	7175	7229	39
21	8.3 7229	7283	7336	7390	7443	7497	7550	7603	7656	7709	7762	38
22	8.3 7762	7815	7868	7921	7974	8026	8079	8132	8184	8236	8289	37
23	8.3 8289	8341	8393	8446	8498	8550	8602	8654	8706	8757	8809	36
24	8.3 8809	8861	8913	8964	9016	9067	9118	9170	9221	9272	9323	**35**
25	8.3 9323	9374	9425	9476	9527	9578	9629	9680	9730	9781	9832	34
26	8.3 9832	9882	9932	9983	*0033	*0083	*0134	*0184	*0234	*0284	*0334	33
27	8.4 0334	0384	0434	0483	0533	0583	0632	0682	0732	0781	0830	32
28	8.4 0830	0880	0929	0978	1027	1077	1126	1175	1224	1272	1321	31
29	8.4 1321	1370	1419	1468	1516	1565	1613	1662	1710	1758	1807	**30**
30	8.4 1807	1855	1903	1951	1999	2048	2095	2143	2191	2239	2287	29
31	8.4 2287	2335	2382	2430	2477	2525	2572	2620	2667	2715	2762	28
32	8.4 2762	2809	2856	2903	2950	2997	3044	3091	3138	3185	3232	27
33	8.4 3232	3278	3325	3371	3418	3464	3511	3557	3604	3650	3696	26
34	8.4 3696	3742	3789	3835	3881	3927	3973	4019	4064	4110	4156	**25**
35	8.4 4156	4202	4247	4293	4339	4384	4430	4475	4520	4566	4611	24
36	8.4 4611	4656	4701	4747	4792	4837	4882	4927	4972	5016	5061	23
37	8.4 5061	5106	5151	5195	5240	5285	5329	5374	5418	5463	5507	22
38	8.4 5507	5551	5596	5640	5684	5728	5772	5816	5860	5904	5948	21
39	8.4 5948	5992	6036	6080	6123	6167	6211	6254	6298	6341	6385	**20**
40	8.4 6385	6428	6472	6515	6558	6602	6645	6688	6731	6774	6817	19
41	8.4 6817	6860	6903	6946	6989	7032	7075	7117	7160	7203	7245	18
42	8.4 7245	7288	7330	7373	7415	7458	7500	7543	7585	7627	7669	17
43	8.4 7669	7712	7754	7796	7838	7880	7922	7964	8006	8047	8089	16
44	8.4 8089	8131	8173	8214	8256	8298	8339	8381	8422	8464	8505	**15**
45	8.4 8505	8546	8588	8629	8670	8711	8753	8794	8835	8876	8917	14
46	8.4 8917	8958	8999	9040	9081	9121	9162	9203	9244	9284	9325	13
47	8.4 9325	9366	9406	9447	9487	9528	9568	9608	9649	9689	9729	12
48	8.4 9729	9769	9810	9850	9890	9930	9970	*0010	*0050	*0090	*0130	11
49	8.5 0130	0170	0209	0249	0289	0329	0368	0408	0448	0487	0527	**10**
50	8.5 0527	0566	0606	0645	0684	0724	0763	0802	0842	0881	0920	9
51	8.5 0920	0959	0998	1037	1076	1115	1154	1193	1232	1271	1310	8
52	8.5 1310	1349	1387	1426	1465	1503	1542	1581	1619	1658	1696	7
53	8.5 1696	1735	1773	1811	1850	1888	1926	1964	2003	2041	2079	6
54	8.5 2079	2117	2155	2193	2231	2269	2307	2345	2383	2421	2459	**5**
55	8.5 2459	2496	2534	2572	2610	2647	2685	2722	2760	2797	2835	4
56	8.5 2835	2872	2910	2947	2985	3022	3059	3096	3134	3171	3208	3
57	8.5 3208	3245	3282	3319	3356	3393	3430	3467	3504	3541	3578	2
58	8.5 3578	3615	3651	3688	3725	3762	3798	3835	3872	3908	3945	1
59	8.5 3945	3981	4018	4054	4091	4127	4163	4200	4236	4272	4308	**0**
	1.0	.9	.8	.7	.6	.5	.4	.3	.2	.1	.0	′
	10 + log cot: 88°											↑

XI. FIVE-PLACE VALUES: SINE AND COSINE

→	0°		1°		2°		3°		4°		
′	Sin	Cos	Sin	Cos	Sin	Cos	Sin	Cos	Sin	Cos	
0	.00000	1.0000	.01745	.99985	.03490	.99939	.05234	.99863	.06976	.99756	**60**
1	029	000	774	984	519	938	263	861	.07005	754	59
2	058	000	803	984	548	937	292	860	034	752	58
3	087	000	832	983	577	936	321	858	063	750	57
4	116	000	862	983	606	935	350	857	092	748	56
5	.00145	1.0000	.01891	.99982	.03635	.99934	.05379	.99855	.07121	.99746	**55**
6	175	000	920	982	664	933	408	854	150	744	54
7	204	000	949	981	693	932	437	852	179	742	53
8	233	000	.01978	980	723	931	466	851	208	740	52
9	262	000	.02007	980	752	930	495	849	237	738	51
10	.00291	1.0000	.02036	.99979	.03781	.99929	.05524	.99847	.07266	.99736	**50**
11	320	.99999	065	979	810	927	553	846	295	734	49
12	349	999	094	978	839	926	582	844	324	731	48
13	378	999	123	977	868	925	611	842	353	729	47
14	407	999	152	977	897	924	640	841	382	727	46
15	.00436	.99999	.02181	.99976	.03926	.99923	.05669	.99839	.07411	.99725	**45**
16	465	999	211	976	955	922	698	838	440	723	44
17	495	999	240	975	.03984	921	727	836	469	721	43
18	524	999	269	974	.04013	919	756	834	498	719	42
19	553	998	298	974	042	918	785	833	527	716	41
20	.00582	.99998	.02327	.99973	.04071	.99917	.05814	.99831	.07556	.99714	**40**
21	611	998	356	972	100	916	844	829	585	712	39
22	640	998	385	972	129	915	873	827	614	710	38
23	669	998	414	971	159	913	902	826	643	708	37
24	698	998	443	970	188	912	931	824	672	705	36
25	.00727	.99997	.02472	.99969	.04217	.99911	.05960	.99822	.07701	.99703	**35**
26	756	997	501	969	246	910	.05989	821	730	701	34
27	785	997	530	968	275	909	.06018	819	759	699	33
28	814	997	560	967	304	907	047	817	788	696	32
29	844	996	589	966	333	906	076	815	817	694	31
30	.00873	.99996	.02618	.99966	.04362	.99905	.06105	.99813	.07846	.99692	**30**
31	902	996	647	965	391	904	134	812	875	689	29
32	931	996	676	964	420	902	163	810	904	687	28
33	960	995	705	963	449	901	192	808	933	685	27
34	.00989	995	734	963	478	900	221	806	962	683	26
35	.01018	.99995	.02763	.99962	.04507	.99898	.06250	.99804	.07991	.99680	**25**
36	047	995	792	961	536	897	279	803	.08020	678	24
37	076	994	821	960	565	896	308	801	049	676	23
38	105	994	850	959	594	894	337	799	078	673	22
39	134	994	879	959	623	893	366	797	107	671	21
40	.01164	.99993	.02908	.99958	.04653	.99892	.06395	.99795	.08136	.99668	**20**
41	193	993	938	957	682	890	424	793	165	666	19
42	222	993	967	956	711	889	453	792	194	664	18
43	251	992	.02996	955	740	888	482	790	223	661	17
44	280	992	.03025	954	769	886	511	788	252	659	16
45	.01309	.99991	.03054	.99953	.04798	.99885	.06540	.99786	.08281	.99657	**15**
46	338	991	083	952	827	883	569	784	310	654	14
47	367	991	112	952	856	882	598	782	339	652	13
48	396	990	141	951	885	881	627	780	368	649	12
49	425	990	170	950	914	879	656	778	397	647	11
50	.01454	.99989	.03199	.99949	.04943	.99878	.06685	.99776	.08426	.99644	**10**
51	483	989	228	948	.04972	876	714	774	455	642	9
52	513	989	257	947	.05001	875	743	772	484	639	8
53	542	988	286	946	030	873	773	770	513	637	7
54	571	988	316	945	059	872	802	768	542	635	6
55	.01600	.99987	.03345	.99944	.05088	.99870	.06831	.99766	.08571	.99632	**5**
56	629	987	374	943	117	869	860	764	600	630	4
57	658	986	403	942	146	867	889	762	629	627	3
58	687	986	432	941	175	866	918	760	658	625	2
59	716	985	461	940	205	864	947	758	687	622	1
60	.01745	.99985	.03490	.99939	.05234	.99863	.06976	.99756	.08716	.99619	**0**
	Cos	Sin	Cos	Sin	Cos	Sin	Cos	Sin	Cos	Sin	′
	89°		88°		87°		86°		85°		←

XI. FIVE-PLACE VALUES: TANGENT AND COTANGENT

→	0°		1°		2°		3°		4°		
′	Tan	Cot	Tan	Cot	Tan	Cot	Tan	Cot	Tan	Cot	
0	.00000	——	.01746	57.290	.03492	28.636	.05241	19.081	.06993	14.301	**60**
1	029	3437.7	775	56.351	521	.399	270	18.976	.07022	.241	59
2	058	1718.9	804	55.442	550	28.166	299	.871	051	.182	58
3	087	1145.9	833	54.561	579	27.937	328	.768	080	.124	57
4	116	859.44	862	53.709	609	.712	357	.666	110	.065	56
5	.00145	687.55	.01891	52.882	.03638	27.490	.05387	18.564	.07139	14.008	**55**
6	175	572.96	920	52.081	667	.271	416	.464	168	13.951	54
7	204	491.11	949	51.303	696	27.057	445	.366	197	.894	53
8	233	429.72	.01978	50.549	725	26.845	474	.268	227	.838	52
9	262	381.97	.02007	49.816	754	.637	503	.171	256	.782	51
10	.00291	343.77	.02036	49.104	.03783	26.432	.05533	18.075	.07285	13.727	**50**
11	320	312.52	066	48.412	812	.230	562	17.980	314	.672	49
12	349	286.48	095	47.740	842	26.031	591	.886	344	.617	48
13	378	264.44	124	47.085	871	25.835	620	.793	373	.563	47
14	407	245.55	153	46.449	900	.642	649	.702	402	.510	46
15	.00436	229.18	.02182	45.829	.03929	25.452	05678	17.611	.07431	13.457	**45**
16	465	214.86	211	45.226	958	.264	708	.521	461	.404	44
17	495	202.22	240	44.639	.03987	25.080	737	.431	490	.352	43
18	524	190.98	269	44.066	.04016	24.898	766	.343	519	.300	42
19	553	180.93	298	43.508	046	.719	795	.256	548	.248	41
20	.00582	171.89	.02328	42.964	.04075	24.542	.05824	17.169	.07578	13.197	**40**
21	611	163.70	357	42.433	104	.368	854	17.084	607	.146	39
22	640	156.26	386	41.916	133	.196	883	16.999	636	.096	38
23	669	149.47	415	41.411	162	24.026	912	.915	665	13.046	37
24	698	143.24	444	40.917	191	23.859	941	.832	695	12.996	36
25	.00727	137.51	.02473	40.436	.04220	23.695	.05970	16.750	.07724	12.947	**35**
26	756	132.22	502	39.965	250	.532	.05999	.668	753	.898	34
27	785	127.32	531	39.506	279	.372	.06029	.587	782	.850	33
28	815	122.77	560	39.057	308	.214	058	.507	812	.801	32
29	844	118.54	589	38.618	337	23.058	087	.428	841	.754	31
30	.00873	114.59	.02619	38.188	.04366	22.904	.06116	16.350	.07870	12.706	**30**
31	902	110.89	648	37.769	395	.752	145	.272	899	.659	29
32	931	107.43	677	37.358	424	.602	175	.195	929	.612	28
33	960	104.17	706	36.956	454	.454	204	.119	958	.566	27
34	.00989	101.11	735	36.563	483	.308	233	16.043	.07987	.520	26
35	.01018	98.218	.02764	36.178	.04512	22.164	.06262	15.969	.08017	12.474	**25**
36	047	95.489	793	35.801	541	22.022	291	.895	046	.429	24
37	076	92.908	822	35.431	570	21.881	321	.821	075	.384	23
38	105	90.463	851	35.070	599	.743	350	.748	104	.339	22
39	135	88.144	881	34.715	628	.606	379	.676	134	.295	21
40	.01164	85.940	.02910	34.368	.04658	21.470	.06408	15.605	.08163	12.251	**20**
41	193	83.844	939	34.027	687	.337	438	.534	192	.207	19
42	222	81.847	968	33.694	716	.205	467	.464	221	.163	18
43	251	79.943	.02997	33.366	745	21.075	496	.394	251	.120	17
44	280	78.126	.03026	33.045	774	20.946	525	.325	280	.077	16
45	.01309	76.390	.03055	32.730	.04803	20.819	.06554	15.257	.08309	12.035	**15**
46	338	74.729	084	32.421	833	.693	584	.189	339	11.992	14
47	367	73.139	114	32.118	862	.569	613	.122	368	.950	13
48	396	71.615	143	31.821	891	.446	642	15.056	397	.909	12
49	425	70.153	172	31.528	920	.325	671	14.990	427	.867	11
50	.01455	68.750	.03201	31.242	.04949	20.206	.06700	14.924	.08456	11.826	**10**
51	484	67.402	230	30.960	.04978	20.087	730	.860	485	.785	9
52	513	66.105	259	30.683	.05007	19.970	759	.795	514	.745	8
53	542	64.858	288	30.412	037	.855	788	.732	544	.705	7
54	571	63.657	317	30.145	066	.740	817	.669	573	.664	6
55	.01600	62.499	.03346	29.882	.05095	19.627	.06847	14.606	.08602	11.625	**5**
56	629	61.383	376	29.624	124	.516	876	.544	632	.585	4
57	658	60.306	405	29.371	153	.405	905	.482	661	.546	3
58	687	59.266	434	29.122	182	.296	934	.421	690	.507	2
59	716	58.261	463	28.877	212	.188	963	.361	720	.468	1
60	.01746	57.290	.03492	28.636	.05241	19.081	.06993	14.301	.08749	11.430	**0**
	Cot	Tan	Cot	Tan	Cot	Tan	Cot	Tan	Cot	Tan	′
	89°		88°		87°		86°		85°		←

XI. FIVE-PLACE VALUES: SINE AND COSINE

→	5°		6°		7°		8°		9°		
′	Sin	Cos	Sin	Cos	Sin	Cos	Sin	Cos	Sin	Cos	
0	.08716	.99619	.10453	.99452	.12187	.99255	.13917	.99027	.15643	.98769	**60**
1	745	617	482	449	216	251	946	023	672	764	59
2	774	614	511	446	245	248	.13975	019	701	760	58
3	803	612	540	443	274	244	.14004	015	730	755	57
4	831	609	569	440	302	240	033	011	758	751	56
5	.08860	.99607	.10597	.99437	.12331	.99237	.14061	.99006	.15787	.98746	**55**
6	889	604	626	434	360	233	090	.99002	816	741	54
7	918	602	655	431	389	230	119	.98998	845	737	53
8	947	599	684	428	418	226	148	994	873	732	52
9	.08976	596	713	424	447	222	177	990	902	728	51
10	.09005	.99594	.10742	.99421	.12476	.99219	.14205	.98986	.15931	.98723	**50**
11	034	591	771	418	504	215	234	982	959	718	49
12	063	588	800	415	533	211	263	978	.15988	714	48
13	092	586	829	412	562	208	292	973	.16017	709	47
14	121	583	858	409	591	204	320	969	046	704	46
15	.09150	.99580	.10887	.99406	.12620	.99200	.14349	.98965	.16074	.98700	**45**
16	179	578	916	402	649	197	378	961	103	695	44
17	208	575	945	399	678	193	407	957	132	690	43
18	237	572	.10973	396	706	189	436	953	160	686	42
19	266	570	.11002	393	735	186	464	948	189	681	41
20	.09295	.99567	.11031	.99390	.12764	.99182	.14493	.98944	.16218	.98676	**40**
21	324	564	060	386	793	178	522	940	246	671	39
22	353	562	089	383	822	175	551	936	275	667	38
23	382	559	118	380	851	171	580	931	304	662	37
24	411	556	147	377	880	167	608	927	333	657	36
25	.09440	.99553	.11176	.99374	.12908	.99163	.14637	.98923	.16361	.98652	**35**
26	469	551	205	370	937	160	666	919	390	648	34
27	498	548	234	367	966	156	695	914	419	643	33
28	527	545	263	364	.12995	152	723	910	447	638	32
29	556	542	291	360	.13024	148	752	906	476	633	31
30	.09585	.99540	.11320	.99357	.13053	.99144	.14781	.98902	.16505	.98629	**30**
31	614	537	349	354	081	141	810	897	533	624	29
32	642	534	378	351	110	137	838	893	562	619	28
33	671	531	407	347	139	133	867	889	591	614	27
34	700	528	436	344	168	129	896	884	620	609	26
35	.09729	.99526	.11465	.99341	.13197	.99125	.14925	.98880	.16648	.98604	**25**
36	758	523	494	337	226	122	954	876	677	600	24
37	787	520	523	334	254	118	.14982	871	706	595	23
38	816	517	552	331	283	114	.15011	867	734	590	22
39	845	514	580	327	312	110	040	863	763	585	21
40	.09874	.99511	.11609	.99324	.13341	.99106	.15069	.98858	.16792	.98580	**20**
41	903	508	638	320	370	102	097	854	820	575	19
42	932	506	667	317	399	098	126	849	849	570	18
43	961	503	696	314	427	094	155	845	878	565	17
44	.09990	500	725	310	456	091	184	841	906	561	16
45	.10019	.99497	.11754	.99307	.13485	.99087	.15212	.98836	.16935	.98556	**15**
46	048	494	783	303	514	083	241	832	964	551	14
47	077	491	812	300	543	079	270	827	.16992	546	13
48	106	488	840	297	572	075	299	823	.17021	541	12
49	135	485	869	293	600	071	327	818	050	536	11
50	.10164	.99482	.11898	.99290	.13629	.99067	.15356	.98814	.17078	.98531	**10**
51	192	479	927	286	658	063	385	809	107	526	9
52	221	476	956	283	687	059	414	805	136	521	8
53	250	473	.11985	279	716	055	442	800	164	516	7
54	279	470	.12014	276	744	051	471	796	193	511	6
55	.10308	.99467	.12043	.99272	.13773	.99047	.15500	.98791	.17222	.98506	**5**
56	337	464	071	269	802	043	529	787	250	501	4
57	366	461	100	265	831	039	557	782	279	496	3
58	395	458	129	262	860	035	586	778	308	491	2
59	424	455	158	258	889	031	615	773	336	486	1
60	.10453	.99452	.12187	.99255	.13917	.99027	.15643	.98769	.17365	.98481	**0**
	Cos	Sin	Cos	Sin	Cos	Sin	Cos	Sin	Cos	Sin	′
	84°		83°		82°		81°		80°		←

XI. FIVE–PLACE VALUES: TANGENT AND COTANGENT

→	5°		6°		7°		8°		9°		
′	Tan	Cot	Tan	Cot	Tan	Cot	Tan	Cot	Tan	Cot	
0	.08749	11.430	.10510	9.5144	.12278	8.1443	.14054	7.1154	.15838	6.3138	**60**
1	778	.392	540	.4878	308	.1248	084	.1004	868	.3019	59
2	807	.354	569	.4614	338	.1054	113	.0855	898	.2901	58
3	837	.316	599	.4352	367	.0860	143	.0706	928	.2783	57
4	866	.279	628	.4090	397	.0667	173	.0558	958	.2666	56
5	.08895	11.242	.10657	9.3831	.12426	8.0476	.14202	7.0410	.15988	6.2549	**55**
6	925	.205	687	.3572	456	.0285	232	.0264	.16017	.2432	54
7	954	.168	716	.3315	485	8.0095	262	7.0117	047	.2316	53
8	.08983	.132	746	.3060	515	7.9906	291	6.9972	077	.2200	52
9	.09013	.095	775	.2806	544	.9718	321	.9827	107	.2085	51
10	.09042	11.059	.10805	9.2553	.12574	7.9530	.14351	6.9682	.16137	6.1970	**50**
11	071	11.024	834	.2302	603	.9344	381	.9538	167	.1856	49
12	101	10.988	863	.2052	633	.9158	410	.9395	196	.1742	48
13	130	.953	893	.1803	662	.8973	440	.9252	226	.1628	47
14	159	.918	922	.1555	692	.8789	470	.9110	256	.1515	46
15	.09189	10.883	.10952	9.1309	.12722	7.8606	.14499	6.8969	.16286	6.1402	**45**
16	218	.848	.10981	.1065	751	.8424	529	.8828	316	.1290	44
17	247	.814	.11011	.0821	781	.8243	559	.8687	346	.1178	43
18	277	.780	040	.0579	810	.8062	588	.8548	376	.1066	42
19	306	.746	070	.0338	840	.7882	618	.8408	405	.0955	41
20	.09335	10.712	.11099	9.0098	.12869	7.7704	.14648	6.8269	.16435	6.0844	**40**
21	365	.678	128	8.9860	899	.7525	678	.8131	465	.0734	39
22	394	.645	158	.9623	929	.7348	707	.7994	495	.0624	38
23	423	.612	187	.9387	958	.7171	737	.7856	525	.0514	37
24	453	.579	217	.9152	.12988	.6996	767	.7720	555	.0405	36
25	.09482	10.546	.11246	8.8919	.13017	7.6821	.14796	6.7584	.16585	6.0296	**35**
26	511	.514	276	.8686	047	.6647	826	.7448	615	.0188	34
27	541	.481	305	.8455	076	.6473	856	.7313	645	6.0080	33
28	570	.449	335	.8225	106	.6301	886	.7179	674	5.9972	32
29	600	.417	364	.7996	136	.6129	915	.7045	704	.9865	31
30	.09629	10.385	.11394	8.7769	.13165	7.5958	.14945	6.6912	.16734	5.9758	**30**
31	658	.354	423	.7542	195	.5787	.14975	.6779	764	.9651	29
32	688	.322	452	.7317	224	.5618	.15005	.6646	794	.9545	28
33	717	.291	482	.7093	254	.5449	034	.6514	824	.9439	27
34	746	.260	511	.6870	284	.5281	064	.6383	854	.9333	26
35	.09776	10.229	.11541	8.6648	.13313	7.5113	.15094	6.6252	.16884	5.9228	**25**
36	805	.199	570	.6427	343	.4947	124	.6122	914	.9124	24
37	834	.168	600	.6208	372	.4781	153	.5992	944	.9019	23
38	864	.138	629	.5989	402	.4615	183	.5863	.16974	.8915	22
39	893	.108	659	.5772	432	.4451	213	.5734	.17004	.8811	21
40	.09923	10.078	.11688	8.5555	.13461	7.4287	.15243	6.5606	.17033	5.8708	**20**
41	952	.048	718	.5340	491	.4124	272	.5478	063	.8605	19
42	.09981	10.019	747	.5126	521	.3962	302	.5350	093	.8502	18
43	.10011	9.9893	777	.4913	550	.3800	332	.5223	123	.8400	17
44	040	.9601	806	.4701	580	.3639	362	.5097	153	.8298	16
45	.10069	9.9310	.11836	8.4490	.13609	7.3479	.15391	6.4971	.17183	5.8197	**15**
46	099	.9021	865	.4280	639	.3319	421	.4846	213	.8095	14
47	128	.8734	895	.4071	669	.3160	451	.4721	243	.7994	13
48	158	.8448	924	.3863	698	.3002	481	.4596	273	.7894	12
49	187	.8164	954	.3656	728	.2844	511	.4472	303	.7794	11
50	.10216	9.7882	.11983	8.3450	.13758	7.2687	.15540	6.4348	.17333	5.7694	**10**
51	246	.7601	.12013	.3245	787	.2531	570	.4225	363	.7594	9
52	275	.7322	042	.3041	817	.2375	600	.4103	393	.7495	8
53	305	.7044	072	.2838	846	.2220	630	.3980	423	.7396	7
54	334	.6768	101	.2636	876	.2066	660	.3859	453	.7297	6
55	.10363	9.6493	.12131	8.2434	.13906	7.1912	.15689	6.3737	.17483	5.7199	**5**
56	393	.6220	160	.2234	935	.1759	719	.3617	513	.7101	4
57	422	.5949	190	.2035	965	.1607	749	.3496	543	.7004	3
58	452	.5679	219	.1837	.13995	.1455	779	.3376	573	.6906	2
59	481	.5411	249	.1640	.14024	.1304	809	.3257	603	.6809	1
60	.10510	9.5144	.12278	8.1443	.14054	7.1154	.15838	6.3138	.17633	5.6713	**0**
	Cot	Tan	Cot	Tan	Cot	Tan	Cot	Tan	Cot	Tan	′
	84°		83°		82°		81°		80°		←

XI. FIVE-PLACE VALUES: SINE AND COSINE

→	10°		11°		12°		13°		14°		
′	Sin	Cos	Sin	Cos	Sin	Cos	Sin	Cos	Sin	Cos	
0	.17365	.98481	.19081	.98163	.20791	.97815	.22495	.97437	.24192	.97030	**60**
1	393	476	109	157	820	809	523	430	220	023	59
2	422	471	138	152	848	803	552	424	249	015	58
3	451	466	167	146	877	797	580	417	277	008	57
4	479	461	195	140	905	791	608	411	305	.97001	56
5	.17508	.98455	.19224	.98135	.20933	.97784	.22637	.97404	.24333	.96994	**55**
6	537	450	252	129	962	778	665	398	362	987	54
7	565	445	281	124	.20990	772	693	391	390	980	53
8	594	440	309	118	.21019	766	722	384	418	973	52
9	623	435	338	112	047	760	750	378	446	966	51
10	.17651	.98430	.19366	.98107	.21076	.97754	.22778	.97371	.24474	.96959	**50**
11	680	425	395	101	104	748	807	365	503	952	49
12	708	420	423	096	132	742	835	358	531	945	48
13	737	414	452	090	161	735	863	351	559	937	47
14	766	409	481	084	189	729	892	345	587	930	46
15	.17794	.98404	.19509	.98079	.21218	.97723	.22920	.97338	.24615	.96923	**45**
16	823	399	538	073	246	717	948	331	644	916	44
17	852	394	566	067	275	711	.22977	325	672	909	43
18	880	389	595	061	303	705	.23005	318	700	902	42
19	909	383	623	056	331	698	033	311	728	894	41
20	.17937	.98378	.19652	.98050	.21360	.97692	.23062	.97304	.24756	.96887	**40**
21	966	373	680	044	388	686	090	298	784	880	39
22	.17995	368	709	039	417	680	118	291	813	873	38
23	.18023	362	737	033	445	673	146	284	841	866	37
24	052	357	766	027	474	667	175	278	869	858	36
25	.18081	.98352	.19794	.98021	.21502	.97661	.23203	.97271	.24897	.96851	**35**
26	109	347	823	016	530	655	231	264	925	844	34
27	138	341	851	010	559	648	260	257	954	837	33
28	166	336	880	.98004	587	642	288	251	.24982	829	32
29	195	331	908	.97998	616	636	316	244	.25010	822	31
30	.18224	.98325	.19937	.97992	.21644	.97630	.23345	.97237	.25038	.96815	**30**
31	252	320	965	987	672	623	373	230	066	807	29
32	281	315	.19994	981	701	617	401	223	094	800	28
33	309	310	.20022	975	729	611	429	217	122	793	27
34	338	304	051	969	758	604	458	210	151	786	26
35	.18367	.98299	.20079	.97963	.21786	.97598	.23486	.97203	.25179	.96778	**25**
36	395	294	108	958	814	592	514	196	207	771	24
37	424	288	136	952	843	585	542	189	235	764	23
38	452	283	165	946	871	579	571	182	263	756	22
39	481	277	193	940	899	573	599	176	291	749	21
40	.18509	.98272	.20222	.97934	.21928	.97566	.23627	.97169	.25320	.96742	**20**
41	538	267	250	928	956	560	656	162	348	734	19
42	567	261	279	922	.21985	553	684	155	376	727	18
43	595	256	307	916	.22013	547	712	148	404	719	17
44	624	250	336	910	041	541	740	141	432	712	16
45	.18652	.98245	.20364	.97905	.22070	.97534	.23769	.97134	.25460	.96705	**15**
46	681	240	393	899	098	528	797	127	488	697	14
47	710	234	421	893	126	521	825	120	516	690	13
48	738	229	450	887	155	515	853	113	545	682	12
49	767	223	478	881	183	508	882	106	573	675	11
50	.18795	.98218	.20507	.97875	.22212	.97502	.23910	.97100	.25601	.96667	**10**
51	824	212	535	869	240	496	938	093	629	660	9
52	852	207	563	863	268	489	966	086	657	653	8
53	881	201	592	857	297	483	.23995	079	685	645	7
54	910	196	620	851	325	476	.24023	072	713	638	6
55	.18938	.98190	.20649	.97845	.22353	.97470	.24051	.97065	.25741	.96630	**5**
56	967	185	677	839	382	463	079	058	769	623	4
57	.18995	179	706	833	410	457	108	051	798	615	3
58	.19024	174	734	827	438	450	136	044	826	608	2
59	052	168	763	821	467	444	164	037	854	600	1
60	.19081	.98163	.20791	.97815	.22495	.97437	.24192	.97030	.25882	.96593	**0**
	Cos	Sin	Cos	Sin	Cos	Sin	Cos	Sin	Cos	Sin	′
	79°		78°		77°		76°		75°		←

XI. FIVE-PLACE VALUES: TANGENT AND COTANGENT

→	10°		11°		12°		13°		14°		
′	Tan	Cot	Tan	Cot	Tan	Cot	Tan	Cot	Tan	Cot	
0	.17633	5.6713	.19438	5.1446	.21256	4.7046	.23087	4.3315	.24933	4.0108	**60**
1	663	.6617	468	.1366	286	.6979	117	.3257	964	.0058	59
2	693	.6521	498	.1286	316	.6912	148	.3200	.24995	4.0009	58
3	723	.6425	529	.1207	347	.6845	179	.3143	.25026	3.9959	57
4	753	.6329	559	.1128	377	.6779	209	.3086	056	.9910	56
5	.17783	5.6234	.19589	5.1049	.21408	4.6712	.23240	4.3029	.25087	3.9861	**55**
6	813	.6140	619	.0970	438	.6646	271	.2972	118	.9812	54
7	843	.6045	649	.0892	469	.6580	301	.2916	149	.9763	53
8	873	.5951	680	.0814	499	.6514	332	.2859	180	.9714	52
9	903	.5857	710	.0736	529	.6448	363	.2803	211	.9665	51
10	.17933	5.5764	.19740	5.0658	.21560	4.6382	.23393	4.2747	.25242	3.9617	**50**
11	963	.5671	770	.0581	590	.6317	424	.2691	273	.9568	49
12	.17993	.5578	801	.0504	621	.6252	455	.2635	304	.9520	48
13	.18023	.5485	831	.0427	651	.6187	485	.2580	335	.9471	47
14	053	.5393	861	.0350	682	.6122	516	.2524	366	.9423	46
15	.18083	5.5301	.19891	5.0273	.21712	4.6057	.23547	4.2468	.25397	3.9375	**45**
16	113	.5209	921	.0197	743	.5993	578	.2413	428	.9327	44
17	143	.5118	952	.0121	773	.5928	608	.2358	459	.9279	43
18	173	.5026	.19982	5.0045	804	.5864	639	.2303	490	.9232	42
19	203	.4936	.20012	4.9969	834	.5800	670	.2248	521	.9184	41
20	.18233	5.4845	.20042	4.9894	.21864	4.5736	.23700	4.2193	.25552	3.9136	**40**
21	263	.4755	073	.9819	895	.5673	731	.2139	583	.9089	39
22	293	.4665	103	.9744	925	.5609	762	.2084	614	.9042	38
23	323	.4575	133	.9669	956	.5546	793	.2030	645	.8995	37
24	353	.4486	164	.9594	.21986	.5483	823	.1976	676	.8947	36
25	.18384	5.4397	.20194	4.9520	.22017	4.5420	.23854	4.1922	.25707	3.8900	**35**
26	414	.4308	224	.9446	047	.5357	885	.1868	738	.8854	34
27	444	.4219	254	.9372	078	.5294	916	.1814	769	.8807	33
28	474	.4131	285	.9298	108	.5232	946	.1760	800	.8760	32
29	504	.4043	315	.9225	139	.5169	.23977	.1706	831	.8714	31
30	.18534	5.3955	.20345	4.9152	.22169	4.5107	.24008	4.1653	.25862	3.8667	**30**
31	564	.3868	376	.9078	200	.5045	039	.1600	893	.8621	29
32	594	.3781	406	.9006	231	.4983	069	.1547	924	.8575	28
33	624	.3694	436	.8933	261	.4922	100	.1493	955	.8528	27
34	654	.3607	466	.8860	292	.4860	131	.1441	.25986	.8482	26
35	.18684	5.3521	.20497	4.8788	.22322	4.4799	.24162	4.1388	.26017	3.8436	**25**
36	714	.3435	527	.8716	353	.4737	193	.1335	048	.8391	24
37	745	.3349	557	.8644	383	.4676	223	.1282	079	.8345	23
38	775	.3263	588	.8573	414	.4615	254	.1230	110	.8299	22
39	805	.3178	618	.8501	444	.4555	285	.1178	141	.8254	21
40	.18835	5.3093	.20648	4.8430	.22475	4.4494	.24316	4.1126	.26172	3.8208	**20**
41	865	.3008	679	.8359	505	.4434	347	.1074	203	.8163	19
42	895	.2924	709	.8288	536	.4373	377	.1022	235	.8118	18
43	925	.2839	739	.8218	567	.4313	408	.0970	266	.8073	17
44	955	.2755	770	.8147	597	.4253	439	.0918	297	.8028	16
45	.18986	5.2672	.20800	4.8077	.22628	4.4194	.24470	4.0867	.26328	3.7983	**15**
46	.19016	.2588	830	.8007	658	.4134	501	.0815	359	.7938	14
47	046	.2505	861	.7937	689	.4075	532	.0764	390	.7893	13
48	076	.2422	891	.7867	719	.4015	562	.0713	421	.7848	12
49	106	.2339	921	.7798	750	.3956	593	.0662	452	.7804	11
50	.19136	5.2257	.20952	4.7729	22781	4.3897	.24624	4.0611	.26483	3.7760	**10**
51	166	.2174	.20982	.7659	811	.3838	655	.0560	515	.7715	9
52	197	.2092	.21013	.7591	842	.3779	686	.0509	546	.7671	8
53	227	.2011	043	.7522	872	.3721	717	.0459	577	.7627	7
54	257	.1929	073	.7453	903	.3662	747	.0408	608	.7583	6
55	.19287	5.1848	.21104	4.7385	.22934	4.3604	.24778	4.0358	.26639	3.7539	**5**
56	317	.1767	134	.7317	964	.3546	809	.0308	670	.7495	4
57	347	.1686	164	.7249	.22995	.3488	840	.0257	701	.7451	3
58	378	.1606	195	.7181	.23026	.3430	871	.0207	733	.7408	2
59	408	.1526	225	.7114	056	.3372	902	.0158	764	.7364	1
60	.19438	5.1446	.21256	4.7046	.23087	4.3315	.24933	4.0108	.26795	3.7321	**0**
	Cot	Tan	Cot	Tan	Cot	Tan	Cot	Tan	Cot	Tan	′
	79°		78°		77°		76°		75°		←

XI. FIVE–PLACE VALUES: SINE AND COSINE

→	15°		16°		17°		18°		19°		
′	Sin	Cos	Sin	Cos	Sin	Cos	Sin	Cos	Sin	Cos	
0	.25882	.96593	.27564	.96126	.29237	.95630	.30902	.95106	.32557	.94552	**60**
1	910	585	592	118	265	622	929	097	584	542	59
2	938	578	620	110	293	613	957	088	612	533	58
3	966	570	648	102	321	605	.30985	079	639	523	57
4	.25994	562	676	094	348	596	.31012	070	667	514	56
5	.26022	.96555	.27704	.96086	.29376	.95588	.31040	.95061	.32694	.94504	**55**
6	050	547	731	078	404	579	068	052	722	495	54
7	079	540	759	070	432	571	095	043	749	485	53
8	107	532	787	062	460	562	123	033	777	476	52
9	135	524	815	054	487	554	151	024	804	466	51
10	.26163	.96517	.27843	.96046	.29515	.95545	.31178	.95015	.32832	.94457	**50**
11	191	509	871	037	543	536	206	.95006	859	447	49
12	219	502	899	029	571	528	233	.94997	887	438	48
13	247	494	927	021	599	519	261	988	914	428	47
14	275	486	955	013	626	511	289	979	942	418	46
15	.26303	.96479	.27983	.96005	.29654	.95502	.31316	.94970	.32969	.94409	**45**
16	331	471	.28011	.95997	682	493	344	961	.32997	399	44
17	359	463	039	989	710	485	372	952	.33024	390	43
18	387	456	067	981	737	476	399	943	051	380	42
19	415	448	095	972	765	467	427	933	079	370	41
20	.26443	.96440	.28123	.95964	.29793	.95459	.31454	.94924	.33106	.94361	**40**
21	471	433	150	956	821	450	482	915	134	351	39
22	500	425	178	948	849	441	510	906	161	342	38
23	528	417	206	940	876	433	537	897	189	332	37
24	556	410	234	931	904	424	565	888	216	322	36
25	.26584	.96402	.28262	.95923	.29932	.95415	.31593	.94878	.33244	.94313	**35**
26	612	394	290	915	960	407	620	869	271	303	34
27	640	386	318	907	.29987	398	648	860	298	293	33
28	668	379	346	898	.30015	389	675	851	326	284	32
29	696	371	374	890	043	380	703	842	353	274	31
30	.26724	.96363	.28402	.95882	.30071	.95372	.31730	.94832	.33381	.94264	**30**
31	752	355	429	874	098	363	758	823	408	254	29
32	780	347	457	865	126	354	786	814	436	245	28
33	808	340	485	857	154	345	813	805	463	235	27
34	836	332	513	849	182	337	841	795	490	225	26
35	.26864	.96324	.28541	.95841	.30209	.95328	.31868	.94786	.33518	.94215	**25**
36	892	316	569	832	237	319	896	777	545	206	24
37	920	308	597	824	265	310	923	768	573	196	23
38	948	301	625	816	292	301	951	758	600	186	22
39	.26976	293	652	807	320	293	.31979	749	627	176	21
40	.27004	.96285	.28680	.95799	.30348	.95284	.32006	.94740	.33655	.94167	**20**
41	032	277	708	791	376	275	034	730	682	157	19
42	060	269	736	782	403	266	061	721	710	147	18
43	088	261	764	774	431	257	089	712	737	137	17
44	116	253	792	766	459	248	116	702	764	127	16
45	.27144	.96246	.28820	.95757	.30486	.95240	.32144	.94693	.33792	.94118	**15**
46	172	238	847	749	514	231	171	684	819	108	14
47	200	230	875	740	542	222	199	674	846	098	13
48	228	222	903	732	570	213	227	665	874	088	12
49	256	214	931	724	597	204	254	656	901	078	11
50	.27284	.96206	.28959	.95715	.30625	.95195	.32282	.94646	.33929	.94068	**10**
51	312	198	.28987	707	653	186	309	637	956	058	9
52	340	190	.29015	698	680	177	337	627	.33983	049	8
53	368	182	042	690	708	168	364	618	.34011	039	7
54	396	174	070	681	736	159	392	609	038	029	6
55	.27424	.96166	.29098	.95673	.30763	.95150	.32419	.94599	.34065	.94019	**5**
56	452	158	126	664	791	142	447	590	093	.94009	4
57	480	150	154	656	819	133	474	580	120	.93999	3
58	508	142	182	647	846	124	502	571	147	989	2
59	536	134	209	639	874	115	529	561	175	979	1
60	.27564	.96126	.29237	.95630	.30902	.95106	.32557	.94552	.34202	.93969	**0**
	Cos	Sin	Cos	Sin	Cos	Sin	Cos	Sin	Cos	Sin	′
	74°		73°		72°		71°		70°		←

XI. FIVE-PLACE VALUES: TANGENT AND COTANGENT

→	15°		16°		17°		18°		19°		
′	Tan	Cot	Tan	Cot	Tan	Cot	Tan	Cot	Tan	Cot	
0	.26795	3.7321	.28675	3.4874	.30573	3.2709	.32492	3.0777	.34433	2.9042	**60**
1	826	.7277	706	.4836	605	.2675	524	.0746	465	.9015	59
2	857	.7234	738	.4798	637	.2641	556	.0716	498	.8987	58
3	888	.7191	769	.4760	669	.2607	588	.0686	530	.8960	57
4	920	.7148	801	.4722	700	.2573	621	.0655	563	.8933	56
5	.26951	3.7105	.28832	3.4684	.30732	3.2539	.32653	3.0625	.34596	2.8905	**55**
6	.26982	.7062	864	.4646	764	.2506	685	.0595	628	.8878	54
7	.27013	.7019	895	.4608	796	.2472	717	.0565	661	.8851	53
8	044	.6976	927	.4570	828	.2438	749	.0535	693	.8824	52
9	076	.6933	958	.4533	860	.2405	782	.0505	726	.8797	51
10	.27107	3.6891	.28990	3.4495	.30891	3.2371	.32814	3.0475	.34758	2.8770	**50**
11	138	.6848	.29021	.4458	923	.2338	846	.0445	791	.8743	49
12	169	.6806	053	.4420	955	.2305	878	.0415	824	.8716	48
13	201	.6764	084	.4383	.30987	.2272	911	.0385	856	.8689	47
14	232	.6722	116	.4346	.31019	.2238	943	.0356	889	.8662	46
15	.27263	3.6680	.29147	3.4308	.31051	3.2205	.32975	3.0326	.34922	2.8636	**45**
16	294	.6638	179	.4271	083	.2172	.33007	.0296	954	.8609	44
17	326	.6596	210	.4234	115	.2139	040	.0267	.34987	.8582	43
18	357	.6554	242	.4197	147	.2106	072	.0237	.35020	.8556	42
19	388	.6512	274	.4160	178	.2073	104	.0208	052	.8529	41
20	.27419	3.6470	.29305	3.4124	.31210	3.2041	.33136	3.0178	.35085	2.8502	**40**
21	451	.6429	337	.4087	242	.2008	169	.0149	118	.8476	39
22	482	.6387	368	.4050	274	.1975	201	.0120	150	.8449	38
23	513	.6346	400	.4014	306	.1943	233	.0090	183	.8423	37
24	545	.6305	432	.3977	338	.1910	266	.0061	216	.8397	36
25	.27576	3.6264	.29463	3.3941	.31370	3.1878	.33298	3.0032	.35248	2.8370	**35**
26	607	.6222	495	.3904	402	.1845	330	3.0003	281	.8344	34
27	638	.6181	526	.3868	434	.1813	363	2.9974	314	.8318	33
28	670	.6140	558	.3832	466	.1780	395	.9945	346	.8291	32
29	701	.6100	590	.3796	498	.1748	427	.9916	379	.8265	31
30	.27732	3.6059	.29621	3.3759	.31530	3.1716	.33460	2.9887	.35412	2.8239	**30**
31	764	.6018	653	.3723	562	.1684	492	.9858	445	.8213	29
32	795	.5978	685	.3687	594	.1652	524	.9829	477	.8187	28
33	826	.5937	716	.3652	626	.1620	557	.9800	510	.8161	27
34	858	.5897	748	.3616	658	.1588	589	.9772	543	.8135	26
35	.27889	3.5856	.29780	3.3580	.31690	3.1556	.33621	2.9743	.35576	2.8109	**25**
36	921	.5816	811	.3544	722	.1524	654	.9714	608	.8083	24
37	952	.5776	843	.3509	754	.1492	686	.9686	641	.8057	23
38	.27983	.5736	875	.3473	786	.1460	718	.9657	674	.8032	22
39	.28015	.5696	906	.3438	818	.1429	751	.9629	707	.8006	21
40	.28046	3.5656	.29938	3.3402	.31850	3.1397	.33783	2.9600	.35740	2.7980	**20**
41	077	.5616	.29970	.3367	882	.1366	816	.9572	772	.7955	19
42	109	.5576	.30001	.3332	914	.1334	848	.9544	805	.7929	18
43	140	.5536	033	.3297	946	.1303	881	.9515	838	.7903	17
44	172	.5497	065	.3261	.31978	.1271	913	.9487	871	.7878	16
45	.28203	3.5457	.30097	3.3226	.32010	3.1240	.33945	2.9459	.35904	2.7852	**15**
46	234	.5418	128	.3191	042	.1209	.33978	.9431	937	.7827	14
47	266	.5379	160	.3156	074	.1178	.34010	.9403	.35969	.7801	13
48	297	.5339	192	.3122	106	.1146	043	.9375	.36002	.7776	12
49	329	.5300	224	.3087	139	.1115	075	.9347	035	.7751	11
50	.28360	3.5261	.30255	3.3052	.32171	3.1084	.34108	2.9319	.36068	2.7725	**10**
51	391	.5222	287	.3017	203	.1053	140	.9291	101	.7700	9
52	423	.5183	319	.2983	235	.1022	173	.9263	134	.7675	8
53	454	.5144	351	.2948	267	.0991	205	.9235	167	.7650	7
54	486	.5105	382	.2914	299	.0961	238	.9208	199	.7625	6
55	.28517	3.5067	.30414	3.2879	.32331	3.0930	.34270	2.9180	.36232	2.7600	**5**
56	549	.5028	446	.2845	363	.0899	303	.9152	265	.7575	4
57	580	.4989	478	.2811	396	.0868	335	.9125	298	.7550	3
58	612	.4951	509	.2777	428	.0838	368	.9097	331	.7525	2
59	643	.4912	541	.2743	460	.0807	400	.9070	364	.7500	1
60	.28675	3.4874	.30573	3.2709	.32492	3.0777	.34433	2.9042	.36397	2.7475	**0**
	Cot	Tan	Cot	Tan	Cot	Tan	Cot	Tan	Cot	Tan	′
	74°		73°		72°		71°		70°		←

XI. FIVE-PLACE VALUES: SINE AND COSINE

→	20°		21°		22°		23°		24°		
′	Sin	Cos	Sin	Cos	Sin	Cos	Sin	Cos	Sin	Cos	
0	.34202	.93969	.35837	.93358	.37461	.92718	.39073	.92050	.40674	.91355	**60**
1	229	959	864	348	488	707	100	039	700	343	59
2	257	949	891	337	515	697	127	028	727	331	58
3	284	939	918	327	542	686	153	016	753	319	57
4	311	929	945	316	569	675	180	.92005	780	307	56
5	.34339	.93919	.35973	.93306	.37595	.92664	.39207	.91994	.40806	.91295	**55**
6	366	909	.36000	295	622	653	234	982	833	283	54
7	393	899	027	285	649	642	260	971	860	272	53
8	421	889	054	274	676	631	287	959	886	260	52
9	448	879	081	264	703	620	314	948	913	248	51
10	.34475	.93869	.36108	.93253	.37730	.92609	.39341	.91936	.40939	.91236	**50**
11	503	859	135	243	757	598	367	925	966	224	49
12	530	849	162	232	784	587	394	914	.40992	212	48
13	557	839	190	222	811	576	421	902	.41019	200	47
14	584	829	217	211	838	565	448	891	045	188	46
15	.34612	.93819	.36244	.93201	.37865	.92554	.39474	.91879	.41072	.91176	**45**
16	639	809	271	190	892	543	501	868	098	164	44
17	666	799	298	180	919	532	528	856	125	152	43
18	694	789	325	169	946	521	555	845	151	140	42
19	721	779	352	159	973	510	581	833	178	128	41
20	.34748	.93769	.36379	.93148	.37999	.92499	.39608	.91822	.41204	.91116	**40**
21	775	759	406	137	.38026	488	635	810	231	104	39
22	803	748	434	127	053	477	661	799	257	092	38
23	830	738	461	116	080	466	688	787	284	080	37
24	857	728	488	106	107	455	715	775	310	068	36
25	.34884	.93718	.36515	.93095	.38134	.92444	.39741	.91764	.41337	.91056	**35**
26	912	708	542	084	161	432	768	752	363	044	34
27	939	698	569	074	188	421	795	741	390	032	33
28	966	688	596	063	215	410	822	729	416	020	32
29	.34993	677	623	052	241	399	848	718	443	.91008	31
30	.35021	.93667	.36650	.93042	.38268	.92388	.39875	.91706	.41469	.90996	**30**
31	048	657	677	031	295	377	902	694	496	984	29
32	075	647	704	020	322	366	928	683	522	972	28
33	102	637	731	.93010	349	355	955	671	549	960	27
34	130	626	758	.92999	376	343	.39982	660	575	948	26
35	.35157	.93616	.36785	.92988	.38403	.92332	.40008	.91648	.41602	.90936	**25**
36	184	606	812	978	430	321	035	636	628	924	24
37	211	596	839	967	456	310	062	625	655	911	23
38	239	585	867	956	483	299	088	613	681	899	22
39	266	575	894	945	510	287	115	601	707	887	21
40	.35293	.93565	.36921	.92935	.38537	.92276	.40141	.91590	.41734	.90875	**20**
41	320	555	948	924	564	265	168	578	760	863	19
42	347	544	.36975	913	591	254	195	566	787	851	18
43	375	534	.37002	902	617	243	221	555	813	839	17
44	402	524	029	892	644	231	248	543	840	826	16
45	.35429	.93514	.37056	.92881	.38671	.92220	.40275	.91531	.41866	.90814	**15**
46	456	503	083	870	698	209	301	519	892	802	14
47	484	493	110	859	725	198	328	508	919	790	13
48	511	483	137	849	752	186	355	496	945	778	12
49	538	472	164	838	778	175	381	484	972	766	11
50	.35565	.93462	.37191	.92827	.38805	.92164	.40408	.91472	.41998	.90753	**10**
51	592	452	218	816	832	152	434	461	.42024	741	9
52	619	441	245	805	859	141	461	449	051	729	8
53	647	431	272	794	886	130	488	437	077	717	7
54	674	420	299	784	912	119	514	425	104	704	6
55	.35701	.93410	.37326	.92773	.38939	.92107	.40541	.91414	.42130	.90692	**5**
56	728	400	353	762	966	096	567	402	156	680	4
57	755	389	380	751	.38993	085	594	390	183	668	3
58	782	379	407	740	.39020	073	621	378	209	655	2
59	810	368	434	729	046	062	647	366	235	643	1
60	.35837	.93358	.37461	.92718	.39073	.92050	.40674	.91355	.42262	.90631	**0**
	Cos	Sin	Cos	Sin	Cos	Sin	Cos	Sin	Cos	Sin	′
	69°		68°		67°		66°		65°		←

XI. FIVE-PLACE VALUES: TANGENT AND COTANGENT

→	20°		21°		22°		23°		24°		
′	Tan	Cot	Tan	Cot	Tan	Cot	Tan	Cot	Tan	Cot	
0	.36397	2.7475	.38386	2.6051	.40403	2.4751	.42447	2.3559	.44523	2.2460	**60**
1	430	.7450	420	.6028	436	.4730	482	.3539	558	.2443	59
2	463	.7425	453	.6006	470	.4709	516	.3520	593	.2425	58
3	496	.7400	487	.5983	504	.4689	551	.3501	627	.2408	57
4	529	.7376	520	.5961	538	.4668	585	.3483	662	.2390	56
5	.36562	2.7351	.38553	2.5938	.40572	2.4648	.42619	2.3464	.44697	2.2373	**55**
6	595	.7326	587	.5916	606	.4627	654	.3445	732	.2355	54
7	628	.7302	620	.5893	640	.4606	688	.3426	767	.2338	53
8	661	.7277	654	.5871	674	.4586	722	.3407	802	.2320	52
9	694	.7253	687	.5848	707	.4566	757	.3388	837	.2303	51
10	.36727	2.7228	.38721	2.5826	.40741	2.4545	.42791	2.3369	.44872	2.2286	**50**
11	760	.7204	754	.5804	775	.4525	826	.3351	907	.2268	49
12	793	.7179	787	.5782	809	.4504	860	.3332	942	.2251	48
13	826	.7155	821	.5759	843	.4484	894	.3313	.44977	.2234	47
14	859	.7130	854	.5737	877	.4464	929	.3294	.45012	.2216	46
15	.36892	2.7106	.38888	2.5715	.40911	2.4443	.42963	2.3276	.45047	2.2199	**45**
16	925	.7082	921	.5693	945	.4423	.42998	.3257	082	.2182	44
17	958	.7058	955	.5671	.40979	.4403	.43032	.3238	117	.2165	43
18	.36991	.7034	.38988	.5649	.41013	.4383	067	.3220	152	.2148	42
19	.37024	.7009	.39022	.5627	047	.4362	101	.3201	187	.2130	41
20	.37057	2.6985	.39055	2.5605	.41081	2.4342	.43136	2.3183	.45222	2.2113	**40**
21	090	.6961	089	.5583	115	.4322	170	.3164	257	.2096	39
22	123	.6937	122	.5561	149	.4302	205	.3146	292	.2079	38
23	157	.6913	156	.5539	183	.4282	239	.3127	327	.2062	37
24	190	.6889	190	.5517	217	.4262	274	.3109	362	.2045	36
25	.37223	2.6865	.39223	2.5495	.41251	2.4242	.43308	2.3090	.45397	2.2028	**35**
26	256	.6841	257	.5473	285	.4222	343	.3072	432	.2011	34
27	289	.6818	290	.5452	319	.4202	378	.3053	467	.1994	33
28	322	.6794	324	.5430	353	.4182	412	.3035	502	.1977	32
29	355	.6770	357	.5408	387	.4162	447	.3017	538	.1960	31
30	.37388	2.6746	.39391	2.5386	.41421	2.4142	.43481	2.2998	.45573	2.1943	**30**
31	422	.6723	425	.5365	455	.4122	516	.2980	608	.1926	29
32	455	.6699	458	.5343	490	.4102	550	.2962	643	.1909	28
33	488	.6675	492	.5322	524	.4083	585	.2944	678	.1892	27
34	521	.6652	526	.5300	558	.4063	620	.2925	713	.1876	26
35	.37554	2.6628	.39559	2.5279	.41592	2.4043	.43654	2.2907	.45748	2.1859	**25**
36	588	.6605	593	.5257	626	.4023	689	.2889	784	.1842	24
37	621	.6581	626	.5236	660	.4004	724	.2871	819	.1825	23
38	654	.6558	660	.5214	694	.3984	758	.2853	854	.1808	22
39	687	.6534	694	.5193	728	.3964	793	.2835	889	.1792	21
40	.37720	2.6511	.39727	2.5172	.41763	2.3945	.43828	2.2817	.45924	2.1775	**20**
41	754	.6488	761	.5150	797	.3925	862	.2799	960	.1758	19
42	787	.6464	795	.5129	831	.3906	897	.2781	.45995	.1742	18
43	820	.6441	829	.5108	865	.3886	932	.2763	.46030	.1725	17
44	853	.6418	862	.5086	899	.3867	.43966	.2745	065	.1708	16
45	.37887	2.6395	.39896	2.5065	.41933	2.3847	.44001	2.2727	.46101	2.1692	**15**
46	920	.6371	930	.5044	.41968	.3828	036	.2709	136	.1675	14
47	953	.6348	963	.5023	.42002	.3808	071	.2691	171	.1659	13
48	.37986	.6325	.39997	.5002	036	.3789	105	.2673	206	.1642	12
49	.38020	.6302	.40031	.4981	070	.3770	140	.2655	242	.1625	11
50	.38053	2.6279	.40065	2.4960	.42105	2.3750	.44175	2.2637	.46277	2.1609	**10**
51	086	.6256	098	.4939	139	.3731	210	.2620	312	.1592	9
52	120	.6233	132	.4918	173	.3712	244	.2602	348	.1576	8
53	153	.6210	166	.4897	207	.3693	279	.2584	383	.1560	7
54	186	.6187	200	.4876	242	.3673	314	.2566	418	.1543	6
55	.38220	2.6165	.40234	2.4855	.42276	2.3654	.44349	2.2549	.46454	2.1527	**5**
56	253	.6142	267	.4834	310	.3635	384	.2531	489	.1510	4
57	286	.6119	301	.4813	345	.3616	418	.2513	525	.1494	3
58	320	.6096	335	.4792	379	.3597	453	.2496	560	.1478	2
59	353	.6074	369	.4772	413	.3578	488	.2478	595	.1461	1
60	.38386	2.6051	.40403	2.4751	.42447	2.3559	.44523	2.2460	.46631	2.1445	**0**
	Cot	Tan	Cot	Tan	Cot	Tan	Cot	Tan	Cot	Tan	′
	69°		68°		67°		66°		65°		←

XI. FIVE-PLACE VALUES: SINE AND COSINE

→	25°		26°		27°		28°		29°		
′	Sin	Cos	Sin	Cos	Sin	Cos	Sin	Cos	Sin	Cos	
0	.42262	.90631	.43837	.89879	.45399	.89101	.46947	.88295	.48481	.87462	**60**
1	288	618	863	867	425	087	973	281	506	448	59
2	315	606	889	854	451	074	.46999	267	532	434	58
3	341	594	916	841	477	061	.47024	254	557	420	57
4	367	582	942	828	503	048	050	240	583	406	56
5	.42394	.90569	.43968	.89816	.45529	.89035	.47076	.88226	.48608	.87391	**55**
6	420	557	.43994	803	554	021	101	213	634	377	54
7	446	545	.44020	790	580	.89008	127	199	659	363	53
8	473	532	046	777	606	.88995	153	185	684	349	52
9	499	520	072	764	632	981	178	172	710	335	51
10	.42525	.90507	.44098	.89752	.45658	.88968	.47204	.88158	.48735	.87321	**50**
11	552	495	124	739	684	955	229	144	761	306	49
12	578	483	151	726	710	942	255	130	786	292	48
13	604	470	177	713	736	928	281	117	811	278	47
14	631	458	203	700	762	915	306	103	837	264	46
15	.42657	.90446	.44229	.89687	.45787	.88902	.47332	.88089	.48862	.87250	**45**
16	683	433	255	674	813	888	358	075	888	235	44
17	709	421	281	662	839	875	383	062	913	221	43
18	736	408	307	649	865	862	409	048	938	207	42
19	762	396	333	636	891	848	434	034	964	193	41
20	.42788	.90383	.44359	.89623	.45917	.88835	.47460	.88020	.48989	.87178	**40**
21	815	371	385	610	942	822	486	.88006	.49014	164	39
22	841	358	411	597	968	808	511	.87993	040	150	38
23	867	346	437	584	.45994	795	537	979	065	136	37
24	894	334	464	571	.46020	782	562	965	090	121	36
25	.42920	.90321	.44490	.89558	.46046	.88768	.47588	.87951	.49116	.87107	**35**
26	946	309	516	545	072	755	614	937	141	093	34
27	972	296	542	532	097	741	639	923	166	079	33
28	.42999	284	568	519	123	728	665	909	192	064	32
29	.43025	271	594	506	149	715	690	896	217	050	31
30	.43051	.90259	.44620	.89493	.46175	.88701	.47716	.87882	.49242	.87036	**30**
31	077	246	646	480	201	688	741	868	268	021	29
32	104	233	672	467	226	674	767	854	293	.87007	28
33	130	221	698	454	252	661	793	840	318	.86993	27
34	156	208	724	441	278	647	818	826	344	978	26
35	.43182	.90196	.44750	.89428	.46304	.88634	.47844	.87812	.49369	.86964	**25**
36	209	183	776	415	330	620	869	798	394	949	24
37	235	171	802	402	355	607	895	784	419	935	23
38	261	158	828	389	381	593	920	770	445	921	22
39	287	146	854	376	407	580	946	756	470	906	21
40	.43313	.90133	.44880	.89363	.46433	.88566	.47971	.87743	.49495	.86892	**20**
41	340	120	906	350	458	553	.47997	729	521	878	19
42	366	108	932	337	484	539	.48022	715	546	863	18
43	392	095	958	324	510	526	048	701	571	849	17
44	418	082	.44984	311	536	512	073	687	596	834	16
45	.43445	.90070	.45010	.89298	.46561	.88499	.48099	.87673	.49622	.86820	**15**
46	471	057	036	285	587	485	124	659	647	805	14
47	497	045	062	272	613	472	150	645	672	791	13
48	523	032	088	259	639	458	175	631	697	777	12
49	549	019	114	245	664	445	201	617	723	762	11
50	.43575	.90007	.45140	.89232	.46690	.88431	.48226	.87603	.49748	.86748	**10**
51	602	.89994	166	219	716	417	252	589	773	733	9
52	628	981	192	206	742	404	277	575	798	719	8
53	654	968	218	193	767	390	303	561	824	704	7
54	680	956	243	180	793	377	328	546	849	690	6
55	.43706	.89943	.45269	.89167	.46819	.88363	.48354	.87532	.49874	.86675	**5**
56	733	930	295	153	844	349	379	518	899	661	4
57	759	918	321	140	870	336	405	504	924	646	3
58	785	905	347	127	896	322	430	490	950	632	2
59	811	892	373	114	921	308	456	476	.49975	617	1
60	.43837	.89879	.45399	.89101	.46947	.88295	.48481	.87462	.50000	.86603	**0**
	Cos	Sin	Cos	Sin	Cos	Sin	Cos	Sin	Cos	Sin	′
	64°		63°		62°		61°		60°		←

XI. FIVE-PLACE VALUES: TANGENT AND COTANGENT

→	25°		26°		27°		28°		29°		
′	Tan	Cot	Tan	Cot	Tan	Cot	Tan	Cot	Tan	Cot	
0	.46631	2.1445	.48773	2.0503	.50953	1.9626	.53171	1.8807	.55431	1.8040	**60**
1	666	.1429	809	.0488	.50989	.9612	208	.8794	469	.8028	59
2	702	.1413	845	.0473	.51026	.9598	246	.8781	507	.8016	58
3	737	.1396	881	.0458	063	.9584	283	.8768	545	.8003	57
4	772	.1380	917	.0443	099	.9570	320	.8755	583	.7991	56
5	.46808	2.1364	.48953	2.0428	.51136	1.9556	.53358	1.8741	.55621	1.7979	**55**
6	843	.1348	.48989	.0413	173	.9542	395	.8728	659	.7966	54
7	879	.1332	.49026	.0398	209	.9528	432	.8715	697	.7954	53
8	914	.1315	062	.0383	246	.9514	470	.8702	736	.7942	52
9	950	.1299	098	.0368	283	.9500	507	.8689	774	.7930	51
10	.46985	2.1283	.49134	2.0353	.51319	1.9486	.53545	1.8676	.55812	1.7917	**50**
11	.47021	.1267	170	.0338	356	.9472	582	.8663	850	.7905	49
12	056	.1251	206	.0323	393	.9458	620	.8650	888	.7893	48
13	092	.1235	242	.0308	430	.9444	657	.8637	926	.7881	47
14	128	.1219	278	.0293	467	.9430	694	.8624	.55964	.7868	46
15	.47163	2.1203	.49315	2.0278	.51503	1.9416	.53732	1.8611	.56003	1.7856	**45**
16	199	.1187	351	.0263	540	.9402	769	.8598	041	.7844	44
17	234	.1171	387	.0248	577	.9388	807	.8585	079	.7832	43
18	270	.1155	423	.0233	614	.9375	844	.8572	117	.7820	42
19	305	.1139	459	.0219	651	.9361	882	.8559	156	.7808	41
20	.47341	2.1123	.49495	2.0204	.51688	1.9347	.53920	1.8546	.56194	1.7796	**40**
21	377	.1107	532	.0189	724	.9333	957	.8533	232	.7783	39
22	412	.1092	568	.0174	761	.9319	.53995	.8520	270	.7771	38
23	448	.1076	604	.0160	798	.9306	.54032	.8507	309	.7759	37
24	483	.1060	640	.0145	835	.9292	070	.8495	347	.7747	36
25	.47519	2.1044	.49677	2.0130	.51872	1.9278	.54107	1.8482	.56385	1.7735	**35**
26	555	.1028	713	.0115	909	.9265	145	.8469	424	.7723	34
27	590	.1013	749	.0101	946	.9251	183	.8456	462	.7711	33
28	626	.0997	786	.0086	.51983	.9237	220	.8443	501	.7699	32
29	662	.0981	822	.0072	.52020	.9223	258	.8430	539	.7687	31
30	.47698	2.0965	.49858	2.0057	.52057	1.9210	.54296	1.8418	.56577	1.7675	**30**
31	733	.0950	894	.0042	094	.9196	333	.8405	616	.7663	29
32	769	.0934	931	.0028	131	.9183	371	.8392	654	.7651	28
33	805	.0918	.49967	2.0013	168	.9169	409	.8379	693	.7639	27
34	840	.0903	.50004	1.9999	205	.9155	446	.8367	731	.7627	26
35	.47876	2.0887	.50040	1.9984	.52242	1.9142	.54484	1.8354	.56769	1.7615	**25**
36	912	.0872	076	.9970	279	.9128	522	.8341	808	.7603	24
37	948	.0856	113	.9955	316	.9115	560	.8329	846	.7591	23
38	.47984	.0840	149	.9941	353	.9101	597	.8316	885	.7579	22
39	.48019	.0825	185	.9926	390	.9088	635	.8303	923	.7567	21
40	.48055	2.0809	.50222	1.9912	.52427	1.9074	.54673	1.8291	.56962	1.7556	**20**
41	091	.0794	258	.9897	464	.9061	711	.8278	.57000	.7544	19
42	127	.0778	295	.9883	501	.9047	748	.8265	039	.7532	18
43	163	.0763	331	.9868	538	.9034	786	.8253	078	.7520	17
44	198	.0748	368	.9854	575	.9020	824	.8240	116	.7508	16
45	.48234	2.0732	.50404	1.9840	.52613	1.9007	.54862	1.8228	.57155	1.7496	**15**
46	270	.0717	441	.9825	650	.8993	900	.8215	193	.7485	14
47	306	.0701	477	.9811	687	.8980	938	.8202	232	.7473	13
48	342	.0686	514	.9797	724	.8967	.54975	.8190	271	.7461	12
49	378	.0671	550	.9782	761	.8953	.55013	.8177	309	.7449	11
50	.48414	2.0655	.50587	1.9768	.52798	1.8940	.55051	1.8165	.57348	1.7437	**10**
51	450	.0640	623	.9754	836	.8927	089	.8152	386	.7426	9
52	486	.0625	660	.9740	873	.8913	127	.8140	425	.7414	8
53	521	.0609	696	.9725	910	.8900	165	.8127	464	.7402	7
54	557	.0594	733	.9711	947	.8887	203	.8115	503	.7391	6
55	.48593	2.0579	.50769	1.9697	.52985	1.8873	.55241	1.8103	.57541	1.7379	**5**
56	629	.0564	806	.9683	.53022	.8860	279	.8090	580	.7367	4
57	665	.0549	843	.9669	059	.8847	317	.8078	619	.7355	3
58	701	.0533	879	.9654	096	.8834	355	.8065	657	.7344	2
59	737	.0518	916	.9640	134	.8820	393	.8053	696	.7332	1
60	.48773	2.0503	.50953	1.9626	.53171	1.8807	.55431	1.8040	.57735	1.7321	**0**
	Cot	Tan	Cot	Tan	Cot	Tan	Cot	Tan	Cot	Tan	′
	64°		63°		62°		61°		60°		←

XI. FIVE-PLACE VALUES: SINE AND COSINE

→	30°		31°		32°		33°		34°		
′	Sin	Cos	Sin	Cos	Sin	Cos	Sin	Cos	Sin	Cos	
0	.50000	.86603	.51504	.85717	.52992	.84805	.54464	.83867	.55919	.82904	**60**
1	025	588	529	702	.53017	789	488	851	943	887	59
2	050	573	554	687	041	774	513	835	968	871	58
3	076	559	579	672	066	759	537	819	.55992	855	57
4	101	544	604	657	091	743	561	804	.56016	839	56
5	.50126	.86530	.51628	.85642	.53115	.84728	.54586	.83788	.56040	.82822	**55**
6	151	515	653	627	140	712	610	772	064	806	54
7	176	501	678	612	164	697	635	756	088	790	53
8	201	486	703	597	189	681	659	740	112	773	52
9	227	471	728	582	214	666	683	724	136	757	51
10	.50252	.86457	.51753	.85567	.53238	.84650	.54708	.83708	.56160	.82741	**50**
11	277	442	778	551	263	635	732	692	184	724	49
12	302	427	803	536	288	619	756	676	208	708	48
13	327	413	828	521	312	604	781	660	232	692	47
14	352	398	852	506	337	588	805	645	256	675	46
15	.50377	.86384	.51877	.85491	.53361	.84573	.54829	.83629	.56280	.82659	**45**
16	403	369	902	476	386	557	854	613	305	643	44
17	428	354	927	461	411	542	878	597	329	626	43
18	453	340	952	446	435	526	902	581	353	610	42
19	478	325	.51977	431	460	511	927	565	377	593	41
20	.50503	.86310	.52002	.85416	.53484	.84495	.54951	.83549	.56401	.82577	**40**
21	528	295	026	401	509	480	975	533	425	561	39
22	553	281	051	385	534	464	.54999	517	449	544	38
23	578	266	076	370	558	448	.55024	501	473	528	37
24	603	251	101	355	583	433	048	485	497	511	36
25	.50628	.86237	.52126	.85340	.53607	.84417	.55072	.83469	.56521	.82495	**35**
26	654	222	151	325	632	402	097	453	545	478	34
27	679	207	175	310	656	386	121	437	569	462	33
28	704	192	200	294	681	370	145	421	593	446	32
29	729	178	225	279	705	355	169	405	617	429	31
30	.50754	.86163	.52250	.85264	.53730	.84339	.55194	.83389	.56641	.82413	**30**
31	779	148	275	249	754	324	218	373	665	396	29
32	804	133	299	234	779	308	242	356	689	380	28
33	829	119	324	218	804	292	266	340	713	363	27
34	854	104	349	203	828	277	291	324	736	347	26
35	.50879	.86089	.52374	.85188	.53853	.84261	.55315	.83308	.56760	.82330	**25**
36	904	074	399	173	877	245	339	292	784	314	24
37	929	059	423	157	902	230	363	276	808	297	23
38	954	045	448	142	926	214	388	260	832	281	22
39	.50979	030	473	127	951	198	412	244	856	264	21
40	.51004	.86015	.52498	.85112	.53975	.84182	.55436	.83228	.56880	.82248	**20**
41	029	.86000	522	096	.54000	167	460	212	904	231	19
42	054	.85985	547	081	024	151	484	195	928	214	18
43	079	970	572	066	049	135	509	179	952	198	17
44	104	956	597	051	073	120	533	163	.56976	181	16
45	.51129	.85941	.52621	.85035	.54097	.84104	.55557	.83147	.57000	.82165	**15**
46	154	926	646	020	122	088	581	131	024	148	14
47	179	911	671	.85005	146	072	605	115	047	132	13
48	204	896	696	.84989	171	057	630	098	071	115	12
49	229	881	720	974	195	041	654	082	095	098	11
50	.51254	.85866	.52745	.84959	.54220	.84025	.55678	.83066	.57119	.82082	**10**
51	279	851	770	943	244	.84009	702	050	143	065	9
52	304	836	794	928	269	.83994	726	034	167	048	8
53	329	821	819	913	293	978	750	017	191	032	7
54	354	806	844	897	317	962	775	.83001	215	.82015	6
55	.51379	.85792	.52869	.84882	.54342	.83946	.55799	.82985	.57238	.81999	**5**
56	404	777	893	866	366	930	823	969	262	982	4
57	429	762	918	851	391	915	847	953	286	965	3
58	454	747	943	836	415	899	871	936	310	949	2
59	479	732	967	820	440	883	895	920	334	932	1
60	.51504	.85717	.52992	.84805	.54464	.83867	.55919	.82904	.57358	.81915	**0**
	Cos	Sin	Cos	Sin	Cos	Sin	Cos	Sin	Cos	Sin	′
	59°		58°		57°		56°		55°		←